THE PECTIC SUBSTANCES

THE PECTIC SUBSTANCES

By Z. I. KERTESZ, *New York State Agricultural Experiment Station, Cornell University, Geneva, N. Y.*

1951

INTERSCIENCE PUBLISHERS, INC., NEW YORK
INTERSCIENCE PUBLISHERS LTD., LONDON

INTERSCIENCE PUBLISHERS, Inc., 250 Fifth Avenue, New York 1, N. Y.

For Great Britain and Northern Ireland:

INTERSCIENCE PUBLISHERS Ltd., 2a Southampton Row, London, W. C. 1

PRINTED IN THE UNITED STATES OF AMERICA
BY MACK PRINTING COMPANY, EASTON, PA.

PREFACE

Pectic substances have interested research workers and technologists in fields far apart. As a result, reports dealing with pectic polyuronides and with the enzymes acting upon them have appeared in a wide range of publications in the various branches of science and technology.

Because of the wide scattering of the literature and the steadily mounting interest in this field, there is need for a comprehensive monograph on the pectic substances. In the present volume an attempt was made to cover all aspects of these interesting compounds. In addition to the emphasis on the interrelations between fragments of information, an effort was made to point out where major loopholes still exist in our knowledge of pectins. This book was not written for the handful of specialists in pectin chemistry. Rather, it is the author's hope that it will be helpful in the orientation of newcomers to the field and aid those interested in problems related in any manner to the pectic substances.

The author wishes to thank his collaborators who participated in his researches and from whom he has learned much. He also takes pleasure in expressing his appreciation to Dr. H. S. Isbell for many valuable suggestions in writing Chapter II, to Drs. J. J. Willaman, Claude H. Hills, and H. H. Mottern for a critical reading of an early draft of Chapter VII, to Dr. R. J. McColloch for aid in the preparation of Table 2 and for many interesting and inspiring discussions, to Mrs. Barbara Imhofe Lamb for making the original drawing for Figure 18, and to Leona W. Greenhill, who prepared the author index.

The author's sincere thanks go to Interscience Publishers, Inc., for encouraging him in the writing of this volume and providing much help during the years while *The Pectic Substances* was in preparation.

The opinions expressed are those of the author and do not necessarily represent the views of his Institution.

Geneva, N. Y.   Z. I. KERTESZ
April, 1951

CONTENTS

PART ONE
THE CHEMISTRY OF PECTIC SUBSTANCES

CHAPTER I

Definitions and Nomenclature

The pectic substances are carbohydrates or, more exactly, carbohydrate derivatives.

The carbohydrates are one of the most important groups of compounds. Excluding water, about three-quarters of the dry substances composing the plant world is made up of carbohydrates and related compounds. The field of carbohydrates is usually divided into (1) the simple sugars (monosaccharides) and (2) polysaccharides. The latter are made up entirely or mostly by the association of one or more variety of sugars.

The simplest true member of the sugar series is glycolaldehyde, CH_2OHCHO, a sweet tasting, crystalline, water-soluble substance. The sugars have the general formula $(CH_2O)_n$ and contain both the carbonyl $=C=O$ and the alcoholic $-CH_2(OH)$ and $=CH(OH)$ groups.[1] In the two groups of most important natural sugars n is either 5, as in the pentoses (arabinose, xylose, ribose), or 6, as in the hexoses (glucose, fructose, mannose, galactose, etc.).

By oxidation of the terminal groups of sugars on carbons 1 or 6, or both, various acids may be derived. Some of these are shown below. Glucuronic acid is of much interest to the physiologist, while D-galacturonic acid is the main building unit of the pectic substances. Both glucuronic and galacturonic acids are *sugar acids* because they contain the carbonyl and alcoholic groups in addition to the carboxyl group COOH characteristic of organic acids:

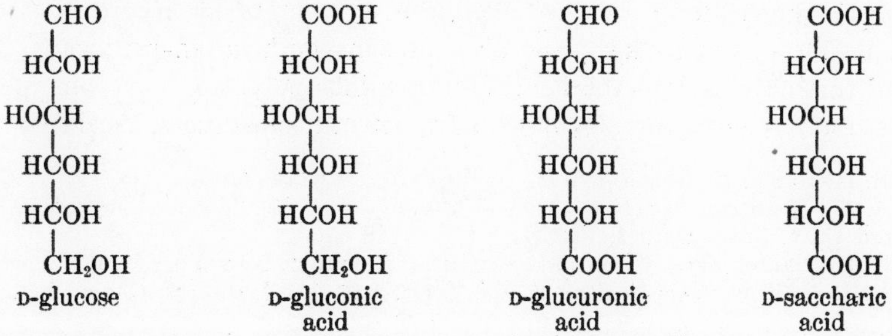

CHO	COOH	CHO	COOH
HCOH	HCOH	HCOH	HCOH
HOCH	HOCH	HOCH	HOCH
HCOH	HCOH	HCOH	HCOH
HCOH	HCOH	HCOH	HCOH
CH_2OH	CH_2OH	COOH	COOH
D-glucose	D-gluconic acid	D-glucuronic acid	D-saccharic acid

[1] E. F. and K. F. Armstrong, *The Carbohydrates*. Longmans, Green, New York, 1934.

CHO   COOH   CHO   COOH

HCOH   HCOH   HCOH   HCOH

HOCH   HOCH   HOCH   HOCH

HOCH   HOCH   HOCH   HOCH

HCOH   HCOH   HCOH   HCOH

CH_2OH CH_2OH COOH   COOH

D-galactose   D-galactonic acid   D-galacturonic acid   D-mucic acid

The disaccharides (sucrose, maltose, lactose, etc.) are derived by elimination of one molecule of water from two molecules of monosaccharides. Similarly the polysaccharides are formed by elimination of $n - 1$ molecules of water from n molecules of monosaccharides. The polysaccharides composed of up to four monosaccharides are designated[2] as *oligosaccharides,* a useful distinction because of the much larger number of basic units in many of the common polysaccharides like cellulose, starch, etc.

Most polysaccharides form colloidal solutions and are difficult to obtain in a pure state. They consist mainly of linear or branched chains of monosaccharide units; others contain a second monosaccharide. Cellulose and starch, both made up of glucose units, are the most important polysaccharides. They are accompanied in plants by lignin, hemicelluloses, and pectic substances. Other important polysaccharides are inulin, and those formed by bacteria.

The terms hemicelluloses and gums are not well defined.[3,4] On hydrolysis they yield mostly glucose, mannose, galactose, arabinose, or xylose. Glucuronic, mannuronic, and galacturonic acids are also components of some hemicelluloses.[3-6] Rarely is it possible to obtain hemicellulose preparations composed of one sugar only; more frequently, on hydrolysis, mixtures of two or more sugars are obtained. Following Karrer's suggestion,[7] the hemicelluloses are grouped according to the composing sugars as hexosans or pentosans or hexosan-pentosans. Norman[3] further classifies the hemicelluloses into polyoses (hexosans, pentosans, etc.), cellulosans (cellulosic framework substances asociated with

[2] B. Helferich, E. Bohne, and S. Winkler, *Ber.,* 63, 989 (1930).

[3] A. G. Norman, *The Biochemistry of Cellulose, the Polyuronides, Lignin, etc.* Oxford Univ. Press, Oxford, 1937.

[4] C. L. Mantell, *The Water-Soluble Gums.* Reinhold, New York, 1947.

[5] R. J. McIlroy, *New Zealand J. Sci. Tech.,* B26, 161 (1944); *J. Chem. Soc.,* 1945, 796.

[6] R. E. Gill, E. L. Hirst, and J. K. N. Jones, *J. Chem. Soc.,* 1946, 1025.

[7] P. Karrer, *Einführung in die Chemie der polymeren Kohlenhydrate.* Akad. Verlagsgesellschaft, Leipzig, 1925.

cellulose, as xylan and mannan), and polyuronides (*cyto-uronides*) which contain uronic acids. The term *polyuronide*, first used by Smolenski,[8] includes the pectic substances.

The pectic substances are polyuronides composed mostly of anhydrogalacturonic acid residues. The basic structure of these materials, the polygalacturonic acids, are now thought to be composed entirely of anhydrogalacturonic acid residues, although some authors[9] still maintain that other carbohydrates, for example arabinose, galactose, sorbose, rhamnose,[10] are attached to the chains of anhydrogalacturonic acid units. Furthermore, there is strong indication that acetyl groups might occur in some pectins, for example, in sugar beet roots (see Chapter IV, section V). The carboxyl groups in pectic polygalacturonides are either free or partially esterified with methyl alcohol or form salts with various cations.

The term *pectin* has been derived from the Greek "πηχτος," meaning to congeal or solidify.[11]

The limits of the term *pectic substances* are not yet sharply defined. This uncertainty is especially acute concerning the minimum molecular size of the pectic polygalacturonic acid or, in other words, the minimum molecular weight (whatever the exact meaning of the term molecule may be in this case) at which a polygalacturonic acid also becomes a pectic acid. As will be shown below, we simply evade this important issue by using the expression *colloidal polygalacturonic acids*, a term which, while still ambiguous, is the best we can manage at the present time.

The characteristics and composition of pectic preparations depend on the source material and on the method of preparation. Most pectic preparations include other substances (galactose, arabinose, etc.), some of which occur with such regularity that they were regarded by many as actual components of the pectic materials. The extreme heterogeneity of the pectic substances contributes a great deal to the uncertainty of definition. During the past decade considerable progress was made in the separation and elucidation of both pectic substances and accompanying materials, resulting in somewhat sharper definition.

The nomenclature of the pectic substances has been very confusing at times. The literature contains well over fifty different terms for the various pectic substances and the meaning of these often overlap and may not be simply explained or, indeed, understood. It is important, there-

[8] K. Smolenski, *Roczniki Chemji*, 3, 86 (1923); 4, 72 (1924).
[9] R. Speiser, *J. Polymer Sci.*, 2, 281 (1947).
[10] C. M. Martin and F. H. Reuter, *Nature*, 164, 373 (1949); W. D. Maclay, R. M. McCready, and H. S. Owens, paper given at the San Francisco Meeting of the American Chemical Society, March, 1949.
[11] H. Braconnot, *Ann. Chim. Phys.*, Sér. 2, 28, 173 (1825).

fore, at the outset, to clarify the nomenclature which will be used in this volume.

Practically every author who made a major effort in this field coined and used a new terminology. The first successful attempt to bring order into this chaos was made in 1926 by a committee of the American Chemical Society. The nomenclature recommended by this committee[12] was subsequently used by most workers in the United States and by many elsewhere. By 1941, however, our knowledge of the chemistry of pectic materials had advanced considerably and a revision of these definitions was undertaken. The *Revised Nomenclature of the Pectic Substances* was reported to the Society in 1943[13] and adopted as official in April, 1944. Wherever applicable, this terminology will be used throughout the present volume.

"Pectic substances. Pectic substances is a group designation for those complex, colloidal carbohydrate derivatives which occur in, or are prepared from, plants and contain a large proportion of anhydrogalacturonic acid units which are thought to exist in a chain-like combination. The carboxyl groups of polygalacturonic acids may be partly esterified by methyl groups and partly or completely neutralized by one or more bases."

The term *pectic substances* appears to be the most satisfactory general designation for this group of compounds. It is undesirable to use *pectin* or *pectins* for this purpose. These substances are described as *carbohydrate derivatives* in contrast to *carbohydrates*. In general, pectic substances are distinguished from polysaccharides by the possession of carboxyl groups. These carboxyl groups are parts of the anhydrogalacturonic acid units characteristic of all pectic substances. Inasmuch as (theoretically at least) galacturonic acid in plants is derived from galactose by oxidation of the alcoholic group on the terminal (6) carbon atom, galacturonic acid as well as the pectic substances are regarded as derivatives of carbohydrates.

"Protopectin. The term *protopectin* is applied to the water-insoluble parent pectic substance which occurs in plants and which, upon restricted hydrolysis, yields pectinic acids."

The original pectic substance occurring in plants has been frequently designated as *pectose*. This term, used by many workers, especially in England, is not suitable because the suffix *ose* is almost exclusively reserved for crystalline sugars. An important exception is *cellulose*, which

[12] C. S. Brinton, W. H. Dore, H. J. Wichmann, J. J. Willaman, and C. P. Wilson, *J. Am. Chem. Soc.,* **49,** 38 (1927).

[13] G. L. Baker, G. H. Joseph, Z. I. Kertesz, H. H. Mottern, and A. G. Olsen, *Chem. Eng. News,* **22,** 105 (1944).

is too firmly established to be changed. To be sure, the term *pectinogen* is most correct of the three, but some workers used it for pectinic acids obtained from the originally insoluble[14] pectic compound rather than, in the true sense, for the parent substance itself. The use of the term in such dual manner gives rise to confusion. Since the name *protopectin* is older and also correct genetically, its use is logical and satisfactory. For a further discussion of protopectin see Chapter III, Section III.

"Pectinic acids. The term *pectinic acids* is used for colloidal polygalacturonic acids containing more than a negligible proportion of methyl ester groups. Pectinic acids, under suitable conditions, are capable of forming gels [jellies] with sugar and acid or, if suitably low in methoxyl content, with certain metallic ions. The salts of pectinic acids are either normal or acid pectinates."

The term *pectinic acid* does not appear in the 1926 nomenclature. Its revival was necessitated by the definition of pectin, given below, according to which pectin must be able to form a sugar-acid jelly.[15] This left without definition compounds which are mostly composed of polygalacturonic acids and contain more than a negligible proportion of methoxyl, but are not necessarily capable of forming the customary pectin-sugar-acid jelly. It appeared desirable, therefore, to reintroduce the name pectinic acid which was first proposed by Chodnew[16] one hundred years ago. The use of this term, according to the present definition, also facilitates the exact description of the chemical characteristics of various salts and derivatives, and brings to the fore their important acidic character. It is used preferably to designate well-defined preparations which are relatively free from extraneous ballast substances. All commercial undiluted pectin preparations are pectinic acids.

"Pectin. The general term *pectin* (or pectins) designates those water-soluble pectinic acids of varying methyl ester content and degree of neutralization which are capable of forming gels with sugar and acid under suitable conditions."

[14] The expressions *soluble* and *solution* are used for pectic substances throughout this volume. In the strict sense of the word, pectic substances as colloids are not soluble in water or capable of forming true solutions. The use of other expressions, however, would be impractical and cause misunderstandings inasmuch as the terminology of colloid chemistry is far from standardized.

[15] The meanings of the terms *jelly* and *gel* as used in this volume should be made clear. There are no clear and generally accepted definitions for these terms. Many authors use them interchangeably. Without any claims of theoretical significance, *jelly* will be used here for the typical product formed from pectin, sugar, and acid under certain conditions. This is the jelly of commerce as defined in federal standards (see Chapter XXVII). The term *gel* is retained for the apparently similar physical state obtained by cooling concentrated solutions or by precipitating certain pectic substances with acid or polyvalent ions. See also Chapter VII, Section 15.

[16] A. Chodnew, *Ann. Chem. Pharm.,* **51**, 355 (1844).

Thus the typical characteristic of a pectin is the formation of the well-known pectin-sugar-acid jelly. There are on the market commercial pectin preparations which are not completely soluble in water but soluble in fruit juices and which do form satisfactory jellies. Such pectins should be regarded as borderline cases. The inclusion of the term *water-soluble* became necessary in order to conform with common usage and to avoid conflict with the specifications given by the *National Formulary*.[17]

The so-called *low-ester* or *low-methoxyl* pectins come within the scope of the term pectin as defined above, because they do form sugar-acid jellies, although not under the same conditions as typical pectins. The line of demarcation between pectins and low-ester pectins is ill-defined. One may state that pectins, in the usual concentrations, will not form jellies in the usual acidity range in the presence of traces of calcium without at least 50% sugar; low-ester pectins will form gels in the presence of traces of calcium at low sugar concentrations but, as a rule, not with sugar alone. There is considerable variation in the degree of esterification at which this change will occur; actually (due to the heterogeneity of pectic preparations), a dividing region exists rather than a line. Various other conditions will also influence the degree of esterification at which a *pectin* becomes a *low-ester pectin*. With all these reservations, one may state that the dividing region is usually about 50% esterification. This matter is further discussed in Chapter III, Section II.

The terminology of low-ester pectins is further complicated by the fact that these compounds must have polyvalent cations (usually calcium) present in order to form gels or jellies which are, at least in part, composed of acid calcium pectinates. It is generally understood, however, that both pectins and low-ester pectins as used in commerce contain added salts of some kind. This is not expressed in the terms *pectin* and *low-ester pectin* but should be taken into consideration in defining the preparations as pectinic acids.

These definitions do not include any term which would be applicable to a completely methylated pectic acid. As will be shown later, such an *ideal pectin* should contain 16.3% methoxyl and has not been isolated as yet. If and when this occurs, a new term will have to be coined. It certainly could not be called a pectinic acid due to the presence of ester groups attached to all carboxyls.

"*Pectic acid.* The term *pectic acid* is applied to pectic substances mostly composed of colloidal polygalacturonic acids and essentially free from methyl ester groups. The salts of pectic acid are either normal or acid pectates."

[17] *National Formulary VIII*. American Pharmaceutical Association, Washington, D. C., 1946.

The reason for the expression, *essentially free from methyl ester groups,* was the apparent presence in pectic acid preparations of some methyl groups. It is likely that most of the *methoxyl* found in pectic acids by various authors was in reality ethanol retained by the preparation rather than methyl groups which were part of the pectic substance itself.[18] The term *colloidal* is used here again to exclude any polygalacturonic acids which contain insufficient anhydrogalacturonic acid units (or lack the necessary structure) and consequently do not show the typical colloidal properties of pectic substances.

The interrelation of these various pectic substances may best be shown in a diagram (Fig. 1). The scheme demonstrates the continuity and overlapping often observed with polymers.

There are a few further points in connection with terminology which must be clarified at this time. Two groups of polysaccharides almost invariably accompany the pectic substances in plants and in crude preparations. Arabans and galactans are not regarded as pectic substances and their presence in pectic preparations is thought to be incidental, or more correctly, the result of great similarity of physical properties. Although there is considerable likelihood that they are in some manner related to the pectic substances, at the present time there is no creditable theory which would clearly state their genetical relationship to the polyuronides. Because of their almost universal presence in pectic preparations they have been included in this volume (see Chapter IV, Section VI).

At this point there is also need to state the meaning of the expressions *free pectinic acids* (free pectins) and *soluble pectic compounds,* as contrasted with *insoluble pectic compounds.* These terms have no precise meaning and are, for the most part, of historical importance. At times, however, they may be employed to great advantage in showing the gross distribution of various pectic materials.

The term *free pectin* is synonymous with *soluble pectic substances,* both meaning fractions which are soluble in cold water without the aid of additional treatments or solvents.[19] Because of the overlapping of the various groups of pectic compounds these expressions have only arbitrary meaning and should always be supplemented with precise descriptions of the procedures applied. Even so, the division is not sharp because the solubility behavior of pectic compounds seems to undergo modification during extended treatment and will always depend on specific conditions, such as acidity, presence of various ions, etc. The *free* or *soluble* fraction may include, under certain conditions, all pectic materials with the ex-

[18] C. H. Hills, C. L. Ogg, and R. Speiser, *Ind. Eng. Chem., Anal. Ed.,* 17, 507 (1945).
[19] M. H. Carré, *Biochem. J.,* 19, 257 (1925).

ception of protopectin. Under ordinary conditions, however, it consists mostly of pectinic acids of fairly high degree of esterification (over 4% methoxyl content). The main reason for the insufficient solubility of other pectinic acids and of pectic acids is the common presence in plant tissues

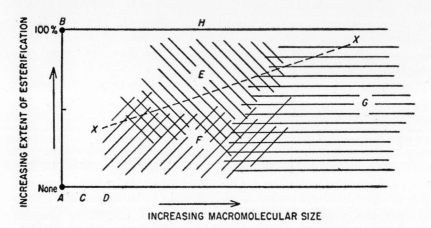

Fig. 1. Schematic illustration of the interrelation of pectic substances.

The basic monomer of the pectic substances is D-galacturonic acid, *A*. Directly above it is D-galacturonic acid methyl ester, *B*. To the right of galacturonic acid are polygalacturonic acids composed of increasing numbers of anhydrogalacturonic acid units. Some of these (near the left, *C*) do not contain enough uronic acid units to show colloidal properties and therefore are not true pectic substances. The threshold of characteristic colloidal behavior is passed at some yet unknown degree of polymerization, *D*, as the size of the polygalacturonic acid increases. At that point the term "pectic acid" becomes applicable. Above the pectic acids are the pectinic acids of various degrees of esterification. Of these, a special group of pectinic acids, the pectins, *E*, contain over 6% methoxyl and are yet of the highest commercial importance. The "low-methoxyl" (low-ester) pectins of 2–7% methoxyl content *F*, are shown directly under the pectins. Protopectins, only vaguely divided from pectinic acids, are on the right side of the scheme, *G*, indicating the contention presented later in Chapter III that protopectins are pectinic acids of large molecular sizes. The "ideal," completely esterified pectinic acids (16.35% methoxyl), not yet found in nature, would fall on the top line, *H*. Note the dotted line *X–X* which roughly divides the whole field into compounds which do or do not form water-insoluble calcium salts and the effect of molecular size and methyl ester content thereupon. Frequent references will be made later in the text to this assumed and idealized interrelationship of pectic substances. For the calculated composition of various pectinic and pectic acids see Tables 6 and 8.

of polyvalent cations which will depress the solubility of both pectic acids and low-ester pectinic acids. This matter will be discussed more fully in Chapters III and VI.

TABLE 1

GLOSSARY OF OBSOLETE TERMS DESIGNATING PECTIC SUBSTANCES

Obsolete term	Author and year
Protopectin	
	Tschirch (1907)
Pectin	Braconnot (1831), Tollens and Tromp de Haas (1895), Ehrlich (1917)
Pectose	Frémy (1840), Mangin (1891), Caldwell (1917), Fellenberg (1918), Wurdack (1923), Carré (Mrs. Branfoot) (1925)
Pectinogen	Clayson, Norris, and Schryver (1921), Nanji, Paton, and Ling (1925)
Pectocellulose	Onslow (1921), Cross (1895)
Lignocellulose	Cross (1895)
"Original pectin" (Genuines Pektin)	Ehrlich (1917)
Propectin	Ehrlich (1917)
"Urpektin"	Ehrlich (1917)
Pectin and Pectinic Acids	
	Braconnot (1825)
	Chodnew (1844)
Pectosic acid	Chodnew (1846), Frémy (1848)
Neutral pectin	Sloep (1928)
Free pectin	Sucharipa (1924)
Soluble pectin	Many authors
Hydratopectin	Ehrlich (1917)
"Rohpektin"	Ehrlich (1917)
Pectic acid	Ehrlich (1917), Link (1930)
Pectinylic acid	Leo, Taylor, and Lindsey (1949)
Pectic Acids and Polygalacturonic Acids	
	Braconnot (1825)
	Ehrlich (1917)
"Gallertsäure"	Braconnot (1831)
Pectin	Vanquelin (1829), Frémy (1848), Onslow (1921), Schryver and Haynes (1916), Tollens and Tromp de Haas (1895)
Cytopectic acid	Clayson, Norris, and Schryver (1921)
Pectosic acid	Frémy (1847)
Degraded or Hydrolyzed Pectinic or Pectic Acids and Polygalacturonic Acids	
Metapectin	Frémy (1848)
Parapectin	Frémy (1848)
"Überpektinsäure"	Chodnew (1844)
Parapectic acid	Frémy (1848)
Metapectic acid	Frémy, Chodnew (1845), Scheibler (1868), Herzfeld (1889), Mangin (1891), Branfoot (1929)
Dipectic acid	Ehrlich et al. (1917–1935)
"Gel-Pektolsäure" "Pektolsäure" "Pektolaktonsäure" Digalacturonic acids a, b, c Tetragalacturonic acids a, b, c, etc.	Ehrlich et al.

Obviously, the term *insoluble pectic substances* will designate those pectic polyuronides which do not dissolve in cold water. This fraction may again include a variety of pectic materials.

In order to facilitate the orientation of those who are not familiar with the terminology described on the previous pages, or those who encounter other terms in the literature, a glossary of obsolete terms designating pectic substances[13] is given in Table 1. It may be noted that it is often impossible to classify certain terms definitely because of insufficient characterization of preparations described by some authors. No attempt has been made to quote all workers who used these terms; only those who made important contributions are listed. The date following the author's name is the earliest printed use of the designation.

CHAPTER II

D-Galacturonic Acid

I. INTRODUCTION

According to the definition, polygalacturonic acids composed of anhydrogalacturonic acid units make up the basic skeleton of all pectic substances. As will be shown below, the characteristics of pectic substances often reflect the properties and behavior of galacturonic acid. For this reason it will be expedient to discuss galacturonic acid and its determination in some detail.

There was a long period in pectin chemistry when the aim of most investigators was to establish the elementary composition of pectic substances. During the nineteenth century no definite chemical conception prevailed concerning the structure of pectic materials except that they were related to the carbohydrates and had the elementary composition typical of these compounds. Tollens and Tromp de Haas[20] assumed that a carbohydrate containing carboxyl groups was present in pectic substances. Smolenski,[21] in 1911, reported the presence in sugar beets of a uronic acid, thought to be glucuronic acid, and in 1917 Suarez[22] noted the occurrence in lemons of "an isomer of glucuronic acid." Later in the same year Ehrlich[23] disclosed the fact that pectic substances were composed principally of galacturonic acid (or more correctly of polymers formed from anhydrogalacturonic acid units). Racemic galacturonic acid was previously described by Fischer and Hertz[24] as "aldehyde mucic acid."

Although galacturonic acid as such is likely to be present in plant tissues, there is no precise information available on this point. As will be seen from the discussion in Chapter VIII, our present methods of

[20] B. Tollens and R. W. Tromp de Haas, *Ann.*, **286**, 278, 292 (1895).
[21] K. Smolenski, *Z. physiol. Chem.*, **71**, 266 (1911).
[22] M. L. Suarez, *Chem.-Ztg.*, **41**, 87 (1917).
[23] F. Ehrlich, *Chem.-Ztg.*, **41**, 197 (1917).
[24] E. Fischer and J. Hertz, *Ber.*, **25**, 1247 (1892).

estimation are not sufficiently specific to show the presence of small proportions of galacturonic acid in the presence of large quantities of other carbohydrates and organic acids.[25]   Galacturonic acid is a component of many natural substances, such as plant gums, mucilages, and as stated before, of some hemicelluloses.[26] Saponins and some bacterial polysaccharides[27] were also reported to contain galacturonic acid. Its most important occurrence, however, is in the pectic substances and the best sources are pectinic and pectic acids. Even crude pectinic acid preparations contain 20 to 60% galacturonic acid in the form of polygalacturonic acid, and some pectic acid preparations have been obtained of such purity that upon hydrolysis they yielded no other substance but D-galacturonic acid.[28]

Of the 16 possible isomeric hexuronic acids only three, D-glucuronic, D-galacturonic, and D-mannuronic acids, have been found to occur in nature. Each of these, as well as its enantiomorph, has been synthesized,[29] and in addition other uronic acids not known to occur in natural products have been prepared by similar means. Of the three isomeric galacturonic acids (D, L, and DL) only the D form has been found in natural products.

1	CHO	CHO
2	HCOH	HOCH
3	HOCH	HCOH
4	HOCH	HCOH
5	HCOH	HOCH
6	COOH	COOH
	D-galacturonic acid	L-galacturonic acid

Examination of the formula of galacturonic acid reveals that it is related to the aldoses and the aldonic acids. As an aldose it gives rise

[25] According to a recent report by T. H. Harris (*J. Assoc. Official Agr. Chem.*, 31, 501 (1948) apple juice contains 0.0013–0.0054 mg. % galacturonic acid. Further work on this subject is needed before these values can be accepted because the apple juice samples used in these determinations were concentrated (*in vacuo*) to 60% solids content. Reducing compounds are known to be formed from pectic substances upon extensive heating (R. C. Merrill and M. Weeks, *J. Am. Chem. Soc.*, 67, 2244 (1945)) and thus the galacturonic acid found by Harris might have been formed as the consequence of the thermal treatment during the preparation of the sample for analysis. This uncertainty is admitted in the statement by Harris that "very little if any galacturonic acid could be detected in good apple juice."

[26] C. Niemann and K. P. Link, *J. Biol. Chem.*, 104, 205 (1934).

[27] M. Heidelberger, F. E. Kendall, and H. W. Scherp, *J. Exptl. Med.*, 64, 559 (1936).

[28] E. L. Hirst, *J. Chem. Soc.*, 1942, 70.

[29] C. Niemann and K. P. Link, *J. Biol. Chem.*, 95, 203 (1932); 104, 195 (1934); 106, 773 (1934); etc.

to pyranose, furanose, and aldehyde derivatives; as an acid it forms salts and other derivatives characteristic of the carboxyl group. The numbering plan commonly used with uronic acids makes the aldehyde carbon number one. This deviates from I.U.C. rule 64 in that the principal function, the carboxyl, is not number one but number six.[30]

Apparently D-galacturonic acid occurs in natural pectic substances only in the pyranoside form. Morell and Link[31] measured the velocity of the acid hydrolysis of α-methyl-D-galacturonide and concluded that the existence of a pyranoside structure in this compound is most probable. Later Levene and Kreider[32] oxidized α-methyl-2,3,4,-trimethyl-L-araboglutaric acid (identified as its dimethylamide). This definitely establishes the pyranoside structure of α-methyl-D-galacturonide methyl ester. Smith[33] obtained the furanose form of methylgalacturonoside from the hydrolysis products of a methylated citrus pectic acid, but apparently the furanose form was produced by the acid hydrolysis of the methylated pectic acid and was not present in the original material.

In contrast to glucuronic and mannuronic acids, D-galacturonic acid does not form a crystalline lactone. Based on information obtained from electrometric titration curves, Wlostowska[34] states that in a water solution of D-galacturonic acid about 5–6% of the carboxyl groups are present in the form of a lactone.

D-galacturonic acid   D-galacturonic
(pyranose modification)   lactone (pyranose
                             modification)

Galacturonic acid usually crystallizes as the monohydrate, $C_6H_{10}O_7.H_2O$ in the α form. The β form, which does not contain water of crystallization, may be prepared from the α form by prolonged boiling in absolute ethanol or by

[30] A. M. Patterson, *J. Am. Chem. Soc.*, **55**, 3905 (1933).
[31] S. Morell and K. P. Link, *J. Biol. Chem.*, **104**, 183 (1934).
[32] P. A. Levene and L. C. Kreider, *J. Biol. Chem.*, **120**, 498 (1938).
[33] F. Smith, *Chem. & Ind.*, **1939**, 363; *J. Chem. Soc.*, **1940**, 1106, 1506.
[34] W. Wlostowska, *Roczniki Chemji*, **10**, 342 (1930).

crystallization from solutions containing high concentrations of ethanol.[35] Both are easily soluble in water but the β isomer is much more soluble in aqueous ethanol. In absolute ethanol, again the a form is more soluble.

Crystals of the monohydrate sinter at 100°C., turn brown at 130–150°, and decompose with carbonization at 156–159°. According to Ehrlich[36] its 2% water solution has an initial $[a]_D^{20}$ of $+98°$ which changes to the final equilibrium rotation value of $+50.9°$. Isbell and Frush[37] report that the mutarotation of the monohydrate follows a course similar to that of a-D-galactopyranose, and that it may be represented by the following equation:

$$[a]_D^{20} = 44.83 \times 10^{-0.0148t} + 10.26 \times 10^{-0.16t} + 51.90$$

This corresponds to the initial value of $+107.0$ and an equilibrium value of $+51.9°$. Pigman[38] gives an equilibrium value $+51.5°$, Collatz[39] $+50.74°$, and Speiser, Hills, and Eddy[40] give $+51.7°$. The average equilibrium value calculated from the nine references in Table 2 is $+51.3°$. Ehrlich and Schubert[35] report the initial $[a]_D^{20}$ of the β form to be $+27°$ which changes to $+55.3°$. Isbell and Frush[41] found the initial $[a]_D^{20}$ of the β form as set free from crystalline sodium galacturonate to be $+21.9°$. The preparation of the pure crystalline β modification is difficult, and apparently the product ordinarily obtained contains more or less of the a modification.

Galacturonic acid reacts with phenlhydrazine, gives the phloroglucinol, orcinol, resorcinol, and naphthoresorcinol tests, and in general all reactions typical of sugars. It reduces Fehling solution and is oxidized by an alkaline solution of iodine. Contrary to previous observations,[42] both galacturonic and glucuronic acids form reductones[43] when heated in an alkaline solution. The proportion of reductone, as measured by titration with 2,6-dichlorobenzenoneindophenol,[44] is equivalent per mole to that formed from glucose and galactose.[45]

The carboxyl group is titratable and forms salts. According to Karrer and Schwarzenbach[46] galacturonic acid has a pK of 3.49 at 23.6°C. Speiser, Hills, and Eddy[40] found a similar value, 3.42 (± 0.01) at 27°C. (K

[35] F. Ehrlich and F. Schubert, *Ber.*, **62**, 1974 (1929).
[36] F. Ehrlich, *Ber.*, **65**, 352 (1932).
[37] H. S. Isbell and H. L. Frush, *J. Research Natl. Bur. Standards*, **31**, 33 (1943).
[38] W. W. Pigman, *J. Research Natl. Bur. Standards*, **25**, 301 (1940).
[39] H. Collatz, *Ber.*, **69**, 485 (1936).
[40] R. Speiser, C. H. Hills, and C. R. Eddy, *J. Phys. Chem.*, **49**, 328 (1945).
[41] H. S. Isbell and H. L. Frush, *J. Research Natl. Bur. Standards*, **32**, 77 (1944).
[42] H. v. Euler and E. Klussmann, *Arkiv Kemi, Mineral. Geol.*, **B11**, Nos. 8, 11, 12 (1933).
[43] T. Reichstein and R. Oppenauer, *Helv. Chim. Acta*, **16**, 988 (1933). N. V. Noury and van der Lande's Exploitatis Maatschappij, Dutch Pat. 56,744 (1944); *C. A.* **41**, 4169 (1947).
[44] Z. I. Kertesz, *J. Biol. Chem.*, **104**, 483 (1934).
[45] Z. I. Kertesz, *unpublished data*, 1935.
[46] P. Karrer and G. Schwarzenbach, *Helv. Chim. Acta*, **17**, 58 (1934).

= 3.81 × 10⁻⁴). Galacturonic acid is thus comparable in strength to formic and malic acids. These latter authors have also obtained titration curves for galacturonic acid and found that it behaves as any monobasic acid with the degree of dissociation depending only on the pH but not changing with the concentration. Recently Isbell and Frush[47] and Pasternack and Regna[48] prepared a number of new crystalline salts of galacturonic acid, some of which contain monovalent and divalent metal in combination with the α-pyranose modification of galacturonic acid. In addition to the reducing group and the carboxyl group, galacturonic acid also contains hydroxyls which may be methylated, acetylated, and substituted in various other ways. Table 2 shows the constants of D-galacturonic acid and of some of its salts and derivatives. A complete list of the known derivatives of galacturonic acid would be several times as long as that given in Table 2 and would be out of place in this volume.[49]

II. PREPARATION OF GALACTURONIC ACID

Obviously, a pure polygalacturonic acid is the most suitable starting material for making galacturonic acid. Its preparation is described in

[47] H. S. Isbell and H. L. Frush, *J. Research Natl. Bur. Standards,* **32,** 77 (1944); **33,** 389 (1944).
[48] R. Pasternack and P. P. Regna, U. S. Pat. 2,338,534 (1944).
[49] For some of the more recent information on this subject see: J. K. N. Jones and M. Stacey, *J. Chem. Soc.,* **1947,** 1340. H. L. Frush and H. S. Isbell, *J. Research Natl. Bur. Standards,* **41,** 609 (1948). H. L. Fraenkel-Conrat and H. S. Olcott, *J. Biol. Chem.,* **161,** 259 (1945).
[50] H. Collatz, *Ber.,* **69,** 485 (1936).
[51] F. Ehrlich and R. Guttmann, *Biochem. Z.,* **259,** 100 (1933).
[52] F. Ehrlich and F. Schubert, *Ber.* **62,** 1974 (1929).
[53] H. S. Isbell and H. L. Frush, *J. Research Natl. Bur. Standards,* **31,** 33 (1943).
[54] S. Johnstin and K. S. Potter, *J. Biol. Chem.,* **110,** 279 (1935).
[55] C. Niemann and K. P. Link, *J. Biol. Chem.,* **104,** 195 (1934).
[56] C. Niemann and K. P. Link, *J. Biol. Chem.,* **106,** 773 (1934).
[57] W. W. Pigman, *J. Research Natl. Bur. Standards,* **25,** 301 (1940).
[58] R. Speiser, C. H. Hills, and C. R. Eddy, *J. Phys. Chem.,* **49,** 328 (1945).
[59] C. Niemann and K. P. Link, *J. Biol. Chem.,* **95,** 203 (1932).
[60] C. Niemann and K. P. Link, *J. Biol. Chem.,* **104,** 743 (1934).
[61] S. Morell and K. P. Link, *J. Biol. Chem.,* **108,** 763 (1935).
[62] H. M. Sell and K. P. Link, *J. Biol. Chem.,* **125,** 229 (1938).
[63] H. S. Isbell and H. L. Frush, *J. Research Natl. Bur. Standards,* **32,** 77 (1944).
[64] R. Pasternack and P. P. Regna, U. S. Pat. 2,338,534 (1944).
[65] C. Niemann, E. Schoeffel, and K. P. Link, *J. Biol. Chem.,* **101,** 337 (1933).
[66] S. Morell and K. P. Link, *J. Biol. Chem.,* **100,** 385 (1933).
[67] H. Ohle and G. Berend, *Ber.,* **58,** 2585 (1925).
[68] H. M. Sell and K. P. Link, *J. Am. Chem. Soc.,* **60,** 1813 (1938).
[69] F. Ehrlich and R. Guttmann, *Ber.,* **66,** 220 (1933).
[70] S. Morell and K. P. Link, *J. Biol. Chem.,* **104,** 183 (1934).
[71] P. A. Levene and L. C. Kreider, *J. Biol. Chem.,* **120,** 597 (1937).
[72] R. S. Tipson, *J. Biol. Chem.,* **125,** 341 (1938).

TABLE 2

Some Derivatives of Galacturonic Acid

Compound	$[\alpha]_D^{22}$ (in water)		Melting point, °C.			Ref. Nos.
	Initial	Final	Melts	Sinters	Decomp.	
α-D-Galacturonic acid.-H₂O	+98°	+51.3° (av.)	—	110	156–159	50–59
β-D-Galacturonic acid	+27°	+56.0° (av.)	—	—	160	52,53
DL-Galacturonic acid	—	0.0°	—	110	156–158	56,57
L-Galacturonic acid	—	−52–56°	156	112–113	156–163	56,60
α-D-Galacturonic acid methyl ester in methanol	+75.5°	+38°	146–148	—	142	61,62
Ba-D-galacturonate	—	24–29°	—	—	180	55
Cd-β-D-galacturonate.-2H₂O	—	+28.4°	—	—	—	63
Ca-α-D-galacturonate.-2H₂O	—	+36.8°	—	—	...	63
K-β-D-galacturonate.-1/2H₂O	—	+31.6°	—	—	—	63
K-Ca-α-D-galacturonate.6H₂O	—	+31.4°	—	—	—	63
Ag-β-D-galacturonate.-1/2H₂O	—	+25.1°	—	—	—	63
Na-β-D-galacturonate	—	+36.0°	—	—	—	52,63
Na-Ba-α-D-galacturonate.6H₂O	—	+27.8°	—	—	—	63
Na-Ca-α-D-galacturonate.6H₂O	—	+32.4–33.0	—	—	—	63,64
Na-Sr-α-D-galacturonate.6H₂O	—	+30.2°	—	—	—	64
Ba-p-bromophenylhydrazone-D-galacturonate	—	—	(over 250)			65
Ba-methyl-D-galacturonate	—	+99.1°	215	—	—	66
K-diacetone-D-galacturonate.1/2H₂O	—	−61–66°	—	—	200	55,67,68
α-Methyl-D-galacturonic acid.2H₂O	—	+128.8° (av.)	109–114	108	120	55,66,69 70,71
2,3,4-Trimethyl-D-galacturonic acid	+126°	+112°	96–98	—	—	72
α-Methyl-D-galacturonic acid methyl ester.H₂O	—	+121–125°	137–140	138	140	55,66,69
Brucine-D-galacturonate.H₂O	—	−7.5°	—	—	189	67
Morphine galacturonate	—	−56.6°	—	—	162–163	52
Cinchonine-D-galacturonate	—	+139°	258	—	—	52

Chapter VI, Section VI. If commercial powdered pectins are used, the sugar and other materials (such as buffers added for standardization) should be separated before hydrolysis. Admixed arabans, galactans, and as much of the ash constituents as possible should also be removed. Thorough extraction with 60% ethanol containing 1% hydrochloric acid at 50 to 60°C. for a few hours, followed by washing with 95% ethanol, is the minimum purification to assure the presence of a low proportion of compounds other than galacturonic acid in the hydrolyzate.

Until about 1932 the polygalacturonic acid was usually hydrolyzed by acids. Ehrlich[73] applied 1% sulfuric acid and Smolenski and Wlostowska[74] 0.5% sulfuric acid at an elevated temperature under pressure. Link and Nedden[75] used boiling 2.5% sulfuric acid for the hydrolysis. These procedures have the common drawback that both prolonged heating and shorter periods of heating under pressure cause the decomposition to proceed beyond hydrolysis with the production of furanoid bodies whose presence makes separation of the galacturonic acid difficult. In the early work the amorphous lead and barium salts were often used for the separation but were not entirely satisfactory. Both the use of acids for hydrolysis and preparation through the lead and barium salts are now obsolete.

The appearance on the market of commercial pectinases in 1931 simplified methods of preparation. By treatment with such enzymes the polygalacturonic acid complex can be completely hydrolyzed without causing further degenerative changes in the galacturonic acid. This was observed in the writer's laboratory as well as by Mehlitz,[76] but it was Ehrlich[77] who first described a complete procedure of preparation using the enzymic hydrolysis. He used an enzyme made from a *Penicillium Ehrlichii* which apparently was not different in its pectinase-forming ability from the molds used for commercial production of the enzymes.[76,78] During the past decade numerous improvements have been made in the enzymic preparation of galacturonic acid.[79] Mottern and Cole[80] employed a purified polygalacturonic acid prepared from commercial pectin and obtained a yield of 27% of galacturonic acid monohydrate from the polygalacturonic acid. Manville, Reithel, and Yamada,[81] in an appendix

[73] F. Ehrlich, *Chem.-Ztg.*, **41**, 197 (1917).
[74] K. Smolenski and W. Wlostowska, *Roczniki Chemji*, **6**, 743 (1926).
[75] K. P. Link and R. Nedden, *J. Biol. Chem.*, **94**, 307 (1931).
[76] A. Mehlitz, German Pat. 680,602 (1932).
[77] F. Ehrlich, *Biochem. Z.*, **250**, 525 (1932); **251**, 204 (1932).
[78] J. J. Willaman and Z. I. Kertesz, U. S. Pat. 1,932,833 (1933).
[79] C. S. Hollander, U. S. Pat. 2,370,961 (1945).
[80] H. H. Mottern and H. L. Cole, *J. Am. Chem. Soc.*, **61**, 2701 (1939).
[81] I. A. Manville, F. J. Reithel, and P. M. Yamada, *J. Am. Chem. Soc.*, **61**, 2973 (1939).

to this method recommended a minor modification of the method and obtained 36% of the theoretical yield.

More recently Pigman[82] used methanol as a solvent in the process. Galacturonic acid is more soluble in this solvent than in the ethanol used previously, increasing the final yield obtained to 74% of the weight of the starting material. This is a great improvement over the ethanol extraction method used until recently for the separation of the galacturonic acid from the digest.

The recent interest in galacturonic acid as a starting material for the synthesis of ascorbic acid[83] resulted in further improvements in its preparation. The main point of interest in these investigations is the use of double salts of galacturonic acid for its separation from the hydrolyzates of pectic substances. These double salts were discovered apparently independently by Pasternack and Regna[84] and Isbell and Frush.[85] The latter authors describe the separation of galacturonic acid in the form of either the sodium calcium or the sodium strontium salt, from pectic acid, from beet pulp, or from citrus residues. Processes using either enzymic or acid hydrolysis are described in detail in the Pasternack and Regna patent. The essence of the apparently superior enzymic method is as follows:

Some 20 g. of a highly active commercial pectinase is dissolved in 6 liters of water and 600 g. of commercial citrus pectin is introduced slowly under constant stirring. The mixture is kept (in the presence of toluol) until there is no further increase in its reducing power measured by the Fehling solution. The amount of enzyme used is regulated in such a manner that the digestion is complete in 10 to 12 days. Afterward the digest is first filtered with the aid of Super-Cel and then concentrated under reduced pressure. Two-thirds of the acidity ascertained by titration of a sample is neutralized with calcium carbonate and the remaining one-third with sodium carbonate. During the addition of the latter, the double sodium calcium salt of galacturonic acid crystallizes readily. After standing, the salt is separated by filtration, washed with water, and dried. The first crop yields about 90% of the available galacturonic acid in the form of the double salt.

With the application of these methods for the separation of the galacturonic acid from digests, interest was revived in the direct preparation of galacturonic acid from agricultural residues rich in pectic polyuronides, especially extracted beet slices.[86] In order to reduce the length

[82] W. W. Pigman, *J. Research Natl. Bur. Standards*, **25**, 301 (1940).

[83] H. S. Isbell, *J. Research Natl. Bur. Standards*, **33**, 45 (1944).

[84] R. Pasternack and P. P. Regna, U. S. Pat. 2,338,534 (1944).

[85] H. S. Isbell and H. L. Frush, *J. Research Natl. Bur. Standards*, **32**, 77 (1944); **33**, 389 (1944).

[86] E. Roboz and Z. I. Kertesz, *unpublished work*, 1948.

of the period required for complete digestion, a combination chemical-enzyme procedure has been developed in the writer's laboratory. In this the beet pulp is first heated to 70°C. in a slurry adjusted to pH 0.8–1.2 for 30–90 minutes. Then the slurry is cooled and the pH adjusted to 10.5 for 30 minutes. Now the mixture is brought to pH 3.5 and the enzymic digestion started. This chemical pretreatment reduces considerably the amount of enzyme required for accomplishing complete hydrolysis as compared with the above procedure. Or, to state the same thing differently, using the same proportion of enzyme, the hydrolysis can be completed more quickly.

The free galacturonic acid may easily be prepared from sodium calcium galacturonate or sodium strontium galacturonate. The following directions for the preparation of galacturonic acid from sodium strontium galacturonate are essentially those given by Frush and Isbell.[87]

One mole of sodium strontium galacturonate (798.2 g.) is added with stirring to 1000 cc. of aqueous 2 N sulfuric acid. The solution is filtered to remove the strontium sulfate and is then concentrated to a volume of 900 cc. at 40°C. in a vacuum still. The strontium sulfate that separates during the evaporation is removed by filtration and the residue on the filter is washed with 100 cc. of hot water. The clear filtrate is seeded with crystalline galacturonic acid hydrate and allowed to cool to room temperature with constant stirring. After crystallization at room temperature is substantially complete, the mixture is placed in a refrigerator for 18 hours. The crystals of galacturonic acid hydrate are collected on a filter and washed with ice water. Isbell and Frush obtained at this step a crop of 407 g. of substantially pure galacturonic acid monohydrate. The mother liquor is concentrated in a vacuum still to a volume of 400 cc. and then diluted with 1 liter of methanol added portionwise over a space of several hours. The crystallization of sodium sulfate is induced by seeding with some sodium sulfate decahydrate. The salt is separated by filtration, washed with methanol, and discarded. The methanol filtrate and the washed liquor are transferred to a vacuum still and the methanol is recovered. The sirupy residue (about 200 cc.) is seeded with galacturonic acid hydrate and the crystals which form in the course of a day are separated by filtration. By concentration of the mother liquor, additional material may be recovered. The total yield obtained by these authors was 607 g. or 95.4% of the theoretical. The galacturonic acid may be recrystallized readily from water or aqueous acetic acid.

If the potassium calcium salt is precipitated from the digest, the first precipitate usually contains some of the sodium present in the liquor since the sodium double salt is more insoluble than the potassium double salt. In addition to those mentioned here, several other double salts as well as normal salts have been prepared by Isbell and Frush. Mutarotation

[87] H. L. Frush and H. S. Isbell, *J. Research Natl. Bur. Standards*, **33**, 401 (1944).

studies[85,88] have shown that some of these contain the α-pyranose modification of galacturonic acid, whereas others contain the β-pyranose form. Some of the important constants of these salts, as well as most of the other known salts and derivatives of galacturonic acid, may be found in Table 2.

The use of various ion-exchange materials has been now extended to the field of carbohydrates and it is more than likely that improved and simplified methods for the separation and purification of galacturonic acid by such means will soon become available. The preliminary information now on hand indicates that ion-exchange agents can be used both for the separation of galacturonic acid from digests and for the transformation of the various salts into free galacturonic acid. This field is being rapidly developed at the present time. A novel idea along these lines is the batchwise treatment of a water slurry of the insoluble double salts of galacturonic acid with cation-exchange resins.[89]

Only reference can be made here to the synthesis of D-galacturonic acid from D-galactose,[90,91] of L-galacturonic acid from L-galactose[92] and from D-galactose,[93] and of DL-galacturonic acid from mucic acid.[94] A simple method for the synthesis of D-galacturonic acid was described more recently by Stacey.[95] Maurer and Drehfahl[96] described a procedure for the direct synthesis of α-methyl-D-galacturonic acid from α-methyl-D-galactose.

III. DETECTION AND IDENTIFICATION OF GALACTURONIC ACID

Galacturonic acid possesses both acidic and reducing properties. It behaves normally like a sugar, giving all the usual reactions which, however, will not be discussed here.[97]

There are a number of color tests for galacturonic acid, of which the oldest is the classical naphthoresorcinol test of Tollens.[98] In the original test equal volumes of uronic acid solution and concentrated hydrochloric acid are boiled for one minute with 1 cc. of a 1% solution of naphthore-

[88] H. S. Isbell and H. L. Frush, *J. Research Natl. Bur. Standards,* **31,** 33 (1943).
[89] E. Roboz, *unpublished work,* 1948.
[90] C. Niemann and K. P. Link, *J. Biol. Chem.,* **104,** 195 (1934).
[91] H. M. Sell and K. P. Link, *J. Am. Chem. Soc.,* **60,** 1813 (1938).
[92] C. Niemann and K. P. Link, *J. Biol. Chem.,* **104,** 743 (1934).
[93] W. Militzer and R. Angier, *Arch. Biochem.,* **10,** 291 (1946).
[94] C. Niemann and K. P. Link, *J. Biol. Chem.,* **95,** 203 (1932).
[95] M. Stacey, *J. Chem. Soc.,* **1939,** 1529.
[96] F. Maurer and G. Drehfahl, *Ber.,* **75,** 1489 (1942).
[97] For these tests see C. A. Browne and F. W. Zerban, *Physical and Chemical Methods of Sugar Analysis.* 3rd ed., Wiley, New York, 1941.
[98] B. Tollens, *Ber.,* **41,** 1788 (1908).

sorcinol in ethanol. After cooling, the mixture is shaken out with an equal volume of ether. The presence of uronic acids is shown by a bluish violet color in the ether phase and the appearance of an absorption band in the yellow, its center lying a little to the right of the D sodium line. Subsequent investigators found that the test is not specific for uronic acids and that the presence of larger quantities of several sugars caused the formation of masking colors. Neuberg and Saneyoshi[99] recommended the use of benzene for the extraction of the color and, according to van der Haar,[100] this method works very well in the presence of about equal quantities of arabinose, xylose, rhamnose, glucose, fructose, mannose, and galactose. In most cases some color is formed during the heating, but the benzene remains colorless unless uronic acids are present. Neuberg and Kobel[101] prefer to use 2 N hydrochloric acid or 50% sulfuric acid in the test which, when carried out in this manner, is sensitive even in the presence of large quantities of various other sugars. In view of recent experiences, neither this modification nor that proposed by Deichmann and Dierker[102] makes the method specific enough for the detection of small amounts of galacturonic acid in the presence of large quantities of other sugars.

Recently Dische[103] described a reaction between uronic acids and carbazole and sulfuric acid, which appears to be suitable for the detection and approximate determination of glucuronic and galacturonic acids. Later[104] the same author described a reaction between carbohydrates and sulfhydryl compounds, which in a specific modification[105] appears to be specific for galacturonic acid. In the test the galacturonic acid and a 4-fold quantity of concentrated sulfuric acid are mixed and cooled. Thereupon 0.1 cc. of a 2.5% solution of cysteine is added and the mixture is kept at room temperature for 24 hours. A green-blue color appears and increases in intensity for another 24 hours. By using light at the proper wave length and measuring the transmission in a photoelectric colorimeter, the sharpness of identification in the presence of impurities can be increased. The method is claimed to be suitable for the quantitative determination of galacturonic acid (and polyuronides) but there is only insufficient evidence on hand to prove its general applicability.

When boiled with concentrated hydrochloric acid, uronic acids undergo complete decarboxylation:

[99] C. Neuberg and S. Saneyoshi, *Biochem. Z.*, **36**, 56 (1911).
[100] A. W. van der Haar, *Anleitung zum Nachweis, zur Trennung und Bestimmung der Reinen und aus Glukosiden usw. erhaltenen Monosaccharide und Aldehydsäuren.* Borntraeger, Berlin, 1920.
[101] C. Neuberg and M. Kobel, *Biochem. Z.*, **243**, 435 (1931).
[102] W. B. Deichmann and M. Dierker, *J. Biol. Chem.*, **163**, 753 (1946).
[103] Z. Dische, *J. Biol. Chem.*, **167**, 189 (1947).
[104] Z. Dische, *Federation Proc.*, **6**, 248 (1947).
[105] Z. Dische, *Arch. Biochem.*, **16**, 409 (1948); *J. Biol. Chem.*, **183**, 489 (1950).

$$C_5H_9O_5COOH \longrightarrow C_5H_4O_2 + CO_2 + 3\ H_2O$$

and furfural, carbon dioxide, and water are formed. Proceeding from this observation, Tollens[106] and his school developed a method for the quantitative determination of uronic acids which will be discussed later. The reaction is also useful for the identification of uronic acids. When the sample containing uronic acids is boiled with 12% hydrochloric acid in a test tube supplied with a connection through which the evolved gases can be bubbled into baryta water, a white precipitate of barium carbonate is formed.[107]

An excess of alkali causes a solution of galacturonic acid to turn yellow. Lime water and baryta water do not form precipitates in a solution of galacturonic acid, but upon heating yellow precipitates occur. Neutral Pb acetate does not precipitate galacturonic acid from solution.

An apparently specific and typical reaction of galacturonic acid has been discovered by Ehrlich.[108]   When a freshly filtered solution of basic lead acetate is added to a solution containing L- or D-galacturonic acid, a white precipitate is formed which dissolves in an excess of the reagent. Upon warming the mixture on a boiling water bath, a pink precipitate occurs which in a few minutes turns brick red and finally brownish red. The latter color is stable and is not affected by prolonged heating. Ehrlich claims that a 0.0005% solution of galacturonic acid still shows a definite reaction. Glucuronic acid gives a precipitate which is first yellowish, then brown; mannuronic acid gives a buff-colored precipitate.

Hot, concentrated nitric acid oxidizes galacturonic acid (and many other compounds such as galactose, quercitol, etc.), largely to mucic acid. The mucic acid is but slightly soluble in water, only 0.33 part being dissolved at 14°C. and 1.6 parts at 100°C. in 100 parts of water. It is insoluble in alcohol and ether.[109,110]   Mucic acid crystallizes readily from the nitric acid solution. The minute granular rhombic prisms may be separated in a fritted glass or Gooch crucible and redissolved in dilute sodium hydroxide solution. This is then acidified with hydrochloric acid and the mucic acid again allowed to crystallize. The characteristic crystals may be identified under the microscope. Mucic acid melts at 213–214°C. and is optically inactive. For further identification mucic acid may be converted into its thallium salt by placing the mucic acid, dis-

[106] K. U. Lefèvre and B. Tollens, *Ber.,* 25, 2569 (1892).
[107] A. D. Dickson, H. Otterson, and K. P. Link, *J. Am. Chem. Soc.,* 52, 775 (1930).
[108] F. Ehrlich, *Ber.,* 65, 352 (1932).
[109] W. H. Kent, *Dissertation,* Göttingen, 1884.
[110] B. Tollens, *Ann.,* 232, 186 (1886).

solved in a drop of dilute ammonium hydroxide, on the microscope slide and adding a small grain of thallium nitrate. The slide is then agitated until the thallium salt is dissolved. Upon standing, prismatic rods of thallium mucate separate out. Photomicrographs of typical crystals of mucic acid and of thallium mucate have been shown by van der Haar[100] and more recently by Hassid and McCready.[111]

Saturated bromine water oxidizes galacturonic acid to mucic acid at room temperature, whereas galactose yields galactonic acid.[112]

Galacturonic acid can also be separated from galactose and other sugars by evaporating the solution containing the material with an excess of barium carbonate. The galacturonic acid is converted into the barium salt which is insoluble in boiling 90% ethanol, whereas galactose and other sugars may be dissolved and removed by the solvent.

The various salts of galacturonic acid as well as the formation of phenylhydrazine and substituted phenylhydrazine derivatives may be used for its identification. For detailed information on this point the reader is again referred to van der Haar's book[100] as well as to Table 2 in which the constants of several salts and derivatives of galacturonic acid are given together with references to the literature.

The separation of galacturonic acid from other compounds on the basis of differential adsorption (chromatography) is comparatively unde- veloped. Lew, Wolfrom, and Goepp,[112a] using column chromatography, observed that, on account of its carboxyl groups, galacturonic acid is more firmly held by the fuller's earth type of clays than are most sugars. Partridge,[112b] using (descending) paper chromatography with a variety of solvents, found that galacturonic acid formed heart-shaped spots and had a lower R_F value than the eleven sugars tested. The low mobility of galacturonic acid was also apparent in two-dimensional paper chroma- tography.[112c] Jermyn and Isherwood[112d] successfully analyzed by this latter method mixtures of galacturonic acid and various sugars. Recently Reid[112e] and Jermyn and Tomkins[112f] studied the paper chromatography of galacturonic acid and of (enzymic) pectin digests.

[111] W. Z. Hassid and R. M. McCready, *Ind. Eng. Chem., Anal. Ed.,* **14**, 683 (1942).

[112] H. Kiliani and S. Kleeman, *Ber.,* **17**, 1296 (1894).

[112a] B. W. Lew, M. L. Wolfrom, and R. M. Goepp, Jr., *J. Am. Chem. Soc.,* **68**, 1449 (1946).

[112b] S. M. Partridge, *Nature,* **158**, 270 (1946).

[112c] S. M. Partridge, *Biochem. J.,* **42**, 238 (1948).

[112d] M. A. Jermyn and F. A. Isherwood, *Biochem. J.,* **44**, 402 (1949).

[112e] W. W. Reid, *J. Sci. Food Agr.,* **1**, 234 (1950).

[112f] M. A. Jermyn and R. G. Tomkins, *Biochem. J.,* **47**, 437 (1950).

IV. DETERMINATION OF GALACTURONIC ACID

As stated before, the analytical methods which may be used for the estimation of galacturonic acid are in most cases also directly applicable to the determination of the polyuronide content of pectic preparations. For this reason they will be given in detail.

Galacturonic acid may be quantitatively determined by: (1) titration as an acid, (2) copper-reducing methods, (3) the Willstätter-Schudel hypoiodite method (oxidation), (4) the amount of furfural, or (5) carbon dioxide formed upon heating with 12% hydrochloric acid, (6) modifications of the Tollens naphthoresorcinol reaction, (7) the sulfuric acid–cysteine method of Dische, and (8) oxidation to mucic acid.

1. Titration with Alkali

Galacturonic acid is a weak acid and its titration with dilute alkali is simple and does not require any discussion. For a study of the acidic properties of galacturonic acid the reader is referred to the recent report of Speiser, Eddy, and Hills.[113]   The calcium acetate titration method of Lüdtke[114] has been also shown to give quite reliable results with galacturonic acid.[115]

2. Estimation by Copper-Reducing Power

The principal chemical methods for the determination of sugars are based upon the property, common to all aldehydes and ketones, of reducing alkaline solutions of certain metals. Of the various metals, copper in alkaline solution has been used most frequently in sugar analysis. Unfortunately, the reaction does not proceed with quantitative precision because the amount of reduced copper depends upon the experimental conditions. Therefore most authors propose a set of standardized conditions and usually supply a table containing the sugar equivalents based on experimental determinations on pure sugars. A great number of copper reduction methods have been described in the literature—a tacit admission that no procedure of outstanding precision and general applicability has as yet been found.

Most of these methods are also useful for the determination of D-galacturonic acid. For those which have to be used in conjunction with tables, values for galacturonic acid must be established. The only such relationship (shown in Table 3) thus far published on galacturonic acid

[113] R. Speiser, C. H. Hills, and C. R. Eddy, *J. Phys. Chem.*, **49**, 328 (1945).
[114] M. Lüdtke, *Biochem. Z.*, **233**, 25 (1931); **268**, 372 (1934); **285**, 78 (1936).
[115] C. C. Unruh, P. A. McGee, W. F. Fowler, Jr., and W. O. Kenyon, *J. Am. Chem. Soc.*, **69**, 349 (1947).

has been worked out by the author[116] for Bertrand's method.[117,118] The essence of Bertrand's procedure is as follows:

A mixture of 20 cc. of copper solution (40 g. of copper sulfate pentahydrate made up to 1 liter), 20 cc. of alkali solution (200 g. of pure Rochelle salt, potassium sodium tartrate, and 150 g. of sodium hydroxide made up to 1 liter), and 20 cc. of (neutral) solution containing the sugar is boiled in a 125-cc. Erlenmeyer flask for exactly three minutes. The solution tested should be free from any other materials which can reduce the alkaline copper solution. The use of 20 to 50 mg. of galacturonic acid in a determination is most suitable for the method. Too vigorous boiling is to be avoided and "bumping" should be eliminated by placing a glass rod in the flask. The color of the mixture should remain blue, indicating an excess of copper. After boiling for three minutes, the flask is removed from the flame, the precipitate of cuprous oxide is allowed to settle for a few minutes, and the liquid is then filtered with suction through a Soxhlet asbestos filter or, even better, through a fritted glass crucible. Care should be taken to have a filter of sufficiently small pore size to prevent the loss of small particles of cuprous oxide. It is advisable to transfer to the filter as little of the cuprous oxide as possible. The precipitate is then washed several times with boiled, distilled water. The wash water, of course, is also filtered, and finally the filter itself is washed several times. The suction flask containing the filtrate and wash water is now replaced by a clean one. The cuprous oxide is dissolved in 10 to 20 cc. of ferric sulfate solution (50 g. of ferric sulfate and 200 g. of concentrated sulfuric acid made up to 1 liter; to this enough 0.1 N potassium permanganate solution is added to turn the solution faintly but permanently pink). It is advisable to dissolve the cuprous oxide first in the flask, then on the crucible, and to wash both the flask and filter thoroughly. The contents of the suction flask are titrated with 0.1 N potassium permanganate solution. At the end point, the color changes sharply from green to pink with one drop. 1 cc. of 0.1 N potassium permanganate is equivalent to 6.35 mg. of copper. The galacturonic acid equivalent of copper may be read from Table 3.

Naturally other copper-reducing methods may also be used for the determination. Pure D-galacturonic acid monohydrate can now be prepared with comparatively little effort or purchased at a fairly low cost. It is relatively simple (although time-consuming) to establish the relation between the amount of galacturonic acid used and the weight of cuprous oxide produced.

A comparatively new principle was introduced into the copper-reducing procedures for sugar determination by Richardson, Higginbotham, and Farrow[119] who pointed out that cuprous oxide is somewhat

[116] Z. I. Kertesz, J. Biol. Chem., 106, 127 (1935).

[117] G. Bertrand, Bull. soc. chim.. 35, 1285 (1906).

[118] Z. I. Kertesz, Recalculated Tables for the Determination of Reducing Sugars by Bertrands's Method. Published by the author, Geneva, New York, 1930.

[119] W. A. Richardson, R. S. Higginbotham, and F. D. Farrow, J. Textile Inst., 27, 131 (1936).

TABLE 3

TABLE FOR ESTIMATION OF GALACTURONIC ACID ($C_6H_{16}O_7$) BY BERTRAND'S COPPER REDUCTION METHOD

Cu, mg.	Galacturonic acid, mg.	Cu, mg.	Galacturonic acid, mg.	Cu, mg.	Galacturonic acid, mg.
14.5	9.1	54	35.7	94	64.4
15	9.6	55	36.4	95	65.2
16	10.2	56	37.1	96	66.0
17	10.8	57	37.7	97	66.6
18	11.5	58	38.4	98	67.4
19	12.2	59	39.1	99	68.1
20	12.8	60	39.9	100	68.8
21	13.4	61	40.5	101	69.6
22	14.1	62	41.2	102	70.4
23	14.7	63	41.9	103	71.0
24	15.5	64	42.6	104	71.8
25	16.1	65	43.3	105	72.5
26	16.7	66	43.9	106	73.4
27	17.4	67	44.6	107	74.1
28	18.0	68	45.3	108	74.8
29	18.7	69	46.0	109	75.5
30	19.4	70	46.7	110	76.2
31	20.0	71	47.5	111	77.0
32	20.7	72	48.2	112	77.7
33	21.3	73	48.9	113	78.4
34	22.0	74	49.6	114	79.2
35	22.6	75	50.3	115	79.9
36	23.3	76	51.0	116	80.7
37	24.0	77	51.8	117	81.4
38	24.7	78	52.6	118	82.2
39	25.4	79	53.3	119	82.9
40	26.1	80	54.1	120	83.7
41	26.8	81	54.9	121	84.4
42	27.4	82	55.5	122	85.0
43	28.2	83	56.2	123	85.8
44	28.8	84	57.0	124	86.6
45	29.5	85	57.8	125	87.4
46	30.2	86	58.5	126	88.1
47	30.9	87	59.3	127	88.9
48	31.6	88	60.0	128	89.6
49	32.3	89	60.8	129	90.4
50	32.9	90	61.6	130	91.1
51	33.7	91	62.2	131	91.9
52	34.4	92	63.0		
53	35.0	93	63.8		

soluble in the hot alkali and that this error should be eliminated. They propose the addition of 2 mg. of glucose to all the reaction mixtures and determine the "glucose equivalent" of the ferrous ammonium sulfate used for titration by determining the amount of cuprous oxide produced by mixtures containing 2 and 4 mg. of glucose. Experience in the author's laboratory[120] indicated that the values obtained with this method for pure galacturonic acid were somewhat lower than those calculated from the glucose values for equivalent amounts of galacturonic acid. Of course, when the Richardson-Higginbotham-Farrow procedure is used for uronic acids or polyuronides, the blank and the titer of the volumetric solution should be determined by the use of galacturonic acid instead of glucose.

3. Estimation by Oxidation with Hypoiodite

Romijn[121] discovered in 1897 that weakly alkaline solutions of iodine oxidize aldoses to the corresponding monobasic acids, while ketoses and nonreducing sugars are only slightly attacked:

$$RCHO + I_2 + 3\ NaOH \rightleftharpoons RCOONa + 2\ NaI + 2\ H_2O$$

Similarly, when galacturonic acid is oxidized by alkaline iodine solution, the aldose group is oxidized and a mucic acid is formed:

$$CHO—(CHOH)_4—COOH + I_2 + 4\ NaOH \rightleftharpoons$$
$$COONa—(CHOH)_4—COONa + 2\ NaI + 3\ H_2O$$

When the oxidation is complete, the solution is acidified and the excess iodine liberated and titrated with thiosulfate. The difference between the amount of iodine added and that found after the reaction is complete is stoichiometrically equal to the amount of aldose oxidized. The quantitative relationship makes possible the estimation of galacturonic acid without the use of the empirical tables necessary with the copper-reducing methods.

In the absence of other hypoiodite-oxidizable substances[122] this method is very suitable for the determination of galacturonic acid. In strongly alkaline solutions the reaction proceeds beyond the oxidation of the aldehyde group and therefore conditions should be carefully chosen to preserve the stoichiometric character of the reaction. Romijn used borax solution to furnish the alkalinity but the oxidation then required about 18 hours at 25°C. Of the many modifications of this method only that given by Willstätter and Schudel[123] will be noted here. These authors found that the time necessary for complete oxidation can be greatly reduced.

[120] J. D. Loconti and Z. I. Kertesz, *unpublished data,* 1941. See also Chapter VII, Section 3.
[121] C. Romijn, Z. *anal. Chem.,* 36, 349 (1897).
[122] According to O. G. Ingles and G. C. Israel (*J. Chem. Soc.,* 1949, 1213), the oxidizing agent is hypoiodous acid (HIO).
[123] R. Willstätter and G. Schudel, *Ber.,* 51, 780 (1918).

To a measured quantity of solution containing the galacturonic acid (or any aldohexose), twice the amount of 0.1 N iodine solution necessary for complete oxidation is added. A quantity of 0.1 N sodium hydroxide solution equivalent to about one and one-half times that of the iodine used is added drop by drop and the mixture allowed to stand for 12 to 15 minutes. The solution is now acidified with dilute sulfuric acid, and the liberated iodine titrated with 0.1 N sodium thiosulfate solution. 1 cc. of the 0.1 N iodine used for the oxidation is equivalent to 9.70 mg. of anhydrous galacturonic acid (or 7.004 mg. of an aldopentose, 9.005 mg. of an aldohexose, 17.11 mg. of a disaccharide as maltose or lactose). Higher concentrations and larger volumes may also be used as long as the proportions remain the same. For very small quantities of galacturonic acid more dilute iodine and thiosulfate solutions should be used.

Myrbäck and Örtenblad[124] made a thorough study of the oxidation of aldoses with iodine in alkaline solution. It is important to add the sodium hydroxide to the solution containing the mixture of sugar or galacturonic acid and iodine dropwise and slowly, at the rate of not more than 60 drops per minute, and with constant swirling. The success of attaining a stoichiometric reaction depends a great deal on the rate at which the alkali is added. Unfortunately, there are many compounds which consume iodine in some manner or other. Nonaldose sugars, as well as glycerol, lactic acid, amino acids, etc., take up a small proportion of iodine. For this reason the method should be applied with caution when used on solutions other than that of pure galacturonic acid.

4. Estimation by Production of Furfural

When pentoses, uronic acids, or more complex materials containing these compounds (pentosans or pectic substances) are heated with 12% hydrochloric acid, furfural (furfuraldehyde) is produced. The furfural can be distilled, determined by one of the many methods described, and calculated as pentose or uronic acid.[125] The yield of furfural is different for the various pentoses and uronic acids and is always below the theoretical yield. By performing the distillation under carefully standardized conditions and using tables and formulas, a determination with a close degree of approximation may be attained.

This method is seldom used for the estimation of pure galacturonic acid because better procedures are available for that purpose. The furfural method is the most common one for the quantitative estimation of L-arabinose, a pentose often accompanying pectic substances in plants. In the presence of pectic substances the determination gives the total

[124] K. Myrbäck and B. Örtenblad, *Svensk Kem. Tid.*, **50**, 72 (1938).
[125] A. Jolles, *Ber.*, **39**, 96 (1906).

amount of arabinose plus galacturonic acid present. The quantity of galacturonic acid can also be estimated by other means, such as by the amount of carbon dioxide produced upon decarboxylation, a method to be discussed below. By calculating the proportion of galacturonic acid present and correcting the amount of furfural (in whatever form furfural is determined) for that amount produced by the galacturonic acid, the quantity of furfural obtained from the arabinose alone can be computed. Unfortunately, the amount of furfural produced from a mixture of substances does not correspond exactly to the sum of furfural produced by each substance separately.

Various reagents have been used to precipitate the furfural, for example, phenylhydrazine, barbituric acid, and phloroglucinol. In these methods the formed compound is weighed. Colorimetric and titrimetric methods have also been proposed.[126,127] The method given below in detail is used most frequently and is the one originally developed by Tollens and Kröber[128] and adopted as an official method by the A. O. A. C.[129] In this procedure the furfural is precipitated with phloroglucinol, and the product is weighed.

When determinations are made by this method, the prescribed procedure should be followed in full detail in order that the tables and formulas should be applicable. Some investigators wash the precipitated phloroglucide with ethanol and still use Kröber's tables. This procedure is unwarranted.

The apparatus commonly used at present for the distillation is essentially the same as that described by Tollens and Kröber. The size of the sample is chosen so that the weight of phloroglucide shall not exceed 0.30 g. The material is placed in a 300-cc. distillation flask, together with several small pieces of recently ignited pumice stone and 100 cc. of 12% hydrochloric acid (sp. gr. 1.06). The flask is closed with a two-hole rubber stopper, one opening of which is fitted to the connecting tube of a condenser, and the other to a small separatory funnel graduated for 30 and 60 cc. The use of apparatus with ground-glass joints is preferred. The flask is placed on a wire gauze, connected with the condenser, and heated gently at first, and then regulated so as to distill 30 cc. of liquid in ten minutes. A glycerol, oil, or metal bath (made from Rose's alloy) offers the advantage of more constant heating and helps to avoid charring on the sides of the flask. The liquid distilled over is replaced by means of a separatory funnel with 30 cc. of 12% hydrochloric acid and the process is continued until

[126] G. E. Youngburg and G. W. Pucher, *J. Biol. Chem.*, **61**, 741 (1924).

[127] J. Griswold, M. E. Klecka, and R. V. O. West, *Ind. Eng. Chem., Anal. Ed.*, **18**, 696 (1946).

[128] B. Tollens and E. Kröber, *J. Landw.*, **48**, 355 (1900); **49**, 7 (1901).

[129] *Official and Tentative Methods of Analysis.* 6th ed., Association of Official Agricultural Chemists, Washington, D. C., 1945.

a total of 360 cc. of distillate has been collected. The 30-cc. portions of hydrochloric acid should be used to wash off any particles adhering to the side of the
flask. The distillate is filtered and placed in a beaker. To the clear filtrate a
solution of phloroglucinol dissolved in 12% hydrochloric acid is added. The
amount of pure phloroglucinol should be about double the amount of furfural
expected. The pure phloroglucinol is prepared as follows: A small quantity of
the phloroglucinol is dissolved in a few drops of acetic anhydride and heated
almost to boiling. Upon the addition of a few drops of concentrated sulfuric acid,
the mixture turns red in the presence of diresorcinol. If the reaction gives
more than a faint coloration, the phloroglucinol should be purified as follows:
To a beaker containing about 300 cc. of hot 12% hydrochloric acid, 11 g. of
phloroglucinol is added in small quantities and with constant stirring until it has
almost entirely dissolved. Some impurities may resist solution, but it is unnecessary to remove them. The hot solution is then poured into a sufficient quantity
of cold 12% hydrochloric acid to make a volume of 1500 cc. and is allowed
to stand overnight, or preferably for several days, to permit the diresorcinol to
crystallize out. It should be filtered immediately before use. The solution may
turn yellow but this does not interfere with its usefulness. For the precipitation
a sufficient volume of this solution is used. The mixture of distillate and phloroglucinol is then stirred thoroughly. It first turns yellow, then green, and soon
the amorphous precipitate of furfural phloroglucide appears, which turns darker
until it becomes almost black. The contents of the beaker are made up to 400 cc.
with 12% hydrochloric acid and allowed to stand overnight. The solution should
be tested with aniline acetate paper to make sure that all the furfural has been
precipitated. (According to Tollens this is prepared by moistening strips of
filter paper with a solution of aniline acetate. When a drop of liquid containing
furfural is placed on it, the paper turns bright cherry red.) It is then carefully filtered through a weighed Gooch or fritted glass crucible. The precipitate
is then washed with 150 cc. of cold water in such a manner that the water is
never completely removed until the very end. The crucible is placed upon a
support so that air has access to the bottom and is dried for 4 hours in an oven
with boiling water jacket. It is then placed in a weighing bottle, cooled in a
desiccator, and weighed. The increase in weight is the amount of furfural phloroglucide obtained from the pentoses and uronic acids.

Kröber's table does not include galacturonic acid. The amount of
furfural phloroglucide formed from pure D-galacturonic acid was determined by Nanji, Paton, and Ling,[130] who found that 1 part of phloroglucide equals 3.66 parts of galacturonic acid. Ehrlich and Schubert,[131]
on the other hand, found a constant ratio of 2.64 and used this figure in
their computations. Later Norris and Resch[132] found a ratio of 2.60, well
in agreement with Ehrlich's results. Ehrlich washed the phloroglucide

[130] D. R. Nanji, F. J. Paton, and A. R. Ling, *J. Soc. Chem. Ind.*, **44**, 252T (1925).
[131] F. Ehrlich and F. Schubert, *Ber.*, **62**, 1974 (1929).
[132] F. W. Norris and C. E. Resch, *Biochem. J.*, **29**, 1590 (1935).

with warm (60°C.) ethanol and reported that about 1.08 to 1.84% of the precipitate was dissolved. Norris and Resch did not use ethanol. Myers and Baker[133] doubted the constancy of the ratio and reinvestigated the problem applying the A. O. A. C. method described above. They found that the factor was indeed not constant, especially when quantities below 0.2 g. are used. These results are shown in Table 4. Myers and Baker also called attention to the fact that Ehrlich and Schubert did not take into consideration the 0.0052 g. of phloroglucide which becomes dissolved in the 400 cc. of 12% hydrochloric acid. If this correction is added to the weight of the phloroglucide, the ratio of galacturonic acid to phloroglucide changes to the figure given in the fourth column of Table 4. When the determination is made on material in which arabinose is the only substance yielding furfural, the values of Kröber for pure arabinose, given in Table 5, can be used. If the determination is performed on a mixture of galacturonic acid (or poly-galacturonide) and arabinose (araban), as is often the case with pectic substances, the procedure is more complicated and one of several possible procedures may be followed.

TABLE 4

FURFURAL PHLOROGLUCIDE OBTAINED FROM GALACTURONIC ACID (ADAPTED FROM MYERS AND BAKER)

Galacturonic acid (anhydrous), g.	Furfural phloroglucide, g.	Ratio of galacturonic acid (anhydrous) to uncorrected phloroglucide	Same, corrected
0.0631	0.0211	2.990	2.400
0.1201	0.0443	2.711	2.426
0.1684	0.0632	2.664	2.462
0.2129	0.0806	2.641	2.481
0.2590	0.0982	2.637	2.505
0.3048	0.1157	2.634	2.521

Ehrlich and Schubert[131] used a procedure based on the presumably contant ratio 1:2.64 between the phloroglucide and galacturonic acid. As noted, the amount of galacturonic acid present in the mixture can be calculated from the quantity of carbon dioxide evolved. From the ratio 1:2.64 the amount of phloroglucide corresponding to the galacturonic acid may be computed and this value then subtracted from the weight of phloroglucide obtained from the mixture of galacturonic acid and arabinose. The residual quantity of phloroglucide is taken as obtained from arabinose and the corresponding value read from Table 5.

TABLE 5
DETERMINATION OF ARABINOSE FROM THE FURFURAL YIELD (KRÖBER)

Furfural phloroglucide, g.	Arabinose, g.	Furfural phloroglucide, g.	Arabinose, g.
0.030	0.0344	0.170	0.1698
0.040	0.0441	0.180	0.1794
0.050	0.0538	0.190	0.1889
0.060	0.0634	0.200	0.1984
0.070	0.0731	0.210	0.2079
0.080	0.0828	0.220	0.2174
0.090	0.0925	0.230	0.2270
0.100	0.1022	0.240	0.2365
0.110	0.1118	0.250	0.2460
0.120	0.1214	0.260	0.2555
0.130	0.1311	0.270	0.2650
0.140	0.1408	0.280	0.2745
0.150	0.1505	0.290	0.2840
0.160	0.1602	0.300	0.2935

Myers and Baker[133] state that in order to obtain accurate results, the solubility of the phloroglucide should be taken into account. In the calculation of the weight of arabinose from the total phloroglucide, 0.0052 must be added to the weight of phloroglucide found. Then the weight of phloroglucide, calculated from column 2 of Table 4 and based on the determination of the carbon dioxide evolved, is subtracted from the corrected weight of total phloroglucide. If the difference is less than 0.03 g., Kröber's table cannot be applied and the corresponding amount of arabinose is derived by multiplying the weight by the factor 1.1108. If the difference is larger than 0.03 g., then Kröber's table is used. But since Kröber's table is based on the uncorrected weight of phloroglucide, 0.0052 must now be subtracted from the difference before the corresponding weight of arabinose is obtained from the table.

Apparently at the present time the method of Myers and Baker is considered to be most suitable for making these computations. However, even slight variations in the details of the determination may influence the results appreciably. It is desirable, therefore, that the procedure be standardized by determinations on known materials. The effect of accompanying substances on the evolution of furfural should be also ascertained, if possible.

Angell, Norris, and Resch[134] studied the mutual effect of various carbohydrates and uronic acids on the amount of furfural produced in mix-

[133] P. B. Myers and G. L. Baker, *Univ. Delaware Agr. Expt. Sta.*, Bull. No. 187 (1934).
[134] S. Angell, F. W. Norris, and C. E. Resch, *Biochem. J.*, **30**, 2146 (1936).

tures. Besides pentoses, other sugars and natural materials may also produce small quantities of furfural in the distillation. These authors suggested the following formula for the calculation of the amount of arabinose:

$$\text{arabinose} = 0.9942P - 1.9081Cp + 0.01313 \ (\pm 0.00305)$$

where P is the weight of the phloroglucide obtained from the mixture of galacturonic acid and arabinose and Cp is the weight of the carbon dioxide obtained by the Lefèvre-Tollens method from the galacturonic acid. The last figure is the probable error found by the authors. For a description of the methods by which the formula was obtained the reader is referred to the original article.

Youngburg[135] in 1927 described a particular adaptation of furfural estimation useful for biological materials. Later Bryant and Joseph[136] and Byrant, Palmer, and Joseph[137] developed the method for the determination of galacturonic acid, polygalacturonic acids, and arabinose in biological materials. In short, the procedure consists of steam distillation of the sample from a solution of 85% phosphoric acid at 170 to 175°C. (338 to 347°F.) and collection of the distillate. Color is developed in an aliquot with aniline and glacial acetic acid and color intensity is measured in a Duboscq colorimeter. A standard made from freshly prepared, vacuum-distilled furfural is used for calibration. Bryant, Palmer, and Joseph deal only with "furfural values" but obviously these may be converted into galacturonic acid or arabinose. The method gave splendid recovery of pectinic acids in the presence of animal organs. It is more suitable for the determination of galacturonic acid in biological materials than is the collection and weighing of the carbon dioxide evolved upon boiling with 12% hydrochloric acid, especially from small quantities of galacturonic acid or polyuronides. Its main drawback is that arabinose and other pentoses as well as some other compounds, such as ascorbic acid, are estimated together with the galacturonic acid.

Cooke[138] studied the kinetics of furfural formation from pentoses and noted that several possibilities exist to improve the precision of the Kröber method and to shorten the time required for the distillation. Rogers[139] recently described an iodine method for more accurate determination of furfural in which the latter is oxidized by iodine in alkaline solution to furoic acid. It is claimed that this method is superior in

[135] G. E. Youngburg, *J. Biol. Chem.*, **73**, 599 (1927).

[136] E. F. Bryant and G. H. Joseph, paper given at the 95th meeting of the American Chemical Society, Dallas, Texas, April, 1938.

[137] E. F. Bryant, G. H. Palmer, and G. H. Joseph, *Ind. Eng. Chem., Anal. Ed.*, **16**, 74 (1944).

[138] Q. G. Cooke, *Paper Trade J.*, **117**, No. 26, 32 (1943).

[139] H. R. Rogers, *Ind. Eng. Chem., Anal. Ed.*, **16**, 319 (1944).

accuracy to the phloroglucinol method, even in the presence of impurities.

5. Estimation by Carbon Dioxide Produced upon Decarboxylation

Uronic acids boiled with 12% hydrochloric acid are completely decarboxylated and, as shown by the equation in part 4 of this Section, yield one molecule of carbon dioxide per molecule of uronic acid. The weight of carbon dioxide multiplied by 4.0 will give the weight of the galacturonic acid in the sample and, in the case of polygalacturonic acids, the weight of polygalacturonic acid is obtained by using the factor of 4.4.

Although the method is based on some earlier work at the University of Göttingen, it is now generally known as the Lefèvre-Tollens method.[106] The procedure has been considerably refined in recent years. In the original method the carbon dioxide was absorbed in a Geissler absorption tower containing potassium hydroxide solution and the increase in weight was determined. There were numerous modifications proposed, among

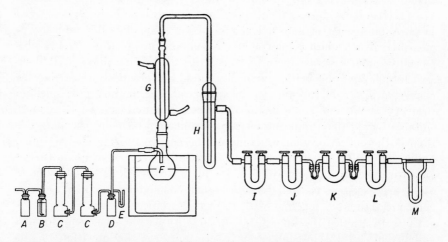

Fig. 2. The Whistler-Martin-Harris uronic acid carbon dioxide apparatus.

them one by Dickson, Otterson, and Link[140] who absorbed the carbon dioxide in a Truog tower. In recent years the use of Ascarite (sodium hydroxide absorbed on asbestos) and of other similar agents for the absorption of carbon dioxide has become more general.

Whistler, Martin, and Harris[141] made a thorough study of the rate

[140] A. D. Dickson, H. Otterson, and K. P. Link, *J. Am. Chem. Soc.*, **52**, 775 (1930).
[141] R. L. Whistler, A. R. Martin, and M. Harris, *J. Research Natl. Bur. Standards*. **24**, 13 (1940).

of evolution of the carbon dioxide from galacturonic acid, pectin, glucose, and some other substances. The apparatus used by these authors is shown in Figure 2. The procedure may be described as follows:

The nitrogen, which is used as the carrier gas for the evolved carbon dioxide, passes first through a safety flask A and then through an alkaline solution of pryogallol B in which the inlet tube is drawn to an orifice to produce fine bubbles. The gas then passes through two absorption towers C, filled with soda lime, into a safety bottle D which is provided with a mercury manometer E, and then enters the 500-cc. reaction flask F. The flask is placed in an oil bath so that the oil level is 3 to 4 mm. lower than the liquid level in the flask. This will prevent the baking of small bits of the sample which may be splashed against the side of the vessel. From the reaction flask the gas passes through a 40-cm. reflux condenser G, which is attached by glass joints, and into a bubbling tower H containing approximately 60 cc. of concentrated sulfuric acid. The gas next passes through the U-tube I which is filled with anhydrous copper sulfate and through tube J which contains phosphorus pentoxide. Then it enters the carbon dioxide absorption tube K which contains Ascarite, backed by phosphorus pentoxide. The absorption tube is connected to the train by means of mercury-cup seals which make rapid change of absorption tubes convenient but which are not essential except when the rate of evolution is to be determined as well as the total amount of carbon dioxide obtained. The tube K is protected by soda lime tube L which is followed by a calibrated flowmeter M for estimating the rate of flow of the nitrogen through the apparatus. The sample to be analyzed is placed in reaction flask F, and covered with 300 cc. of 12% (sp.gr. 1.06) hydrochloric acid. If needed, thorough wetting of the sample can be attained by evacuating the air in the flask. Nitrogen, at the rate of about 10 l. per hour, is passed through the apparatus until the tube K shows no further gain in weight. This operation requires about 30 minutes, during which the temperature of the bath is slowly raised to 50°C. (122°F.). When the apparatus is free from carbon dioxide the bath temperature is brought to 130°C. (266°F.). The use of electric immersion heaters is recommended for the maintenance of bath temperature by thermostatic control. The point of zero time is taken when this reaction temperature is reached.

The length of time required to sweep the carbon dioxide from the reaction flask into the absorption tube should be determined beforehand by the use of a known quantity of sodium carbonate. Whistler, Martin, and Harris placed this in a small glass tube sealed with paraffin. When the temperature of the bath was raised, the paraffin plug loosened and allowed the acid to come in contact with the sample of sodium carbonate. In their experiments the time required to carry all of the carbon dioxide into the Ascarite tube was less than 30 minutes. The procedure should be continued for 6 hours or until the absorption tube fails to show an increase during a 30 minute period.

Freudenberg, Gudjons, and Dumpert[142] proposed a new apparatus for the determination of uronic acids which appears to have merit, especially because of its simplicity. No reports on the usefulness of this procedure are available as yet.

The rate of evolution of carbon dioxide from pure galacturonic acid is rapid and practically complete in a few hours. On the other hand, under the conditions applied in the method, most carbohydrates yield a small quantity of carbon dioxide which is liberated slowly and at a practically constant rate. Evidence of the presence of true uronic acid groups in a mixture may be obtained by ascertaining the rate of liberation of the carbon dioxide. A characteristic curve for a mixture of uronic acids and other carbohydrates has a sharp break during the first hour.

When pectic preparations are analyzed by the carbon dioxide method, the effect of small quantities of other sugars may be neglected because the quantity of carbon dioxide derived from such sources is negligible. According to Whistler, Martin, and Harris[141] the amount of carbon dioxide evolved from 1 g. of glucose in 6 hours is only 1.5% of that from 1 g. of galacturonic acid. On the other hand, if material rich in carbohydrates but containing little galacturonic acid is analyzed, the amount of carbon dioxide evolved will have to be corrected for the non-uronic acid carbon dioxide. For this purpose the rate of carbon dioxide evolution from the mixture should be followed for at least 6 hours and the results plotted. Since the production and absorption of the carbon dioxide from the galacturonide component is complete after the first hour or two, the slope of the curve after that time will be a measure of the non-uronide carbon dioxide. By determining, from the slope of this curve, the rate at which the carbon dioxide was evolved from the non-uronide components during the first hours of the determination, the final value can be corrected to obtain the amount of uronide carbon dioxide.

The determination of pure galacturonic acid by this method gives the theoretical recovery and is one of the most dependable procedures used in analyzing pectic substances. A recent modification of the procedure by McCready, Swenson, and Maclay[143] employs 19% hydrochloric acid and a heating temperature of 145°C. (293°F.). This method gives identical yields with those obtained by the method of Whistler, Martin, and Harris but requires only 1.5 to 2 hours of heating and, as shown in Figure 3, the apparatus is also simpler.

Air is purified through an Ascarite or soda lime column A and then passes through mercury valve B and tube C into the reaction flask D. The latter is a

[142] K. Freudenberg, H. F. Gudjons, and G. Dumpert, *Ber.*, **74**, 245 (1941).
[143] R. M. McCready, H. A. Swenson, and W. D. Maclay, *Ind. Eng. Chem.*, *Anal. Ed.*, **18**, 290 (1946).

100-cc. round-bottomed, long-necked boiling flask with standard ground-glass joint. Oil bath E is maintained at 145°C. by a thermoregulator and immersion heater. The evolved gases pass upward in condenser F through trap G containing 25 g. of 20-mesh granulated zinc or tin and finally into the absorption flask H and absorption tower I. The lower end of the tower consists of a medium-porosity fritted Pyrex glass disc sealed to the end of the tube and is placed 1–2 mm. above the bottom of the flask. Soda lime tower J and capillary tube regulator K complete the apparatus through which 1.7–2.0 l. of carbon dioxide-

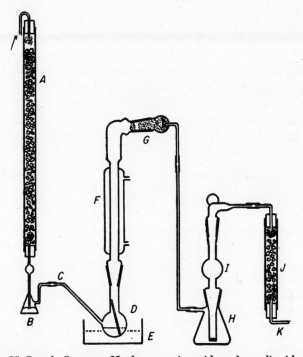

Fig. 3. The McCready-Swenson-Maclay uronic acid carbon dioxide apparatus.

free air per hour is sucked by a water aspirator connection attached at K. The pectinic acid or other sample (about 0.25 g.) is placed into vessel D with 30 cc. of 19% hydrochloric acid while 25 cc. of 0.25 N sodium hydroxide and 5 drops of butanol-1 are placed in the absorption chamber. At the end of the reaction period the absorption tower is washed down into the adsorption flask, then 10 cc. of 10% barium chloride dihydrate and 2 drops of phenolphthalein indicator are added and the contents are titrated with 0.10 N hydrochloric acid.

This procedure has been found very useful in the case of preparations rich in polyuronides, but in cases where interfering substances are present, the method of Whistler, Martin, and Harris is preferable. Micromethods based on the same principles have been described by Buston[144] and by Burkhart, Baur, and Link[145]; a manometric semimicro method was described by Voss and Pfirschke[146] and a manometric micromethod by Tracey.[147] When hydriodic acid is used instead of hydrochloric acid, the carbon dioxide yield is consistently lower (about 93%) than the theoretical value.[148]

6. Measurement of Colored Naphthoresorcinol Complex

Measurement of the blue-violet compound[149] formed by the reaction of uronic acids with naphthoresorcinol[150] (1,3-naphthalenediol) may also be applied to the quantitative determination of galacturonic acid. After a number of unsuccessful attempts to find conditions under which a reproducible relationship between the amount of uronic acid and the intensity of the color exists, Kapp[151] described standardized conditions for the reaction. More recently Ratish and Bulowa[152] published an article on the determination of glucuronic acid in biological media. This method was found by the author to be directly applicable to the determination of galacturonic acid. The essence of the procedure is as follows:

The naphthoresorcinol reagent is prepared by adding 0.1 g. of this compound to 50 cc. of distilled water, and then keeping the solution in an incubator at 37°C. for 24 hours. The solution is then filtered and kept in a dark bottle in the refrigerator. The reagent should not be used when it is more than 4 or 5 days old and it should be checked against pure galacturonic acid every day. The ether used for the extraction of the color should be washed with a 1% solution of ferrous sulfate to remove oxidizing agents. The ferrous sulfate is in turn removed with several portions of distilled water.

To 2 cc. of the sample (after removal of proteins, if these are present) 2 cc. of the naphthoresorcinol solution and 2 cc. of concentrated hydrochloric acid are added. The mixture is heated (preferably in a glass-stoppered test tube) in a boiling water bath for 45 minutes, then cooled in cold (or ice) water for 10 minutes. Now 2 cc. of ethanol (95%) and 15 cc. of prepared ether are added and the mixture is shaken vigorously in a corked or glass-stoppered flask for 30 to 60 seconds. The two layers are permitted to separate (quick centrifuging has been found more efficient) and the water phase removed with a pipette

[144] H. W. Buston, *Analyst,* **57,** 220 (1932).
[145] B. Burkhart, L. Baur, and K. P. Link, *J. Biol. Chem.,* **104,** 171 (1934).
[146] W. Voss and J. Pfirschke, *Ber.,* **70,** 631 (1937).
[147] M. V. Tracey, *Biochem. J.,* **43,** 185 (1948).
[148] B. Vollmert, *Z. Lebensm.-Untersuch. u. Forsch.,* **89,** 347 (1949).
[149] The pigment formed might be dinaphthylmethane (A. H. Guerrero and R. T. Williams, *Nature,* **161,** 930 (1948)) or a xanthane derivative (K. Mayer, H. S. Bloch, and E. Chaffee, *Federation Proc.,* **1,** 125 (1942)).
[150] B. Tollens, *Ber.,* **41,** 1788 (1908).
[151] E. M. Kapp, *J. Biol. Chem.,* **134,** 143 (1940).
[152] H. D. Ratish and J. G. M. Bulowa, *Arch. Biochem.,* **2,** 381 (1943).

inserted into the container. The light transmission of the ether solution is measured by any of the customary methods using light in the region of 565 millimicrons. A blank and controls to establish the calibration curve are run simultaneously.

Very good results were obtained by this method for 10 to 50 micrograms of galacturonic acid monohydrate. Unfortunately, obstacles were encountered when attempts were made to determine galacturonic acid in the presence of other sugars. Small proportions of glucose and galactose do not seem to interfere but both arabinose and fructose in proportion exceeding the amount of galacturonic acid may completely destroy the reliability of the method. Attempts to change the procedure and to use the extracting solvents suggested by Neuberg and Kobel[153] did not remedy the situation, nor can the more recent method of Deichmann and Dierker[154] be used in presence of large excesses of pentoses.

7. Measurement of Colored Complex Formed with Sulfuric Acid and Cysteine

This recently described method[155] for the colorimetric determination of galacturonic acid will give good results in pure solutions. Hexoses form a yellow color under the experimental conditions already noted in Section III of this Chapter, but the absorption is inconsequential at a wave length of 540 millimicrons, at which the measurements are made. On the other hand, pentoses show a sharp maximum of absorption at this wave length although their presence can be recognized from the shape of the absorption curve. Further work on this method is needed to establish its usefulness for the determination of galacturonic acid in the presence of carbohydrates commonly occurring in plant material.

8. Determination as Mucic Acid

The determination of galacturonic acid as mucic acid is not very satisfactory. Evaporation with 24% nitric acid on the steam bath, as proposed by Tollens,[156] is the usual procedure of oxidation. The reaction is also given by galactose which is often present in pectic preparations, as well as by galactonic acid, lactose, dulcitol, and quercitol. The yield of mucic acid from galactose is only about 75% of the theoretical value but it is fairly constant with pure galactose. The procedure of Tollens as given in the Official Methods of the A. O. A. C.[129] for galactose is likely to give comparable results with galacturonic acid. Ehrlich and Schubert[131]

[153] C. Neuberg and M. Kobel, *Biochem. Z.*, **243**, 435 (1931).
[154] W. B. Deichmann and M. Dierker, *J. Biol. Chem.*, **163**, 753 (1946).
[155] Z. Dische, *Federation Proc.*, **6**, 248 (1947).
[156] B. Tollens, *Handbuch der Kohlenhydrate.* 3rd ed., 1914.

obtained 77% of the theoretical yield with pure galacturonic acid and used a factor of 1.33 for calculating the amount of galactose from the mucic acid. The corresponding factor for (anhydrous) galacturonic acid would be 1.43 which, used with Ehrlich's results, gives 110.1% recovery. The author, using the Tollens method as given by the A.O.A.C. and the factor of 1.43, obtained a recovery of 91%.

Many workers consider the Tollens procedure unreliable. Van der Haar[157] devised a modification of the method, the superiority of which has been confirmed by Wise and Peterson.[158] Tables rather than factors are used in this method but unfortunately it has not yet been tested systematically with galacturonic acid.

By oxidation of glucuronic acid by bromine water in the cold and repeated recovery of the mucic acid dissolved in the mother liquor Ehrlich and Schubert[131] reached a recovery of 98% of the calculated yield of mucic acid.

In a recent report Frush and Isbell[159] state that in the presence of bromides galacturonic acid may be transformed into mucic acid by electrolytic oxidation in an almost quantitative yield. Chlorous acid might also be effectively used for the oxidation of galacturonic acid to mucic acid.[160] There are no reports as yet on the application of these procedures for the quantitative estimation of galacturonic acid. Because of the limited applicability of mucic acid for the estimation of galacturonic acid, no details of the procedures will be given here. The reader is referred to the handbooks and original articles cited.

[157] A. W. van der Haar, *Anleitung zum Nachweis zur Trennung und Bestimmung der Reinen und aus Glukosiden usw. erhaltenen Monosaccharide und Aldehydsäuren.* Borntraeger, Berlin, 1920.
[158] L. E. Wise and F. C. Peterson, *Ind. Eng. Chem.,* 15, 611 (1923).
[159] H. L. Frush and H. S. Isbell, paper given at the 104th Meeting of the American Chemical Society, Buffalo, N. Y., September, 1942.
[160] H. S. Isbell, U. S. Pat. 2,338,115 (1944).

CHAPTER III

Composition and Structure of Pectic Substances

There is neither space nor need at this point to discuss in full detail the evolution of our ideas concerning the composition and structure of pectic substances. There are several excellent historical reviews of this subject in the literature.[161,162] In this volume the emphasis is on present conceptions concerning pectic substances and historical data will be given only where they add to the clarity of the discussion.

This method of approach has not been chosen purely to save printing ink. One of the difficulties in pectin chemistry is the large number of confusing and contradictory statements in the literature. For those who enter this field it is more confusing than illuminating to recapitulate all that has been said during the past 120 years on this topic. In this statement there is no intention to belittle the merits and accomplishments of workers of the nineteenth century who did their researches under the handicap of general lack of knowledge of carbohydrate chemistry. Many of their contributions were remarkable indeed. But most of the work was done on preparations which contained a great deal of admixed materials. No doubt, this is still often the case but the difference is that we now recognize the fact that pectic substances are heterogeneous and that most preparations are mixtures of true pectic substances and other related or just incidentally present materials.

According to our present conception the basic skeleton of pectic substances is composed of galacturonic acid residues. In the past, arabinose and galactose have often been thought of as building blocks of these structures,[162a] but most authorities agree that, while often present, they do not participate directly in the fundamental skeleton of pectic substances. They may, however, have some relation to pectic materials and, if present,

[161] M. H. Branfoot (M. H. Carré), "A Critical and Historical Study of the Pectic Substances of Plants," Dept. of Scientific and Ind. Res., Special Report No. 33, H. M. Stationery Office, London, 1929.

[162] M. A. Joslyn and H. J. Phaff, *Wallerstein Lab. Communs.*, 10 (29), 39 (1947).

[162a] E. L. Hirst and J. K. N. Jones in *Advances in Carbohydrate Chemistry*. Vol. II, Academic Press, New York, 1946, p. 235.

they certainly do influence some important properties of pectic preparations. They are therefore dealt with in some detail in Chapter V. In addition, recent work seems to indicate that sorbose[163] and rhamnose[164] may
also occur in pectic substances. From the little information available at
the present time (1950) it would seem that, even if these two carbohydrates can be proven to be attached to the polygalacturonic acid chains
rather than occur as "ballast," their proportion is so small that they might
occur in or attached to the polygalacturonic acid chains at long intervals.
Further reports on this point must be awaited before the possible significance of the sorbose and rhamnose found in pectic preparations can be
clearly assessed.

A true polygalacturonic acid or pectic acid upon analysis will show
only the presence of galacturonic acid residues. Such pure materials have
now been actually prepared.[165] For this reason a discussion of the composition of these compounds is superfluous. The composition of commercial pectins, pectinic and pectic acids, and pectic acid prepared by the
most important methods of preparation will be discussed in Chapter
XXII.

I. PECTIC ACIDS

1. Introduction

According to the definition given on page 6, all pectic substances contain a large proportion of polygalacturonic acids which are built from
anhydrogalacturonic acid units. The simplest pectic structure, therefore,
is a polygalacturonic acid which has just enough component units to attain colloidal properties and thus become a pectic acid. In addition to being the simplest structure within the scope of our discussion, pectic acid
may be also regarded as the structure from which all other pectic substances are derived by the addition of various groups or by increasing the
size of the molecular unit. Discussions of the pectic compounds usually
start with the most complicated ones and progress to the relatively simpler
members. It appears more logical to discuss first the simplest of all pectic
compounds, the pectic acids, and then progress to the more complicated
pectinic acids, pectins, and protopectin.

Until 1917 the chief aim of most investigators was to establish the elementary composition of pectic substances and to find a lead toward their
composition through the interpretation of the analytical results. Because

[163] C. M. Martin and F. H. Reuter, *Nature*, **164**, 373 (1949).
[164] W. D. Maclay, R. M. McCready, and H. S. Owens, paper given at the San
Francisco Meeting of the American Chemical Society, March, 1949.
[165] E. L. Hirst, *J. Chem. Soc.*, **1942**, 70.

of the previously emphasized ever-varying composition of these preparations, different results were obtained by most workers leading to a variety of loosely defined theories concerning the structure of pectic materials. At the turn of the century there was no tenable theory about the structure of the pectin molecule. The presence of carbohydrates and some material of acidic properties, however, was recognized. As we have stated before, the recent era in pectin chemistry started in 1917, when Suarez[166] reported the presence of a uronic acid and Ehrlich,[167] in the same year, announced that the basic building block of pectic substances is galacturonic acid. This important discovery inspired new lines of attack. Now the components from which pectic and pectinic acids are built were known and rapid progress followed in the ensuing years.

The researches of Ehrlich and collaborators[168-170] and of others[171-173] clearly indicated that a polygalacturonic structure is common to all pectic substances, from whatever source they are obtained. In his first publications Ehrlich[167] did not describe the manner in which the galacturonic acid units are associated in pectins. He called it a "polygalacturonic acid" without any definition of the size or structure of the molecule.

In 1923 Smolenski[174] advanced the idea, based partly on experimental work and partly on reasoning by analogy with other carbohydrates, that the polygalacturonic acid structure of pectic substances may contain eight galacturonic acid units made up of four digalacturonic acids connected by lactone linkages to give the octa structure:

$$\begin{bmatrix} C_5H_8O_4-O-C_5H_7O_3 \\ | \quad\quad\quad\quad | \\ COOH \quad\quad COOH \end{bmatrix} -O- \begin{bmatrix} C_5H_7O_3-O-C_5H_7O_3 \\ | \quad\quad\quad\quad | \\ COOH \quad\quad COOH \end{bmatrix} -O- \text{ etc.}$$

Later Smolenski abandoned the idea of this octa structure in favor of a polygalacturonic acid of undefined constitution and degree of polymerization. He noted occasional increase of free carboxyl groups in various pectinic acid and pectic acid preparations and assumed on this basis the possible presence of lactone linkages. As will be seen below, this possibility has been revived recently in connection with some of the recent views concerning the structure of pectic substances. Unfortunately, many important contributions of Smolenski were long overlooked because of the inaccessibility of his original publications.

[166] M. L. Suarez, Chem.-Ztg., 41, 87 (1917).
[167] F. Ehrlich, Chem.-Ztg., 41, 197 (1917).
[168] F. Ehrlich and R. Sommerfeld, Biochem. Z., 168, 263 (1926).
[169] F. Ehrlich and F. Schubert, Biochem. Z., 169, 13 (1926).
[170] F. Ehrlich and A. Kosmahly, Biochem. Z., 212, 162 (1929).
[171] F. W. Norris and S. B. Schryver, Biochem. J., 19, 676 (1925).
[172] T. Fellenberg, Biochem. Z., 85, 118 (1918).
[173] R. Sucharipa, Die Pektinstoffe. Serger and Hempel, Braunschweig, 1925.
[174] K. Smolenski, Roczniki Chemji, 3, 86 (1923).

Without knowledge of the work of Smolenski, in 1925, Ahmann and Hooker[175] suggested a galacturonic acid–galactonic acid unit as the basic building block of pectic acid. It was assumed that at least six of these double units were linked to form pectic acid. This structure, assumed to contain 12 molecules, was larger than all those proposed previously. While positive evidence was still lacking that such a structure exists in the pectic substances, it clearly indicated the increasing desire to reconcile the constitution and colloidal properties of the pectic substances. Also in 1925, Nanji, Paton, and Ling[176] published an article which proposed a cyclic structure for pectic acid. Their purest calcium pectate preparations had a galacturonic acid anhydride content of 70.56%. These authors reached the conclusion that the basic structure of pectic substances is a six-membered ring, composed of four galacturonic acid units and one molecule each of arabinose and galactose:

Nanji-Paton-Ling formula for pectic acid

Such a structure contains four free carboxyl groups and should yield a calcium salt containing 7.36% calcium; they found 7.34% in the purest preparation. It also contains, according to the formula, 69.7% galacturonic acid anhydride, 14.3% anhydroarabinose, and 16.5% anhydrogalactose. The analytical results substantiated this assumed composition but provided no actual evidence that the unit was a six-membered ring. This conclusion was reached purely on the basis of two considerations that (1) all components of the complex molecule must be present in the proportion of at least one whole molecule per pectin unit, and (2) the actual proportions of the components are increased by the exclusion of water with increasing polymerization and unit size. The six-membered ring structure was disproved later on several grounds. Norris and Resch[177] found that the calculations used by Nanji, Paton, and Ling to estimate the portion of the furfuraldehyde yields derived from the galacturonic acid were incorrect and thus gave the wrong proportion of arabinose. It was also found that pectin preparations often contain a higher proportion of methyl ester than is compatible with the hexa structure.[178]

[175] C. F. Ahmann and H. D. Hooker, *Univ. Missouri Agr. Expt. Sta.*, Research Bull. No. 77 (1925).

[176] D. R. Nanji, F. J. Paton, and A. R. Ling, *J. Soc. Chem. Ind.*, 44, 252T (1925).

[177] F. W. Norris and C. E. Resch, *Biochem. J.*, 29, 1590 (1935).

[178] P. B. Myers and G. L. Baker, *Univ. Delaware Agr. Expt. Sta.*, Bull. No. 187 (1934).

During the twenties and early thirties the name of Ehrlich was insepa-rably associated with pectin chemistry. In 1926 Ehrlich and co-workers[168-170] published a series of articles on the pectic substances of various plants and described the presence of digalacturonic acids. These views were further elaborated[179] by the disclosure in 1929 that the funda-mental chemical units on which all pectic substances are based are tetra-galacturonic acids. Accordingly pectic substances derived from different sources vary in both composition and constituent units, but all contain tetragalacturonic acid structures as their basic skeleton. The linkages be-tween the four galacturonic acid units have been assumed to be similar to those found in other polysaccharides, and the low reducing power of pec-tins was taken as an indication that the linkages involve the aldehydic groups. At first the tetragalacturonic acid was presumed to exist in only three distinct modifications. " Tetragalacturonic acid a" was supposed to be in a normal tetraanhydro form. The addition of one molecule of water and opening of the amylene oxide ring was claimed to transform this into "tetragalacturonic acid c." Both the "a" and "c" modifications could be converted into "tetragalacturonic acid b," in which the ring was opened and a monolactone formed. In this latter unit only three of the carboxyls were directly titratable while the fourth was assumed to be saponifiable by treatment with alkali. The opening of the ring in "tetragalacturonic acid b" was thought to be responsible for its increased reducing power. According to the formula this increase should be equivalent to one alde-hydic group per molecule of "tetragalacturonic acid b." These three units are now only of historical interest. The structure of the alleged "tetra-galacturonic acid a" is shown below:

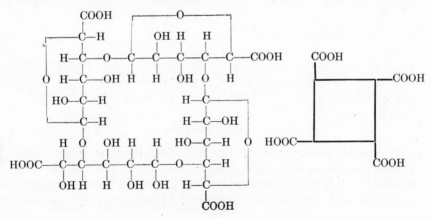

Ehrlich's tetragalacturonic acid structure

[179] F. Ehrlich and F. Schubert, *Ber.*, **62**, 1974 (1929).

Later Ehrlich modified his views and introduced several new terms (pectolic acid, gelpectolic acid, pectolactonic acid, etc.), while some of those previously described (the digalacturonic acids, some of the tetragalacturonic acids) never occurred again in his writings. It is obvious to us now that he was the victim, as were so many before him, of the heterogenity of the pectic substances.

Myers and Baker[178] criticized Ehrlich's work on the basis that he dealt with pectic materials excessively degenerated during the process of extraction and concentration. They argued that Ehrlich's pectins ("hydratopectins") had negligible jellying power and they were thus unsuitable for the determination of structure and molecular size. Upon analysis of high-grade pectins extracted from orange peel, they found arabinose in amounts too low and the galacturonic acid content too high to be accounted for by Ehrlich's formula. Myers and Baker thought that pectin (of high jellying power) is an octagalacturonic acid which contains, in addition, one molecule each of galactose and arabinose, two molecules of acetic acid, and seven molecules of methyl alcohol. The octagalacturonic acid was assumed to be formed from two tetragalacturonic acid units with the elimination of one molecule of water in a manner similar to that postulated by Smolenski.

In spite of the now dominant opinion that the pectic substances are linear polymers containing mostly the same repeating building unit, it would seem unwise to discard categorically the possibility that some kind of ring structures might exist in pectic substances. As will be shown on the following pages, there is some suspicion that polygalacturonic acid units might associate in some manner. If such interchain linkages between two polygalacturonic acid units occur at more than one point, what one might consider as a ring structure could exist. It is most unlikely, however, that comparatively small regular units like tetragalacturonic acid units would represent the maximum degree of polymerization in pectic substances. It is of interest to note that quite recently Macara[180] suggested that the pectinic acids in fruit juices consist of a ring structure formed from four anyhydrogalacturonic acid units and one molecule of galactose.

2. Structure

It is rather arbitrary to separate the discussion of structure from that of size and shape since these properties are of course intimately interrelated.[181] It is hoped, however, that by grouping the arguments on these points the still very confusing picture might be presented in a more helpful manner.

[180] T. Macara, reprint of a lecture given before the Royal Institution of Great Britain, April 16, 1937.
[181] H. Mark, *Physical Chemistry of High Polymer Systems*. Interscience, New York, 1940.

The contention that the pectin molecule has any given constant size and that it contains either four, five, six, or eight, or any other number of galacturonic acid residues, became increasingly untenable as new information concerning the structures of starch, cellulose, and other polysaccharide macromolecules was accumulated. To many workers it appeared unlikely that such a group of compounds could show so many properties similar to other polysaccharides and yet have an entirely different type of structure. It appeared unreasonable, furthermore, that the highly colloidal nature of the pectic materials could be caused by small molecules containing four or even eight galacturonic acid residues. As a consequence, the decade from 1930 to 1940 showed a gradual return to the view that the polygalacturonic acid nucleus of the pectic substances has a large and essentially indefinite size.

From a study of the physical properties of pectic substances, Meyer and Mark[182] in 1930 assumed that these are built in a manner similar to cellulose, namely from galacturonic acid residues coupled into long chains with glycosidic linkages. Corbeau and also Burgers,[183] who studied pectin threads with x-rays, concluded that the pectinic acid molecule must be very much elongated. But Morell, Baur, and Link[184] were the first ones to disprove definitely the tetragalacturonic acid theory as well as the alleged ring structure of pectic substances. These workers methylated pectic acid by Fischer's method.[185]   The methylpolygalacturonic acid methyl ester (polyester glycoside or methyl polygalacturonide) was purified and after saponification with dilute alkali (which does not affect the glycosidic methyl end group marked with an asterisk in the formula shown below) gave a methoxyl content lower than Ehrlich's formula for tetragalacturonic acid would require. Some of these results are shown in Table 6.

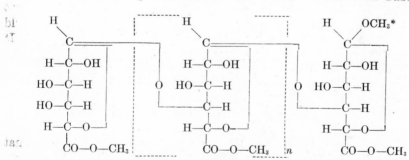

Link *et al.* formula for pectin (as shown on a
completely esterified polygalacturonic acid)

[182] H. Meyer and H. Mark, *Der Aufbau der hochmolekularen Naturstoffe.* Akad. Verlagsgesellschaft, Leipzig, 1930.

[183] L. Corbeau and also W. G. Burgers, both cited by G. van Iterson, Jr., *Chem. Weekblad,* **30,** 2 (1933). Apparently unpublished data.

[184] S. Morell, L. Baur, and K. P. Link, *J. Biol. Chem.,* **105,** 1 (1934).

[185] E. Fischer and A. Speier, *Ber.,* **28,** 3252 (1895).

TABLE 6

METHOXYL CONTENTS OF METHYLPOLYGALACTURONIDES OF VARYING MOLECULAR
SIZES (MORELL, BAUR, AND LINK)

| | | Per cent CH_3O | |
		Polyester glycoside	Polyacid glycoside
Calculated for	4 units..........	20.15	4.21
	8 units..........	18.00	2.15
	9 units..........	17.82	1.92
	10 units..........	17.67	1.73
Found....................................		18.00	2.18

These analyses indicated that the polygalacturonic acids studied by
Morell, Baur, and Link must have contained a minimum of 8–10 units
in the polymer chain. Since this was the case after such severe and prolonged heating with acid that a considerable proportion of the polygalacturonic acid was reduced to (mono) galacturonic acid, it seemed
safe to assume that the average number of galacturonic acid residues in
the polygalacturonic acid as it existed in the plant must have contained
considerably more than 8 or 10 anhydrogalacturonic acid units. In view
of present knowledge on the retention of organic solvents like ethanol by
pectic preparations (see Chapter VIII, Section 6), one must reconsider
the figures obtained in these methyl determinations because they are likely
too high on account of retained traces of solvents. In a recent extension of
this work, Jansen, MacDonnell, and Ward[186] have shown that when such
precautions are followed, the residual methoxyl content of the methyl
glycoside of polygalacturonic acid is only 0.85%, indicating polygalacturonic acid units composed of about 21 anhydrogalacturonic acid residues. The structural formula suggested by Link and associates is still
widely used. This formula differs from that of the naturally occurring
pectic substances only by the presence of the glycosidic methyl group
(marked with an asterisk) which has been introduced during the methylation. The true spatial relationships are better represented by a hexagonal
formula suggested by Haworth and now widely used. The following diagram shows a part of a polygalacturonic acid (pectic acid) chain (without
end units):

[186] E. F. Jansen, L. R. MacDonnell, and W. H. Ward, *Arch. Biochem.*, **21**, 149
(1949).

That the structure of pectic substances is to a certain extent similar to that of cellulose was demonstrated by the researches of some German workers. Applying the methods of cellulose research, Henglein and Schneider[187] prepared nitropectin and found that it shows properties similar to those of nitrocellulose. Nitropectin is likely to be composed of elongated threadlike molecules because when the rapidly flowing material is solidified in a film, its tensile strength is considerably greater longitudinally than transversely. The molecules of these esters appear to be less extended than the cellulose molecule,[188] perhaps because of the presence of strongly polar carboxyl groups. From this work the conclusions were drawn that polygalacturonic acids contain a great number of galacturonic acid residues and that the differences between the various preparations of pectic substances are caused by: (1) molecular size (number of combined units), (2) degree of esterification of the carboxyl groups of the component galacturonic acid units, and (3) the proportion of accompanying "ballast" material such as pentosans and hexosans. Possible structural variations might be added as a fourth major factor.

For some time it was assumed, purely on the basis of analogy, that the galacturonic acid residues in polygalacturonic acids are linked through positions 1 and 4. That the glucose units in cellulose are connected in this manner is now well established. When Schneider and co-workers[187,188] prepared nitropectin and this compound behaved similarly to nitrocellulose, this was regarded as additional indication that the linkages between the individual building units in pectin must be similar to those in cellulose. One of the results of the presence of 1,4 linkages is the low reducing ability of pectic acids, pectins, and pectinic acids toward alkaline copper solutions. We shall deal with the reducing power of pectic substances in Chapter VII.

Levene and Kreider[189] oxidized polygalacturonic acid with periodic acid and found that L-tartaric acid was formed. This indicated that the connection between the galacturonic acid groups was either through 1 and 4 or 1 and 5 positions. Knowing that galacturonic acid occurs in nature only in the pyranoside form, the only possible linkage was through carbon atoms 1 and 4. It should be noted that, according to Beaven and Jones[190] and Smith,[191] during the methylation of polygalacturonic acids transformations may occur which cause the appearance of furanoside structures in such drastically treated samples. In spite of this it is the opinion of Hirst,[165] who reviewed this matter a short time ago, and of

[187] F. A. Henglein and G. Schneider, *Ber.*, **69**, 309 (1936).
[188] G. Schneider and U. Fritschi, *Ber.*, **69**, 2537 (1936).
[189] P. A. Levene and L. C. Kreider, *J. Biol. Chem.*, **120**, 591 (1937).
[190] G. H. Beaven and J. K. N. Jones, *J. Soc. Chem. Ind.*, **58**, 363 (1939).
[191] F. Smith, *J. Soc. Chem. Ind.*, **58**, 363 (1939).

Beaven and Jones and of Smith that the coupling of adjacent galacturonic acids in naturally occurring polygalacturonic acids is always through the 1 and 4 positions.

According to the definition given in Chapter I, polygalacturonic acids must show a colloidal nature in order to be classified as pectic materials. There is no information on how many galacturonic anhydride units must be linked to give a polygalacturonic acid of colloidal nature, but the lower polymers, containing up to at least four units (the "oligogalacturonic acids"), will probably prove to be crystallizable and outside the scope of the above definition.

At the present time there is no unanimity among various workers in this field concerning the macromolecular structure of the pectic substances. As we have seen, it is known that most of the individual units of anhydrogalacturonic acid are combined through 1,4 linkages. It seems more than likely that the structure of the macromolecule is more complicated. There are many who are willing to go far in reasoning by analogy, and to apply to the pectic substances most of the knowledge accumulated in research on starch and cellulose. Other schools of thought propose that full advantage be taken of the methods and lines of reasoning developed with other polysaccharides but that nothing should be assumed to be actually analogous unless and until there is sufficient evidence to prove that this is the case. These different approaches resulted in some very stimulating discussions.

The views of most workers in this field may be classified into a few general types of structures which might account for the typical colloidal, viscous, and jelly-forming properties: (1) The linear polygalacturonic acids formed exclusively by 1,4 linkages contain enough units to build large colloidal molecules. (2) Such individual units of polygalacturonic acids are further combined in some manner. This latter might include branching or laminated structures such as were shown to exist in starch[192,193] or any other type of association between the individual polygalacturonic acids. (3) One cannot exclude the possibility that the typical properties result more from specific shapes rather than structures although these latter will obviously depend on the existence of certain specific structural elements. Let us see what arguments might be used for any of these hypotheses.

According to hypothesis (1) the polygalacturonic acid structure of the pectic substances is built up of a great number of anhydrogalacturonic acid residues, all connected with 1,4 linkages of equal strength and vulnerability. The picture of such a molecule is obvious and simple. A sufficient

[192] W. N. Haworth, *Proc. Roy. Soc.* (*London*), **186,** 1 (1946).
[193] K. H. Meyer, P. Gurtler, and P. Bernfeld, *Nature,* **160,** 900 (1948).

number of units must be associated to lend the molecule typical colloidal properties and the high molecular weights noted on the following pages. Schneider and Fritschi[188] support this view with the results of osmotic molecular weight determinations performed on nitropectin and on acetylpectin produced therefrom. The average molecular weights did not change materially during the preparation of these derivatives. Were the large molecular sizes due to aggregates, it would be impossible, they claim, to perform acetylation of nitropectin without appreciable degradation.

According to hypothesis (2) the basic structure of the pectic substances might involve linkages of different types and of different degrees of vulnerability. It does not matter, from the standpoint of this conception, whether a linkage participating in the construction of the large molecule is actually chemically different or is only caused to behave differently due to internal stresses, asymmetry, or any other reason or reasons. Let us examine this latter possibility which is much more complicated (and therefore more flexible) than is structure (1).

Smaller groups of associated anhydrogalacturonic acid residues may bundle or aggregate into larger structures. There are many ways in which this may occur. One of these is the assumption that the "basic units" may be formed by primary valence bonds (*Hauptvalenzketten*), and these combined by other types of linkages into larger structures. A similar manner of construction has been suggested previously for other naturally occurring polymers.[194] The basic polygalacturonic acid units composed of n molecules of anhydrogalacturonic acid molecules, linked by primary valences, may or may not contain a sufficient number of member units to attain colloidal properties. These "primary" polygalacturonic chains $(G)_n$ associate into larger units $[(G)_n]_m$ by linkages which are thought to be more vulnerable to destruction than the 1,4 glycosidic linkages connecting the adjoining individual anhydrogalacturonic acid units.[195] The formation of such more complex structures or "molecular associations"[196] is the property of long chains containing more than a minimum number of anhydrogalacturonic acid molecules. When such chains are reduced in length below this minimum (as by enzymic hydrolysis, for instance), the "secondary" structure may also be destroyed. Thus, the essence of this type of structure would be the presence of diffrent types of linkages between some of the anhydrogalacturonic acid units or between chains of polygalacturonic acids. In turn, the main significance of

[194] G. V. Caesar, in R. W. Kerr, *Chemistry and Industry of Starch*. 2nd ed., Academic Press, New York, 1950.

[195] Z. I. Kertesz, *J. Am. Chem. Soc.*, **61**, 2544 (1939).

[196] R. Speiser, M. J. Copley, and G. C. Nutting, *J. Phys. Colloid Chem.*, **51**. 117 (1947).

different linkages is that some of these will resist fissure more than will others.

There is some indication, mostly from physical measurements, that the polygalacturonic acids are linked together end to end or at least in some manner giving definitely elongated shape. Such a structure was postulated by Smolenski[174] in the description of a polygalacturonic acid composed of digalacturonic acid units. It is likely that such typical properties of pectic compounds as high viscosity and the ability to form jellies, for instance, are due to the "super" structure and are not exhibited to any great extent by unassociated polygalacturonic acids.

The "secondary" or "super" structure may be due to ester, lactone, or anhydride bridges[197] between the $(G)_n$ chains. The participation of intramolecular acid groups in forming such linkages within any given polygalacturonic acid chain is not likely, because of the large distances between these groups. On the other hand, such connection between neighboring chains of polygalacturonic acids are distinctly possible. For example, the linking of polygalacturonic acid chains through an anhydride bridge may occur as follows:

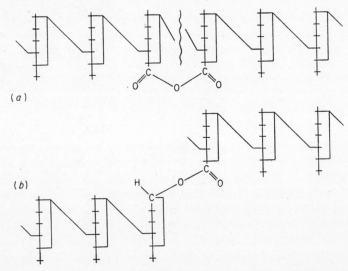

(a)

(b)

The possible occurrence of such linkages involving the carboxyl groups may explain the fact that the equivalent weight of even pure and highly viscous polygalacturonic acids (pectic acids) does not reach the calculated values. The vulnerability of pectic compounds to treatment with alkali may be also explained by this working hypothesis. The acidic character

[197] J. D. Loconti, *Master's Thesis*, Cornell University, 1940.

of pectinic acids increases during degradation by prolonged heating without the simultaneous corresponding hydrolysis of methyl ester linkages. This, again, may be the result of the liberation of carboxyl groups which were engaged in some manner in the structure of the macromolecule. We shall return to these observations in Chapter VII.

As will be seen below, the ester content of isolated pectinic acids hardly ever even approaches the theoretical value of 16.35% methoxyl. This may be taken as an indication that some acid groups are in some manner otherwise engaged in the structure of pectinic acids. Protopectin is now believed by some to represent very large (and therefore water-insoluble) pectinic acid molecules. During the solubilization of protopectin, fissure of some of the linkages involving carboxyl groups occurs, accounting for the free acid groups found in all water-soluble pectinic acids. The existence of polyvalent ions in bonding pectinic acids into protopectin as suggested by Henglein[198] is only a special case of this sort.

Schneider and Fritschi[188] state that linkages involving the carboxyl groups are not likely to occur in pectic substances but their argument, in the writer's view, is more an argument for than against the possible role of these groups. They have methylated nitropectin and reached 91–96% of the theoretically possible methylation without simultaneous degradation of the polygalacturonic acid as judged from viscosity measurements. More drastic methylation resulted in complete esterification of the carboxyl groups, but this could be attained only after definite degradation occurred, resulting in a 62% drop in the specific viscosity. This indeed may indicate that some carboxyl groups in the original macromolecule participated in some manner in the formation of a "superstructure" and could be methylated only after they were set free. Some destruction of the original structure is demonstrated by the drop in viscosity. These authors also note that applying the glycosidic methyl end group method of Link and co-workers,[184] the residual methoxyl values obtained for partially degraded, first methylated and then saponified, nitropectins were so low that a minimum molecular weight of only 20,000 (100 units) must be assumed.

Luckett and Smith[199] comment on the fact that the methyl ester of trimethylmethylgalacturonoside was not detected among the hydrolysis products of methylated pectic acid. This may indicate either that the polygalacturonic acid chains are very long or that the end groups are involved in some manner in the structure of the macromolecule and are therefore not free to be methylated. This assumption is contrary to the approximately 2 to 3% reducing power shown by purified pectinic acids (see

[198] F. A. Henglein, *J. makromol. Chem.*, **1**, 121 (1943).
[199] S. Luckett and F. Smith, *J. Chem. Soc.*, **1940**, 1506.

Chapter VII, Section III), or rather makes the significance of reducing power values found for pectinic acids more doubtful.

Snellman and Säverborn[200] measured the streaming double refraction of some pectinic acids and believe that these are composed of long particles arranged in bundles. The behavior of pectinic acids in these experiments may be explained by the existence of some "secondary" manner of association of the polygalacturonic acid units. Bock and Einsele[201] are of the opinion that the polygalacturonic acid units may branch similarly to starch. If this is actually the case, the possible variations which may occur in both the length and shape of molecules of equal weight would increase several fold.

Some recent results obtained from the enzymic hydrolysis of pectic acids by a tomato enzyme[202] indicate the formation of some "limit polygalacturonides" reminiscent of the "limit dextrins" obtained from starch. This might indicate that there is some break in the continuity of the polygalacturonic acid molecule caused either by the occurrence of branchings or of a different type of linkage or structural element. Similar "interruptions" in the continuity of the cellulose molecule by glucuronic acid[203] and by nonglucosidic residues of odd character[204] have been considered in the formation of interchain bonds in other polysaccharides. By the action of this tomato enzyme on pectic acid, units of polygalacturonic acid giving an average of over five anhydrogalacturonic acid residues can be obtained. This observation might be regarded as a further indication of the existence of different types of interpolygalacturonic acid linkages in pectic acid. Since the publication of our report on this enzyme, which has been provisionally named a "depolymerase," several similar observations appeared in the literature (see Chap. XIV, Section III).

Much systematic study is needed before we shall have any definite knowledge of all the types of linkages which participate in the building of large polygalacturonic acid molecules. The idea presents itself that the basic polygalacturonic acid chains are built with primary valences while the "super" structure or structures are formed by hydrogen bonds. Saric and Schofield[205] recently suggested the existence in pectic acids of such hydrogen bridges linking the carboxyl groups. The participation of hydrogen bonds in similar structures such as cellulose and starch has been previously postulated and seems to be one of the dominant ideas in the

[200] O. Snellman and S. Säverborn, *Kolloidchem. Beihefte,* **52,** 467 (1947).

[201] H. Bock and R. Einsele, *J. prakt. Chem.,* **155,** 225 (1940).

[202] R. J. McColloch and Z. I. Kertesz, *Arch. Biochem.,* **17,** 197 (1948).

[203] H. Mark, *Anal. Chem.,* **20,** 104 (1948).

[204] E. Pacsu, *Textile Research J.,* **16,** 243, 318, 490, 534 (1946); *J. Polymer Sci.,* **2,** 565 (1947).

[205] S. P. Saric and R. K. Schofield, *Proc. Roy. Soc. London,* **A125,** 431 (1946).

field of polymolecular structures of polysaccharides rich in hydroxyl groups.[296]

R
|
O
\
  H   H   R   R
     \ / | |
      O   H—C—O—H⋯O=C—OH
      | | |
      R   R

Possible intermolecular hydrogen bonding between
two hydroxyl and hydroxyl and carboxyl groups

Naturally, the location of the active hydrogen bonds will depend on the spatial configuration and other factors which, to a certain extent, also determine the strength of the bond.

If the contention that chains of pectic acids are connected in any manner different from the glycosidic 1,4 linkages can be proven to be correct, the possibility occurs of obtaining from such structures split products similar in some manner to some of the ring structures of Ehrlich. The difference would be that the linkages would not all be of the same type. Bock[207] assumed the occurrence of such structures during the hydrolysis of protopectin, but there is no evidence thus far to prove their existence.

It will be apparent from the foregoing discussion, that pectic acid is a polyanhydro-a-D-galacturonic acid containing the pyranose ring and linked glycosidically through positions 1 and 4. Some other types of linkages are likely to exist in the macromolecule, but we have no exact evidence on this point. As will be shown in Chapter IV, pectic acids as we know them now are heterogeneous mixtures of macromolecules of various sizes.

3. Shape and Size

Pectic acid has elongated molecules. If we consider the pectic polygalacturonic acids as showing identical structure throughout, then, neglecting for the moment stereochemical and other similar considerations, there are two extreme forms of molecules under conditions where interaction between molecules does not occur: (1) the polymer may take the shape of a completely extended chain of monomeric units; or (2) the chain may be folded tightly into a spherical body. All configurations between these two extremes are theoretically possible. If interaction between polygalacturonic acid units exists, the number of possible different shapes becomes great.

[296] L. Pauling, *The Nature of the Chemical Bond and the Structure of Molecules and Crystals*. Cornell Univ. Press, Ithaca, 1940.

[207] H. Bock, *Dissertation*, Technische Hochschule, Karlsruhe, 1943.

There is no reason to assume, furthermore, that the shape of any macro-molecule of this sort is constant; thus the solvent[208] and other external conditions[209] will determine the prevalent shape of the polymer molecule.[210,211]

Linear polymers, twisting or rotating about single bonds, might take up an enormous number of different configurations. Each configuration of the chain will correspond to a definite distance between its ends, usually designated as the "effective length" of the molecule.[212] The degree of flexibility of the macromolecules allowing twisting or kinking[211] depends on the structure of the chain and is likely to be limited in both configurational variations. Although this subject has received considerable attention in recent years, especially in the case of cellulose and cellulose derivatives, much more systematic work is needed on pectic substances before a discussion of this matter will have enough solid foundation to become useful. Many authors dealt with the spatial arrangement of polygalacturonic acids but most of them simply reason by analogy with cellulose. Reinicke[213] developed a graphic scheme showing the spatial configuration of polygalacturonic acids in which the interrelation of various atoms is shown by placing tetrahedrals into cubes. The latter always meet on edges and thereby limit the spherical shape of the model. Reinicke concluded that the polygalacturonic acids must occur in two optical isomers, a point not thus far confirmed.

A recent x-ray study of spun sodium pectate and pectic acid fibers by Palmer and Lotzkar,[214] and Palmer and Hartzog[215] has yielded some interesting information on the spatial structure of these molecules. Polygalacturonides differ from other polysaccharides in that the C—O glycosidic bond forms an angle of 90° with the plane of the pyranose ring in contrast with the 20° bond angle in cellulose, for instance. The rings therefore bear a trans relationship to each other and the galacturonide chain has the configuration of a three-fold screw axis and an identity period in the fiber direction of 13.1 Å. These authors draw the conclusion that, as a result of this structure, polygalacturonic acid chains are likely to be less flexible than cellulose or alginic acid chains. From a later study of the x-ray diffraction of various pectin esters (acetate, propionate, butyrate, laurate, myristate, and palmitate), Palmer and Ballantyne[216] con-

---

[208] T. Alfrey, A. Bartowics, and H. Mark, *J. Am. Chem. Soc.*, **64**, 1557 (1942).
[209] H. Campbell and P. Johnson, *Trans. Faraday Soc.*, **40**, 221 (1944).
[210] W. Kuhn and H. Kuhn, *J. Colloid. Sci.*, **3**, 11 (1948).
[211] A. F. Siriani, L. M. Wise, and R. L. McIntosh, *Can. J. Research*, **B25**, 301 (1947).
[212] C. E. H. Bawn, *Research*, **1**, 343 (1948).
[213] R. Reinicke, *Chem.-Ztg.*, **63**, 472 (1939).
[214] K. J. Palmer and H. Lotzkar, *J. Am. Chem. Soc.*, **67**, 883 (1945).
[215] K. J. Palmer and M. B. Hartzog, *J. Am. Chem. Soc.*, **67**, 2122 (1945).
[216] K. J. Palmer and M. Ballantyne, *J. Am. Chem. Soc.*, **72**, 736 (1950).

cluded that the polygalacturonic acid chains in these compounds have two-fold screw symmetry and that the interchain separation per carbon atom in the ester chain is 0.78 Å. The investigations of Wuhrmann and Pilnik[217] by a similar technic also indicated folded chains in pectic acid fibers.

On the basis of a variety of measurements, Säverborn[218] drew some conclusions concerning the shape of the molecules of pectic and pectinic acids. He found the thickness of the particles quite constant, being of the magnitude of 10 Å., except for pectins of exceptionally high molecular weight. The length of the molecules ranged from 730 to 4500 Å., but the different methods of measurements gave results which often varied several fold. Results of some of these measurements are shown in Table 7.

TABLE 7

PARTICLE DIMENSIONS IN SOME PECTINIC ACIDS (ADAPTED FROM SÄVERBORN)

Source of pectinic acid	Degree of polymerization[a]	Average length in Å., from			Average thickness in Å., from	
		Sedimentation velocity	Viscosity	Streaming birefringence	Sedimentation velocity	Streaming birefringence
Apple pomace.....	1900	1200	1700	2630	10	7
Lemon peel.......	2500	1600	2400	3780	10	7
Beet slices........	1800	1200	1600	—	10	—

[a] Calculated from the molecular weights and assuming a polymerizing unit equal to the glucose in cellulose: 5.15 Å.

It is clear that the particles of pectinic acids are elongated in shape. Essentially a similar shape can be assumed for the pectic acids which might be derived (without causing any degradation) from these pectinic acids. The removal of the ester groups may have a noticeable effect on the over-all dimensions, inasmuch as it will alter the degree of hydration; however, this is not likely to affect the ratio of thickness to length of the particles. The hydration of polymers like pectic substances is one of the main factors casting uncertainty over the absolute values obtained in such measurements and their interpretations. Recently Owens, Lotzkar, Schultz, and Maclay[219] made viscosity and osmotic pressure measurements on a series of pectinic acids. The length–diameter ratios calculated from the intrinsic viscosities by means of the Simha[220] equation gave values

[217] K. Wuhrmann and W. Pilnik, *Experientia*, 1, No. 9, 1 (1945).
[218] S. Säverborn, *A Contribution to the Knowledge of the Acid Polyuronides,* Almqvist and Wiksells, Uppsala, 1945.
[219] H. S. Owens, H. Lotzkar, T. H. Schultz, and W. D. Maclay, *J. Am. Chem. Soc.,* 68, 1628 (1946).
[220] R. Simha, *J. Phys. Chem.,* 44, 25 (1940).

from 53 to 165, indicating rigid, rodlike structures for these pectinic acids in aqueous salt solutions.

Let us turn now to the matter of molecular size. Whatever the exact structure of the pectic acids may be, it is certain that highly colloidal pectic substances possess molecular weights in the same ranges as those found for other macromolecular polymers. Nearly all important properties, especially mechanical characteristics of high polymers which are of such great practical importance, depend on the molecular weight and therefore the great interest taken in such measurements is entirely understandable. As will be shown, we have as yet only fragmentary information on this point. For one, pectin samples are made up of mixtures of units of various sizes. Considerable progress has been made in the determination of this heterogeneity of pectic substances, yet practically all work in the past was done on ill-defined mixtures of pectic substances of various molecular sizes. We shall discuss this point in Chapter IV.

Before mentioning numerical values obtained by any methods, the nature of averages encountered in such investigations should be considered. Any mean molecular weight will depend on the proportional distribution of smaller and larger molecules to an extent determined by the nature of the method of estimation. By the cryoscopic, osmotic, and end-group methods the number of molecules will be counted regardless of their size and thus the molecular weight will be number-average (M_n). Other methods such as viscosity or sedimentation velocity measurements will give weight-average molecular weights (M_w) in which the larger particles will play a dominant role. Kraemer and Lansing[221] gave the following formulas for the calculation of such values:

$$M_n = \frac{1}{\Sigma \dfrac{f_i}{M_i}}$$

$$M_w = \Sigma f_i M_i$$

where f_i is the fractional weight of M_i molecular weight in the mixture. To illustrate with a simple example: A mixture of 99 parts of a polymer composed of 1000 units and 1 part composed of 100,000 units will give $M_n = 1010$ while $M_w = 1999$ or almost twice the former value. The M_n and M_w values are identical for a homogeneous sample. In heterogeneous samples of polymers the difference between M_n and M_w is an index of the heterogeneity. There are many methods for the calculation of M_n and M_w values during hydrolysis or degradation of any kind of polymer com-

[221] E. O. Kraemer and W. D. Lansing. *J. Phys. Chem.*, **39**, 153 (1935).

pounds but a detailed discussion of this topic is beyond the scope of the present volume. There is ample literature on this subject.[222-224] The point which must be emphasized here is that in dealing with molecular weights of polymer compounds the methods by which the values were obtained should be always borne in mind.

As an introduction to discussing the results which may be found in the literature, it may be mentioned that Ehrlich and Schubert[225] used the cryoscopic method for the determination of the molecular weight of various pectic preparations and obtained results in the neighborhood of 1300. As has been stated before, such values are either just incorrect or have been obtained on preparations so extensively degraded that they should not be called true pectic substances. The cryoscopic method was later applied by Morell, Baur, and Link[226] to some purified methylglycoside of polygalacturonic acid methyl ester prepared by refluxing pectinic acid for 66 hours with methanol containing 5% hydrochloric acid. Even these excessively treated preparations indicated (by the cryoscopic method) molecular weights higher than those found by Ehrlich.

A great deal of work has been done toward determining the molecular weight ranges in pectic substances. The methods which may be, at times at least, regarded as useful for obtaining such information are as follows: (1) end-group determinations (reducing power); (2) cryoscopic, osmotic, and diffusion methods; (3) ultracentrifugal (sedimentation velocity and equilibrium) methods; and (4) viscosity measurements. The behavior of pectic substances under conditions of such measurements will be discussed in Chapter VII.

Assuming the existence of certain conditions, the measurement of end groups seems to offer a good possibility of measuring the (number-average) molecular weight of pectic substances. Unfortunately, methodological difficulties cast doubt upon the results obtained. Taking the reducing power determinations at face value, the results in the range of 2.5 to 7.5% (expressed as anhydrogalacturonic acid) indicate average degrees of polymerization of 13 to 40 anhydrogalacturonic acid units. This corresponds to approximate molecular weights in the range of 2500 to 7500. Such values are out of range of those found by physical measurements and are, in addition, not in harmony with our general ideas concerning the molecular weights of colloidal polymers. The possible significance of

[222] See: H. Mark, *Physical Chemistry of High Polymer Systems*, Interscience, New York, 1940, and other books in the series (*High Polymers*).
[223] W. H. Durfee and Z. I. Kertesz, *J. Am. Chem. Soc.*, **62**, 1196 (1940).
[224] G. Herdan, *Research*, **3**, 35 (1950).
[225] F. Ehrlich and F. Schubert, *Ber.*, **62**, 1974 (1929).
[226] S. Morell, L. Baur and K. P. Link, *J. Biol. Chem.*, **105**, 1 (1934).

these values is that they may represent some kind of component units forming the larger pectinic acid and pectic acid molecules.

The results obtained for pectic substances by measurement of the osmotic pressure are equally disappointing. As stated before, large molecules produce low osmotic pressures and therefore even minute impurities will have a great influence. The osmotic behavior of colloidal solutions also deviates markedly from ideal solutions.[227]   The few results obtained for water solutions of pectinic acids are of little significance.

Schneider and Fritschi[188] determined by osmotic methods the (number-average) molecular weight ranges of a number of derivatives and found for acetylpectin prepared from nitropectin values in the range of 30,000 to 100,000. When nitropectin was directly prepared from pectinic acid, values in the range 30,000 to 50,000 were obtained, but when the nitration was performed after demethylation the range was 20,000 to 40,000. These authors also illustrated the heterogeneity of such preparations. A sample of nitropectin which gave the molecular weight of 45,000 was fractionated by precipitation from acetone solution with water. The percentage distribution of the fractions and their average molecular weights were:

```
Lower than  30,000........20%
30,000  to  50,000........40%
50,000  to  70,000........35%
70,000  to  90,000........ 5%
```

The question remains, of course, just how much significance may be attributed to results obtained for derivatives. Schneider and co-workers seem to feel that the values represent the weights of the macromolecules. The values, however, seem to be lower than those obtained by several other methods discussed below.

Measurements with the ultracentrifuge[228] are regarded by many workers as the most dependable means of determining the size of large molecules. Thus far all results for pectic substances were reported from the University of Uppsala in Sweden. Svedberg and Gralén[229] obtained (weight-average) molecular weights ranging from 16,000 to 50,000 for pectic substances in unpurified extracts from apples, pears, plums, lily bulbs, and orange albedo. Säverborn[230] used some of the older standard methods for the preparation of pectinic acids and obtained results ranging from 33,000 to 117,000. It is certain that in most of these preparations there was a considerable proportion of nonpectic polysaccharides. This

[227] H. W. Melville, *Trans. Faraday Soc.*, 32, 258 (1936).
[228] T. Svedberg and K. D. Pedersen, *The Ultracentrifuge*. Oxford Univ. Press, London, 1940.
[229] T. Svedberg and N. Gralén, *Nature*, 142, 261 (1938).
[230] S. Säverborn, *Kolloid-Z.*, 90, 41 (1940).

author also determined the molecular weight range of some nitropectins and found it to be 50,000–100,000. Ingelman and Tiselius[231,232] determined the approximate molecular weight of beet pectinic acid by this method and obtained results indicating 90,000. If this later value is correct, the previously held opinion that the pectinic acids of beets are of low molecular magnitude is wrong. Recent reports that pectin capable of forming a jelly may be isolated from beets tend to confirm the results of Ingelman and Tiselius. Recently Säverborn[218] published an extensive treatise dealing with the physicochemical properties of polyuronides. This author obtained for a series of samples the molecular weight values shown in Table 8. Säverborn concluded from these results that, while in general there

TABLE 8

MOLECULAR WEIGHT VALUES CALCULATED FOR PECTIC SUBSTANCES FROM SEDIMENTATION VELOCITY MEASUREMENTS (ADAPTED FROM SÄVERBORN)

No.	Preparation	Medium used in the measurement	Molecular weights
1	Commercial apple pectin, jelly grade 320	0.2 N sodium chloride	67,000
2	Same, neutralized with sodium hydroxide	0.2 N sodium chloride	58,000
3	Pectic acid from No. 1	0.2 N sodium carbonate	62,000
4	Lemon pectin	0.2 N sodium chloride	89,000
5	Same, neutralized as No. 2	0.2 N sodium chloride	75,000
6	Beet pectin	0.2 N sodium chloride	62,000
7	Red currant pectin	0.2 N sodium chloride	42,000
8	Carrot pectin	0.2 N sodium chloride	58,000
9	Flax pectin	0.2 N ammonium oxalate	64,000

seems to be good agreement between the molecular weights of pectic preparations obtained from the same source, there is considerable apparent discrepancy between the molecular weights of various preparations and their ability to form sugar-pectin-acid gels. Beet pectin gave molecular weight values similar to those obtained from apple pectin yet it shows decidedly inferior jellying properties. Säverborn draws the conclusion that differences in composition and perhaps in constitution account for this phenomenon. For instance, beet pectins apparently contain acetyl groups while such groups do not occur in apple and citrus pectin. The hypothesis of Bock[207] based on the occurrence of ionic bonding by polyvalent ions[198] in pectinic acids may be the explanation for this discrepancy. Bock assumed that in the hydrolysis of beet protopectin fragments containing such ionic bonds will be obtained and that such polygalacturonides containing ionic bridges in addition to the normal 1,4 glycosidic linkages between adjoining anhydrogalacturonic acids will cause the observed anomaly. We shall return to Bock's theory later.

[231] A. Tiselius and B. Ingelman, *Förh. Svenska Socker.*, 1942, II, 16 pp.
[232] B. Ingelman and A. Tiselius, *Förh. Svenska Socker.*, 1943, II, 16 pp.

There has been more controversy about the meaning of viscosity measurements of dilute solutions of high polymers than almost any other subject in high polymer chemistry. The method, as will be shown in Chapter VII, has many limitations and the results obtained by it should always be confirmed by some absolute determinations. This, in the case of pectic substances and many other natural polymers, is very difficult. The validity of molecular weight calculations based on viscosity measurements in water solutions is altogether questionable, even if such data conform to a given equation. On the basis of viscosity measurements, Baker and Goodwin[233] calculated the value of 280,000 for the (weight-average) molecular weight of a sample of apple pectinic acid. Schneider and Bock[234] gave the comparative values of 56 to 190 for pectinic acids from apple pomace and citrus peel, 25 for pectinic acid from fermented apple pomace, and 17 for pectinic acid from beets. Säverborn[230] calculated the molecular weights 67,000, 89,000, and 62,000 from the viscosities of solutions of commercial apple pectin, lemon pectin, and beet pectin, respectively. Recently Owens, Lotzkar, Schultz, and Maclay[219] determined the intrinsic viscosities of a series of pectinic acids in the presence of 0.155 M sodium chloride and obtained values from 27,000 to 115,000. These authors stated that the molecular weight values did not change significantly with changes in the ester contents, and that therefore the flexibiliy of the polygalacturonide chains is apparently not affected by the enzymic removal of the methoxyl groups. They also state that the influence of hydration, flexibility, and heterogeneity will make such values somewhat inaccurate and that attempts to fractionate the samples without degradation were unsuccessful.

More significance may be attached to molecular weight determinations based on the viscosity of nonwater solutions of various derivatives. Henglein and Schneider[235] first applied viscosity methods to the determination of molecular weights in such preparations. Using a nitrated purified pectic acid containing 9.5% nitrogen, they found the molecular weight to be approximately 20,000. Nitropectins obtained from extracted sugar beet slices by direct nitration showed molecular weights in the range of 25,000 to 50,000, depending on the method of treatment. A further word of caution should be sounded here concerning the interpretation of such viscosity measurements on nitropectin. Staudinger and Sohn[236] found that at times derivatives obtained from carbohydrates show an abnormally high viscosity giving apparent molecular weight values higher than those

[233] G. L. Baker and M. W. Goodwin, *Univ. Delaware Agr. Expt. Sta.*, Bull. No. 216 (1939).

[234] G. Schneider and H. Bock, *Ber.*, **70**, 1617 (1937).

[235] F. A. Henglein and G. Schneider, *Ber.*, **69**, 309 (1936).

[236] H. Staudinger and A. W. Sohn, *Ber.*, **72**, 1709 (1939).

found in the starting material. Schneider and Fritschi,[237] who note this possibility (together with the frequent irregularities apparently caused by strongly polar groups), are of the opinion that the molecular weights given here represent true minimum values for the pectic substances investigated.

Schneider and Bock[234] determined the average molecular weights of the pectic acid prepared from a series of extracts obtained from apple pomace. These values, shown in Table 9, were obtained by viscosity determinations made on carefully nitrated samples and confirm the observation of Säverborn that the first extracts from fruits usually contain pectic materials of the highest molecular weight and viscosity.

Lüdtke and Felsner[238] state that nitropectin prepared from purified flax pectin has, depending on the method of preparation used, molecular weights of 145,000 to 227,000. Here again the viscometric method was used. Later Bock and Einsele[201] found that the nitropectin prepared from flax straw has a molecular weight of 11,000 to 16,000, while that from retted flax gave values ranging from 3000 to 10,000. Direct nitration gave somewhat higher values, ranging for flax straw pectin from 26,000 to 30,000. Even for indicative values the discrepancy between the observations of Lüdtke and Felsner, and of Bock and Einsele is considerable.

TABLE 9

MOLECULAR WEIGHTS OF NITRATED PECTINIC ACIDS OF DIFFERENT ORIGINS (ADAPTED FROM SCHNEIDER AND BOCK)

Source of pectinic acid	Molecular weights
Apple pomace	
First extract	280,000
Second extract	220,000
Third extract	170,000
Fourth extract	90,000
Lemon albedo	220,000
Orange albedo	150,000
Beet slices	20,000 to 25,000

In recent contributions to this subject, Hills, Mottern, Nutting, and Speiser,[239] and Speiser and Eddy[240] studied the molecular size and molecular size distribution in nitrated pectinic acid preparations. The degradation during nitration is believed by the latter authors to be only of such small extent that the molecular weight values obtained by subsequent vis-

[237] G. Schneider and U. Fritschi, *Ber.*, **69**, 2537 (1936).
[238] M. Lüdtke and H. Felsner, *Ann.*, **549**, 1 (1941).
[239] C. H. Hills, H. H. Mottern, G. C. Nutting, and R. Speiser, paper given at the 108th Meeting of the American Chemical Society, New York, September, 1944.
[240] R. Speiser and C. R. Eddy, *J. Am. Chem. Soc.*, **68**, 287 (1946).

cosity measurements should represent reasonably similar values to that of the starting material. The nitrated pectinic acids were fractionated from acetone by the addition of toluene, a method which we shall discuss in Chapter VII, Section VII. From molecular weights obtained for various fractions the number- and weight-average molecular weights were calculated on the assumption that each fraction was substantially homogeneous. The (weight-average) molecular weight values for the orginal pectinic acids were 125,000 and 105,000. Deesterification with acid reduced these values by about 30%. Speiser and Eddy also mention a sample of acid-deesterified pectinic acid which after the deesterification gave a molecular weight of 199,000. From the previous observations one could assume a considerably higher weight-average molecular weight in the starting sample which is not described in the paper. Enzymic deesterification did not reduce the (weight-average) molecular weight, an observation in good harmony with the statements of Owens *et al.* The number-average molecular weight values for the original pectinic acids were found to be 61,400 and 83,400 and these values did not appear to change during acidic deesterification, a fact not yet adequately explained. Speiser and Eddy conclude that, contrary to the contention of some workers in the field,[241] it is unlikely that different types of linkages between anhydrogalacturonic acid units or polygalacturonide chains would exist in pectinic acids.

This short discussion is sufficient to show the disharmony between the results of different authors on various pectic substances. This confused state of the question of molecular weight of pectic substances is, however, hardly surprising if two points, noted before, are once again borne in mind. First of all, the pectic substances do represent ranges of molecular weights and the averages found will depend on the sizes of the component members as well as on their proportional distribution. Second, the values obtained may be weight or number averages and even within either of these groups may vary according to the method of determination used.

This discussion would be incomplete without the mention of synthetic polygalacturonic acids. Unfortunately, the technic of synthesis through the 1-phosphates[242,243] has not yet been applied to polyuronides. Myers[244] in 1939 obtained a patent on "synthetic pectin" produced by the heating of the lactone of galacturonic acid under vacuum in the presence of a catalyst. The resulting polygalacturonic acid was claimed to be similar to the "octagalacturonic" acid described by Myers and Baker[245] and was

[241] Z. I. Kertesz, *J. Am. Chem. Soc.*, **61**, 2544 (1939).

[242] G. T. Cori and C. F. Cori, *J. Biol. Chem.*, **116**, 119 (1936).

[243] C. S. Hanes, *Proc. Roy. Soc. (London)*, **B128**, 421 (1940); **129**, 174 (1940).

[244] P. B. Myers, U. S. Pat. 2,156,223 (1939).

[245] P. B. Myers and G. L. Baker, *Univ. Delaware Agr. Expt. Sta.*, Bull. No. **187** (1934).

assumedly able to form gels in the manner typical for pectins. No detailed report on the properties of these synthetic polygalacturonic acids can be found in the literature and thus we are still awaiting an objective evaluation of the procedure and of the products obtained.

The properties of pectic acids will be discussed in Chapter VII in detail. For the preparation of pectic acids see Chapter VI, while methods of their commercial scale preparation will be dealt with in Chapters XVIII–XXVI.

II. PECTINIC ACIDS AND PECTINS

According to the definition given in Chapter I, polygalacturonic acids containing more than a negligible proportion of methoxyl groups are pectinic acids. If the pectinic acid, in addition, is capable of forming a jelly with sugar and acid, it is also designated as a pectin. All pectins are pectinic acids but not all pectinic acids are pectins. The relationship between polygalacturonic acids and pectinic acid may be illustrated in the following diagram in which G—COOH represents individual anhydrogalacturonic acid residues:

G—COOH	G—CO—O—CH$_3$	G—CO—O—CH$_3$
G—COOH	G—COOH	G—CO—O—CH$_3$
G—COOH	G—CO—O—CH$_3$	G—CO—O—CH$_3$
G—COOH	G—COOH	. . .
G—COOH	G—COOH	. . .
. . .	G—COOH	. . .
. . .	G—CO—O—CH$_3$	. . .
. . .	. . .	. . .
	. . .	. . .
G—COOH		. . .
G—COOH	G—COOH	. . .
. . .	G—CO—O—CH$_3$	G—CO—O—CH$_3$
. . .	G—CO—O—CH$_3$	G—CO—O—CH$_3$
. . .	. . .	. . .
. . .	. . .	
etc.	etc.	etc.
Polygalacturonic acid or pectic acid	Pectinic acid (pectin)	"Ideal" (fully esterified) pectinic acid

The existence of methyl ester groups in pectic substances was discovered by Fellenberg,[246] who sought an explanation of the frequent occurrence of methanol in fruit juices and wines. He proved that the methanol was derived from the pectic materials present in all fruits. Fellenberg then isolated some pectinic acids and determined their methyl ester content. He also showed that the methyl ester groups can be easily removed from the pectinic acids by treatment with alkali. Gel formation from pectin solutions upon the addition of fruit juices and calcium salts,

---

[246] T. Fellenberg, *Mitt. Lebensm. Hyg.*, **4**, 122, 273 (1913).

previously ascribed to the action of the enzyme pectase,[247] also proved to be essentially a demethylation of pectinic acids, followed by the formation of low-ester (acid) calcium pectinates or calcium pectate.

We have no ground to assume at this time that the polygalacturonic acid structure of a pectinic acid is principally different from that of pectic acids. Pectic acids are usually prepared from pectinic acids by demethylation. Changes other than deesterification may occur as a result of the removal of the ester groups with alkali or acid, but the occurrence of such changes is not definitely established and their possible nature is unknown (see Chap. VII on this point). On the other hand, it is most unlikely that enzymic deesterification would cause changes in addition to the removal of the ester groups.

There is a remote possibility that certain colloidal properties such as electrical charge or extent of hydration, for instance, may depend on the presence or absence of the methyl ester groups, and that such properties may be of importance for the formation of the complex pectin molecule. There is no experimental evidence at this time to show that this is the case.

The chemical composition of pectinic acids, obviously, will differ from that of the polygalacturonic and pectic acids by the presence of various proportions of methyl ester groups. Fellenberg and many later investigators were much disturbed by the variations in the methyl ester content of different pectinic acid preparations. Indeed, pectinic acids of a wide range of methoxyl content may be prepared from the same raw material upon making only slight alterations in the procedures. It is now clear that these variations are caused mainly by the following three factors: (1) the natural variations in the methyl ester content of the pectic substances as they occur in nature; (2) the degree of demethylation which occurs during extraction, purification, and preparation; and (3) the "dilution" of the preparations with admixed materials, mostly arabans and galactans.

There was a period in the history of pectin chemistry, when many workers, such as Fellenberg,[246] Ehrlich and collaborators,[248-250] Nanji, Paton, and Ling,[251] Myers and Baker,[245] and others, thought that a definite proportion of the carboxyl groups in pectinic acids is esterified but these views are now outmoded. Our conception of pectic substances as linear polymer macromolecular compounds also defines the theoretical maximum methoxyl content of pectinic acids. For the pectin molecule of Nanji, Paton, and Ling (illustrated on page 46) the maximum value was

[247] E. Frémy, *J. pharm.*, 26, 368 (1840).
[248] F. Ehrlich and R. Sommerfeld, *Biochem. Z.*, 168, 263 (1926).
[249] F. Ehrlich and F. Schubert, *Biochem. Z.*, 169, 13 (1926).
[250] F. Ehrlich and A. Kosmahly, *Biochem. Z.*, 212, 162 (1929).
[251] D. R. Nanji, F. J. Paton, and A. R. Ling, *J. Soc. Chem. Ind.*, 44, 252T (1925).

11.8%. Ehrlich's tetragalacturonic acid, upon esterification of all four carboxyl groups, could contain a maximum of 15.9% methoxyl, while a polygalacturonic acid containing 25 or more anhydrogalacturonic acid units will contain, upon esterification of all carboxyl groups, 16.3% methoxyl. This value of 16.3% has not been found as yet in any isolated pectinic acid: in fact, the highest values are in the neighborhood of 14%. It should be noted, however, that since we know that the pectinic acid preparations of most authors also contained substances other than polygalacturonic acids, the actual percentage of methoxyl groups on the basis of the polyuronide content may have at times been over 14%. The apple pectinic acid prepared by Hirst and Jones,[252] for instance, upon analysis showed 49.2% polygalacturonic acid and 9.5% methoxyl content. Recalculated on the polyuronide basis, the methoxyl content was 16.2%, a figure very close to the theoretical maximum value. It is likely, however, that the methoxyl content was actually lower than 16.2%. Hills, Ogg, and Speiser[253] and also Jansen, Waisbrot, and Rietz[254] observed that when ethanol is used in the preparation of pectic substances some ethanol is retained even when the sample is dried under vacuum. Consequently, when the Zeisel[255] method or any of its modifications[256,257] now customarily used for the determination of the methyl ester content is applied, the results are erroneously high. Since most investigators used ethanol for the isolation and purification of pectic preparations and applied the Zeisel method for the determination of the ester content, it is more than likely that in many cases the results reported in the literature are higher than were the true methyl ester contents. The simple methods developed for the elimination of this difficulty with absorbed ethanol are given in Chapter VIII, Section VI-3.

Recently Schlubach and Hoffmann-Walbeck[257a] reported 14.9% methoxyl in a pectinic acid sample isolated from unripe apples. This finding, however, should be regarded with reservation because ethanol precipitation and the Zeisel method were used without attempts to remove residual traces of ethanol.

It is impossible to say, therefore, just how closely the theoretical maximum methoxyl value was ever approached. Indeed, as noted before, if an ideal, completely methylated polygalacturonic acid is ever isolated, a new

[252] E. L. Hirst and J. K. N. Jones, *J. Chem. Soc.*, **1939**, 454.
[253] C. H. Hills, C. L. Ogg, and R. Speiser, *Ind. Eng. Chem., Anal. Ed.*, **17**, 507 (1945).
[254] E. F. Jansen, S. W. Waisbrot, and E. Rietz, *Ind. Eng. Chem., Anal. Ed.*, **16**, 523 (1944).
[255] S. Zeisel, *Monatsh.*, **6**, 989 (1885); **7**, 406 (1886).
[256] E. P. Clark, *J. Assoc. Official Agr. Chem.*, **15**, 136 (1932).
[257] J. B. Niederl and V. Niederl, *Micromethods of Quantitative Organic Analysis.* 2nd ed., Wiley, New York, 1942.
[257a] H. H. Schlubach and H. P. Hoffmann-Walbeck, *Makromol. Chem.*, **4**, 5 (1949).

term will have to be coined for it since it could not be called a pectinic acid because it will not have free acid groups.

The pectinic acids occur in nature with a wide variation in methoxyl content. Both soluble pectinic acids and those obtained from protopectin show this diversity. Obviously, the methoxyl contents of various pectinic

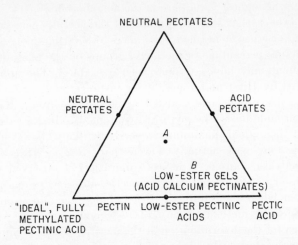

Fig. 4. Schematic illustration of the interrelation of pectic acid, pectates, pectinic acids and pectinates.

The average molecular weight is not illustrated but is assumed to be of sufficient magnitude to give good jelly and gel forming characteristics. The lower right corner of the triangle represents pectic acid, the left corner the "ideal," fully methylated, neutral methyl ester. The base line represents pectinic acids from 0 to maximum methoxyl contents, including pectins and low-ester (low-methoxyl) pectins. The top of the triangle represents neutral pectates, the right side acid pectates, the left side neutral pectinates. The inner field of the triangle represents the innumerable possible acid pectinates. As an example, point A in the center represents a pectinic acid containing an equal third of its acid groups free, methylated and combined in salt formation. The area around B indicates the acid pectinates as in low-ester gels. Such a diagram is useful in "mapping" the characteristics of acid pectinates which are rapidly gaining prominence with the advent of low-ester pectins.

acid preparations represent averages. This point will be further discussed in Chapter IV. At times the wide variations in the ester content are perceptible and may be shown by the differences in the methoxyl contents of fractions successively precipitated.

An important function of the methyl ester groups is in influencing the solubility of pectinic acids. Generally speaking, the solubility in water increases with a greater proportion of methyl ester. In the presence of even very minute quantities of certain ions, especially of polyvalent cations, the pectinic acids of less than 7% methoxyl content may be dissolved only with difficulty or they may be entirely insoluble in water.

While pectins are pectinic acids which are able to form jellies with sugar and acid under certain conditions, the "low-ester" (low-methoxyl) pectins constitute a further special group of pectinic acids which possess some 3 to 7% methoxyl and are consequently greatly influenced by the presence of polyvalent cations such as calcium. The interrelation of pectic acids, pectinic acids, pectin, low-ester pectins, and their salts is illustrated by the diagram given in Figure 4. For the purpose of simplicity this diagram assumes that the pectic material in question is composed of large molecules containing the same number of anhydrogalacturonic acid units.

Concerning the structure, shape, and size of pectinic acid molecules, reference is made to the discussion of pectic acid on preceding pages. As stated before, we have no reason to assume that in these respects pectinic acids are different from pectic acids. The properties of pectinic acids will be discussed in Chapter VII, while the methods of manufacture, composition, evaluation, etc., of commercial pectinic acids and pectins may be found in Part Four (Chapters XVIII–XXVI) of this volume.

Buston and Nanji[258] reported the synthesis of methyl esters of polygalacturonic acids by heating the silver salt of pectic acid with methyl iodide under slight pressure. The resulting product is said to have resembled natural pectin and showed the typical ability to form sugar-acid jellies. Bennison and Norris,[258a] using the methylation procedure given by Buston and Nanji, were unable to obtain methylated products capable of forming sugar-acid jellies. Hinton[259] methylated pectinic acids with dimethyl sulfate and increased the methoxyl content from 9.7 to 11.0 and 13.2%. The jellying power of these latter two preparations was lower than that of the starting material, indicating that molecular size degradation occurred concurrently with the esterification.

III. PROTOPECTIN

The existence of a distinct water-insoluble pectic compound, protopectin, has been assumed ever since pectic substances became known. Protopectin, while insoluble in water, is exceedingly susceptible to a long list of reagents and treatments of widely divergent nature. When exposed to these it gives rise to soluble pectic compounds of various characters.

[258] H. W. Buston and H. R. Nanji, *Biochem. J.*, 26, 2090 (1932).
[258a] E. W. Bennison and F. W. Norris, *Biochem. J.*, 33, 1443 (1939).
[259] C. L. Hinton, *Fruit Pectins, Their Chemical Behaviour and Jellying Properties.* Chem. Publishing Co., New York, 1940.

The nature of protopectin is one of the most intricate problems in pectin chemistry and there is no theory at this time which would explain its behavior and properties to our complete satisfaction. Even the theories of the most modern schools of thought have the earmarks of working hypotheses rather than of well-substantiated facts. One of the reasons for this uncertainty is the extreme difficulty of separating protopectin from other water-insoluble components of plant tissues without causing changes which must be regarded as indicative of degradation or decomposition. Furthermore, the line of division between the water-insoluble protopectin and soluble pectic compounds is arbitrary and the extent of separation will depend greatly on the conditions applied. Ripa[260] is the only one who claimed to have isolated pure protopectin. There is considerable doubt concerning the correctness of his contentions, or at least, of their general applicability.

Ever since the times of Frémy[261] and Mangin,[262] most investigators held the view that protopectin is a combination of pectinic acids with cellulose. There was great divergence, however, in the types of combinations which the various workers assumed to exist between the two components. It ranged from actual chemical linkages to loose absorption. The classical theory was perhaps best presented by Fellenberg[263] who suggested that protopectin was a compound formed by the union of cellulose with pectinic acids, probably with the elimination of water molecules and that heat and acid hydrolysis split up this combination and produce soluble pectic compounds and cellulose. This view was also supported by Carré[264] who found that when weighed samples of apple and pear tissues, previously extracted with water and ethanol, were treated with hot dilute acid, soluble pectinic acids, insoluble cellulose, and a small amount of mineral matter were produced. The weight of soluble pectinic acids yielded by the hydrolysis added to the weight of the insoluble residue and the mineral matter gave a total very closely approximating the weight of the material taken for examination; this suggested that the protopectin underwent decomposition to yield the above components. Carré, as well as many other workers who investigated this matter, noted the great variation in the proportions in which the two assumed components (soluble pectic compounds and cellulose) occurred in protopectins derived from various sources.

Ripa[260] suggested that in protopectin all unesterified carboxyl groups

[260] R. Sucharipa (now Ripa), *J. Am. Chem. Soc.*, **46**, 145 (1924).

[261] E. Frémy, *J. pharm. compt. rend.*, **49**, 561 (1859), etc.

[262] L. Mangin, *Compt. rend.*, **107**, 144 (1888), etc.

[263] T. Fellenberg, *Biochem. Z.*, **85**, 118 (1918).

[264] M. H. Branfoot (M. H. Carré), "A Critical and Historical Study of the Pectic Substances of Plants," Dept. of Sci. and Ind. Res., Special Report No. 33, H. M. Stationery Office, London, 1929.

of the pectic compound are linked with cellulose. Accordingly, if a protopectin yields pectinic acids of high average methyl ester content, it could
have been bound only to a comparatively small proportion of cellulose
units and vice versa. Ripa presented very interesting evidence of this
theory which, however, does not hold up under critical evaluation with
our present knowledge. He extracted citrus albedo with ethanol and ether,
then with slightly acidified warm water. This latter was assumed to dissolve all pectic compounds which were rendered insoluble in the albedo
by the presence of calcium and magnesium. Afterward the sample was
treated with Schweitzer's reagent to remove the "free" cellulose, followed
by the removal of the copper with a 2% solution of acetic acid. The resulting preparation, according to. Ripa, contained only protopectin. He
then proceeded to expose a sample of this material successively to the
action of: (1) boiling water under 1.5 atmosphere pressure for 30 min.,
(2) hot 50% sucrose solution, and (3) hot 0.5% ammonium oxalate solution. The solubilized pectinic acids were separated and their methoxyl
content determined. In addition, the amount of "free" cellulose produced
was also established. The results of this experiment are shown in Table
10.

TABLE 10

PROGRESSIVE DECOMPOSITION OF RIPA'S "PROTOPECTIN"

Sample	Pectin, %	CH_3O, %	Cellulose, %
Acid–water extracted pectin	*7.6*	*11.3*	—
1. "Pressure pectin"	3.3	10.2	16.3
2. "Sucrose pectin"	1.0	8.0	16.7
3. "Ammonium oxalate pectin"	9.7	2.0	23.9

From this experiment Ripa drew the following conclusions: The "free"
pectinic acid obtained by acid–water extraction shows the highest
methoxyl content, 11.3%, which, he thought, may be near to complete
esterification of all carboxyl groups. Treatment (1) liberated some pectinic acids of high methoxyl contents which, for this reason, had only a
low proportion of the carboxyl groups available for linkage to cellulose.
On the other hand, the fractions obtained by treatments (2) and especially by (3) produced pectinic acids of low methoxyl contents which,
therefore, were associated with a larger proportion of cellulose. Ripa concluded that all free carboxyl groups in the pectinic acid component of
protopectin are connected to cellulose and that this is the reason why
protopectin is neutral and yet upon treatment produces pectic compounds
of acidic nature.

With our meager knowledge of protopectin it may be a fallacy to say that Ripa was completely wrong, but it is fair to state that his theory has now been greatly discredited. First of all, we know now that the theoretical maximum methoxyl content of pectinic acids is over 16% and that preparations containing over 14% have been reported. Many questioned the effect of the very high alkalinity of Schweitzer's reagent used by Ripa on pectic component of protopectin. As shown in Chapter VII, Section II, pectic substances in general have little resistance to the action of alkali. Emmett and Carré[265] tried to repeat Ripa's work on apples and pears but were entirely unsuccessful. Ripa also assumed (for no good reason) that the calcium and magnesium which are always present in protopectin are adsorbed rather than combined in the stoichiometrical formation of salts with the free carboxyl groups.

That the presence of calcium and magnesium in protopectin may have a great deal to do with its insolubility in water has been often mentioned in the botanical literature. In contrast to the cellulose complex theory which culminated in the postulations of Ripa, Ehrlich[266] believed that the insoluble pectic compound of the middle lamella is a calcium magnesium salt of pectin ("dimethoxy-diacetyl-arabino-galacto-tetragalacturonic acid"), in loose combination with araban. Upon treatment with hot water or acid, hydrolysis occurs and both components become soluble in water. In criticism of the cellulose complex theory Ehrlich quoted the fact that typical protopectin often becomes entirely water soluble upon treatment with cold dilute acid which simultaneously removes calcium and magnesium from the preparation. The views that calcium and magnesium are responsible for the insolubility of protopectin were shared by Smolenski and Wlostowska,[267] who state that the protopectin in beet pulp is a polymer of the calcium salt of pectin ("monomethyl-araban-galactan-acetyl-digalacturonic acid").

Dauphiné[268] thought that protopectin is rendered insoluble by the presence of small quantities of protein material and Colin and Chaudun[269] assumed that in protopectin the pectinic acids are strongly adsorbed on cellulose. Tutin[270] suggested that the insolubility of protopectin is due solely to mechanical difficulties of penetration by the solvent, but Carré[264] showed quite clearly that this insoluble pectic substance really existed and that it could be solubilized by treatment with hot dilute acids, hot 0.5% ammonium oxalate, or even hot water.

[265] A. M. Emmett and M. H. Carré, *Biochem. J.,* 20, 6 (1926).
[266] F. Ehrlich, *Cellulosechemie,* 11, 1 (1930).
[267] K. Smolenski and W. Wlostowska, *Roczniki Chem.,* 7, 591 (1927).
[268] A. Dauphiné, *Compt. rend.,* 196, 1738 (1933); 199, 307 (1934).
[269] H. Colin and A. Chaudun, *Compt. rend.,* 198, 2116 (1934); 202, 973 (1936).
[270] F. Tutin, *Biochem. J.,* 17, 510 (1923).

When pectinic acids are degraded, they become increasingly soluble in water. Stating the same fact in another manner, it can be assumed that very large pectin molecules would show the water-insolubility typical of protopectin.[271,272] Thus protopectin may be large molecules which upon partial degradation become noticeably soluble in water. This relation between protopectin and pectinic acids may be similar to that which exists between water-insoluble starch and soluble starch and dextrins. The structure of protopectin, accordingly, would be represented by the schematic illustrations given for the pectin macromolecule in Figure 1. The presence of cellulose in protopectin preparations might be regarded as the consequence of its insolubility similar to that of this protopectin macromolecule. One of the main advantages of this hypothesis is that it brings protopectin into a logical and continuous relationship with other pectic substances. Such a position for protopectin was shown in Figure 1.

This line of thinking may be extended by assuming that the building of larger molecules may be accomplished by different types of linkages. Anhydride, lactone, and ester linkages again present themselves as definite possibilities, as they did in the case of the structures for pectic and pectinic acids. But the consistent presence of calcium in water-insoluble protopectins may indicate that this ion—and perhaps other polyvalent ions—may also participate in the linking of polygalacturonic acid units into higher types of structures. Indeed, Nanji, Paton, and Ling,[273] as well as Nanji and Norman,[274] state that the presence of small quantities of iron and calcium can give formerly soluble pectinic acids the typical characteristics of protopectin. If polyvalent ions link carboxyl groups of different polygalacturonic acid chains, an increase in the molecular size and weight will result. It has been assumed above that this increase in itself may result in the lowering of the solubility; obviously, the presence of the metallic ions will also work in the same direction.

This idea of the existence of calcium linkages in protopectin was recently developed further by Henglein[275] who postulated that protopectin is formed by the association of polygalacturonic acid chains among each other, and perhaps even with cellulose, exclusively through calcium linkages. The ability of cellulose to participate in building protopectin in such a manner has been made more plausible by the finding of carboxyl groups in native cellulose.[276] Thus the existence of a calcium linkage between

[271] J. Bonner, Jahrb. Wiss. Botanik, 82, 377 (1936).
[272] Z. I. Kertesz, paper given at the Memphis Meeting of the American Chemical Society, April, 1942.
[273] D. R. Nanji, F. J. Paton, and A. R. Ling, Trans. Soc. Chem. Ind., 44, 253 (1925).
[274] D. R. Nanji and A. G. Norman, Biochem. J., 22, 596 (1928).
[275] F. A. Henglein, J. makromol. Chem., 1, 121 (1943).
[276] E. Schmidt, R. Schnegg, W. Jandebeur, M. Hecker, W. Simson, J. W. Pedlow. and M. Atterer, Ber., 68, 542 (1935).

a pectinic acid and cellulose is a distinct possibility. The structure of protopectin, according to Henglein's description, is shown below. With alterations in the proportion of calcium and the degree of esterification of the participating pectinic acids, the degree of interlocking and the properties of the protopectin are changed. With highly esterified pectinic acids only a small degree of interlocking with calcium is possible, while the reverse is true in the case of comparatively low-ester pectinic acids. Depending on the similarity or dissimilarity of the participating units, Henglein distinguishes between "hetero-acidic" and "iso-acidic" protopectin. In addition to cellulose, proteins may also participate in the formation of such complexes. There is the possibility of hexosans and pentosans being attached to the polyuronide complex inasmuch as, according to Henglein, these also contain small proportions of carboxyl groups.

Bock[277] developed these ideas further from the standpoint of the fissure of such "meshed" protopectin and distinguished between "intramolecular cleavage" of the 1,4 glycosidic linkages (at X in the formula given below) in the polygalacturonic acids and "intermolecular cleavages" as occurring by the removal of polyvalent ions which bond the polygalacturonic acids in the complex (as at Y). We shall return to this matter in Chapter XXI in the discussion of the manufacture of beet pectin, and it may suffice to say here that Bock suggests that, by variations of the acidity and tem-

```
              G
     X →      G                           G      Y
              G                           G      |
              G                           G      ↓
              G        G        G         G—Ca—G
              G        G        G         G      G
              G—Ca—G   G        G         G      G
              G        G        G         G      G
     X →      G        G        G—Ca—G    G      G
              G        G—Ca—G   G         G  .   G
              G        G        G         G      G  ← X
              G—Ca—G   ＼ G     G         G      G
              G        G        G         G—Ca—G
              G        G        G         G      G
              G        G—Ca—G   G         G      G
              G
              G        ↑
                       Y
```

Henglein's protopectin structure

perature, fissure of the "meshed" protopectin structure may occur at different places and thus give either true polygalacturonic acids or fragments of polygalacturonic acids bonded by polyvalent ions.

It may be noted that this theory is essentially a special form of the supposition that protopectin is a large molecule which may be composed

[277] H. Bock, *Dissertation*, Technische Hochschule, Karlsruhe, 1943.

entirely of pectinic acid units. Even so, the more positive formulation of such views by Henglein and Bock is the first ray of light in a long time in the sterile field of protopectin chemistry. Interestingly enough, one may regard it as a reintroduction of some of the older ideas to modern macro-molecular chemistry. It is difficult to say at this time whether it represents actual conditions as they exist, but there will likely be some truth to it. Deuel, Huber, and Anyas-Weisz[278] have already stated that it is unlikely that such ion bridges would participate in the formation of protopectin as well as in 3-dimensional gel structures. At any rate, this theory will probably provide incentive for further investigations, whether the purpose of these will be to support or disprove the Henglein-Bock thesis.

In view of the newly discovered highly insoluble double salts of galacturonic acid (see Chapter II) it is inescapable to consider the possibility that protopectin is insoluble because of the formation of some similar double salts of polygalacturonic acids. Sodium galacturonate is easily soluble in water. Calcium galacturonate is soluble only to the extent of 4.9 g. per 100 cc. of water at 20°C. At the latter temperature, however, sodium calcium galacturonate is soluble only to the extent of 1.8 g. per 100 cc. Since both sodium and calcium (and magnesium) commonly occur in protopectin, the possibility exists that protopectin is insoluble in water through the formation of some kind of double salts.

Our present very inadequate knowledge of protopectin may be summarized as follows: The insolubility of protopectin may be caused by (1) its association with cellulose, (2) the presence of polyvalent ions, (3) its large molecular size, or (4) combinations of these factors.

A discussion of the manufacture of protopectin-like commercial preparations is to be found in Chapter XXV.

[278] H. Deuel, G. Huber, and L. Anyas-Weisz, *Helv. Chim. Acta*, **33**, 563 (1950).

CHAPTER IV

Some Further Possible Components of Pectic Substances

A survey of the literature shows that until recent years most investigators worked with impure pectic preparations with undefined polygalacturonic acid contents. It is little wonder, therefore, that many other substances have at times been thought to be components of the pectinic acid molecule. Reports of new components were most frequent before the discovery of galacturonic acid in 1917. But even after this date, many investigators sought the composition of a molecule of definite size and therefore the regular occurrence of any compound in hydrolyzates tempted them to incorporate these into the hypothetical molecular structures. The experimental difficulties in the determination of various components, such as arabinose, galactose, methylglycosides, and acetic acid, in the presence of galacturonic acid added much to the confusion.

I. METHYLPENTOSE

Fellenberg[279] claimed to have identified a methylpentose in pectic preparations and consequently incorporated this compound into his formula for pectin. Analytical methods for estimating the various components of pectic preparations were rather undeveloped at that time; e.g., it was not known that galacturonic acid may be quantitatively decarboxylated by hot acid and that it also yields furfuraldehyde. Later Ehrlich and Haensel[280] found in pectinic acid isolated from ramie bast a methylpentose, thought to have been rhodeose (D-fucose). The methylpentose, however, was not actually crystallized and its existence was assumed on the basis of indirect evidence. There is no reason now to assume that methylpentoses are building units of pectinic acids, although their possible presence in crude pectic preparations derived from plant sources rich in methylpentoses cannot be denied. They can, however, be assumed to be soluble in the ethanol–water mixtures usually applied for the precipitation of pectic substances and therefore would probably

[279] T. Fellenberg, *Mitt. Lebensm. Hyg.*, **5**, 172, 225 (1914).
[280] F. Ehrlich and R. Haensel, *Cellulosechemie*, **16**, 97 (1935).

be removed during the course of preparation. One cannot escape the suspicion that Fellenberg, as well as Ehrlich and Haensel, may have dealt with some galacturonic acid methyl esters of low molecular weights, perhaps mixed with some other polysaccharides composed of a few units of arabinose or galactose. The pectinic acids (Pektinsäure) from which Ehrlich and Haensel obtained the alleged methylpentose contained only 34 to 53% polygalacturonic acid.

II. XYLOSE

Bauer[281] in 1901 reported that xylose is a constituent of orange pectin. Later workers failed to find this pentose among the hydrolytic products of pectin preparations. In 1926 Ehrlich and Schubert[282] reintroduced the idea that xylose is a component of flax pectin, but subsequent work by Henderson[283] and Norris[284] on much more highly purified pectic preparations from flax did not confirm the presence of this carbohydrate. Since the pectinic acid preparation of Ehrlich and Schubert contained only 55% polygalacturonic acid, it is likely that some xylan (usually present in flax) was extracted and subsequently precipitated together with the true pectic substances. Xylans are common components of plants, especially of straw, wood, and other materials rich in cellulose,[285] and it is therefore not surprising to find some xylose in crude pectic preparations made from such sources.

III. GALACTONIC ACID

On the basis of titrations of pectinic acid and pectic acid preparations, Ahmann and Hooker[286] postulated the occurrence of galactonic acid units in the pectin molecule. The validity of this assertion has been questioned by practically all subsequent workers in pectin chemistry. There is no direct evidence whatsoever that galactonic acid occurs even as an impurity in pectic preparations.

IV. ACETONE

Tutin[287] claimed that, upon the treatment of pectin preparations with cold dilute alkali, acetone in the proportion of two molecules to one

[281] R. W. Bauer, *Landw. Vers.-Stat.*, **41**, 477 (1892); **43**, 191 (1894).
[282] F. Ehrlich and F. Schubert, *Biochem. Z.*, **169**, 13 (1926).
[283] S. T. Henderson. *J. Chem. Soc.*, **131**, 2117 (1928).
[284] F. W. Norris, *Biochem. J.*, **23**, 195 (1929).
[285] A. G. Norman, *The Biochemistry of Cellulose, the Polyuronides, Lignin*, etc. Oxford Univ. Press, Oxford, 1937.
[286] C. F. Ahmann and H. D. Hooker, *Univ. Missouri Agr. Expt. Sta.*, Research Bull. No. 77 (1925).
[287] F. Tutin, *Biochem. J.*, **15**, 494 (1921).

molecule of methanol was produced. Sehryver and Haynes,[288] Farnell,[289] and Sucharipa,[290] who thoroughly investigated this matter, were unable to confirm this observation.

V. ACETIC ACID (ACETYL GROUPS)

Smolenski[291] in 1924 reported that, upon the treatment of crude or purified pectinic acids from sugar beet with cold alkali or dilute mineral acid, acetic acid is split off. In subsequent publications of Ehrlich and collaborators[292] acetic acid always occurred among the hydrolysis products of pectin preparations derived from various plant sources, especially beets. The amount of acetic acid ranged up to 12%. Consequently, acetic acid has been assumed to be one of the constituents of Ehrlich's pectin molecule in which it usually appears with two molecules per one "tetragalacturonic acid" unit. Later Nelson[293] found only 0.37% acetic acid in pectinic acid from lemon peel, 0.45% in that from apples, 0.79% in tomato pectinic acid, but 6.0% in sugar beet pectinic acid. The low proportion of acetic acid in all these preparations is noteworthy. Nelson felt that the acetyl group may be a constituent of beet pectinic acid, but is not of pectinic acids in general. The proportion of acetic acid in the pectins prepared by Myers and Baker[294] was only 1.9 to 4.7%. These authors did not attach much significance to the acetic acid content of their preparations but nevertheless incorporated an acetic acid molecule into their postulated general structure for pectin.

Schneider and Bock[295] reexamined this matter and concluded that the alleged occurrence of acetyl groups may have been caused by the harsh treatment of the pectic preparations with hot alkali. The methods used by Ehrlich and by Myers and Baker both involved treatment first with 0.5 N sodium hydroxide in the cold for 2 hours, followed by refluxing with 0.05 N sodium hydroxide for 5 hours. Schneider and Bock state that acetyl groups may have been formed during the decomposition of the polygalacturonic acid by the hot alkali. Decarboxylation occurs under such conditions and it is plausible to assume that some formic acid may be formed as an end product.

[288] S. B. Schryver and D. Haynes, *Biochem. J.*, 10, 539 (1916).

[289] R. G. W. Farnell, *Intern. Sugar J.*, 25, 630 (1923).

[290] R. Sucharipa (now Ripa), *J. Am. Chem. Soc.*, 46, 145 (1924).

[291] K. Smolenski, *Roczniki Chemji*, 4, 72 (1924).

[292] F. Ehrlich, "Festschrift zur Feier des 25 jahrigen Bestehens der Technischen Hochschule Breslau, June, 1935," pp. 129–141, contains a good summary of the views held by Ehrlich.

[293] E. K. Nelson, *J. Am. Chem. Soc.*, 48, 2945 (1926).

[294] P. B. Myers and G. L. Baker, *Univ. Delaware Agr. Expt. Sta.*, Bull. No. 187 (1934).

[295] G. G. Schneider and H. Bock, *Ber.*, 70, 1617 (1937).

Schneider and Bock attempted to find acetyl groups in pectic preparations by saponification with p-toluolsulfonic acid in ethanol or in 2.5 and 5.0% sulfuric acid solutions in water. This method gave very good results on cellulose acetate and acetylpectin but gave no indication of the presence of acetyl groups in the pectic preparations from fruits. Acetyl groups were also absent from nitropectin. Thus they claimed that the acetic acid (or what appeared as such) found by the various authors was either formed during the harsh treatment of the pectic substances during analysis or may have been derived from admixed compounds present as impurities.

Recent tests in the writer's laboratory[296] showed that both formic and acetic acids are formed from glucose and galacturonic acid during heating with alkali in the manner used by Ehrlich and by Myers and Baker. When a sample of citrus pectin was refluxed with 0.15% sodium hydroxide for 4 hours, no volatile acids were formed. But when 0.5% alkali was used in a similar test, the citrus pectin yielded what appeared to be 3.7% acetic acid and 5.5% formic acid as determined by common methods.[297]

One must conclude from this discussion that acetyl groups are not likely to occur in pectin preparations made from fruits and that if such are found they may have been formed during the various chemical manipulations. On the other hand, all work with beet pectin samples has shown acetyl groups even in the most purified preparations. Henglein and Vollmert[298] state in a recent article that the acetyl groups may occur both in beet pectin and in the accompanying arabans and galactans. These authors believe that the acetyl groups occur in the form of an ester. Yet, even in recently postulated structures of beet pectinic acid, acetyl groups do not appear[299] in spite of the fact that analyses of recent investigators[300,301] still consistently find acetyl groups in such preparations but none in fruit pectin.

Pippen, McCready, and Owens[302] recently reported some results obtained on acetylated citrus pectin. Preparations containing 3.5–5.2% acetyl failed to form sugar-acid-pectin jellies, while upon removal of the acetyl groups jelly could be made with these preparations in the usual manner. The conclusion drawn by these authors is that the presence of acetyl groups prevents jelly formation. It should be noted that the

[296] B. Crowley and Z. I. Kertesz, unpublished data, 1948.
[297] Official and Tentative Methods of Analysis. 6th ed., Association of Official Agricultural Chemists, Washington, D. C., 1945.
[298] F. A. Henglein and B. Vollmert, Makromol. Chem., 2, 77 (1948).
[299] H. Bock, Dissertation, Techn. Hochschule. Karlsruhe, 1943.
[300] H. S. Isbell and H. L. Frush, J. Research Natl. Bur. Standards, 33, 389 (1944).
[301] S. Säverborn, Dissertation, University of Uppsala, 1945.
[302] E. L. Pippen, R. M. McCready, and H. S. Owens, paper given at the San Francisco, California, meetings of the American Chemical Society, March 29, 1949.

introduction of acetyl groups will reduce the solubility of pectinic acids in water and this factor alone might have been the cause of the differences observed by Pippen, McCready, and Owens.

The situation is confused by the fact that in the writer's laboratory a recently prepared beet pectin sample proved to be 75 jelly grade (see Chap. XXIII, Sect. IV) in spite of the presence of several per cent of acetyl groups.

Thus, there seems to be little doubt concerning the presence of acetyl groups in beet pectin preparations but further work is needed to clarify the following questions: (1) whether these acetyl groups are attached to the polygalacturonic acid skeleton; (2) by what type of linkages; and (3) in exactly what manner the presence of such groups influences the jelly-forming ability of beet pectin.

VI. ACCOMPANYING ARABANS AND GALACTANS

According to the terminology used in this volume, only the colloidal polygalacturonic acids and their derivatives are regarded as true pectic substances. Up to the present time, however, very few pure pectic preparations have been obtained as indicated by the polygalacturonic acid contents which ranged, even in samples used for research purposes, from 30 up to 95%. It has been already noted that a pure polygalacturonic acid which yields only galacturonic acid upon hydrolysis has been described by Hirst.[303]

Some of the nonpectic materials which make up 5 to 70% of these crude preparations occurred so regularly together with the pectic substances that they were regarded by some as components of the pectic and pectinic acid molecules. Arabinose and galactose have been frequently described as the hydrolysis products of preparations of pectinic acids and little wonder, therefore, that the belief that they are components of the pectin molecule for a time gained almost universal acceptance. As a consequence, these sugars also appeared in the structures postulated for the various pectic substances by Fellenberg,[279] Nanji, Paton, and Ling,[304] Ehrlich,[282] Myers and Baker,[294] and others. Nor is the opinion that arabinose and galactose are not parts of the pectin molecule shared as yet by all workers in the field.[305] The nomenclature used by certain groups of investigators has also prolonged the confusion by lack of clear definition. According to the terminology used by most British workers, for instance, the term *pectin* still includes pectic acids (poly-

[303] E. L. Hirst, *J. Chem. Soc.*, 1942, 70.
[304] D. R. Nanji, F. J. Paton, and A. R. Ling, *Trans. Soc. Chem. Ind.*, 44, 253 (1925).
[305] R. Speiser, *J. Polymer Sci.*, 2, 281 (1947).

galacturonic acids) as well as arabans and galactans. In our view,[306] however, arabans and galactans (or arabinose and galactose) are admixed materials and are outside of the scope of definition of the pectic substances.

While the participation of arabinose and galactose as structural components of pectin materials was generally accepted until a few years ago, the experimental results obtained concerning the proportions of these constituents in pectic preparations were disturbing indeed. The amount of arabinose and galactose varied greatly with the source of material, as well as with any changes in the procedure of preparation. Myers and Baker,[294] for example, extracted pectinic acids from lemon albedo by heating it for different lengths of times at various temperatures and at a number of different pH values. The extracted pectins were precipitated with ethanol. All these preparations upon analysis showed at least 80% polygalacturonic acid content. On the other hand, the arabinose content ranged from 3.1 to 7.7% and the galactose content from 0.1 to 6.4%.

These variations caused those who attempted to formulate pectin molecules of definite size to tread on uncertain ground. While arabinose and galactose were included in some manner in the hypothetical structures, it was generally assumed that some or all of the arabinose and galactose are bound in a "labile" manner and that they are split off from the "pectin molecule" with ease. Only after the introduction of the linear polymer conception of polygalacturonic acids was the incidental nature of these polyoses widely accepted. Several authors had expressed the opinion earlier that the arabinose found in pectic preparations may not actually be a part of the molecule. McKinnis[307] claimed that the arabinose found in acid digests of pectic substances is derived from the galacturonic acid by decarboxylation, but Conrad,[308] in a very thorough study, failed to detect arabinose among the acid decomposition products of galacturonic acid. Later (1936) Bonner,[309] as well as Olsen, Stuewer, Fehlberg, and Beach,[310] expressed the opinion that some arabinose and galactose units may be scattered in the polygalacturonic acid chain. Schneider and Fritschi[311] carefully considered this possibility and reached the conclusion that arabinose and galactose do not occur in the polygalacturonic acid chain itself or as side chains attached to it, but are merely admixed with the pectic preparations.

[306] G. L. Baker, G. H. Joseph, Z. I. Kertesz, H. H. Mottern, and A. G. Olsen, Chem. Eng. News, 22, 105 (1944).
[307] R. B. McKinnis, J. Am. Chem. Soc., 50, 1911 (1928).
[308] C. M. Conrad, J. Am. Chem. Soc., 53, 2282 (1931).
[309] J. Bonner, Botan. Rev., 2, 475 (1936).
[310] A. G. Olsen, R. F. Stuewer, E. R. Fehlberg, and N. M. Beach, Ind. Eng. Chem., 31, 1015 (1939).
[311] G. Schneider and U. Fritschi, Ber., 69, 2537 (1936); 70, 1611 (1937).

Before discussing some of the evidence on the admixed nature of these
two hemicelluloses, one may state that most arabans and galactans are
likely to be linear polymers.[312] As highly colloidal compounds, they
behave in many respects similarly to soluble pectic substances and
thus may be included in pectic preparations. They are soluble in water
and are precipitated by high concentrations of ethanol. A certain degree
of segregation of these hemicelluloses from pectic substances may be
accomplished by the use of low concentrations of ethanol. In the past
most pectin preparations were precipitated with ethanol of too high a
concentration (over 70%) causing the almost universal simultaneous
precipitation of admixed polysaccharides. The term *ballast materials*[305]
has been extensively used for such impurities derived from the original
plant tissue and composed mostly of nonpectic polysaccharides.

TABLE 11

EFFECT OF ETHANOL EXTRACTION ON REMOVAL OF ADMIXED MATERIALS FROM CITRUS
PECTINIC ACID (ADAPTED FROM SCHNEIDER AND BOCK)

Concentration of ethanol, %	Per cent in the precipitated pectinic acid		
	Anhydrogalact-uronic acid	Methoxyl	Methoxyl (on anhydrogalact-uronic acid basis)
100	70.3	9.5	13.5
79	72.1	9.8	13.6
67	76.2	10.3	13.5
53	83.9	11.4	13.6

Ehrlich[292] tried to find some order in the occurrence of polyuronides,
arabinose, and galactose in pectin preparations and found that the araban
("Tetraaraban") accompanying pectin ("Hydratopektin") may be completely removed by extraction with 70% ethanol. The residual preparation
still contained both arabinose and galactose which, according to Ehrlich,
were components of the soluble pectin ("Pektinsäure"). Schneider and
Bock[295] emphasized that in reality fractionation rather than complete
separation is accomplished by extraction with 70% ethanol because only
the araban molecules of smaller size are soluble in this solvent, while the
high molecular weight (size) fractions remain with the pectinic acids.
Gaponenkov[313] studied this araban extracted with 70% ethanol and
determined its molecular weight by osmotic methods. The results indicated
molecular weight ranges of 6000 to 7000. Upon the use of ethanol–water

[312] E. L. Hirst and J. K. N. Jones, in W. W. Pigman and M. L. Wolfrom, *Advances
in Carbohydrate Chemistry*. Vol. II, Academic Press, New York, 1946, p. 235.
[313] T. K. Gaponenkov, *Colloid. J. U. S. S. R.*, 2, 561 (1936) (*C. A.*, 31, 1649 (1937);
J. Applied Chem. U. S. S. R., 9, 1364 (1936) (*C. A.*, 31, 2552 (1937)).

mixtures with ethanol concentrations below 70%, more araban—of assumedly higher molecular weight—may be dissolved. As an indirect illustration of the procedure of separation, some of the results of Schneider and Bock[295] are shown in Table 11. These authors purified citrus pectinic acid by extraction with ethanol–water mixtures.

The use of low ethanol concentrations resulted in an increase in the polygalacturonic acid content, i.e., removal of admixed components. When the results are recalculated in the manner advocated in Chapter VIII, it becomes apparent that the methoxyl content of the pectinic acid was identical in all cases. Similar results were obtained by Schneider and Bock on pectinic acids prepared from orange peel and apple pomace. Obviously, the extent and ease of removal of arabans and galactans will also depend on the molecular size distribution of these substances.

The arabans accompanying the pectic materials in plants are relatively easily hydrolyzed by dilute acids.[282] The same is true, to a lesser degree, of the galactans which are also usually hydrolyzed before the pectinic acids are greatly degraded. Therefore, pectinic acids prepared from protopectin by prolonged extraction with dilute acid will have the araban component mostly degraded and the galactan component partly degraded to such an extent that they will be almost completely removed when the pectinic acid is precipitated with ethanol concentrations of 50 to 55%. Schneider and Bock prepared pectinic acids free from arabinose and galactose by this method.

The comparative ease with which galactans and especially arabans may be hydrolyzed is one of the factors causing the variations in the arabinose and galactose contents of the pectic preparations of different workers. A further reason is the experimental difficulties encountered in the quantitative determination of small amounts of arabinose in the presence of large proportions of galacturonic or polygalacturonic acids, a subject already discussed in Chapter II.

Schneider and Bock[295] analyzed several samples of commercial high jelly grade pectins made in the United States and found arabinose and galactose absent. This they attribute to the acid hydrolysis used in the manufacture. The precipitation by aluminum salts (see Chapters XIX–XX) may also facilitate the separation of the pectinic acids from the accompanying hemicelluloses. Henglein and Schneider[314] found that nitropectins prepared from a variety of sources contained neither arabinose nor galactose.

The view that arabans and galactans present in crude pectic preparations are admixed rather than in any chemical combination with the polyuronide

[314] F. A. Henglein and G. Schneider, Ber., **69**, 309 (1936).

components has been recently confirmed by Hirst and Jones.[315] These authors prepared pectin from apple pomace by boiling the latter with water, followed by precipitation of the filtered extract with three times its volume of methanol containing 1% hydrochloric acid. The pectin precipitate was washed with methanol, and dried under vacuum at 40°C. (104°F.). It was then further purified by being dissolved in water, followed by filtration and precipitation with ethanol. The pentosan (araban) component could be removed by gentle hydrolysis with 0.05 N sulfuric acid at 90°C. for 4 hours. The filtered solution was poured into ethanol and the mixture of pectinic acid and galactan washed free from sulfuric acid. The alcoholic solution contained arabinose equivalent to about 20% of the original preparation. The polygalacturonic acid (pectic acid) was prepared from the pectic acid–galactan mixture by dissolving it in 1 N sodium hydroxide, followed by precipitation with hydrochloric acid and re-precipitation four times in this manner. Finally, the pectic acid was precipitated as calcium pectate and the free acid liberated therefrom by trituration with acid ethanol. The pectic acid was once more dissolved in sodium hydroxide, precipitated with hydrochloric acid, washed with water, dehydrated with ethanol, and dried under vacuum. The composition of these preparations is shown in Table 12.

TABLE 12

COMPOSITION OF CRUDE APPLE PECTIN AND OF PECTINIC ACID–GALACTAN MIXTURE AND PECTIC ACID (POLYGALACTURONIC ACID) PREPARED THEREFROM (ADAPTED FROM HIRST AND JONES)

	Crude apple pectin	Pectinic acid– galactan complex	Pectic acid
Equivalent weight[a]	364	250	185
Anhydrogalacturonic acid, %	49.2	73.0	96.7
Pentosan (as araban), %	20	0	0
Galactan (estimated by difference[b]), %	25	21	(4)

[a] See Chapter VIII, Section VIII.
[b] See Chapter II.

The successive removal of arabans and galactans is clearly shown by these analyses. Hirst and Jones also confirmed the finding of Ehrlich,[282] Schneider and Bock,[295] and others that part of the araban may be removed by extraction with 70% ethanol.

It has been suggested that the arabans and galactans may be linked to the polyuronide structure by means other than primary valence bonds. Speiser, Eddy, and Hills[316] claim to have obtained evidence that the arabans occurring with pectic substances are attached to the polyuronide chain by hydrogen bonds. These workers determined the activation energy

[315] E. L. Hirst and J. K. N. Jones, *J. Chem. Soc.*, **1939**, 454.
[316] R. Speiser, C. R. Eddy, and C. H. Hills, *J. Phys. Chem.*, **49**, 563 (1945).

for the removal of the araban and the galactan and found that the former was of the order of magnitude of 4000 calories, while the latter was of the order of 13,000 calories. This is taken as evidence that the arabans are attached to the polygalacturonic acid molecules by hydrogen bonds while the galactans are not. It would appear, however, that unless entirely new and specific methods were used for the determination in the progress of the "removal," the differences in the activation energy may simply show different rates of hydrolysis of the arabans and galactans. Differences in the rates of disappearance of the two hemicelluloses upon acid treatment may not necessarily indicate removal from the polygalacturonic acid chains. This is even more likely to be the case because, in the writer's opinion, their presence in the preparation was due to the similarity of behavior of these three compounds rather than the existence of a complex of hemicelluloses and polyuronides.

The araban portion of the crude apple pectin was further investigated by Hirst and Jones[312] who state that methylation experiments indicate the presence of the furanose form of the arabinose. This araban appears to be identical with the araban previously isolated by them[317] from crude pectic preparations made from shelled and deskinned peanuts (*Arachis hypogaea*). The araban may have a branched chain structure. Ehrlich and Schubert[282] claimed to have isolated a "tetraaraban" associated with pectic substances, but it is likely that the material they dealt with was a mixture of arabans of degraded nature.

The galactan occurring together with pectic substances was isolated in the pure state by Hirst, Jones, and Walder[318] from white lupine (*Lupinus albus*) seeds. The galactan here occurs together with relatively small proportions of araban and pectic acid. After the isolation of the polysaccharide fraction the araban was removed therefrom by hydrolysis with 0.01 N acid and the pectic acid precipitated as the water-insoluble calcium pectate. The residual polysaccharide gave galactose upon hydrolysis. The rate of hydrolysis indicated that the galactose in the galactan had a pyranose structure. Methylation experiments proved the presence of 1,4 linkages between the a-D-galactose units.

From the practical point of view it is of interest that the pentose (arabinose) component of crude pectin preparations may be removed without changing the jelly-forming ability of the preparation.[319]

There is a great deal of additional evidence, even if mostly indirect in nature, to show the incidental nature of galactans and arabans—or arabinose and galactose—in pectin preparations. Therefore, it is safe

[317] E. L. Hirst and J. K. N. Jones, *J. Chem. Soc.*, 1938, 502.
[318] E. L. Hirst, J. K. N. Jones, and W. O. Walder, *J. Chem. Soc.*, 1947, 1225.
[319] G. H Joseph, *Bull Natl. Formulary Comm.*, 9, 18 (1940).

to conclude that, while these substances frequently occur in preparations of pectinic acids, pectins, and pectic acids, their presence cannot be regarded as proof that they are components of the pectin molecule. It appears a much safer course to admit the impure nature of most pectic preparations and regard their presence in pectic preparations as the result of similar physical properties.

At present it appears that an obvious genetic relationship does not exist among these polysaccharides (see Chapter XI). This does not mean, however, that such a relation may not exist in a manner unknown to us at the present time. We know little of the means by which the carbohydrate constituents of plants are transformed or, indeed, formed. It may be just as wrong to assume that arabans and galactans or arabinose and galactose may not at some time be in actual association with pectic substances. Practically all the chemical work performed in the past dealt with water-soluble pectinic acids, pectins, or derivatives of these compounds. The nature of protopectin is still unknown and, therefore, it may be unwarranted to neglect the possibility that in protopectin these polysaccharides may be associated in some manner with the pectic component. The observations listed above, however, seem to justify the opinion that their presence in all pectic preparations is incidental—at least until conclusive evidence to the contrary is produced.

CHAPTER V

Heterogeneity of Pectic Substances

The heterogeneity of pectic substances must be obvious to all who are familiar with macromolecular polymers. The existence of a definite molecular size in the case of pectic substances was almost universally believed, however, until a few years ago and it may therefore not be in vain to discuss this point.

Due to constitutional peculiarities, the pectic substances offer several possibilities for nonhomogeneity. Some of these will be mentioned here in an attempt to explain the variations encountered in pectic preparations. Let us assume, for the purpose of simplicity, that the pectic substances possess a straight polygalacturonic acid skeleton built of identical anhydrogalacturonic acids connected in an identical manner, and disregard, for the moment, the possibilities of branchings and additional ("secondary") structures.

As it will be shown in Chapter XI, we do not have any definite information on the genesis and fate of pectic materials in plants. The only constructive theory, namely, that the polygalacturonic acids are directly derived either by the oxidation of arabans or the reduction of the galactans, had to be discarded for the present at least. It is most likely that the polygalacturonic acids are formed by an association of individual galacturonic acid anhydride molecules (polymerization). Thus, in a plant tissue where pectin is produced, at any given time there must be a whole series of pectic compounds in various stages of polymerization, therefore showing diversity in the number of associated anhydrogalacturonic acid units. Any pectic preparation made from plant tissues has as its starting material a mixture of polygalacturonic acids of different sizes.

It has been also observed that during certain phases of plant life the pectic compounds undergo degradation and decomposition. This process is well indicated in the case of apples, pears, tomatoes, peaches, etc., by the decreasing colloidality of the pectinic acids which may be isolated from overmature fruit and by the simultaneous decrease in the proportion of pectic substances in the tissue. Such degradations (*Abbildung*) again are apt to increase the heterogeneity of the pectic components by causing a wider distribution with regard to molecular size. Thus, we already have two variants, namely, the size of polygalacturonic acid chains and the relative proportions in which they may occur (see Fig. 5 below).

Further differences may appear among pectinic acids because of the existence of esterified carboxyl groups in the polygalacturonic acid chains. As was mentioned on the previous pages, the methoxyl content values of a pectinic acid preparation are averages. It is unlikely that in any preparation of pectinic acid all the various polygalacturonic acids would contain the same proportion of methoxyl groups. A polygalacturonic acid may contain many, few, or no methyl ester groups at all. Furthermore, the methyl ester groups may be distributed in a uniform or in an irregular

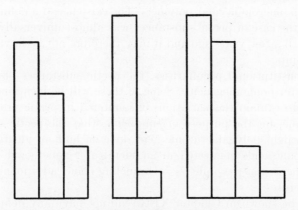

Fig. 5. Schematic illustration of the molecular size heterogeneity in polygalacturonic acids.

The number-average molecular weights of the three samples shown are the same (4) yet the differences in the distribution of various sizes will cause variations in their behavior and usefulness. The weight-average molecular weights of the three samples are 4.6, 6.1 and 5.5, respectively.

manner along the polygalacturonic acid chains. In the case of pectinic acids, therefore, three additional variants exist, namely, the proportion of methyl esters, their distribution among the individual polygalacturonic acid chains, and the manner of spacing of methyl ester groups on the individual polygalacturonic acid units. Some of these simple possibilities are schematically indicated in Figures 6 and 7.

In the case of "super" structures discussed in Chapter III and involving various types of linkages other than the 1,4 glycosidic bridge, many new possible variations may exist. These are indeed so obvious and at the same time so endless that it is hardly profitable to discuss them. If the pectin macromolecule is branching, as Bock and Einsele[320] postulate, the

[320] H. Bock and R. Einsele, *J. prakt. Chem.*, **155**, 225 (1940).

variation in different possible compounds is again increased. The two ends of the polygalacturonic acid molecule are not identical: one end has a reducing group and thus the molecule is asymmetrical. It is conceivable

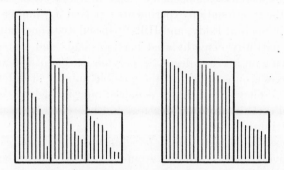

Fig. 6. Schematic illustration of the heterogeneity caused by different methyl ester contents.

The two samples of pectinic acids are identical with regard to molecular size and size distribution, but the distribution of the methyl ester groups within any given molecular size group is different even if the average degree of esterification is the same. Thus the samples will show different behavior especially in acidic properties and reactivity toward polyvalent ions.

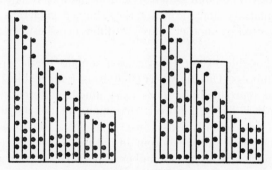

Fig. 7. Schematic illustration of variations in the distribution of methyl ester groups.

A further variation based on Figure 6. Here the difference between the two samples is in the spacing of the ester groups on the polygalacturonic acid units. The significance of such variations is yet unknown except perhaps from the standpoint of enzymic hydrolysis (see p. 356).

that this factor may also increase the heterogeneity of certain pectic materials.

Changes of some kind leading to increased heterogeneity are apt to occur during the extraction and treatment of pectic substances. These, however, may be more than counteracted by the common use of precipitation methods since the latter are likely to effect the removal of some fractions and thus increase homogeneity. Some illustrations of this point may be found in the fractionation experiments reported in Chapter VII, Section VII. Recently Speiser, Eddy, and Hills[321] speculated concerning the heterogeneity of partially demethylated pectinic acids and stated that, in a sample showing an average degree of polymerization of 500 and with half of the carboxyl groups esterified, the possible number of different pectinic acids is 10^{150}. They stated that it is indeed improbable that such a preparation would contain any two identical molecules or even a random sampling of distribution.

Finally, one should mention the possibility of differences caused by salt formation involving the carboxyl group, which may again be different in proportion, distribution among polygalacturonic acids, and spacing on the polygalacturonic acid.

Almost all pectic and pectinic acid preparations studied prior to 1935 were impure and consisted of mixtures of pectic substances with accompanying materials. Of these the arabans and galactans were the most significant, because they were present in quantities up to 50% and because their colloidal behavior must have greatly influenced the characteristics of the preparations. The point which should be made here is that the variations in the quantity and nature of the admixed galactans and arabans was, and still often is, another source of differences between pectic preparations.

Thus, the possible extent of variation among pectic preparations is practically limitless. One may say that it is remarkable that so much similarity and reproducibility does exist among different lots of pectic preparations. It is likely, however, that many of the possible structural variations do not actually exist, just as most of the possible isomeric sugars have not been found to occur in nature. Therefore, the variations may not be limitless even if the number of possible different pectinic acids must be expressed by astronomical figures.

At the present time pectin chemistry is not much beyond a clear realization that problems of heterogeneity exist. Our methods of segregation into more homogeneous fractions as well as the definition of the heterogeneity of pectic preparations are both in their infancy. Of the several attempts at fractionation only the recent work of Speiser and Eddy[322] will be mentioned. These authors studied the changes in the molecular size distribution as affected by various methods of deesterification. The pectinic acids

[321] R. Speiser, C. R. Eddy, and C. H. Hills, *J. Phys. Chem.*, **49**, 563 (1945).
[322] R. Speiser and C. R. Eddy, *J. Am. Chem. Soc.*, **68**, 287 (1946).

were nitrated by the method of Henglein and Schneider[323] and precipitated from acetone solution by the gradual addition of toluol. Speiser and Eddy made a whole series of assumptions in connection with these measurements and appear to have obtained some indication of the changes caused by the various treatments in the molecular weight distribution. While such experimental technic is a very useful approach in gaining information on the problem of heterogeneity, there are many irregularities which are still unexplained and the many assumptions which must be made for the calculations will cause the results obtained to bear less significance.

It will be clear from the discussion of weight- and number-average molecular weights in Chapter III, that the closer the weight- and number-average values approach equality, the more homogeneous is the sample with regard to molecular weight. The unhomogeneity of macromolecular materials may also be characterized by the nonuniformity coefficient[324] calculated from data obtained in determination of sedimentation velocities in the ultracentrifuge.[325] Obviously, such values will again only characterize the heterogeneity with regard to molecular size and not in other respects.

There is little doubt that the development of methods to increase the homogeneity of samples of pectic substances is one of the most important problems of pectin chemistry. This may also be the key to the large-scale use of low-ester pectins, whose practical application seems to be retarded by extensive and changing heterogeneity. Better methods of estimating and defining the multiple heterogeneity of pectic substances are also much needed.

[323] F. A. Henglein and G. Schneider, *Ber.*, **69**, 309 (1936).
[324] W. D. Lansing and E. O. Kraemer, *J. Am. Chem. Soc.*, **57**, 1369 (1935).
[325] S. Säverborn, *Dissertation*, University of Uppsala, 1945.

CHAPTER VI

Preparation and Purification of Pectic Substances in the Laboratory

A detailed discussion of the methods used for the extraction and purification of pectic substances is important since such procedures are necessarily involved in studying their composition, structure, and properties. On the following pages methods will be given for the separation with maximum purity of the various pectic substances from plant sources. While these methods are often similar to those used in the quantitative determination and commercial-scale production of the pectic materials, the yields obtained and the time and cost involved in the preparation will be overlooked in the present discussion. The methods of quantitative estimation and commercial production will be dealt with later in Chapters VIII and XVIII–XXVI, respectively.

The pectic substances constitute in most cases only a small fraction of plant tissues. It is necessary, therefore, to separate them from the other plant components. Some of these latter may be removed with ease, while others may attach themselves to the pectic materials with considerable tenacity. The method of preparation and the extent of purification will depend on the purpose for which the pectic substance is to be used. In the commercial production of pectic materials, an equitable balance between desirable purity and cost of purification will have to be maintained and therefore such preparations at times contain a considerable proportion of nonpectic components. Even in the laboratory preparation of a pectic substance it is of governing importance whether the object is quantitative estimation or rather purification for subsequent studies of physical and chemical behavior. It is often necessary to obtain pectic preparations which will not change during the course of a contemplated investigation. This purpose is best served by the preparation of the pectic substances in the form of dry powders which have been found to show little deterioration during storage.

The methods of extraction, preparation, and purification will effect some degree of fractionation of the large number of different compounds which may be grouped under any general name such as pectinic acid, for instance. Such fractionation may also occur at the time when other compounds and "ballast" substances are removed by extraction with comparatively low ethanol concentrations.

If the aim of the investigator is to preserve some plant tissue for future work on its pectic components, it is customary to inactivate any naturally present enzymes which may act upon the pectic constituents during storage. The best method is to slice or otherwise add the plant material in small pieces to a considerable volume of boiling 95% ethanol,[326] not allowing the ethanol concentration to drop below 70%. The material is then allowed to stand in fresh 95% ethanol for at least a few hours, filtered through cloth, squeezed free of ethanol, and dried in air.[326a] It is undesirable to preserve and store the plant tissue in ethanol for long periods of time, but if this is necessary the sample should be kept at temperatures around or below 0°C. in order to minimize the possible effect of acids and other agents. The practice of adding calcium carbonate at the time of preservation in ethanol may be useful in studies of many plant constituents, but it is definitely undesirable when the pectic components are to be studied.

I. PREPARATION OF PROTOPECTIN

It has been made clear in Chapter III that the true nature and even the chemical composition of protopectin are still unknown. The classical definition, similar to the nomenclature used in this volume, defines protopectin as the water-insoluble parent pectic substance which occurs in plants. Therefore, the separation of protopectin from pectinic and pectic acids must be undertaken on the basis of this differential solubility in water. Unfortunately, this definition, while the best we may have at the present time, is far from being either clear or precise. There is now no general agreement on the methods which should be applied for the removal of the soluble components from plant tissues and preparations during the course of separating the protopectin from the more soluble pectinic and pectic acids. In addition, some salts, especially those of pectic acids or of low-ester pectinic acids, will show a disturbing degree of similarity in their solubilty behavior to protopectin. Actually, in the majority of cases it is not possible to reach a stage where no further soluble pectic substance is removed, since apparently even cold water effects extremely slow but continuous hydrolysis (solubilization) of proto-

[326] G. Bertrand and A. Mallèvre, *Compt. rend.*, **119**, 1012 (1894).

[326a] Z. I. Kertesz and R. J. McColloch, *New York State Agr. Expt. Sta.*, Bull. No. 745 (1950).

pectin.[327]   Therefore, the proportion of solvent used, particle size of the plant tissue, presence of other colloids and electrolytes, and duration and temperature of treatment will determine the line of demarcation obtained and, in addition, will also influence the sharpness of the separation.

The influence of experimental conditions is of such magnitude that Tutin,[328] who found that the degree of solubility of the pectic substances of fruits depends greatly on the extent of disintegration of the tissue, questioned the existence of a water-insoluble pectic compound in plants. The dominant opinion at this time, however, is that protopectin does exist as a compound insoluble in water, even if it is more similar to pectinic acids in its composition and structure than has previously been suspected.

Some regard calcium as a component of protopectin, while others remove most of the calcium and magnesium by treatment with dilute acid. The majority of workers in this field now prefer not to use an acid treatment, but only cold water for the removal of other pectic constituents in the preparation of protopectin. The purest preparations may be obtained from fruit tissues upon removal of all components soluble in water, alcohol, and ether. According to some authors, these extractions may be followed by removal of cellulose by Schweitzer reagent (ammoniacal solution of cupric hydroxide). Constituents other than cellulose may also be removed by this latter solvent and it is more than probable that, in addition, some alterations in the insoluble pectic component are also caused. For lack of better methods, this procedure using extraction with water, alcohol, and ether and the one using, in addition, Schweitzer reagent will be described.

1. The "Classical" Procedure

From certain plant tissues the majority of components other than cellulose and protopectin may be quite easily removed by extraction. The selection of the plant tissue is of highest importance. Unripe fruits, citrus albedo, and apple pomace are suitable starting materials because they contain a comparatively large proportion of protopectin and a low proportion of other components which behave similarly to protopectin.

If enzymes acting upon pectic substances are present, these should first be inactivated by rapid heating. This is best accomplished by slicing the plant tissue rapidly into a large volume of boiling 95% ethanol. The proportions are chosen so that the final ethanol concentration is not below 70%. The mixture is again brought to a boil and then cooled. After standing overnight, it is drained through silk cloth, pressed dry, and suspended in 95% ethanol. After standing

[327] F. Hardy, *Biochem. J.,* **18,** 2 (1924).
[328] F. Tutin, *Biochem. J.,* **17,** 510 (1923).

for at least a day, the mixture is drained through cloth, squeezed dry, and rubbed in a large mortar until the alcohol evaporates. A few minutes in a 100°C. oven will take off the last traces of moisture. This ethanol treatment removes most of the sugars and the dried material may now be ground in a Wiley mill to pass a 1-mm. screen. Some authors recommend even finer grinding because this will facilitate subsequent extractions. Ripa[329] recommends grinding into a fine powder and sifting through a bolting cloth, but filtrations become much more difficult with finely ground tissues.

The ground powder is extracted several times with comparatively large volumes (at least 25 cc. per g. of dry powder) of cold distilled water until only traces of soluble pectin are removed. In most instances at least 3 to 5 extractions are needed, although "60 to 80 extractions," as mentioned by Branfoot,[330] may be superfluous. Ample soaking time (5 to 6 hours) and vigorous agitation will increase the efficiency of extraction but the temperature should not be raised above 20 to 25°C. (68 to 77°F.) lest excessive solubilization of the protopectin may occur. Some authors recommend that low proportions of

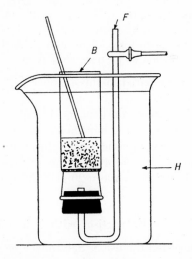

Fig. 8. The Weihe-Phillips extractor.

acid be used in these extractions but it is likely that such a procedure will cause some changes in components which would otherwise fall within the definition of protopectin. As it has been mentioned in Chapter III, some cations such as calcium may be essential parts of the protopectin molecule and therefore the removal of such cations is regarded as undesirable. Centrifuging has been found

[329] R. Sucharipa (now Ripa), *J. Am. Chem. Soc.*, **46**, 145 (1924).
[330] M. H. Branfoot (M. H. Carré), "A Critical and Historical Study of the Pectic Substances of Plants." Dept. of Sci. and Ind. Res., Special Report No. 33, H. M. Stationery Office, London, 1929.

to offer the most efficient means of separation of the suspended tissue from the extraction water.

After exhaustive extraction with cold water, the material is extracted with 95% ethanol until this solvent does not remove any more solids. The use of hot ethanol has often been recommended for the sake of more efficient extraction but again the heat may cause changes in the protopectin and therefore cold ethanol is preferred even if this procedure takes a longer time. Afterward the residue is extracted with ether until it is completely void of materials soluble in this solvent, and then rubbed dry in a large mortar.

Recently Weihe and Phillips[331] described an apparatus, shown in Figure 8, which will simplify such extraction operations.

The sample and the solution used for the extraction are contained in vessel B which has a fritted glass bottom. The contents of B are kept warm by the water contained by beaker H. Upon completion of the extraction, the liquid is sucked through the fritted glass disc and removed through tube F. This expedient method of extraction eliminates the necessity of transferring the extraction mixture as well as the occurrence of possible losses due to adhesion of some of the extract to the filter paper. In order to retain the full working efficiency of the fritted glass disc, it is important that during the process the plant material never be sucked dry enough to form a firm cake. The Weihe-Phillips extractor is also useful in the extraction of pectinic acids from plant tissues.

A crude protopectin prepared in this manner will contain (in addition to the water-insoluble pectic constituents) cellulose, lignin, and perhaps some protein and other minor constituents. It will also contain, as a rule, some mineral constituents (ash), but should be free from water-soluble pectic constituents, sugars, organic acids, glucosides, pigments, oils, etc. The polyuronide content of such preparation, determined by methods described in Chapter II, will be between 20 and 80%, depending on the raw material used.

2. Preparation by Extraction with Schweitzer Reagent

Mangin[332] first suggested the use of Schweitzer reagent for the removal of cellulose from protopectin preparations. A more recent advocate of the use of this reagent for the preparation of "pure" protopectin has been Ripa,[329] whose work on this subject was discussed in Chapter III, Section III in some detail. The procedure used by Ripa is as follows.

A crude protopectin prepared from lemon peel by the extraction method given above is used as the starting material. The completely dry preparation is first ground thoroughly in a mortar and then the mortar, together with the sample, is chilled to about 5°C. Thereupon some freshly prepared Schweitzer

[331] H. D. Weihe and M. Phillips, *J. Agr. Research*, 74, 77 (1947).
[332] L. Mangin, *J. Bot.*, 6, 13, 207, 363 (1892); 7, 37, 121, 325 (1893).

reagent (made in the usual manner with cooling of the ammonium hydroxide) is added dropwise and mixed thoroughly in the mortar with the protopectin. More reagent is then added until the proportion is 30 to 40 cc. of reagent for every gram of crude protopectin used. After mixing, the contents of the mortar are transferred to a glass-stoppered flask, the mortar is once more rinsed with the reagent, and the mixture is kept at ice box temperatures for 2 to 3 days. At that time the insoluble portion of the mixture is removed by means of a fritted glass filter or by any other suitable method and the whole procedure is repeated. Acidification of the extract precipitates cellulose which, according to Ripa, represents the "free cellulose" fraction of the preparation. A third extraction usually fails to remove any more cellulose. Now the residual powder is soaked in dilute (1 or 2%) acetic acid until no more copper can be removed. Afterward it is separated from the acid, washed rapidly with ice water until the acetic acid is completely removed, rinsed with ethanol, and dried at 100°C. under vacuum.

Ripa claims that such a preparation represents an almost pure protopectin from which pectinic acids may be prepared by any of the conventional methods. The composition of some protopectin preparations prepared by Ripa were given in Table 10.

Thus the known methods for the preparation of protopectin depend on the successive and successful removal of the various other chemical constituents from the plant tissue. The classical method of preparation gives a protopectin which is obviously far from pure, while the use of Schweitzer reagent produced good results only in the hands of Ripa and with lemon peel as starting material. Carré[330] suggests the use of zinc chloride and ammonium hydroxide for the removal of the cellulose but there is insufficient evidence to show that this reagent is preferable to Schweitzer reagent.

II. EXTRACTION OF PECTINIC ACIDS FROM PLANT TISSUES

At times plant materials, especially ripe fruits, contain pectinic acids in the dissolved state. This dissolved fraction usually represents only a part of the total quantity of pectinic acids which may be obtained by extraction with water and various other agents. Such extractions were performed by Braconnot[333] more than one hundred years ago and are still the usual method of obtaining soluble pectic compounds.

A preliminary treatment of the plant material with ethanol is favored by most workers. Such extraction of the finely ground tissues with 95% ethanol will remove sugars, some acids, and many other components. If there is any possibility that the tissue contains enzymes which act upon pectic substances, these should be inactivated. The two matters may well

[333] H. Braconnot, *Ann. chim. phys.*, **28**, 173 (1825); **30**, 96 (1825).

be combined by slicing the tissue into boiling 95% ethanol, followed by
cooling, filtration, and further washing with ethanol, as given above for
protopectin.

1. Extraction of Water-Soluble ("Free") Pectinic Acids

The solution of pectinic acid which may be obtained by expressing the
cell sap from certain plant tissues contains the so-called "free" pectinic
acid fraction. When the tissue is treated with hot water, acids, or any
one of a long list of other agents, further quantities of pectinic acids and
pectic acids may be obtained by the solubilization of the pectic components which were originally insoluble in water. This is mentioned here
to make it clear that most pectinic acid samples extracted by the use
of heat and chemical agents, but without preliminary extractions with
cold water, may include some of the originally soluble pectic components
as well as pectinic acids derived from protopectin and other water-insoluble pectic substances.

Let us assume now that the purpose of the investigation is to study the
properties of the originally water-soluble pectic constituents.

The extraction is performed on the well-ground tissue with successive portions
of distilled water at 20 to 25°C. (68 to 77°F.). Some sand may be used to
facilitate thorough grinding. A Waring Blendor may also be used, although
with caution, as a substitute for mortar grinding. The extraction is not strictly
comparable, first because cells are parted but mostly not cut by the Blendor.
Second, a great deal of air is whipped into the solution which might cause
changes in pectic constituents, especially with plant tissues containing ascorbic
acid (see Chapter VII, Section VI). Third, the liquid in the Blendor may warm
up rapidly when the machine is used longer than a few seconds, thus introducing variations in the extraction temperature.

The extracts are then separated either by filtration or centrifuging and
turned into solid preparations by any of the methods given (Section IV, this
Chapter). Since the distinction between the soluble and insoluble pectic compounds is arbitrary, rigid adherence to all details of the chosen extraction procedure is imperative. The Weihe-Phillips apparatus shown in Figure 8 is eminently useful for the extraction of pectinic acids from plant tissues.

2. Extraction with Solubilizing Agents

Just as in the case of the extraction of the "free" or originally soluble
pectinic acids, the condition of the plant tissue is very important. Generally speaking, the sample should be finely ground to assure successful
extraction. The efficiency of both solubilization and actual dissolution
is greatly enhanced when the tissue consists of fine particles. On the
other hand, the difficulties of separation increase considerably as the
particles become smaller. In the preparation of research samples much

more thorough grinding can be afforded than in commercial production. The separation of the extract from the tissue in the case of finely ground plant material is best accomplished by a high-speed centrifuge, followed by filtration through shark skin filter paper.[334] One important benefit of fine grinding is much more rapid extraction of the pectinic acids, necessitating shorter exposure to the detrimental influences of heat, acid, or other chemicals.

Extraction with hot water is the simplest and oldest method for removing the pectinic acids from plant tissues, but this procedure has many disadvantages. First of all, the water dissolves various other compounds from the plant tissue some of which might be of acidic nature. Consequently, the extraction is performed at an hydrogen ion activity (pH) which may not be the same for various extractions from the same sample of plant tissue. If the sample was previously extracted with ethanol, this difficulty is reduced but may not be entirely eliminated. A further disadvantage of hot-water extraction is the long periods of heating which are required for essentially complete removal of the pectinic acids. As will be shown in Chapter VII, pectic substances undergo degradation during such heat treatment. The use of hot-water extraction is one of the most vulnerable points in the important and extensive researches of Ehrlich,[335] who heated his preparations on the steam bath for this purpose. A critical reading of his reports leaves no doubt that the pectinic acids which this author extracted from almost any plant material must have become extensively degraded. Indeed, most of the pectinic acid (*Hydratopektin*) samples obtained by Ehrlich had low solution viscosities and were probably useless in making pectin-sugar-acid jellies. For this reason some workers, such as Myers and Baker,[336] Schneider and Bock,[337] and others, do not even regard the preparations obtained and studied by Ehrlich as typical pectinic acids or pectins.

The same holds true for pectinic acids extracted under increased pressure, as recommended by Verdon.[338] The length of treatment required in the latter case is only a fraction of that needed by hot water at atmospheric pressure, yet, the loss of colloidal properties and caramelization will be apparent even when such elevated temperatures are carefully applied.[339]

[334] Available in rolls from the Schleicher & Schüll Co. of New York, or in a round shape with diameters up to 50 cm. from laboratory supply houses. This paper has been found eminently suitable for work with pectic substances.

[335] F. Ehrlich, *Cellulosechemie*, **8**, 8 (1930), etc.

[336] P. B. Myers and G. L. Baker, *Univ. Delaware Agr. Expt. Sta.*, Bull. No. 187 (1934).

[337] G. Schneider and H. Bock, *Ber.*, **70**, 1617 (1937).

[338] E. Verdon, *J. pharm. chim.*, **5**, 347 (1912).

[339] M. H. Carré, *Biochem. J.*, **16**, 704 (1922).

A long list of various agents has been recommended for the extraction of pectinic acids from plant tissues. Of these the use of acids,[335] glycerol,[340] ammonium oxalate,[333] sucrose solutions,[330] and polyphosphates[341-343] may be mentioned. Alkaline compounds such as sodium hydroxide,[327] sodium carbonate,[344] and ammonium hydroxide[345] have also been proposed, but it is obvious now that, while these may be suitable for the extraction of pectic acids, the alkaline medium will demethylate the pectinic acids. For this reason alkaline reagents are altogether unsuitable for our purpose.

The usual method of protective extraction is to use a dilute hot solution of a highly dissociated acid. The literature contains many statements giving combinations of the three principal factors which determine the efficiency of extraction, namely, pH, temperature, and duration of heating. A fourth factor, dilution, may be added as being of secondary importance. It would be of little service to the reader to relate the details of procedures used in the past. A more useful plan may be to discuss briefly the significance of these factors and then describe a procedure of universal applicability for the protective extraction of pectinic acids. The role of the various factors in the commercial extraction of pectinic acids will be discussed in detail in Chapter XIX.

There is a wide range of acidities at which pectinic acids may be successfully extracted from plant tissues. The dominant idea in extraction for research purposes is to prevent any great extent of degradation and hydrolysis, as well as deesterification. In addition to rendering the insoluble pectic constituents water-soluble, the acid solution also acts on the pectinic acids already in solution. For this reason it is desirable, in the present case, to use only slightly acid extractants and to remove frequently the extracted pectinic acids. The use of acid in the extraction procedure has the added advantage that it reduces the proportion of hemicelluloses in the extract. Hydrochloric acid in 0.05 N concentration (at 90°C. for 4 hours) has been shown by Hirst and Jones[346] to be sufficient to hydrolyze the araban to such a degree that it is not precipitated by 66% ethanol. Therefore the araban "ballast" will either be eliminated or at least greatly reduced in quantity during such acid extraction.

The careful control of extraction temperatures is important for several

[340] C. van Wisselingh, *Jahrb. Wiss. Bot.*, **31**, 629 (1898).
[341] G. L. Baker and C. W. Woodmansee, *Fruit Products J.*, **23**, 164 (1944).
[342] W. D. Maclay and J. P. Nielsen, U. S. Pat. 2,375,376 (1945).
[343] R. M. McCready, A. D. Shepherd, and W. D. Maclay, *Fruit Products J.*, **27**, 36 (1947).
[344] M. V. Regnault, *J. pharm.*, **24**, 201 (1838).
[345] R. G. W. Farnell, *Intern. Sugar J.*, **25**, 248 (1923), etc.
[346] E. L. Hirst and J. K. N. Jones, *J. Chem. Soc.*, **1939**, 454.

easons. Hot acid renders the insoluble pectic constituent soluble in a much shorter period of digestion than is the case when lower temperatures re used. The dissolving of the solubilized pectinic acids is also more rapid in a hot solution. On the other hand, hot acid causes degradation of the xtracted pectic materials. This latter reaction is greatly accelerated at emperatures above 80°C. and the range 60 to 90°C. is therefore used y most workers. Extraction at 80°C., as used in the procedure given be-ow, is comparatively safe and efficient, provided that the extracts are emoved frequently and thus are not unduly exposed to heating for an ex-essive period. Hinton[347] states that extraction at 80 or 90°C. with 0.05 N ydrochloric acid results in much less demethylation of the pectinic acid han at the boiling point. If complete extraction is sought without previous xtraction of the water-soluble pectic fraction, or by performing only one xtraction with acid, the heating period would have to be prolonged; n such cases even 80°C. may be too high for the protective preparation f the pectinic acids. The time of extraction recommended by various uthors runs from 30 minutes to several hours. The two-hour period ecommended below for the extraction where several such treatments are sed has the benefits of longer extraction without much danger of de-radation of the previously extracted pectic materials. The dilution is f minor significance in the laboratory preparation of pectinic acids. It chosen in such a manner as to allow satisfactory extraction and to void undue difficulties in the separation of the individual extracts from he tissue sample.

The following procedure is recommended for the extraction of "free" nd "solubilized" pectinic acids from plant tissues.

The sample is first treated with large portions of 95% ethanol or, if pectic nzymes are present, is sliced or poured slowly into boiling 95% ethanol. The hanol-insoluble materials are filtered off, washed with more 95% ethanol, hanol–ether mixture, and finally with ether. Thereupon the sample is pressed, ried, and ground as described above, or directly resuspended in water. The resid-al small ethanol or ether content will not interfere with the extraction, on the ntrary, it will assure better "wetting" of the sample by water. The sample thoroughly mixed with the water, using about 50 cc. per gram of dry material. he water-soluble pectinic acids are then extracted as directed above, Sect. 1. fterward the residue is resuspended in 0.05 N hydrochloric acid and the mixture eated to 80°C. in a water bath for 2 hours with occasional stirring. It is then ooled, centrifuged, or filtered, and the insoluble residue again treated with 05 N hydrochloric acid in the same manner.

If the sample is sufficiently well dispersed in the solvent, more than 99% : all pectinic acid is usually extracted by three treatments with hot acid and

[347] C. L. Hinton, *Fruit Pectins, Their Chemical Behaviour and Jellying Properties.* hem. Publishing Co., New York, 1940.

four or five acid extractions are usually sufficient for complete extraction of pectinic acids. To obtain assurance that this has been accomplished, a small sample of the clear filtrate is mixed in a test tube with twice its volume of ethanol. After vigorous shaking, the tube is observed in a beam of light directed toward it from the side, using a black background. If precipitated particles appear in the mixture, the extraction should be continued.

The combined extracts are then purified and made into solid preparations by any of the procedures given below. This method of extraction has been successfully used in the writer's laboratory and elsewhere for a number of years. It is almost identical with the procedure given by Hinton[347] for the preparation of some fruit pectinic acids. The Weihe-Phillips apparatus[331] shown in Figure 8 may again be recommended for all these operations.

Various ion exchange agents may also be used in the extraction of pectinic acids from plant tissues since some of the pectic compounds in plant tissues may be rendered insoluble by calcium and other polyvalent cations.[348,349] Norris and Schryver[350] found that by using a solution of ammonium oxalate instead of water, the solubilization of the insoluble pectic constituents proceeded more rapidly. The same principle was later covered by the patents issued to Nanji and Paton,[351] the German Pomosin-Werke,[352] and Myers and Rouse.[353] Recently the use of polyphosphates[341,354] was suggested for the extraction of pectinic acids, especially in cases where acidities above pH 2.2 are to be used. While the experimental evidence which may be found in the literature concerning the general usefulness of polyphosphates is not convincing, it is clear that in the presence of calcium and magnesium salts (as in the case of unpurified raw materials) they are helpful. In the procedure recommended above, where the extraction is performed by successive portions of hot 0.05 N hydrochloric acid, no benefits are expected from the use of polyphosphates because the calcium and other divalent ions are removed by the first few extractions. Furthermore, difficulties are often encountered in completely removing the polyphosphates used in the extraction from the solutions obtained and even from the precipitated pectins. The usefulness of polyphosphates in commercial extraction of pectin will be discussed in Chapter XIX, Section III-4.

[348] A. Chodnew, Ann., 51, 355 (1844).
[349] E. Frémy, Ann. chim. phys., 24, 5 (1848).
[350] F. W. Norris and S. B. Schryver, Biochem. J., 19, 676 (1925).
[351] D. R. Nanji and F. J. Paton, U. S. Pat. 1,634,879 (1927).
[352] Pomosin-Werke (Fischer and Co.), Belg. Pats. 444,825 and 444,872 (1942); C A., 39, 566, 1480 (1925).
[353] P. B. Myers and A. H. Rouse, U. S. Pat. 2,323,483 (1943).
[354] B. A. Gilmore and C. J. Munter, Can. Pat. 376,632 (1937).

III. PURIFICATION OF PECTINIC ACID SOLUTIONS

The fruit juices, plant extracts, and solutions used in the following procedures must be completely clear and entirely void of suspended particles.
They may be clarified by efficient centrifuging or filtration, or both. It
has been found expedient to use diatomaceous earth filter aids even in
the laboratory, especially in the case of viscous solutions or for those
containing large proportions of fine cellular debris. The filtration of
laboratory samples does not give much difficulty, though viscous solutions
of pectinic acids at times require some experience in handling. The
methods of filtration will be discussed later in Chapter XIX in connection
with the commercial manufacture of pectinic acids and pectins.

If the pectinic acids in a solution are not accompanied by compounds
which may find their way into the final solid preparations, the precipitation may be performed without any preliminary purification. Sugars,
fruit acids, metallic ions, and many ash constituents will be removed for
the most part by successive precipitations with acid ethanol, for instance.
On the other hand, some of the accompanying hemicelluloses and starch,
as well as some cations, attached to the carboxyl groups of the pectinic
acid are at times difficult to remove. It has already been shown in Table
11 that the arabans and galactans may be eliminated in the course of
ethanol precipitation. Special treatment of the solutions will be required
in the presence of starch, combined ash constituents, and of some other
compounds which may be absorbed or occluded during precipitation.

1. Removal of Starch

The pectinic acid extracts prepared from apple pomace or from starchy
vegetable matter often contain starch. Some of the starch in such solutions
undergoes rapid reversion or retrogradation and settles out in the container. This is the basis of the method of purification recommended by
Spencer[355] in which the solution is permitted to stand for prolonged periods
in the presence of an antiseptic. If a solution containing starch is frozen
and then defrosted, this will also precipitate most of the starch from the
solution. It is more expedient, however, to remove the starch by less
time-consuming methods, such as by treatment with amylolytic enzymes.
Such a treatment was originally described by Douglas[356] for the clarification and purification of commercial pectin extracts. In the past, such
commercial diastase preparations were seldom void of traces of enzymes

---

[355] G. Spencer, *J. Phys. Chem.*, **34**, 654 (1930).
[356] R. Douglas, U. S. Pat. 1,235,666 (1917).

which acted upon the pectinic acids. However, the author had occasion to test several new preparations of amylolytic enzymes produced for this purpose which did not seem to have any effect on the pectic constituents in solution. Some of these enzymes are now commercially available. In the laboratory it is customary to use a somewhat diluted and filtered solution of saliva which is rich in amylase (ptyalin) but void of pectin-digesting enzymes.[357,358] A trace of chloride (sodium chloride) should be present in the mixture to assure activation of the salivary amylase and the pH of the solution should be adjusted to about 6.0 to 6.5. Of course, it is desirable to purify the pectinic acid afterward by any of the usual methods in order to remove the salts and hydrolysis products as well as the ptyalin itself.

The removal of starch from solutions of pectinic acids during the course of quantitative estimation and commercial production will be discussed in Chapters VIII and XIX, respectively.

2. Purification by Dialysis and Electrodialysis

The utilization of semipermeable membranes for the separation of colloids and crystalloids is one of the standard methods of colloid chemistry. There are a number of papers and patents on the application of dialysis and electrodialysis to the purification of pectinic acids. Fellenberg[359] recommended dialysis for the purification of soluble pectic substances. Griggs and Johnstin[360] dialyzed a dilute solution of pectinic acid in a parchment bag against 0.01 N hydrochloric acid for a week, followed by dialysis against water for four or five days. The ash content of the pectinic acid was reduced from the initial 2.60% to 0.18%. Unfortunately, the pectinic acid undergoes considerable degradation during such lengthy treatment. Various regenerated cellulose (Cellophane) bags and tubes (sausage casings) are now more commonly used for dialysis than parchment.

Electrodialysis is more efficient. Emmett[361] used this method for the purification of pectic and pectinic acid after preliminary purification by precipitation with ethanol. The apparatus used by Emmett is shown in Figure 9. The process is similar to that described by Schwerin[362] and by

[357] Z. I. Kertesz, *J. Nutrition*, 20, 289 (1940).

[358] J. B. Sumner and G. F. Somers, *Chemistry and Methods of Enzymes*. Academic Press, New York, 1943.

[359] T. Fellenberg, *Biochem. Z.*, 85, 45 (1918).

[360] M. A. Griggs and R. Johnstin, *Ind. Eng. Chem.*, 18, 623 (1926); see also G. Spencer, *J. Phys. Chem.*, 34, 429 (1930).

[361] A. M. Emmett, *Biochem. J.*, 20, 564 (1926).

[362] B. Schwerin, U. S. Pat. 1,235,064 (1917).

Knaggs, Manning, and Schryver[363] for glue, gelatin, and similar substances.

A small parchment dialyzer (I) is suspended within bell jar B having a parchment-covered bottom. This is dipped into a large glass container (D) filled with distilled water, at the bottom of which is a layer of mercury to serve as the cathode (M). The small inner dialyzer contains distilled water and is dipped into the pectin solution (P) contained in the bell jar. Through the cork of the bell jar pass glass tubes for filling and emptying the apparatus and a glass tube filled with mercury, to the end of which a platinum electrode about 2 cm. long is fused to serve as the anode. Emmett used a lighting circuit of 220 v., d.c., and kept the current at 0.25 amp. by means of an external resistance. The heating effect is reduced to a minimum by placing the electrodes as close together as

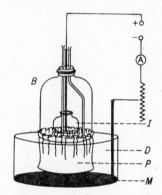

Fig. 9. Emmett's electrodialysis apparatus for pectin.

possible, thereby decreasing the resistance. Cooling may be effected by exposing a large surface of water in the outer container. With daily changes of water Emmett succeeded in reducing the ash content of a pectinic acid solution from the initial 3.1 to 0.5% in three days.

Nanji and Paton[351] used electrodialysis for the removal of acids from pectinic acid extracts without the necessity of neutralizing them. Edson,[364] in a study of the physicochemical properties of pectins, used electrodialysis of pectinic acid solutions first against 0.01 N hydrochloric acid and then against water. A final ash content of 0.18% was reached by this author for several batches in one week's time.

Gortner and Hoffman[365] in 1933 described an interesting method of electrodialysis which, in addition to the purification of pectinic acid

[363] J. Knaggs, A. B. Manning, and S. B. Schryver, *Biochem. J.*, **17**, 473 (1923); **18**, 1079 (1924).
[364] L. E. Edson, *Dissertation,* Columbia University, New York, 1928.
[365] R. A. Gortner and W. F. Hoffman, U. S. Pat. 1,915,568 (1933).

solutions, was claimed to be useful for the separation of pectic constituents from plant material.

The main feature of the apparatus, shown in Figure 10, is a boxlike structure divided into three compartments (A, B, C) by walls of semipermeable membranes. Sections A and C contain carbon electrodes D and the raw material is placed into the middle compartment B. Current is now passed through the apparatus, causing the migration of the cations through the diaphragms. Gortner and Hoffman recommend the packing of the middle compartment with a fibrous material to increase efficiency. The apparatus has been claimed to be useful for the production of pectinic acid solutions from plant tissues where the pectinic acids are immobilized by the formation of calcium and magnesium compounds. The details of the operation indicated in the patent specification reveal several difficult features which may be the reason why (to the writer's knowledge) this method has not been used for either commercial production or laboratory purification of pectic substances.

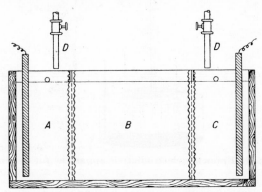

Fig. 10. Gortner and Hoffman's electrodialysis apparatus.

Dialysis and electrodialysis have never been extensively used in pectin research. Fortunately, much easier, more dependable and expedient methods for the removal of ash constituents are now available through the use of ion exchange materials as described below.

3. Removal of Ash Constituents with Ion Exchange Resins

Zeolites and related products capable of ion exchange have been known and used for many years but found limited application for purposes other than water purification. Mainly as the result of the work of Adams and Holmes,[366] resinous ion exchangers became available in 1935 and, in turn, were found useful for a variety of purposes including the de-ashing of pectin solutions.

[366] B. A. Adams and E. L. Holmes, British Pat. 2,191,853 (1940).

Commercial ion exchange resins have been used by a number of workers for the de-ashing of pectinic acid solutions. The Pomosin-Werke in Germany obtained a patent on such a method in 1942.[352] Williams and Johnson[367] applied synthetic resins Amberlite 1R-100 and 1R-4[368] for the removal of ash constituents prior to the determination of pectinic acids by electrodeposition. The method is simple and efficient. Figure 11 shows the apparatus used by Williams and Johnson.

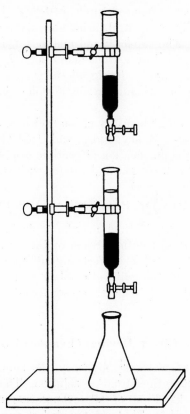

Fig. 11. Ion-exchange de-ashing of a pectin solution according to Williams and Johnson.

The exchange columns are prepared in glass tubing 2.4 cm. in diameter and 19.0 cm. in length, constricted at one end to a 0.6-cm. outlet. Some 10 g. (drained weight) of the resin, supported by a glass wool mat at the lower end, is used in each tube. The upper column is used for the cation exchange, and is filled

[367] K. T. Williams and C. M. Johnson, *Ind. Eng. Chem., Anal. Ed.*, **16**, 23 (1944).
[368] Manufactured by the Rohm and Haas Co., Philadelphia, Pa.

with the 1R-100 resin. The effluent drips directly into the lower column filled with the 1R-4 resin which removes the acids. Williams and Johnson used dilute (0.10 to 0.04%) solutions of pectinic acids. The columns are first rinsed with two 10- or 15-cc. portions of the solution and the rinsings are discarded. The main portion of the solution is then put through at the rate of approximately 3 cc. per minute.

The concentration of pectinic acid in the solution is not changed by passing through the columns. The ash content of pectinic acid solutions treated in this manner is reduced to about 0.05%. The resin system has been used successfully on neutral, acid, and alkaline aqueous solutions of pectic substances. The capacity and methods of regeneration of these resins have been described by various manufacturers in many pamphlets. This field is now being rapidly developed and significant further improvements[369] in the use of exchange resins for de-ashing pectin solutions can be expected.

These views concerning the utility of ion exchange resins are not shared by all workers. Lampitt, Money, Judge, and Urie[370] are pessimistic about their application in the purification of pectinic acid solutions and recommend precipitation methods and dialysis for such purposes.

IV. PREPARATION OF PECTINIC ACIDS IN SOLID FORM

There are several methods which may be applied for the preparation of solid pectinic acids from solution. Some of these, such as direct drying under various conditions, do not effect any additional purification, while others, such as precipitation with ethanol or as metallic salts, may remove much of the admixed nonpectic substances as well as certain pectic fractions.

1. Direct Drying (Evaporation)

The evaporation of water is obviously the simplest method of obtaining a solid preparation from a solution. This method, however, has several drawbacks. First of all, evaporation usually involves the application of heat and heat is to be avoided as much as possible during the protective preparation of pectinic acids. A second difficulty is that, unless the evaporation is performed with vigorous stirring, a leathery, jellylike layer often occurs on the surface as the solution is concentrated. This is especially common with highly viscous solutions of pectinic acids. Such layers might interfere with further evaporation. The occurrence of

[369] R. W. Porter, *Food Inds.*, 20, 691 (1948).
[370] L. H. Lampitt, R. W. Money, B. E. Judge, and A. Urie, *J. Soc. Chem. Ind.*, 66, 121 (1947).

such semisolid masses can also be observed on the walls of vessels in which the agitated solution is evaporated. It is important, for this reason, to evaporate pectinic acid solutions in thin, preferably rapidly moving layers. When such concentrates are dried, they again should be spread thin in order to avoid the formation of a leathery surface.

The fact that direct drying does not effect fractionation and purification of the solids in the solution is one reason why precipitation methods are usually preferred. On the other hand, it is desirable at times to obtain all the solids which were contained in an extract. Such procedures may also be used for the commercial production of pectin and have been applied occasionally in research work. If a pectin extract must be dried in this manner, it should be concentrated first, and then dried under reduced pressure, at temperatures not exceeding about 50°C. (122°F.) with the simultaneous application of drying agents. The acid-ethanol soluble components of pectinic acids dried in this manner may be effectively removed from the solid preparation by the "dry extraction" method described below, Section 5.

Drying of pectinic acid solutions from the frozen state has recently been investigated in the writer's laboratory.[371] Vacuum dehydration of a frozen solution of pectinic acid was very successful.

About 200 cc. of a 2% solution of a highly purified pectinic acid was measured into a porcelain dish and frozen at −18°C. The dish was then placed in an experimental vacuum dehydrator[372] and dried at 50 microns (McLeod gauge) pressure. The temperature of the solution was in the neighborhood of −40°C. for the greater part of the drying and below room temperature until all the water was evaporated. The pectinic acid was obtained in a spongy, fluffy condition. The dry mass had the dimensions originally occupied by the solution and upon examination proved to be built up of many thin films of pectinic acid.

The preparation behaved similarly to pectinic acid films dried on heated drums,[373] inasmuch as it dissolved in cold water with ease. Since freezing itself does not destroy the colloidal properties of a viscous pectinic acid solution[374,375] it is apparent that by dehydration from the frozen state a pectinic acid solution may be dried without any major degradative effect. There is little doubt that this method of drying experimental samples will attain considerable significance when vacuum dehydration equipment is developed further and is generally available for laboratory research.

[371] J. C. Moyer and Z. I. Kertesz, *unpublished work*, 1946.
[372] J. C. Moyer and E. Stotz, *Farm Research*, 12, (1), 16 (1946).
[373] R. Sucharipa (now Ripa), U. S. Pat. 1,519,561 (1925).
[374] D. Haynes, *Biochem. J.*, 8, 553 (1914).
[375] J. S. Caldwell, *Washington Agr. Expt. Sta.*, Bull. No. 147 (1917).

2. Precipitation with Ethanol

Ever since Braconnot[333] first applied it for this purpose, ethanol has been generally used for the preparation of solid pectinic acids. It is now clear that the attempts of investigators to use a high concentration of ethanol for the precipitation of pectinic acids did not improve purity but, on the contrary, caused the simultaneous precipitation of other materials, especially hemicelluloses. Ehrlich[376] discovered that some or most of the arabans and galactans which occur with the pectic substances may be removed by extraction with 70% ethanol, but the relation between the purity of the precipitate and the concentration of ethanol employed for the precipitation did not become clear until the researches of Schneider and Bock[337] were published. Table 11 (Ch. IV) shows that the lower the ethanol concentration used for the precipitation the more admixed nonpectic material will remain in solution. It is of importance to realize, in addition, that such precipitation may effect separation of pectinic acids of various molecular sizes, since some of these may be soluble in ethanol concentrations above 50%. Such pectinic acids are described in Chapter XIV, Section II.

The flocculation of pectinic acids by ethanol depends on the presence of traces of electrolytes because in their absence the pectinic acid particles might remain colloidally dispersed. Emmett and Carré[377] showed that pectinic acids may fail entirely to precipitate upon the addition of ethanol to solutions containing less than 0.025% pectinic acid. Bourquelot and Hérissey[378] found that the addition of small quantities of hydrochloric acid facilitated flocculation by ethanol. This is accomplished even better, according to Hinton,[347] by using a small quantity of sodium chloride. Elwell and Dehn[379] recommend the addition of a trace of calcium chloride. Precipitability with ethanol also depends on the colloidal characteristics of the pectinic acid which, in turn, are governed mostly by the molecular size and degree of methylation. When traces of hydrochloric acid, sodium chloride, or calcium chloride are used in conjunction with ethanol, the pectinic acids can be completely precipitated even from very dilute solutions.

Unfortunately, the insolubility of pectinic acids in ethanol is shared by many other organic substances commonly found in plant tissues and fruit extracts. The most important of these are hemicelluloses (arabans, galactans, and xylans, etc.) and the calcium and potassium salts of fruit acids. The mere fact that the quantity of an ethanol precipitate from a

[376] F. Ehrlich, *Z. angew. Chem.*, **40**, 996 (1928).
[377] A. M. Emmett and M. H. Carré, *Biochem. J.*, **20**, 564 (1926).
[378] E. Bourquelot and H. Hérissey, *J. pharm. chim.*, **7**, 473 (1898).
[379] W. E. Elwell and W. M. Dehn, *Plant Physiol.*, **14**, 809 (1939).

fruit extract usually diminishes by successive resolution and reprecipitation is proof that a less soluble fraction, which may be only partly composed of pectinic acids, is being separated from a more soluble fraction which is mostly nonpectic in nature. To illustrate the progress of purification by ethanol precipitation, some figures given by Hinton[347] are shown in Table 13.

TABLE 13

PURIFICATION OF AN ETHANOL PRECIPITATE FROM APPLE JUICE

No. of times precipitated from 50% ethanol	Calcium pectate yield, on ash-free ethanol precipitate basis, %
1	86
2	99
3	101

The table shows that successive portions of nonpectic materials were removed by repeated precipitation. It may be added that the calcium pectate yield[380] of highly purified pectinic acids is usually in the neighborhood of 110% and therefore 92–96% purity was apparently attained by Hinton using ethanol even without the addition of acid.

A final concentration of 55% ethanol in the mixture has been found quite suitable for the precipitation of pectinic acids. Filtration at this concentration is still fairly efficient, although—especially in the presence of low-grade pectins—it occasionally becomes tedious. Ethanol concentrations below 55% are almost certain to give some difficulty. If the proportion of admixed materials is considerable, preliminary precipitation with an ethanol concentration of 70 to 80% is often beneficial in removing the bulk of the nonpectic materials. When this is followed by precipitation from a final concentration of 55% ethanol, the filtration is much easier.

Sugars are weakly absorbed or occluded on alcohol precipitates made from pectinic acid solutions, which is in marked contrast to the tenacity with which the precipitates retain traces of acids and salts. Therefore, the use of hydrochloric acid in the course of ethanol precipitation of pectinic acid has some advantages in addition to facilitating precipitation. In most naturally occurring pectinic acids there are some cations attached to the free acid groups of the polygalacturonic acids. When the purpose of the operation is to prepare as pure pectinic acids as possible without degradation, the use of 0.05 N hydrochloric acid (as calculated for the final mixture) will materially assist in the removal of ash constituents. Griggs and Johnstin[360] found in a test that three subsequent ethanol

[380] M. H. Carré and D. Haynes, *Biochem. J.*, 16, 60 (1922).

precipitations of a sample of pectinic acid gave an ash content of 2.60%, while the equal number of precipitations from ethanol containing 0.01 N hydrochloric acid reduced the ash to 0.69%.

It is perhaps superfluous to note at this point that, when pectinic acids are precipitated by ethanol, the latter should always be added dropwise and with vigorous agitation to the solution or extract. The reverse procedure, recommended some time ago by Tarr[381] and Halliday and Bailey,[382] will cause temporarily high ethanol concentrations, resulting in the precipitation of constituents which then may not easily dissolve in the final ethanol–water mixture. After precipitation, it is advisable to let the mixture stand for several hours. It may then be filtered through filter paper and resuspended in 95% ethanol for the purpose of dehydration. Again standing for at least a few hours is advisable. The precipitate is then filtered off, washed with some more 95% ethanol and finally with ether, and rubbed in a porcelain mortar until free from the odors of alcohol and ether.

In the preparation of larger quantities of material or of pectinic acids of comparatively low colloidality (molecular weight) and degree of esterification, the use of filter paper is very bothersome. Silk or rayon cloth has been found more suitable for the filtration of such precipitates. After filtration the precipitate should be squeezed as dry as possible on the cloth, scraped off, and rubbed dry in a mortar.

By the use of acid ethanol precipitation the ash content of a pectinic acid may be reduced in most cases to about 0.5% but not much below this figure. For the removal of the residual ash the pectinic acid solution should be treated with ion exchange resins as described and then again precipitated with ethanol. The ash content may be reduced below 0.1% in this manner.

For routine precipitation of pectic constituents it is now customary to use a 2-fold volume of 95% ethanol containing enough hydrochloric acid to make the final concentration 0.05 N. The final ethanol concentration in such a mixture is about 60%.

3. Precipitation with Acetone

Acetone, similarly to ethanol, precipitates pectinic acids from solutions. Some authors prefer acetone to ethanol because the former gives a firmer coagulum and is easier to recover. However, acetone must be used at a lower concentration than ethanol because at higher strengths it precipitates more nonpectic materials than does ethanol. Hinton found[347] that starting with a 0.1% solution of pectinic acid and adding acetone slowly until 50% concentration is reached gave good results and that repeated

[381] L. W. Tarr, *Univ. Delaware Agr. Expt. Sta.*, Bull. No. 134 (1923).
[382] E. G. Halliday and G. R. Bailey, *Ind. Eng. Chem.*, 16, 595 (1924).

precipitation at this acetone concentration did not essentially diminish the weight of the precipitate. This he took as an indication that only a small proportion of nonpectic admixed materials was originally precipitated by the 50% acetone. The total volume of the mixture also appeared to make less difference than in the case of ethanol. Much of what has been said above in connection with ethanol precipitation will hold in the case of acetone. Hinton recommends the addition of a small quantity of sodium chloride to the acetone to aid flocculation.

As will be shown in Chapter XIX, isopropyl alcohol has also been widely used for the precipitation of pectic materials from solution, especially in commercial practice. For laboratory preparation the use of ethanol or acetone is preferable.

4. Precipitation with Metallic Salts

This method was developed for the commercial preparation of citrus pectin,[383] but it may be applied equally well to pectinic acids derived from other sources and to laboratory samples. The pectinic acid is precipitated from a clear solution with a colloidal agent having the opposite charge, usually aluminum hydroxide. It has been claimed that the method is purely a case of coprecipitation caused by neutralization of particle charges, while others maintain that during the precipitation, as described below, salt formation occurs.

The solution of the pectinic acid is first brought to a pH of 4.0 to 4.2 with ammonium hydroxide. This operation and the subsequent precipitation are performed with vigorous stirring in order to avoid the creation of local alkalinization and consequent demethylation of the pectinic acid. The exact amount of 25% aluminum sulfate solution required for complete precipitation is first determined on a small sample. The required quantity of aluminum sulfate solution is then added slowly to the pectinic acid solution. The aluminum hydroxide is precipitated together with the pectinic acid. The precipitate is filtered off and washed quickly with cold water. It is then suspended in acidified 95% ethanol, acetone, or isopropyl alcohol, filtered on a Büchner funnel with suction, and washed with the acid–solvent mixture until free from aluminum. It is then rinsed with 95% ethanol until free from acid, rinsed with ether, pressed free from the solvents, and rubbed dry in a large porcelain mortar.

This procedure gives good separation of pectinic acids from nonuronide polysaccharides. Both the type and the extent of segregation are different from those obtained with ethanol.

As will be shown in Chapters XIX and XX, a somewhat different procedure is used in the commercial production of pectins where the

[383] E. Jameson, F. N. Taylor, and C. P. Wilson, U. S. Pat. 1,497,884 (1924).

quantity of ethanol (or isopropyl alcohol) applied must be kept at a minimum in order to avoid excessive cost of manufacture.

Copper salts have also been used for the preparation of pectinic acids. While there are some claims that precipitation with copper is preferable to aluminum, there is not enough published information available to substantiate this claim. Usually a 1% solution of copper sulfate penta-hydrate is applied after the pH of the pectinic acid solution has been adjusted to about 2.0. Only a comparatively small amount of copper sulfate solution is needed to precipitate the pectinic acid. A difficulty with the use of copper and of other metal salts is their removal from the pectin precipitate. The presence of even traces of copper will have a definite undesirable effect when such pectins are used in various food products. We shall return to this point in Chapter XIX.

5. Purification of Dry Preparations by Extraction

Components of pectinic acid preparations such as sugars, fruit acids, and certain ash constituents, may often be efficiently removed by extraction of the finely powdered dry pectinic acid with acidified ethanol. An ethanol concentration of about 80% containing 0.05 N hydrochloric acid is suitable for this purpose. The 80% ethanol is preferred to higher concentrations because the admixed nonpectic materials will dissolve more easily in this mixture, and yet hydration of the solid pectinic acids will not occur. The same procedure may be used for the removal of aluminum or copper when these were used for the precipitation of the pectinic acid. The use of hot acid-containing solvents is undesirable because of the chemical changes which this might cause in the pectinic acids.

The extraction, even in the cold, should be performed as rapidly as possible. In the laboratory it is advisable to apply at least 50 cc. of solvent for every gram of pectinic acid. The mixture is vigorously shaken or stirred, and then centrifuged or filtered; this procedure is repeated until the solvent fails to extract any more admixed materials from the sample. The pectinic acid is then treated with 95% ethanol until all the hydrochloric acid is removed, rinsed with an ethanol–ether mixture and finally with ether, and quickly dried at room temperatures below 60°C. or by rubbing in a mortar.

V. PREPARATION OF LOW-ESTER (LOW-METHOXYL) PECTINS (PECTINIC ACIDS)

The low-ester pectinic acids contain 3 to 7% methoxyl and show some peculiar properties. During the past decade considerable interest has developed in this group of compounds and therefore present knowledge concerning their preparation will be summarized below. This field is now being rapidly developed and improvements in the preparation and use of low-ester pectins are likely to become known by the time this text is printed.

Although pectinic acids of low average degrees of esterification undoubtedly occur in nature, it is customary to prepare the low-ester pectins by the partial deesterification of pectinic acids of more than 7% methoxyl content. The reason for this preference is that low-ester pectins occurring in nature seem to show some undesirable properties, perhaps indicating low average molecular sizes, undesirable degrees of heterogeneity, or both. There are three essentially different methods for the preparation of low-ester pectins. The deesterification might be performed: (a) *in situ*, prior to extraction of the pectinic acid, (b) during extraction, or (c) after the pectinic acid is extracted and separated from the residual plant tissue.

1. Partial Deesterification Prior to Extraction

Partial deesterification can be accomplished by the use of alkali (in the water phase), by the use of alkali contained in a solvent which will not hydrate and dissolve the pectic compounds, or by treatment with a gas or gaseous mixture which performs the same function as alkali. In addition, partial deesterification can be accomplished by the use of enzymes[384] naturally present in some raw materials used, such as citrus peel, for instance.

There are some objections which apply to all these methods. Since the demethylating reagent is in contact with the tissue particles, it penetrates the latter gradually. This results in a time differential in the action, or, to put it differently, the extent of demethylation in the outer layers of the particles will be more advanced than in the inside layers. The result will be a more heterogeneous preparation (with regard to ester content) than when solutions of pectinic acids are demethylated as under (c). Heterogeneity in low-ester pectins is of great importance on account of the calcium requirements of these compounds in the formation of low-sugar jellies. For this reason the use of *in situ* deesterification with alkali is not recommended where exact information is sought. The situation might be changed once we have better methods for the isolation and characterization of different fractions of pectinic acid mixtures. Work toward this end is now in progress at several laboratories.

Owens, McCready, and Maclay[384] described an apparently more suitable method in which the enzyme naturally present in the tissue is used for

[384] H. S. Owens, R. M. McCready, and W. D. Maclay, *Ind. Eng. Chem.*, **36**, 936 (1944).

the deesterification. Of course, this method is only applicable where the demethylating enzyme (pectin-methylesterase, see Chapter XIV) is present in the tissue used. The essence of this *in situ* deesterification in the case of citrus peel is as follows.

A slurry is prepared from ground citrus peel and water (1:3). Then 0.5 N sodium hydroxide is added with constant and vigorous stirring until the desired pH (around 8) is reached. This pH is maintained by the addition of alkali until the required degree of deesterification has been attained. This is calculated on the basis of a previous experiment in which the total ester content of the pectinic acids in the citrus peel has been ascertained. After the desired demethylation has been reached, the pH is dropped to about 3 to 4 by the addition of sulfur dioxide or sulfuric acid. Then 0.1% sodium hexametaphosphate (on the basis of the peel used) is added, the pH is readjusted to 3 to 4, and the slurry is boiled for 10 to 15 minutes. Thereupon the pectin extract is filtered, cooled, and precipitated with ethanol or in any other manner described below.

There is some uncertainty concerning the enzymic nature of this method because, according to the results of Owens, McCready, and Maclay, no deesterification occurs at pH 6, a somewhat remarkable observation in view of the pH optimum of the pectin-methylesterase of citrus peel.[385] It is noteworthy that deesterification also occurs with apple pomace, which according to some observations,[386] does not contain the required pectin-methylesterase. However, the method has been rather extensively used in research work and has therefore been described.

A recent article by Ward, Swenson, and Owens[387] confirmed the suspected high heterogeneity (with regard to methyl ester content) in low-ester pectins prepared by this method.

2. Partial Deesterification during Extraction

It is more than likely that some degree of deesterification will occur during the extraction of pectinic acids from plant tissue by almost any method. Since it is commonly known that prolonged heating with strong acid causes other undesirable changes in addition to deesterification, either dilute acid at high temperatures and a short period of heating or strong acid at low temperatures and a prolonged period of treatment is applied. Methods of the latter type were used before the discovery of low-ester pectins for the purpose of increasing the setting time (see Chapter XXII) of pectins[388] or in order to render them precipitable by calcium.[389]

[385] L. R. MacDonnell, E. F. Jansen, and H. Lineweaver, *Arch. Biochem.*, **6**, 389 (1945).

[386] Z. I. Kertesz, *Plant Physiol.*, **18**, 308 (1943).

[387] W. H. Ward, H. A. Swenson, and H. S. Owens, *J. Phys. & Colloid Chem.*, **51**, 1137 (1947).

Olsen and Stuewer[390] described a procedure for the preparation of low-ester pectins, at low temperatures and high acidity, directly from the raw material.

The starting material (citrus peel or apple pomace) is mixed with hydrochloric acid barely sufficient to moisten the tissue but concentrated enough to give a pH of about 0.7. This mixture is kept at 40°C. and samples are removed at various times for the determination of the progress of solubilization (extraction) and deesterification. When these processes have advanced to the desired point, the pH is raised to about 3 and the pectinic acid extracted. Polyphosphates may be used as in the procedure given in Section 1. The treatment with strong acid will also hydrolyze a considerable proportion of the hemicelluloses occurring in the tissue and will thus increase the purity of the pectinic acid, which can be precipitated with ethanol or other means from the clarified extract.

Baker and Goodwin[391] recommend treatment of the pomace or albedo at 50°C. with an acid solution of pH 1.25.

The heating should last for about 36 hours in order to obtain the best yield of a pectin with about 5% methoxyl content. These authors used six times as much acid solution as the weight of the dry pomace before the preliminary purification.[392] At the end of the acid treatment the pH is raised to 4.5 and the extract is pressed from the pomace. Starch is removed by treatment with an amylase (see above), and the extract is filtered clear with a filter aid and transformed into a solid preparation by any of the customary methods.

3. Deesterification of Isolated Pectinic Acids

For research purposes the most suitable method for the preparation of low-ester pectins is the deesterification of pectinic acid preparations dissolved in water. The methods described below are equally applicable to extracts made from plant tissues and purified in some manner discussed previously and to solutions (dispersions) prepared from solid pectinic acids and pectins. These latter might be also purified beforehand. Deesterification in solution can be controlled easily and can be assumed to progress fairly uniformly throughout the experimental mixture.

There are three methods for the deesterification of pectinic acids in solution: (a) by the use of acids, (b) by the use of alkali, and (c) by the use of enzymes.[393] The comparative merits of these three methods are

[388] W. C. Platt, U. S. Pat. 2,020,572 (1929).
[389] L. Wallerstein, U. S. Pat. 2,008,999 (1935).
[390] A. G. Olsen and R. Stuewer, U. S. Pat. 2,132,577 (1938).
[391] G. L. Baker and M. W. Goodwin, U. S. Pat. 2,133,273 (1938).
[392] G. L. Baker, Univ. Delaware Agr. Expt. Sta., Bull. No. 204 (1936).
[393] G. L. Baker in E. M. Mrak and G. F. Stewart, Advances in Food Research. Vol. I, Academic Press, New York, 1948, p. 395.

not entirely clear at this time, although the differences in the low-ester pectins obtained by the use of various agents are well recognized.

(a) Acid Deesterification

As noted above, there are several patents dealing with the acid deesterification of pectinic acids. Some of these were granted before the principle of low-ester pectins and the formation of low-sugar jellies with their aid was clearly understood. Some of these procedures aimed at altering the "setting time" (Chapter XXII) of pectins and have been used since 1929 to produce pectins of the slow-set type. Others described acid deesterification methods applied to render pectins precipitable with acids or calcium.[394] Hills, White, and Baker[395] described the following method for acid deesterification.

An approximately 3% solution of pectin is adjusted to pH 0.3 with hydrochloric acid and is then kept at 50°C. The mixture first thickens and then sets to a gel. This latter reaction is claimed to occur at a time when the methoxyl content reaches 6% but considerable variation in this respect might be expected. When the desired extent of deesterification is attained, ethanol is added to the mixture and it is washed free from acid. Thereafter it is partially neutralized with dilute alkali, washed again with ethanol, pressed out, and dried.

Here again, as in the extraction of pectinic acids from plant tissues, no generally applicable formula can be supplied. The aim will be to accomplish deesterification with as little degradation of the macromolecular structure as possible. It is now the general opinion that this can best be accomplished at high acidities as used above, but at temperatures below 50°C. The velocity of deesterification increases as the pH of the solution is lowered. According to Speiser, Eddy, and Hills,[396] the rate constants fall on a straight line when plotted against hydrochloric acid concentrations. Therefore the velocity of deesterification will depend directly neither on the hydrogen ion activity nor on the ionic strength. Merrill and Weeks[397] confirmed this observation.

The advantage of acid deesterification is the simultanous extensive hydrolysis of the admixed hemicelluloses. The removal of these "ballast materials" does not occur during alkaline or enzymic deesterification and for this reason the preparation obtained after the acid treatment will in many instances show a higher polygalacturonide content than before. The outstanding drawback of acid deesterification is its slowness. At

[394] L. Wallerstein, U. S. Pat. 2,008,999 (1945).
[395] C. H. Hills, J. W. White, and G. L. Baker, Proc. Inst. Food Technol., 1942, 47.
[396] R. Speiser, C. R. Eddy, and C. H. Hills, J. Phys. Chem., 49, 563 (1945).
[397] R. C. Merrill and M. Weeks, J. Phys. Chem., 50, 75 (1946).

pH 0.3 the deesterification proceeds at less than 1/100 of the rate of alkaline saponification at pH 11 at the same temperature.

The partial deesterification of isolated pectinic acids may also be accomplished without dissolving the preparation in water. Joseph[398] recommends the use of an acid or an acid gas dissolved in an organic solvent, usually ethanol. The same objections given above for the deesterification of pectinic acids before extraction also apply here. Such treatment is apt to give highly heterogeneous preparations from the standpoint of methyl ester content.

(b) Alkaline Deesterification

The fact that treatment with alkali gradually removes the ester groups from pectin has been observed by Fellenberg[359] and many other investigators. Before the development of the field of low-ester pectins Mnookin[399] used partial demethylation with alkali.

The chief difficulty with alkaline deesterification is that the removal of ester groups is in most cases accompanied by degradation. This effect of alkali on pectic substances is well appreciated and is dealt with in some detail in Chapter VII, Section 2. Baier and Wilson[400] and Wilson[401] recommend careful demethylation at pH values below 8.5 and at temperatures not exceeding 35°C. Under such conditions the saponification proceeds slowly but apparently without much degradation. McDowell[402] described a partially alkali-demethylated pectinic acid which retained its colloidal properties. This author used cold alkali and recommended reaction temperatures near the freezing point.

During recent years several thorough studies on this subject have been reported. McCready, Owens, and Maclay[403] deesterified commercial citrus pectin at pH values of 10, 11, and 12 and at temperatures ranging from 5 to 35°C. At pH 10 the temperature coefficient of the rate of degradation was higher than that for the rate of deesterification and for this reason 15°C. is recommended for the reaction. In order to obtain useful preparations, a temperature of 5°C. or below must be used at pH values of 11 to 12. Deesterification with ammonium hydroxide is slower than with sodium hydroxide but the former offers advantages because low-ash preparations may be prepared more readily when ammonium hydroxide is used. The ammonium chloride formed from the latter during acidification is much

[398] G. H. Joseph, U. S. Pat. 2,273,527 (1942).
[399] N. M. Mnookin, U. S. Pat. 2,253,389 (1941).
[400] W. E. Baier and C. W. Wilson, Ind. Eng. Chem., 33, 287 (1941).
[401] C. W. Wilson, U. S. Pat. 2,132,065 (1938); reissue No. 21,077 (1939).
[402] R. H. McDowell, British Pats. 541,528 (1942) and 555,842 (1943).
[403] R. M. McCready, H. S. Owens, and W. D. Maclay, Food Ind., 16, 794, 906 (1944).

more soluble in the ethanol–water mixtures frequently used for the precipitated low-ester pectin than is sodium chloride.

An important consideration in this connection is the activation of deesterification by certain ions, especially cations. Lineweaver,[404] Lineweaver and McCready,[405] and McCready, Owens, and Maclay[403] investigated this subject and found that, by the use of certain cations such as
magnesium or calcium, the rate of saponification can be increased several
fold. The choice of a salt will depend on the experimental conditions and
especially on the contemplated methods for the separation of the low-
ester pectin. As an example a somewhat modified procedure given by
Lineweaver and McCready is quoted.

1 liter of a solution containing 2% citrus pectin of about 10% methoxyl content
is adjusted to pH 10.5 with 0.5 N sodium hydroxide and maintained at this point
by continuous addition of alkali with vigorous stirring until half of the methyl
ester is removed. The time required without activation for this reaction is
80–85 minutes. The addition of 5.8 g. of sodium chloride reduces the time to
45–50 minutes, while with the addition of 3.7 g. of anhydrous calcium chloride
50% deesterification is reached in 18–20 minutes. After deesterification the mixture
is adjusted to pH 5, mixed with an equal volume of 95% ethanol, allowed to
stand for one hour, and is then thoroughly stirred and pressed out in a hydraulic
press. The precipitate is suspended in ethanol or, in the case where calcium chloride is used, in acid ethanol. This procedure is repeated until the salts are
removed. Thereupon the precipitate is again pressed out and dried under
vacuum below 50°C.

An interesting method of deesterification is that in which ammonia is
used.[406] The demethylation might be performed on a dry pectin powder
suspended in ethanol containing ammonia or the dry powder might be
exposed in a desiccator to the vapors from ammonium hydroxide containing over 28% ammonium hydroxide or using ammonia gas under pressure. However, under these conditions deesterification is not the only reaction which occurs. The extent of esterification decreases but at the
same time some type of compound different from an ammonium salt and
suspected to be an amide, —$COONH_4$, is formed. The nitrogen is retained
by the pectinic acid even after treatments which would produce free carboxyl groups as in the purification of pectinic acids deesterified with
sodium or potassium hydroxide. Thus, the resulting compound has methyl
ester, carboxyl, and amide groups and cannot be called a low-ester pectin
in the sense used in this discussion.

[404] H. Lineweaver, *J. Am. Chem. Soc.*, **67**, 1292 (1945).
[405] H. Lineweaver and R. M. McCready, U. S. Pat. 2,386,323 (1945).
[406] G. H. Joseph, A. H. Kieser, and E. F. Bryant, *Food Tech.*, **3**, 85 (1949).

(c) Enzymic Deesterification

We have already discussed in Section (a) the *in situ* deesterification of pectinic acids by the esterase which occurs in some raw materials. Paul and Grandseigne,[407] Mehlitz,[408] and Hills, White, and Baker have studied the use of pectin-methylesterase for the deesterification of prepared pectinic acids. The method is rapid and easy to control. It appears, however, that low-ester pectins prepared by the use of enzymes show certain undesirable characteristics (such as a critical calcium concentration) when used in gel preparations. The reasons for the differences between low-ester pectins prepared by the enzymic method and by other methods are not well understood. It has been suggested that the enzyme removes the ester groups one by one progressing along the polygalacturonic acid chain while alkali and acid are assumed to remove these at random.

An important consideration is the purity of the enzyme used. The pectin-methylesterase should be in such a condition that the removal of the enzyme from the pectinic acid should not be difficult once the deesterification is accomplished. The preparations used should also be free from enzymes which hydrolyze pectinic acids. (For a discussion of pectin-methylesterase, its sources, preparation, and properties, see Chapters XIV and XV.)

Pectin-methylesterase occurs in tomatoes, eggplant, tobacco stems, alfalfa, citrus peel, and a number of other plants. Of the various sources, the pectin-methylesterase of tomatoes[409] has been used most frequently. Unfortunately, tomatoes seem to contain pectin-hydrolyzing enzymes[410-412] and therefore special precautions must be taken to perform the enzymic deesterification under conditions which will prevent the former enzymes from degrading the pectinic acid.

Tests in the writer's laboratory on some commercial pectin-methylesterases indicated the complete absence of hydrolytic activity at pH 3.5 even during prolonged exposure. Such enzymes now are used in the treatment of pectinic acids to change the setting time (see Chapter XXII).

Hills, White, and Baker[395] and several other investigators have used tomato pectin-methylesterase for the preparation of low-ester pectins.

[407] R. Paul and R. H. Grandseigne, *Bull. assoc. chim. sucr. dist.*, 46, 233 (1929); *C. A.*, 24, 2511 (1930).

[408] A. Mehlitz, *Biochem. Z.*, 256, 145 (1932).

[409] Z. I. Kertesz, *Food Research*, 3, 481 (1938).

[410] L. R. MacDonnell, E. F. Jansen, and H. Lineweaver, *Arch. Biochem.*, 6, 389 (1945).

[411] H. H. Mottern and C. H. Hills, *Ind. Eng. Chem.*, 38, 1153 (1946).

[412] R. J. McColloch, J. C. Moyer, and Z. I. Kertesz, *Arch. Biochem.*, 10, 479 (1046).

Mottern and Hills[411] reported the results of a detailed study of the preparation of low-ester pectin from apple pomace. The procedure for the enzymic deesterification given below is based on the work of these authors.

The pectin extract or solution is filtered until it is clear and an aliquot is assayed for pectin methyl ester by any of the procedures given in Chapter VIII, Section VI-2. The solution is adjusted to pH 6.5 and 40° C. and a tomato enzyme extract is added. Such extracts when prepared by methods now recommended[412] (see Chapter XIV, Section IV-2) contain the sodium chloride required for the activation[413] of the pectin-methylesterase. If removal of starch or dextrins is desired, Clarase or preferably ptyalin (filtered human saliva) is also added at this time. The pH of 6.5 is now maintained by continuous addition of 0.5 N sodium hydroxide from a buret. The solution is vigorously stirred during all these operations. The reaction is allowed to proceed until the required degree of deesterification (as calculated from the determination of the ester content) is attained. The mixture is then immediately acidified with 1:5 sulfuric acid to pH 4.0 and heated to 90°C. for 3 minutes. Thereupon the mixture is cooled and precipitated with an equal volume of 95% ethanol and is pressed on a hydraulic press. The precipitate is disintegrated in 95% ethanol, allowed to stand for about 2 hours, pressed again, and dried.

The advantage of precipitation at pH 4.0 consists in the partial neutralization of the acid groups, resulting in preparations which are quite easily dispersible in water. Mottern and Hills used polyphosphates in the extraction of the pectin from the apple pomace and cite the beneficial action of such compounds from the standpoints of extraction, dispersibility, and calcium tolerance. For further information on these points the reader is referred to the original article and to various other chapters of this volume.

4. Precipitation of "Low-Ester" Pectins with Acids or Calcium

It has been known for some time that, as the ester content of a pectinic acid is lowered, it eventually becomes precipitable with acid. McCready, Owens, Shepherd, and Maclay[414] recently investigated the effects of various factors on the precipitability of low-ester pectinic acids with acid and found that—depending on the method of deesterification used—some 90% or more of the pectinic acid could be recovered by this method at methoxyl contents of 4 to 7%. The concentration of the pectinic acid in the solution does not make much difference. The pH required for the precipitation of more than 90% of the pectinic acid is in most cases below 2.0. These authors recommend the following procedure.

[413] H. Lineweaver and G. A. Ballou, *Arch. Biochem.*, 6, 373 (1945).

[414] R. M. McCready, H. S. Owens, A. D. Shepherd, and W. D. Maclay, *Ind. Eng. Chem.*, 38, 1254 (1946).

The solution containing the low-ester pectin is adjusted to about 15°C. and mixed with sufficient acid to give a pH of about 1.3. The mixture is stirred slowly to break up lumps and to insure complete precipitation. The free liquid is then drained off in some manner and the mixture pressed in a hydraulic press to a solids content of 30%. The excess acid (and any agents used for deesterification) are removed by suspending the precipitate in about the original volume of water and, after stirring, the wash water is drained off and the precipitate pressed as described above. This procedure is repeated several times, then the pressed precipitate is dried at 66°C. under vacuum and ground to pass a 100-mesh screen.

A pectinic acid with a sufficient proportion of free carboxyl groups may also be precipitated from solution by the soluble salts of alkaline earth metals such as calcium chloride. This procedure was described some time ago by Wallerstein[389] before the low-ester pectins were generally known. Wallerstein recommended partial deesterification (which we have already discussed), followed by precipitation of the pectinic acid with calcium at pH values in the range of 4 to 7. This method, useful at times for the separation of the low-ester pectinic acid, may be summarized as follows.

The pH of the solution containing the low-ester pectin is adjusted to about 4, after which a 0.1 M solution of calcium chloride is added dropwise and with vigorous stirring. The addition of the calcium salt is continued until the clear part of the liquid does not give a precipitate with calcium chloride. The acid calcium pectinate which is formed is separated by filtration or by other means, pressed free from the mother liquor, and washed with 80% ethanol containing 0.05 N hydrochloric acid until free from calcium. It is then washed with 95% ethanol until free from hydrochloric acid, pressed out, and dried. Or the precipitate obtained is separated, pressed, dried and ground, and extracted with 95% ethanol containing 0.05% hydrochloric acid ("dry extraction"). It is then washed again with 95% ethanol and dried. For laboratory preparations the removal of calcium prior to drying is more suitable.

The advantages of these methods of precipitation consist mostly in that with acid or calcium the pectinic acids are almost quantitatively precipitated, while many other compounds present in the solution are not removed from the liquid phase. Many such admixed materials would be precipitated by ethanol and thus find their way into the solid preparation of low-ester pectin. Acid and calcium precipitation are also much cheaper than the use of ethanol.

VI. PREPARATION OF PECTIC ACIDS

Pectic acids ("polygalacturonic acids of colloidal nature") differ from pectinic acids by the absence of the methyl ester groups. Pectic acid seems to occur as such or in the form of salts in some plant tissues, especially in those which are lignified. It is rather difficult to extract the pectic acid from such sources and for this reason it is usually prepared by the demethylation of pectinic acids. If a plant tissue containing pectinic acids is extracted with an alkaline solvent of pectic materials, deesterification accompanies the extraction.

The complete demethylation of pectinic acids into pectic acids may be performed by the use of acid, alkali, or enzymes. Inasmuch as all these procedures have advantages as well as disadvantages, they will be discussed briefly below. The reader is also referred to the discussions of partial deesterification on the pages immediately preceding this section.

1. Complete Demethylation with Acid

While the removal of the ester groups by acid shows certain advantages over removal by alkali, there is no procedure as yet which would accomplish complete deesterification by acid without extensive degradation. One of the difficulties is that acid deesterification proceeds rather slowly. After removal of about two-thirds of the ester groups, the rate of the reaction seems to decrease considerably and, as a result, prolonged treatment is required for complete deesterification. It is believed, however, that the advantages of acid deesterification (discussed on previous pages in connection with the low-ester pectins) will maintain interest in this problem and will lead to improvements which will make the preparation of pectic acid by acid treatment feasible. Hills and Speiser[415] prepared a pectic acid of high purity by prolonged treatment with acid. The extent of degradation suffered by this sample during acid treatment for more than 800 hours is not known.

2. Complete Demethylation with Alkali

The treatment of pectinic acids for the purpose of demethylation and preparation of compounds of diminishing methyl ester contents was applied by many of the early workers but it was Fellenberg[416] who first knowingly prepared low-ester pectins and pectic acids by progressive saponification. He treated a pectinic acid solution with 0.5 to 1.0% sodium hydroxide for 2 minutes and then acidified the solution with hydrochloric acid, whereby gellike pectic acid was immediately precipitated. The pectic acid was dispersed in a large volume of boiling water and reprecipitated with ethanol containing hydrochloric acid. Fellenberg also reported the fact, which was often overlooked later, that pectic acid of sufficient purity may be dissolved in hot water, but that the presence of

[415] C. H. Hills and R. Speiser, *Science*, 103, 166 (1946).
[416] T. Fellenberg, *Biochem. Z.*, 85, 118 (1918).

electrolytes causes a marked decrease in the solubility. The pectic acid of Fellenberg was a white powder and was entirely void of methyl ester groups.

Mottern and Cole[417] used saponification with alkali in ethanol for the preparation of pectic acid. The procedure described by these authors is as follows.

100 g. of powdered pectinic acid is suspended in 250 cc. of 50% ethanol in a mixing bowl with a capacity of 2 liters. To obtain adequate mixing the use of stirrers of the egg-beater type is recommended. When the pectinic acid is thoroughly wetted by the ethanol and is uniformly dispersed, 10 g. of calcium chloride dissolved in 250 cc. of water is added. The addition of the calcium salt controls the swelling of the pectic acid particles so that a grainy precipitate can be obtained; this will facilitate washing and filtration. It is now also known that the calcium ions will enhance the progress of the saponification, a point which we have discussed above. Then 250 cc. of 3 N sodium hydroxide solution is added with constant stirring and this is continued until a smooth pasty mass is obtained. This is permitted to stand for 15 minutes, after which the clear supernatant liquid is decanted. The mixture is neutralized with hydrochloric acid and sufficient excess is added to give a concentration of about 1.5% acid; the mixture is then boiled for 10 minutes with vigorous stirring. The pectic acid is filtered off with suction and washed with cold water containing 10 cc. of concentrated hydrochloric acid per liter. The hydrochloric acid is removed with 50% ethanol, the precipitate is washed with 95% ethanol and finally with ether, and dried in a mortar. This method will give a pectic acid of fair purity; it is, however, rather drastic and may degrade the macromolecule to a certain extent.

In recent years many attempts were made to prepare pectic acid by the use of alkali under carefully controlled conditions. We have noted that Baier and Wilson[400] and Wilson[401] recommend demethylation at a pH not exceeding 8.5 and at a temperature not appreciably above 35°C. The pectic acid preparations obtained in such a manner appear to retain their colloidal properties much better than when a great excess of alkali is used. A further improvement in this direction is the method of McDowell[402] where temperatures close to the freezing point are used in combination with carefully controlled alkalinization. Reference should also be made to some observations of McCready, Owens, and Maclay[403] on alkaline deesterification, discussed previously in connection with low-ester pectins.

Although the removal of the last traces of ash, araban, and galactan from pectic acids is very difficult, pectic acids of a high degree of purity have been prepared by numerous workers. Practically all procedures used

[417] H. H. Mottern and H. L. Cole, *J. Am. Chem. Soc.*, 61, 2701 (1939).

treatments with an excess of alkali and thus partial degradation may be assumed to have occurred in most cases. As an example of the preparation of pure pectic acid, the procedure used by Hirst and Jones[418] will be given.

The already purified pectinic acid preparation is dissolved in normal sodium hydroxide and the pectic acid precipitated from a dilute solution (0.5%) by the addition of hydrochloric acid. It is then washed with water, reprecipitated four times from the calculated quantity of dilute sodium hydroxide solution, and finally converted to the sodium salt and again made up to a 0.5% solution. Addition of calcium chloride solution will precipitate calcium pectate, which is first freed from calcium chloride by washing with hot water and then decomposed by trituration with ethanol containing 0.05 N hydrochloric acid. The resulting pectic acid is once more dissolved in sodium hydroxide solution and precipitated with acid. The pectic acid is washed with water, followed by ethanol, and dried at 100°C. under a vacuum.

The equivalent weight of such a preparation made by Hirst and Jones was 185, very close to the theoretical value of 176. Its uronic anhydride (polygalacturonic acid) content, as determined by the carbon dioxide method, was 96.7%. Hirst[419] later noted a pectic acid prepared by precipitation with copper and calcium and then further purified by methods as yet unpublished. The equivalent weight of this pectic acid, according to Hirst, was close to 176. It showed upon hydrolysis no other substances than D-galacturonic acid.

On the basis of the information in the literature the following procedure is recommended for the laboratory preparation of pectic acid.

Pectinic acid is first purified to the maximum extent and a solution containing it is treated at room temperature with small increments of dilute sodium hydroxide solution until pH 8.5 is reached. This pH is maintained with further additions of alkali until it does not change during a 15-minute period. The solution is then treated with a sufficient excess of hydrochloric acid to precipitate the pectic acid. This latter is separated by filtration, washed with little hot water and redispersed in water with the addition of enough alkali to bring the precipitate into solution. It is then purified by letting it pass through the ion exchange columns described in Section III-c of this Chapter. The de-ashed solution is precipitated with a double volume of 95% ethanol containing 0.01% hydrochloric acid, is filtered off, washed free from acid with ethanol, rinsed with a mixture of ethanol and ether followed by ether, and dried in the usual manner.

[418] E. L. Hirst and J. K. N. Jones, *J. Chem. Soc.*, 1939, 454.
[419] E. L. Hirst, *J. Chem. Soc.*, 1942, 70.

3. Complete Demethylation with Enzymes

Under suitable conditions the enzymic demethylation of pectinic acids proceeds rapidly until about two-thirds of the ester groups are removed. Afterward the reaction slows down a great deal and complete demethylation, to the writer's knowledge, has not been attained as yet by this method. Hills, White, and Baker[395] reported a value of 1.8% for the residual methoxyl content of pectinic acid deesterified by prolonged enzyme action. Hills, Ogg, and Speiser[420] more recently succeeded in reducing the residual methoxyl content to 0.70% in the case of pectinic acids which have not been previously demethylated by acids. Jansen, Waisbrot, and Rietz[421] found that alfalfa pectin-methylesterase will deesterify pectinic acids to 0.5% methoxyl content. Apparently acid and alkaline demethylation hydrolyze off some of the methyl ester groups which, for reasons as yet unknown, resist the action of the enzyme.

Thus, treatment of pectinic acids by pectin-methylesterase is not suitable at this time for the production of pectic acid completely free from ester groups. Judging from the experience with enzyme-produced, low-ester pectins, this method would provide the safest way for the deesterification of pectinic acids without causing other changes. Perhaps after an explanation has been found for the apparently unreasonable resistance of the small proportion of methyl ester groups, a method will be developed to overcome this obstacle and to effect complete demethylation by the enzyme.

[420] C. H. Hills, C. L. Ogg, and R. Speiser, *Ind. Eng. Chem., Anal. Ed.*, **17**, 507 (1945).
[421] E. F. Jansen, S. W. Waisbrot, and E. Rietz, *Ind .Eng. Chem., Anal. Ed.*, **16**, 523 (1944).

CHAPTER VII

Some Properties of Pectic Substances

The pectic substances show almost endless variation in properties and behavior. Since our methods of definition and characterization are so limited, it is not surprising that contradictions are numerous in the literature concerning the behavior of pectic substances under different conditions. The divergence, however, is even more disheartening in the interpretation of these observations. This is due mainly to the uncrystallized state of our knowledge of the structure of pectic substances, which leaves too great latitude for personal interpretation.

The titles under which the various observations are classified here are not claimed to adhere to any given system: common usage is the directing thought in the grouping. At times several different types of observations are manifestations of the same property and are closely interrelated. This is emphasized whenever the fact stands out clearly enough to make such discussions more than mere speculation.

I. ACIDIC PROPERTIES OF PECTIC SUBSTANCES

The pectic substances of the cell wall appear to be neutral in nature. Just how the pectinic acids which are undoubtedly present in the protopectin of the middle lamella are neutralized is not clear at this time. Some investigators believe that they may be completely esterified while many others, including Ehrlich,[422] think that the pectinic acids are neutralized by salt formation. Because of our lack of exact knowledge concerning the nature of protopectin (see Chapter III, Section III) it is hardly profitable at this time to speculate on this point.

Pectic substances showing definite acidic properties also occur in plants, dissolved in the plant sap, or at least in a soluble condition. The sap of certain plants, especially fruits, contains (in solution) pectinic acids of various degrees of esterification. Pectic acid, in the form of acid salts, may be found in certain woody tissues. We shall deal below

---

[422] F. Ehrlich, *Cellulosechemie*, **11**, 140 (1930).

with the acidic properties of pectic and pectinic acids which have either been found in plant tissues as such or have been obtained by processes of solubilization such as were discussed in Chapter VI.

1. Acidic Character of Pectic Acids

The acidic properties of both pectic and pectinic acids were well recognized by some of the early workers, such as Frémy[423] and Chodnew.[424] The reason for the great variations in the extent of acidity observed by these authors became clear only upon the discovery that some of the acid groups in pectinic acids occur in the free form while others occur in the form of the methyl ester.[425] Pectic acid with the maximum of free carboxyl groups was prepared by some of the earliest investigators of pectin chemistry. The acidic groups of pectic acids have been used throughout the past one hundred years to supply information concerning the combining and equivalent weights of these compounds. Chodnew prepared calcium, barium, lead, silver, and copper pectates for the purpose of determining their stoichiometric properties. Olsen,[426] who recently recalculated these results, found that they indicate an equivalent weight for pectic acid between 206 and 207. As will be shown below, these values are in remarkable agreement with some of those reported in recent years.

Of course, the calculated equivalent weights for the pectic acid molecule will depend on whether the molecule is assumed to contain any units other than anhydrogalacturonic acid. The opinion that pectic acids are composed solely of galacturonic acid residues has already been emphasized. The calculated composition of a series of pectic and pectinic acids is shown in Table 14. On the basis of the assumption that the pectic acid molecule contains an average of at least 100 anhydrogalacturonic acid residues, the calculated equivalent weight is 176. Since any property of a pectic acid preparation is an average derived from often widely varying components, it is likely that in most preparations some polygalacturonic acids occur which are of smaller than average molecular size—and therefore of larger equivalent weight. In assuming the value of 176, furthermore, complete freedom from nongalacturonide constituents must be presupposed. Similarly, it must be assumed that all carboxyl groups are free and not engaged in the formation of methyl esters or salts or in any other manner. Any of these factors would result in an apparent increase in the observed equivalent weight.

[423] E. Frémy, J. pharm. chim., 26, 368 (1840).
[424] A. Chodnew, Ann., 51, 355 (1840).
[425] T. Fellenberg, Mitt. Lebensm. Hyg., 4, 122 (1913).
[426] A. G. Olsen, Science, 86, 486 (1937).

Ahmann and Hooker[427] determined the equivalent weight of a pectic acid from apple pectin and found a value of 195. This is quite close to the theoretical value considering the obviously impure state of their pectic acid. These authors found a number of "kinks" in the electrometric titration curves and concluded that pectic acid contains eight carboxyl groups, an observation which is of purely historical interest at present. Sloep[428] found the equivalent weight of a pectic acid to be 205. Bonner[429]

TABLE 14

CALCULATED MOLECULAR WEIGHTS AND COMPOSITIONS OF POLYGALACTURONIC ACIDS AND DERIVATIVES

No. of units	Mol. wt.	Equiv. wt.	Mol. wt. of (neutral) Ca pectate	Ca in Ca pectate, %	Mol. wt. of (neutral) methyl ester	Methoxyl in (neutral) methyl ester, %
(1)[a]	(194)	(194)	(213)	(9.4)	(208)	(14.9)
2	370	185	408	9.8	398	15.6
5	898	180	993	10.1	968	16.0
10	1,778	178	1,968	10.2	1,918	16.2
25	4,418	177	4,893	10.2	4,768	16.3
50	8,818	176	9,768	10.2	9,518	16.3
100	17,618	176	19,518	10.3	19,018	16.3
500	88,018	176	97,518	10.3	95,018	16.3
1000	176,018	176	195,018	10.3	190,018	16.3

[a] Galacturonic acid.

estimated the equivalent weight of purified pectic acid from its sodium salt and obtained an average value of 206. He also determined the equivalent weight by titration and found values from 201 to 207. Loconti[430] in the writer's laboratory obtained the value of 204 for purified citrus pectic acid. All these values should be considered in view of the difficulties observed during the removal of the last traces of ash constituents, and during purification of pectic compounds in general.

Hills and Speiser[431] recently described a pectinic acid of high molecular weight which showed an average residue weight of 178. This sample, apparently still of high molecular weight, was prepared by prolonged acid treatment. Hirst and Jones[432] found the value of 185. The lowest value yet reached was reported by Hirst,[433] who noted that the theoretical

[427] C. F. Ahmann and H. D. Hooker, *Univ. Missouri Agr. Expt. Sta.*, Research Bull. No. 77 (1925).
[428] A. C. Sloep, *Dissertation*, Univ. of Delft, 1928.
[429] J. Bonner, *Proc. Roy. Acad. Amsterdam*, **38**, 346 (1935).
[430] J. D. Loconti, *Master's Thesis*, Cornell Univ., 1940.
[431] C. H. Hills and R. Speiser, *Science*, **103**, 166 (1946).
[432] E. L. Hirst and J. K. N. Jones, *J. Chem. Soc.*, **1939**, 454.
[433] E. L. Hirst, *J. Chem. Soc.*, **1942**, 70.

value of 176 had been obtained for a very pure pectic acid composed entirely of galacturonic acid residues. The procedure by which this pectic acid was obtained was not described in sufficient detail. The possibility exists that harsh methods caused considerable loss of colloidal properties of the pectic acid but there is no information available on this point.

These results substantiate the view that pectic acids are polygalacturonic acids and do not contain other constituent units.

Phenolphthalein indicator was used by most investigators in these studies. Bonner[429] states that, judging from the shape of the titration curves, the use of this indicator is warranted. Olsen, Stuewer, Fehlberg, and Beach[434] recommended titration to pH 7.5 and Hinton[435] recommends an indicator mixture which shows an end point at pH 7.5.

The titration curve for pectic acid resembles that of a monobasic acid and has only one inflection point. The pK values calculated show a steady increase from 2.77 to 4.18 near the end of the titration (pH 5.37).

2. Acidic Character and Methyl Ester Content of Pectinic Acids

The acidic character of pectinic acids is a much more complicated affair than that of the pectic acids. The pectinic acids occur with a great variety of average degrees of methylation and, in addition, with a great variety of qualitative and quantitative distribution patterns. Salt formation is again an additional factor. It has been suggested that the methyl ester content of a pectinic acid preparation should be expressed on the basis of its polygalacturonic acid content. One may go one step further and express the free acidity as a proportion of the total carboxyl groups. Such an expression has been recommended by Hinton,[435] who used the ratio of combined to total acid groups, and more recently by Speiser, Eddy, and Hills[436] and Hills and Speiser,[431] who used such ratios for the characterization of pectin preparations. We shall return to the matter of characterization in Chapter VIII.

In the formation of pectinates the proportion of the free carboxyl groups determines the proportion of cation with which the pectinic acid combines. Table 15 shows calculated values for the "combining weights" of pectinic acids containing 100 anhydrogalacturonic acid units with different degrees of esterification.

[434] A. G. Olsen, R. F. Stuewer, E. R. Fehlberg, and N. M. Beach, *Ind. Eng. Chem.*, 31, 1015 (1939).
[435] C. L. Hinton, *Fruit Pectins, Their Chemical Behavior and Jellying Properties*, Chem. Publishing Co., New York. 1940.
[436] R. Speiser, C. R. Eddy, and C. H. Hills, *J. Phys. Chem.*, 49, 563 (1945).

TABLE 15

CALCULATED COMPOSITION, MOLECULAR AND COMBINING WEIGHTS OF PECTINIC ACIDS
OF DIFFERENT DEGREES OF METHYLATION

Ratio: Free COOH / Total COOH	Methoxyl, %	Molecular weight	Combining weight
1.0[a]	0	17,618	176
0.8	3.3	17,898	224
0.6	6.5	18,178	303
0.4	9.8	18,458	462
0.2	13.0	18,738	937
0.0[b]	16.3	19,018	—

[a] Pectic acid.
[b] Such completely methylated pectinic acids are not known to occur in nature.

Ahmann and Hooker[427] and Edson[437] reported titration curves for apple and citrus pectinic acids. Speiser, Hills, and Eddy[438] recently made a thorough study of the acidic behavior of pectinic acids, and obtained titration curves by the method of Briggs[439] for a number of different preparations. Some of these curves are shown in Figure 12. In subsequent calculations pH 7.5 was used as the point of equivalence, although these authors state that the true equivalence actually occurs at a pH somewhat higher than this value. The true equivalence point appears to be a complicated function depending on the concentration of carboxyl groups and dissociation constants, but these authors say that the error in using pH 7.5 is small. The behavior of a pectinic acid resembles qualitatively that of a monobasic acid in that it has only one buffer range. Similar conclusions were drawn by Deuel[440] from a study of potentiometric titration behavior of pectinic acids. This resemblance to monobasic acids might be only superficial because the titration curves are more like those of some polybasic acids such as citric or saccharic acids, for instance, whose buffer ranges are so close together that they overlap and produce only one composite buffer range. At a given pH, an increase in the concentration of the pectinic acid will cause an increase in the degree of dissociation. Hinton[441] observed the same effect for orange, currant, and strawberry pectinic acids. No noticeable differences occur in the acid behavior of pectinic acids of widely different molecular weights; the acid behavior of these acids cannot be treated in a definitive way by existing theoretical methods of approach because the carboxyl groups are apparently not free from

[437] L. E. Edson, *Dissertation*, Columbia Univ., 1928.
[438] R. Speiser, C. H. Hills, and C. R. Eddy, *J. Phys. Chem.*, 49, 328 (1945).
[439] D. R. Briggs, *J. Phys. Chem.*, 39, 867 (1934).
[440] H. Deuel, *Mitt. Lebensm. Hyg.*, 34, 41 (1943)
[441] C. L. Hinton, *Biochem. J.*, 34, 1211 (1940).

mutual interactions. Speiser, Hills, and Eddy found, however, that empirically the logarithm of the titration constant for a pectinic acid is a linear function of the logarithm of the degree of neutralization and is also a linear function of the square root of the concentration of ionized carboxyls. Furthermore, for the latter case, the experimental lines for

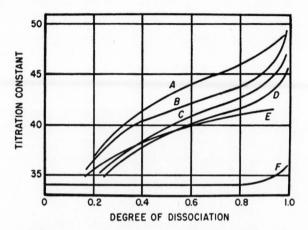

Fig. 12. Titration curves for pectinic acids and galacturonic acid (adapted from Speiser, Hills, and Eddy).

Curves *A*, *B* and *E* represent a pectinic acid with 10% esterification in concentrations of 1, 2 and 4%, respectively. Curve *C* was obtained with pectinic acid of 33% esterification in a 1.98% solution. Curve *D* shows results obtained on a pectinic acid of 44% esterification in a 1.94% solution. Curve *F* represents galacturonic acid. The titration constant was plotted in terms of its negative logarithm. Degree of dissociation represents the ratio of free carboxyl groups to the total concentration of carboxyl groups in equivalents per liter.

all pectinic acid samples extrapolate to the same intercept for zero degree of dissociation. It is of interest to note that arabic and polyacrylic acids have been found to behave similarly.[438,442]

We shall return later to the importance of the proportion of free acid groups in pectinic acids from the standpoint of jelly making and to the determination of free and esterified carboxyl groups (Chapter VIII).

II. BEHAVIOR OF PECTIC SUBSTANCES TOWARD ACIDS AND BASES

In the early days of pectin chemistry many investigators sought clues to the composition and structure of the pectic substances by treating

[442] W. Kern, *Z. physik. Chem.*, **A181, 249 (1938)**.

them with acid or alkali and isolating the decomposition products. Little information was gained by these experiments. On the contrary, an immense number of partial decomposition products were found, isolated, and duly described and this contributed greatly to the general confusion.

With our present knowledge of the components of pectinic and pectic acids, we may again employ treatment with acid and alkali to elucidate the structure of these compounds; and, indeed, some interesting observations have been made through this line of approach.

1. Effect of Acids

Protopectin is solubilized by acid treatment even when cold dilute acid is used. Just how this process of solubilization occurs is as yet unknown. Various schools of thought claim that the acid acts through removal of bivalent cations, by hydrolyzing the cellulose–pectinic acid complex, or by simple hydrolysis of a large and thus water-insoluble molecule. The various arguments for and against these hypotheses were presented in Chapter III, Section III.

Temporary exposure to cold dilute acids does not alter pectinic or pectic acids. In fact, acids of considerable strength are well tolerated in the cold. The first noticeable effect of acid treatment is the removal of ester groups. This reaction proceeds very slowly; Hinton,[435] for instance, found that keeping a pectinic acid in 0.05 N hydrochloric acid at 20°C. caused removal of only 0.02% of the latter groups in one hour and of 4% in 14 days. Treatments with strong acid in the cold or with even dilute acid at temperatures over 50°C. cause progressive demethylation at a much faster rate.

It is now generally assumed that demethylation is one of the first changes occurring in pectinic acids as the result of acid treatment. As more concentrated acids, prolonged treatment, and especially acids at higher temperatures are used, noticeable degradation of the pectinic acid occurs. Since the structure of the pectinic acid macromolecule is not known, it is difficult to say just what these changes are. If the pectinic acid macromolecule is constructed with some linkages different from 1,4 glycosidic connections between anhydrogalacturonic acid residues, it is likely that some of these will suffer fissure before the 1,4 glycosidic connections are extensively severed. However, there are many workers who believe that the first effect of acid on the polygalacturonic acid structure is the hydrolysis of the 1,4 linkages. This question is difficult to decide at this time because our major tool for the determination of fissures is the measurement of increases in the reducing power. The increase in this property to indicate hydrolysis of any extent is so small that our present methods are hardly suitable for the detection of such changes. As will be shown in Section III below, this is true because any change in the physical condition of the pectic substance will also alter the reducing power. Hydrolysis of the polygalacturonic acid chains certainly does occur during harsh and prolonged treatment with acid. As the concentration of the acid and the reaction temperatures are raised, decarboxylation and further decomposition of the galacturonic acid which is formed will take place.

The decarboxylation of uronic acids by hot acids attracted much attention ever since Lefèvre and Tollens[443] observed this reaction and developed a method of quantitative estimation based on it (Chapter II). The decarboxylation proceeds slowly in dilute hot acids. Conrad[444] made a thorough study of the conditions influencing the rate of decarboxylation and found that, when a pectinic acid was boiled in 2% sulfuric acid solution, 16 hours were needed for 30% decarboxylation. Even in 5% sulfuric acid only 59% decarboxylation occurred in 16 hours. When uronic acids are boiled in 12% hydrochloric acid the decarboxylation is complete in a few hours.

Pectic acids, again, can withstand prolonged exposure to cold acids of considerable strength. The use of higher acid concentrations and elevated temperatures causes changes similar to those described above for pectinic acids, with the exception of demethylation. Conrad[444] states that calcium pectate is much more resistant to the decarboxylating action of hot acid than are pectinic acids.

2. Effect of Bases

The behavior of bases toward pectic substances is of much interest. Upon the addition of an excess of potassium or sodium hydroxide crude protopectin is decomposed. The pectinic acids which either constitute or are a part of protopectin are completely demethylated and eventually become dissolved in the excess alkali. Some insoluble residue consisting at least partly of cellulose will remain. The presence of more than traces of alkaline earth elements may change this reaction inasmuch as repeated treatments with alkali are required to dissolve the calcium pectate which is formed since this can be accomplished only after removal of the calcium ion.[445] When plant tissue or crude protopectin preparations are treated with an excess of calcium or barium hydroxide, hard and difficultly soluble masses are formed. In order to dissolve these in alkali they must first be treated with an acid to remove the calcium or barium. The

[443] K. U. Lefèvre and B. Tollens, *Ber.*, **40**, 4513 (1907).
[444] C. M. Conrad, *J. Am. Chem. Soc.*, **53**, 1999 (1931).
[445] J. D. Loconti and Z. I. Kertesz, *Food Research*, **6**, 499 (1941).

cellulose which is apparently a component of protopectin will again remain as a residue.

Upon the careful addition of potassium or sodium hydroxide to a dilute solution of pectinic acid the free acid groups are engaged in salt formation, giving first acid, and then neutral pectinates. Of course, the solution will not become alkaline until this latter point is reached and further alkali is then added. As soon as the reaction of the solution becomes alkaline, demethylation commences. This consumes the alkali and the pH of the solution soon drops. The demethylation occurs with great velocity and the bulk of the ester groups may be removed in a few minutes at room temperature. Under certain conditions the saponification of the methyl ester proceeds with stoichiometric regularity and may be used for the controlled partial or almost complete demethylation of the pectinic acid. The consumption of alkali, therefore, can also be used as a method of estimating the ester content of pectinic acids. Detailed information on the deesterification of pectinic acids by alkali was given in Chapter VI.

Demethylation may not be the only reason why a pectinic acid consumes alkali. There are many observations in the literature that the consumption of alkali increases as the excess of alkali or its concentration, or the duration of treatment, or the temperature of the reaction is raised. It is difficult to evaluate clearly the significance of these reports because of the doubt cast upon the validity of most methoxyl values reported in the past for pectinic acids (see Chapter VIII). It will suffice to say that the main difficulty is that the calculated "theoretical" quantity of alkali required for the demethylation depends either directly or indirectly on the Zeisel method of determination, which when used for pectic material prepared with ethanol, isopropanol, or acetone may give values several per cent higher than the true methoxyl contents. For this reason, it would be fruitless to discuss the values reported by various workers before this retention of solvents became known. As a general illustration some observations of Hinton[435] on an apple pectinic acid may be quoted. These results, given in Table 16, have been recalculated for the original solution used by Hinton because he expressed the alkali consumption on the basis of the diminishing calcium pectate yields (Chapter VIII). The solution used in this experiment contained 0.34% pectinic acid (expressed as calcium pectate) and the concentration of the alkali in the mixture was 0.1 N. Even at room temperature the alkali consumption increases throughout the experimental period. The effect is greatly enhanced by increasing the reaction temperature to 37°C. It is evident that, after the rapid attainment of the initial value of about 13, some secondary consumption of the alkali proceeds at a velocity strongly dependent on the temperature. Hinton states that loss of colloidality is clearly observable upon the precipitation of pectic acid or calcium pectate from the solutions showing the increased alkali consumption. Similar results were obtained by Hinton for strawberry, gooseberry, and plum pectinic acids. The rate of "secondary"

TABLE 16

ALKALI CONSUMPTION OF PECTINIC ACID SOLUTION (ADAPTED FROM HINTON)

Time	NaOH consumed, g./100 g. original pectinic acid (expressed as Ca pectate)		
	16–17°C.	26°C.	37°C.
5 minutes............	12.5	12.9	13.5
30 minutes...........	12.9	13.0	13.5
3 hours..............	13.0	13.6	14.5
23 hours.............	13.7	14.8	17.8
6 days..............	16.2	18.9	21.1

alkali consumption was not always the same for the various cases, but the effect of higher temperatures was (without exception) to increase the alkali consumption considerably. In the temperature range used the proportion apparently consumed for the demethylation during the first five minutes was almost independent of the reaction temperature. Variations in the pectinic acid concentration did not markedly change the phenomenon, while diminishing the alkali concentration to 0.04 N only reduced the rate of the secondary reaction but did not alter its character.

Hills, Ogg, and Speiser,[446] in a study of the methyl ester content of low-ester pectins, observed the same slow secondary increase in alkali consumption at 25°C. in reaction mixtures containing dilute sodium hydroxide. The "theoretical" 100% consumption value, correctly known in this case, was passed within 30 minutes by the mixtures containing the higher concentration (about 0.05 N) of alkali. The various pectinic acids studied behaved quite differently and in two hours yielded values up to 115% of the calculated amounts of alkali. An excessive use of alkali was also observed by these authors when other reagents, such as alkaline salts, organic bases, or carbonate buffers, were used. We may once again conclude that it is certain that such "excessive" consumption of alkali exists and that an investigation of this behavior of pectinic acids would be of great interest and importance. Meanwhile it may be suggested that perhaps the "secondary" consumption of alkali might be caused by reactions leading to the degradation of the superstructure of the polygalacturonide units. The suggestion has been made by Loconti[430] that some unusually strong anhydride or lactone linkages are responsible for the

[446] C. H. Hills, C. L. Ogg, and R. Speiser, *Ind. Eng. Chem., Anal. Ed.,* **17,** 507 (1945).

commonly observed low equivalent weights of pectic acids. It may be assumed that these linkages are attacked in an alkaline solution, causing degradation of the molecular structure and changes of the colloidal properties accompanied by consumption of additional alkali. The fact that treatment with alkali has such a degrading effect is well known. Molecular weight determinations made by Schneider and Fritschi[447] on nitropectins prepared with or without preliminary saponification with alkali also indicated molecular weights about 25% lower for the alkali-treated samples.

Gel formation upon the addition of a strong alkali to solutions of pectinic acids or pectates or upon the addition of a weak alkali to more concentrated solutions of pectinic acids or pectates has often been observed. The formation of such gels can be reversible or irreversible. When sodium or potassium hydroxide is used, the gel dissolves in an excess of the alkali or even upon dilution with water. On the other hand, calcium and barium hydroxide cause—under similar conditions—the formation of hard gels which do not dissolve in an excess of the reagent. When using dilute solutions of calcium or barium hydroxide, there is a temporary formation of a gel, followed by flocculation and precipitation. These reactions obviously depend on the different solubility properties of various pectates.

An interesting observation reported by Ehrlich,[448] but doubtlessly observed by many earlier workers, is the temporary yellow coloration of any solution of pectic materials upon the addition of an excess of strong alkali. After the appearance of the yellow color the mixture becomes turbid. Shortly afterward the yellow color disappears for the most part and a precipitate may occur in the solution. Ehrlich claimed that the precipitate is the sodium salt of "tetragalacturonic acid" but it is now clear that it is probably a sodium pectate of degraded pectic acid.

Recent observations in the writer's laboratory indicate that the disappearance of the yellow color from alkaline solutions of pectic compounds is much slower in the absence of oxygen.[449] Ascorbic and alginic acids also give this color with alkali. At the present time there is considerable interest in the relationship between the appearance of the yellow color and the occurrence of specific structural configurations.[450,451]

The effect of various salts on the pectic substances will be dealt with later in the discussion of solubility and precipitability characteristics (see Section XIII).

[447] G. Schneider and U. Fritschi, *Ber.*, **69**, 2537 (1936).
[448] F. Ehrlich, *Z. angew. Chem.*, **40**, 1312 (1927).
[449] R. J. McColloch and A. Rosen, *unpublished work*, 1948.
[450] N. Clauson-Kaas and F. Limborg, *Acta Chem. Scand.*, **1**, 619 (1947).
[451] L. N. Owen, S. Peat, and J. K. N. Jones, *J. Chem. Soc.*, 1941, 339.

III. REDUCING POWER OF PECTIC SUBSTANCES

The ability to reduce alkaline copper solutions and many other reagents has often been used for the characterization and estimation of carbohydrates. This property, shown by all monosaccharides and uronic acids, depends on the presence of aldehyde or ketone groups. We have already discussed the reducing power of galacturonic acid (see Chapter II), the monomer building unit of the basic structure of pectic substances.

In comparison with the reducing power of the monosaccharides, that of polysaccharides and pectic substances appears to be much more complicated. According to our present ideas most polysaccharides are composed of chains of monomer units. In the formation of such polymers usually all the reducing aldehyde groups with the exception of those on the terminal units are engaged in linking the component monomers. If a polymer is built as a straight chain, it has only one free reducing group, as shown by the formula on page 49. If the polymer is branched, several reducing groups may exist at the ends of various branch chains. For a homogeneous sample of a linear polymer the measurement of the proportion of free reducing groups gives a direct measure of the chain length, while for a mixture of polymers of different sizes a number-average value is obtained.

The reducing power of pectic substances is still a rather confused subject; at this time further progress seems to be blocked by methodological difficulties. As shown in Chapter V, the pectic substances are heterogeneous mixtures and it would therefore be difficult to arrive at results other than average values. Furthermore, due to the presence of carboxyl groups, the pectic substances show solubility properties quite different from those of the common polysaccharides; this factor influences the reducing power as determined by several reagents. Finally, our knowledge of the structure of pectic polyuronides is still insufficient at this time to warrant the definite assumption of a homogeneous linear structure in pectic substances.

When the reducing power is expressed in the manner used here, the average number of component anhydrogalacturonic acid units in the polygalacturonic acid structure is obviously equal to:

$$\frac{100}{\text{per cent of reducing power}}$$

This of course assumes nonbranching polygalacturonic acid chains. In this case it is also assumed that the reducing power of an aldehyde group at the end of a polygalacturonic acid chain is the same as in the galacturonic acid monomer. This calculation is valid, furthermore, only if the polygalacturonic acid chains contain anhydrogalacturonic acid units exlusively and no galactose, sorbose, and rhamnose molecules, as believed by some authorities. If it is proved that the polygalacturonic acid chains are branched, reducing power values will have little meaning as an indication of the average degree of polymerization. In the latter case both the number and the location of the branchings will profoundly affect the relation between free aldehyde groups and chain lengths.

TABLE 17

REDUCING POWER OF APPLE AND CITRUS PECTINIC ACID PREPARATIONS AND PECTIC ACID AND CALCIUM PECTATE PREPARED THEREFROM (FROM LOCONTI AND KERTESZ)

| | Reducing power as per cent anhydrogalacturonic acid on polygalacturonic acid basis | | | | | |
| | Citrus | | | Apple | | |
Method used	Pectinic acid	Pectic acid	Calcium pectate	Pectinic acid	Pectic acid	Calcium pectate
Alkaline copper methods						
1. Richardson et al.	3.23	0.95	0.94	3.00	—	—
2. Somogyi-Shaffer-Hartman	7.52	—	—	—	—	—
Hypoiodite	2.93^a	2.35^a	1.31^a	2.69^a	2.18^a	—
Potassium ferricyanide	6.80	3.73	1.72	4.47	2.74	1.89
Dinitrosalicylic acid	2.53	—	2.63	3.12	—	2.83

^{a} Minimum values.

After this introduction it is not surprising that the information in the literature on the reducing power of pectic substances is indeed confusing. Norman[452] remarks in his excellent book, that "pectin is completely non-reducing." Similarly, Baier and Wilson[453] state that "pectates are not readily oxidized" and Ehrlich[454] claims that one of his pectinic acids ("gelpectolic acid") shows "not even traces of a reducing power against Fehling solution." Deschreider and Driesche[455] found no reducing ability in purified pectins. On the other hand, Baur and Link[456] determined the reducing power of apple and citrus pectinic acids by the hypoiodide method[457] and found values of 2.6 and 3.8%, respectively (expressed as per cent of galacturonic acid in the preparations). Ehrlich[458] also measured, in the same manner, the reducing power of many of his other preparations and obtained values ranging from 4 to 9%. Hinton[435] attaches definite significance to the reducing value of pectinic acids and reports for orange pectin of high purity reducing power of 2.5–3.5% and values ranging from 2.9 to 27% for laboratory preparations.

[452] A. G. Norman, The Biochemistry of Cellulose, the Polyuronides, Lignin, etc. Clarendon Press, Oxford, 1937.
[453] W. E. Baier and C. W. Wilson, Ind. Eng. Chem., 33, 287 (1941).
[454] F. Ehrlich, Festschrift zur Feier des 25 jahrigen Bestehens der Techn. Hochschule Breslau. June, 1935, p. 129.
[455] A. R. Deschreider and S. van Den Driesche, Food Manuf., Feb., 1948, p. 77.
[456] L. Baur and K. P. Link, J. Biol. Chem., 109, 293 (1935).
[457] R. Willstätter and G. Schudel, Ber., 51, 780 (1918).
[458] F. Ehrlich, Emzymologia, 3, 185 (1937); etc.

Owing to this confusion and to the lack of comprehensive reports on this topic in the literature, it seems desirable to record here in some detail some observations made in the writer's laboratory.[459] The results reported in Table 17 were obtained on two samples of pectinic acids purified by precipitation with 70% ethanol. The pectic acid was prepared by careful demethylation with alkali and the calcium pectate by the Poore modification of the Carré and Haynes methods (see Chapter VIII), using the same pectinic acids as starting materials.

1. Alkaline Copper Methods

The Bertrand,[460] the Munson and Walker,[461] and other similar methods which involve removal by filtration of the produced cuprous oxide were found to be practically useless because of the difficulties experienced in filtering the solutions. In addition to cuprous oxide, copper pectates (and pectinates?) are also formed in these solutions, which usually makes filtration difficult and often impossible. Most of these difficulties disappear in partially degraded or decomposed pectic substances.

Of the alkaline copper methods in which no filtration is required, the Shaffer and Somogyi[462] modification of the Shaffer and Hartman[463] procedure was tried first. Results in the range of 6 to 8.5% reducing power (expressed as per cent of anhydrogalacturonic acid on the polygalacturonic acid basis throughout this discussion) were consistently obtained. The average of 7.52% shown for a citrus pectinic acid in Table 17 is almost twice as high as the value obtained by other methods for this preparation. The alkaline copper method which gave the most consistent results was that of Richardson, Higginbotham, and Farrow[464] in which a correction is made for the amount of cuprous oxide dissolved in the reagent. This method, discussed previously in Chapter II, gave regular and reproducible results when amounts of pectinic acid ranging from 20 to 120 mg. were used in the reaction mixtures.

A further important point in favor of this method is that the reducing values did not change when the heating time was varied from the standard of 3 hours to 1–5 hours. The results obtained with two preparations of pectinic acids are shown in Table 17.

[459] J. D. Loconti and Z. I. Kertesz, *unpublished work*, 1940.

[460] G. Bertrand, *Bull. soc. chim.*, 35, 1285 (1906). Apparently this method was first proposed by H. Schwarz, *Ann.*, 84, 84 (1852).

[461] L. S. Munson and R. H. Walker, *J. Am. Chem. Soc.*, 28, 663 (1906); 34, 202 (1912).

[462] P. A. Shaffer and M. Somogyi, *J. Biol. Chem.*, 100, 695 (1933).

[463] P. A. Shaffer and A. F. Hartman, *J. Biol. Chem.*, 45, 349 (1921).

[464] W. A. Richardson, R. S. Higginbotham, and F. D. Farrow, *J. Textile Inst.*, 27, 131 (1936).

Unfortunately, our confidence in these results was shaken by the reducing power values obtained for pectic acid and calcium pectate. These were considerably below the figures found for the reducing power of the pectinic acids from which they were prepared. This "loss" in reducing power was not due to fractionation because the low values could be essentially duplicated when the saponification to pectic acid and subsequent precipitation as calcium pectate were accomplished in a small volume and the whole mixture of precipitate and supernatant liquid was used for the determination. The "mother liquor" from the precipitation of calcium pectate was also tested separately for reducing power but showed little or none. When sodium citrate was added to the reaction mixtures in order to keep the pectic substances in solution, the reducing power increased several fold but without sufficient regularity to warrant further discussion. The reproducibility of the reducing power values obtained for calcium pectate samples prepared from any given pectinic acid preparation was noteworthy. One might think that the precipitability of a pectic acid as calcium pectate is a function of the molecular size and that it is for this reason that these fairly consistent average reducing power values were obtained. It is conceivable that calcium pectates would precipitate only in the case of large molecules which in turn would show low reducing power. This, however, is not the situation. When calcium pectate preparations were made from a sample of pectic acid undergoing enzymic hydrolysis, a series of different calcium pectate samples was obtained which showed up to 11.5% reducing power expressed in the above manner. Such behavior is not surprising considering the great changes which may be observed in the appearance of the calcium pectate precipitates from a pectic substance undergoing degradation or decomposition.

In one case the calcium pectate precipitate was homogenized after precipitation. The reducing power of this latter sample was 2.11% as compared with the average value of 1.65% obtained without homogenization.

2. Hypoiodite Method

This method, described in its modern form by Willstätter and Schudel,[457] has been found very useful for simpler carbohydrates, including uronic acids. Inasmuch as difficulties were encountered in the use of alkaline copper solutions with pectinic acids due to the formation of precipitates, it was hoped that this method would give reliable results. It was previously applied to pectinic acids by a number of investigators, such as Ehrlich,[458] Baur and Link,[456] Hinton,[435] and the writer.[465] However, when increased amounts of iodine or pectinic acid were used in the oxidiz-

[465] Z. I. Kertesz, *J. Am. Chem. Soc.*, **61**, 2544 (1939).

ing mixture a temporary dark coloration often appeared and the apparent reducing power increased considerably. Rather consistent results were obtained when the pectinic acid and the iodine excess were both kept low, but even in these ranges there was no satisfactory proportionality between the amount of pectinic acid used in a test and the reducing power. For this reason even the values obtained under these latter conditions have been considered unreliable. The dark coloration was not due to metal contamination or starch, and it occurred in commercial and laboratory preparations (from apples, lemon peel, bean pods, beet pulp, etc.) of pectinic acids, as well as after enzymic hydrolysis of the pectinic acids. Some of the minimum values obtained by this method are included in Table 17. Determinations in the presence of a large excess of iodine or large proportions of pectinic acid or both indicated the possible existence of a second level of oxidation, usually in the neighborhood of 12% reducing power.

3. Potassium Ferricyanide Method

The Hagedorn and Jensen[466] method was also tried in this work. As shown in Table 17, the results were definitely higher than those obtained by all other methods except that of Somogyi, Shaffer, and Hartman. Again, the results obtained for pectic acids prepared from the pectinic acids were lower and those for calcium pectates were the lowest.

4. Dinitrosalicylic Acid Method

This method, described by Sumner,[467] gave consistent results and did not show the difference, observed with most other procedures, between the reducing powers of pectinic acid and calcium pectate. The results obtained for purified citrus and apple pectinic acids are shown in Table 17. This procedure was considered to be the most promising method for the determination of the reducing power of pectinic acids.

The reducing power of the purified pectinic acids shown in Table 17 is in the range of 2.5 to 7.5%. This corresponds to 13 to 40 units in the polygalacturonic acid and indicates comparatively low molecular weights (2500 to 8000), far from the 20,000 to 300,000 indicated by the results obtained by other means by Schneider and co-workers and others (see Chapter III). A certain degree of disharmony between molecular weight determinations by different methods is not surprising. Even when discrepancies due to differences in homogeneity are allowed for, there seems to be basic disagreement between the molecular weight values calculated

---

[466] H. C. Hagedorn and B. N. Jensen, *Biochem. Z.,* **135,** 46 (1923).
[467] J. B. Sumner, *J. Biol. Chem.,* **47,** 4 (1921). J. B. Sumner and S. F. Howell, *J. Biol. Chem.,* **108,** 51 (1935).

for pectic substances from their reducing power and those calculated from other physical properties. It would indeed appear that many of the reducing groups in the polygalacturonic acid are not engaged in the 1,4 linkages in such a manner as to block them. This, in turn, might indicate branching molecules or a type of loose association which does not resist the treatments used in the customary methods of determining the reducing power. The values obtained for pectic acid and calcium pectate were in most cases definitely lower than those obtained for the parent pectinic acid. In these insoluble compounds some of the reducing groups may be blocked or imbedded and are thus unable to exert any action. This condition is indicated by the fact that homogenization increases the apparent reducing power of calcium pectate. Hirst, Plant, and Wilkinson[468] suggest that in starch the micellar structure may mask some of the reducing groups. Of course, if this "blocking" occurs at all in the pectic substances, it will only accentuate the disharmony between the molecular weights calculated from the observed reducing power values and those from physical measurements.

It is clear from this discussion that our knowledge of the factors which govern the reducing power of pectic substances is as yet insufficient. Hinton[435] has shown some relationship between the jellying power and reducing power of pectins, but doubts whether a constant relationship exists between these two properties in different preparations. Recently Lampitt, Money, Judge, and Urie[469] have stated that the reducing power is of no value for the quantitative determination of pectinic acids.

It might be noted that the reducing power of all pectic substances increases during enzymic hydrolysis. This subject will be discussed later in Chapter XIV. The effect of heat on the reducing power of pectinic acids will be discussed in the following section.

IV. THERMAL DEGRADATION AND AGING OF PECTINIC ACID SOLUTIONS

Solid pectinic acids with less than 10% moisture content change little during long periods of storage at room temperature. Solutions of pectinic acids, however, show a gradual irreversible loss of viscosity which is designated as "aging" or degradation. This reaction will also occur in solutions kept near the freezing point and tests in the writer's laboratory indicate that it takes place even when the solution is kept frozen for longer periods. The reaction velocity is gradually increased as the temperature of the solution is elevated from room temperature.

[468] E. L. Hirst, M. M. T. Plant, and M. D. Wilkinson, *J. Chem. Soc.*, 1932, 2375.
[469] L. H. Lampitt, R. W. Money, B. E. Judge, and A. Urie, *J. Soc. Chem. Ind.*, 66, 121 (1947).

This loss of viscosity is of both theoretical and practical importance. The changes which occur might give information concerning the molecular structure of pectinic acids. In practice the importance of thermal degradation lies in the fact that the pectinic acid solutions are heated in almost all processes of manufacture. Recently some interest in this subject was shown in connection with the use of pectinic acids as blood plasma substitutes (see Chapter XXVIII, Section 1-4). In this case the usefulness of the solution depends on its osmotic efficiency rather than on the high viscosity. Since the latter is at times actually objectionable, means were sought to produce nonviscous solutions of pectinic acids which would have the other beneficial characteristics.

Some of the early investigators, such as Sauer and Sanzenbacher,[470] believed that aging and thermal degradation represent two different phenomena. It is now generally accepted that they are the same reaction or set of reactions occurring at different rates. One point which may have to be taken into consideration in this connection is the reduced solubility of oxygen in heated solutions of pectinic acids as contrasted with cold solutions. The role of such oxygen in the degradation is unknown at present.

The effect of heating can be studied in two different ways. First, the changes which occur in a pectinic acid solution can be observed. Such studies have been made by Sauer and Sanzenbacher,[470] Myers and Baker,[471] the author,[465,472] Hinton,[473] and Merrill and Weeks.[474] A set of such data is shown in Table 18. The second method is to observe the changes on solid preparations made from such heated solution of pectinic acid. The observations made on such an ethanol precipitate[472] are shown in Table 19. The information concerning the effect of various factors on thermal degradation is summarized below.

The drop in viscosity upon heating is the outstanding and most obvious change which occurs. The rate of viscosity loss increases with elevation of the heating temperature and with continued heating. We shall return later to the temperature coefficient of this reaction. The concentration of the solution has little influence on the rate of viscosity loss.[474] The loss of viscosity seems to be more rapid when the pH of the solution of a pectinic acid is either lowered below or is elevated above the usual range of pH 3–4 within which the pH values of most unadjusted

[470] E. Sauer and K. Sanzenbacher, *Kolloid Z.*, **79**, 55 (1937).
[471] P. B. Myers and G. L. Baker, *Univ. Delaware Agr. Expt. Sta.*, Bull. No. 187 (1934).
[472] Z. I. Kertesz, *unpublished data*, 1945.
[473] C. L. Hinton, *Fruit Pectins, Their Chemical Behavior and Jellying Properties.* Chem. Publishing Co., New York, 1940.
[474] R. C Merrill and M. Weeks, *J. Am. Chem. Soc.*, **67**, 2244 (1945).

TABLE 18

EFFECT OF HEATING ON PECTINIC ACID SOLUTIONS

Temperature	Heating time, hours	Specific viscosity (at 30°C.)	$[\alpha]_D^{20}$ (+) [a]	pH	Free acidity,[a,b] %	Methoxyl,[a] %	Reducing power,[a,c] %	Calcium pectate, %	Volume of wet calcium pectate, cc./mg.
80°C.	0	3.38	240°	3.40	25	—	—	0.47	—
	2	3.00	238°	3.39	23	—	—	—	—
	7	1.65	—	3.23	27	—	—	0.44	—
	13	0.70	241°	3.21	27	—	—	0.43	—
	20	—	237°	3.27	27	—	—	0.38	—
	28	0.45	224°	3.18	32	—	—	0.37	—
	32	0.11	239°	3.07	36	—	—	0.32	—
	46	0.07	219°	3.08	39	—	—	—	—
98°C.	0	2.83	250°	3.48	25	10.0	3.21	0.54	2.4
	2	1.14	249°	3.36	25	10.0	3.76	0.53	2.1
	4	0.68	249°	3.38	25	9.9	4.32	0.53	1.8
	6	0.41	240°	3.30	25	9.8	5.58	0.50	1.5
	8	0.30	240°	3.31	27	9.7	6.48	0.50	0.9
	10	0.22	234°	—	27	9.6	7.46	0.48	1.0
	24	0.07	213°	3.29	32	—	13.38	0.39	1.0

[a] Calculated on the basis of the initial pectinic acid content.
[b] As anhydrogalacturonic acid.
[c] As anhydrogalacturonic acid, per cent of original polygalacturonic content.

pectinic acid solutions fall. From the results given by Myers and Baker[471] and Hinton[473] it would seem that the jellying power decreases hand in hand with the viscosity. The effect of temperature appears to

TABLE 19

PROPERTIES OF A PREPARATION MADE BY ETHANOL PRECIPITATION FROM 0.5% PECTINIC ACID SOLUTION HEATED AT pH 3.4 (UNADJUSTED) FOR 8 HOURS AT 98°C.

Property	Pectinic acid	
	Original	Degraded
Approximate yield, %	(100)	72
Specific viscosity (0.25%, 30°C.)	1.62	0.08
Specific optical rotation (0.5% soln.)	+237.00°	+236.2°
Calcium pectate yield, %	107.0	103.2
Methoxyl, %	10.3	10.3
Acidity (as anhydrogalacturonic acid), %	31.1	36.1
pH (0.5% soln.)	3.40	3.18
Reducing power (as anhydrogalacturonic acid, per cent of original polygalacturonic acid content)	3.2	5.8

be much more important than that of pH changes within the range 2–5. Fellenberg[475] and Wendelmuth[476] have assumed that the decrease in viscosity is caused by deesterification. Myers and Baker[471] proved that this is not the case since they found no essential change in the methyl ester content of a solution the specific viscosity of which was reduced from 9.7 to 0.8 by refluxing for 5 hours. Later work of other investigators confirmed this point.[472,477] The methoxyl contents of the solid pectinic acids prepared from heated solutions by the writer (see Table 19) and by Owens, Lotzkar, Merrill, and Peterson[477] were also similar to that of the starting material.

It has been generally observed by all investigators that the acidity of the pectinic acid solution increases during heating. The same increase in acidity is noticeable in the solid degraded pectinic acids mentioned above. The pH value of the solutions drops as the titratable acidity increases. The major significance of these observations consists of the fact that the increase in acidity does not appear to be a result of deesterification. We shall return to this point later.

The limitations of reducing power measurements have been emphasized on preceding pages. The author found[465] that the changes in this

[475] T. Fellenberg, *Biochem. Z.*, **85**, 118 (1918).
[476] G. Wendelmuth, *Kolloid Beihefte*, **19**, 115 (1924).
[477] H. S. Owens, H. Lotzkar, R. C. Merrill, and M. Peterson, *J. Am. Chem. Soc.*, **66**, 1178 (1944).

property during the heating of pectinic acids were negligible or non-existent. Hinton[473] found a slight but rather irregular increase, while Merrill and Weeks[474] state that only a small increase in the reducing power occurs during large changes in the viscosity. In later experiments the author found a small but fairly regular increase in the reducing power of a pectinic acid solution heated to 98°C.

Reference is now made to the statement that reducing groups in the pectic substances may be blocked: if this is the case, a definite increase might be expected merely from the elimination of colloidal properties. Even disregarding this factor, the increase in reducing power as we measure it seems insufficient to account for the loss of viscosity strictly on the basis of severance of 1,4 glycosidic linkages.

Table 18 shows the changes in the optical rotation of a heated pectinic acid solution. The decrease is slow and irregular but surprisingly enough the essentially nonviscous solutions obtained by prolonged heating show only a small drop in optical rotation. Similarly, the degraded pectin preparation characterized in Table 19 shows no significant drop in optical rotation, while the degraded citrus pectin described by Owens, Lotzkar, Merrill, and Peterson[477] shows a slight increase over the mother preparation. Table 18 also shows that the calcium pectate yield obtained from this solution decreased very slowly. The differences in appearance of the calcium pectate precipitates were quite impressive, and an attempt was made to express this effect of thermal degradation in a quantitative manner. Calcium pectate precipitates were allowed to settle in small graduated cylinders overnight. Then the volume taken up by the precipitate was read and divided by the weight of calcium pectate, found upon completion of the determination. These figures, shown in the right hand column of Table 18, indicate the rapidly decreasing "colloidality" of the precipitate. The important point, however, is that even as the volume decreased to 42% of the original value, the weight of the precipitate was still 72% of that in the starting solution. Therefore, the kind of macromolecular structure which will cause a pectic substance to give a calcium pectate precipitate is not identical with the structure which lends pectinic acids their typical viscous and jelly-forming characteristics.

To call the meaning of all these observations obscure is an understatement. Let us see, nevertheless, what possible explanations might be suggested to explain the above facts.

A theory to explain the interrelationship between the changes which occur during thermal degradation and the structure of pectinic acids was suggested by the writer in 1939[465] (see Chap. III). The essence of this hypothesis is that pectinic acids are built from comparatively small units of polygalacturonic acids which are then further combined into the typical colloidal pectinic acid macromolecules. The reducing power and optical rotation are properties of the component units G_m, while the high viscosity and jelly-forming abilities are due to the $(G_m)_n$ superstructure. As suggested before (without conclusive evidence), the "secondary" structure might be built up, in part at least, through the carboxyl units and the latter can be free upon treatment with alkali or upon thermal degradation. Hence, a pectinic acid could be degraded without corresponding increase in the reducing power or, in other words, without hydrolysis of the 1,4 glycosidic linkages in the polygalacturonic acids.

One might, of course, criticize this point of view on the basis that too much emphasis has been put on the reducing power determinations which are admittedly unreliable. However, in addition to the data shown above, Merrill and Weeks also observed the lack of increase in reducing power and the absence of drop in the optical rotation during thermal degradation. These authors note that the activation energies calculated for the viscosity losses indicate the breaking of primary valences in the polygalacturonic acid chains, even if this apparently does not result in an increase in the reducing power and a drop in the optical rotation. On the assumption that the concentration of the pectinic acid seems to have little influence on the rate of degradation, they assume that the degradation is a first-order reaction and quoted Schulz[478] to the effect that the oxidative or hydrolytic degradations of macromolecules are first-order reactions. They assume, furthermore, that pectinic acids degraded at different temperatures will show the same size-distribution pattern. This seems to be quite unlikely. Merrill and Weeks arrive at the conclusion that the thermal degradation constitutes regular fissure of the 1,4 glycosidic bonds rather than destruction of secondary structures or aggregates. No satisfactory explanation is offered by these authors for the behavior of the reducing power values and of the optical rotation.

It would be unreasonable to conclude at this time that the former theory is right while the conclusions of Merrill and Weeks are wrong. Further investigation and, even more, more complete knowledge of the structure of the pectinic acid macromolecule are needed to give a conclusive answer.

V. FORMATION OF REDUCTONES OR REDUCTIC ACID FROM PECTIC SUBSTANCES

It was noted in Chapter II that compounds capable of reducing 2,6-dichlorobenzenoneindophenol indicator are formed when galacturonic

[478] G. U. Schultz, Z. physik. Chem., B51, 127 (1942).

acid is heated. Compounds of this kind, collectively designated as "reductones," have attracted considerable attention in recent years on account of their occurrence in cooked, preserved, and stored food materials, where their presence might interfere with the direct determination of ascorbic acid.[479] Pectic substances, when heated with acid or alkali, give rise to similar decomposition products.

Reichstein and Oppenauer[480] heated pectic acid in a 5% solution of sulfuric acid in an autoclave at 150°C. for 90 minutes. Yellow, crystalline reductic acid $C(OH):C(OH).CO.CH_2.CH_2$ was obtained in 7% yield. The reductic acid had a m.p. of 213–213.5°C. and, by sublimation at 0.2 mm. pressure and 150°C., it could be purified to give white crystals. These authors produced the same compound from xylose and galacturonic acid, but not from glucose, furfural, and several other compounds. Reductic acid closely resembles ascorbic acid but has no antiscorbutic activity. In order to confirm the validity of the above structure, Reichstein and Oppenauer[481] prepared a number of derivatives of reductic acid.

More recently Snow and Zilva[482] prepared reductic acid by heating pectinic acid solutions with different acids. In the presence of 0.25% citric acid no indophenol-reducing substances were formed on heating at 90°C. for 6 hours, and only negligible amounts when heated in 0.5 N sulfuric acid for 3 hours. On heating with stronger acid, increasing quantities of reductone-like substances were formed. The pH values of the mixtures were not given. Snow and Zilva state that the formation of a brown coloration does not accompany the production of these highly reducing compounds as is the case with sugars. This is a somewhat surprising observation in view of the great facility with which galacturonic acid forms yellow and brownish reaction products.[483] The indophenol-reducing material which is formed was thought to be reductic acid; it reacted completely with formaldehyde.[484,485] These authors state that the formation of reductic acid from pectic substances may not be as common in foods as has been suspected.

Reductic acid may be produced from pectin by heating it with 2–9% phosphoric acid in an autoclave at about 150°C.[486] The formation of

[479] F. Wokes, J. G. Organ, J. Duncan, and F. C. Jacoby, *Biochem. J.*, **37**, 695 (1943).
[480] T. Reichstein and R. Oppenauer, *Helv. Chim. Acta*, **16**, 988 (1933); *C. A.*, **28**, 108 (1934).
[481] T. Reichstein and R. Oppenauer, *Helv. Chim. Acta*, **17**, 390 (1934); *C. A.*, **28**, 3718 (1934).
[482] G. A. Snow and S. S. Zilva, *Biochem. J.*, **38**, 458 (1945).
[483] J. L. Seaver and Z. I. Kertesz, *J. Am. Chem. Soc.*, **68**, 2178 (1946).
[484] G. A. Snow and S. S. Zilva, *Biochem. J.*, **37**, 630 (1943).
[485] L. W. Mapson, *J. Soc. Chem. Ind.*, **62**, 223 (1943).
[486] N. V. Noury and van der Lande's Exploitatie Matschappij, Dutch Pat. 56,744 (1944); *C. A.*, **41**, 4169 (1947).

compounds of this nature has also been observed by the writer (and no doubt by others) during the heating of alkaline solutions of pectic acid.

VI. OXIDATIVE DEGRADATION AND DECOMPOSITION OF PECTIC SUBSTANCES

When treated with oxidizing agents, aldohexoses are transformed first to monobasic and then to dibasic acids. Galacturonic acid, which may be regarded as the partial oxidation product of galactose, is easily transformed into the corresponding dicarboxylic acid, mucic acid. The complex reaction which occurs through the action of oxidizing agents or systems on pectic substances will be designated here as "oxidative degradation," although the mechanism of this transformation is far from clear.

Nanji and Chinoy[487] assumed that the methyl ester groups protect pectinic acids from oxidation. A number of oxidizing agents, however, have been shown to affect the pectic substances; of these hydrogen peroxide, ascorbic acid, and a combination of these two reagents are the most noteworthy and will be discussed below. Bromine water, in the presence of calcium carbonate, acts on pectinic acids very slowly.[488] Pallmann and Deuel[489] compared chlorine, bromine, iodine, and chlorine dioxide (ClO_2) in 0.01 M concentrations and found that, while the first two had approximately equal degrading effects on pectinic acid in solution (as measured by viscosity), the latter two agents showed no action whatsoever in 72 hours.

Periodic acid, one of the most widely used oxidizing agents in organic chemistry, causes the degradation and decomposition of starch, cellulose, xylan, etc., and, as expected, also effects rapid degradation of a pectinic acid in solution as shown by a drop in viscosity.[490] Using this reagent, Levene and Kreider[491] found levotartaric acid among the oxidation products of pectic acid. Potassium permanganate in alkaline solution rapidly degrades pectin. Scheele, Svensson, and Rasmusson[492] have used this reaction for the quantitative removal of pectic substances from macerated potatoes. The oxidation of pectinic acids by permanganate in acid solution is much slower. The rate of the reaction (as measured by viscosity changes) in both cases is much lower than with comparable quantities of periodic acid or hydrogen peroxide.

[487] H. R. Nanji and J. J. Chinoy, *Biochem. J.*, 28, 456 (1934).
[488] A. G. Norman and F. W. Norris, *Biochem. J.*, 24, 402 (1930).
[489] H. Pallmann and H. Deuel, *Experientia*, 1, 89 (1945).
[490] H. Deuel, *Helv. Chim. Acta*, 26, 2002 (1943).
[491] P. A. Levene and L. C. Kreider, *Science*, 85, 610 (1937).
[492] C. Scheele, G. Svensson, and J. Rasmusson, *Landw. Versuchsstat.*, 127, 67 (1936).

1. Degradation by Hydrogen Peroxide

The decomposition of organic compounds by peroxides has been extensively studied. Reference may be made here to such reports dealing with the degradation of starch,[493] cellulose and cellulose derivatives,[494] and agar-agar.[495] The fact that hydrogen peroxide degrades pectinic acids in solution has been reported by the author,[496] and by Deuel.[490] Most of the discussion below will be based on the work of the latter author who dealt with this topic extensively.

The action of hydrogen peroxide on a pectinic acid solution is noticeable even at very low concentrations. In the presence of 4 milligram per cent of hydrogen peroxide, the specific viscosity of a 0.2% pectinic acid solution is reduced (at 25°C.) more than 50% in one day. A 10-fold

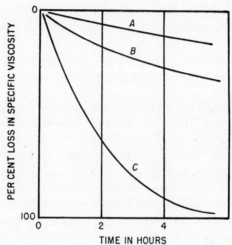

Fig. 13. Loss of viscosity in a pectin solution (pH 6.0) upon the addition of ascorbic acid (A), hydrogen peroxide (B) or both (C).

increase in the peroxide concentration does not increase the rate of the reaction further. Heating, however, increases its velocity. An increase in the titratable acidity accompanies the degradation; the reducing power, as determined by the hypoiodite method, will first increase and then decrease rapidly. When the degradation is performed at elevated temperatures, some reductone-like decomposition products are also formed.

[493] C. Wurster, *Ber.*, **22**, 145 (1889).
[494] J. Jurisch, *Z. angew. Chem.*, **54**, 305 (1941); etc.
[495] A. Fernau, *Biochem. Z.*, **102**, 246 (1920).
[496] Z. I. Kertesz, *Plant Physiol.*, **18**, 308 (1943).

These, as will be shown below, are able to cause degradation of pectinic acids even after the removal of all peroxide. One may assume, therefore, that the degradation, once started, will proceed as an autocatalytic reaction. Deuel states that, upon extensive degradation of pectinic acid, carbon dioxide, formic acid, and formaldehyde occur among the decomposition products. The viscosity changes in a pectinic acid solution in the presence of hydrogen peroxide are shown in Figure 13.

The oxidative degradation of pectinic acids by peroxide is catalyzed by the addition of many compounds. Of these ascorbic acid is of the greatest interest and will be dealt with separately below. Neuberg and Miura[497] observed that the addition of iron salts catalyzed the oxidation by peroxide of many macromolecular substances such as glycogen, starch, and others. The effect on pectinic acids of a combination of peroxide and ferrous acetate (Fenton reagent[498]) was studied by Norman and Norris.[488] The reaction is strongly exothermic and produces degradation products which resemble hemicelluloses. Upon hydrolysis with 1% sulfuric acid, the degraded pectinic acid yields galactose and galacturonic acid, which Norman and Norris thought to have existed in the form of galactose mono- and digalacturonic acids. Deuel found that 1.3 mg. of ferrous sulfate added to a mixture of 100 cc. of 0.25% pectinic acid and 9 mg. of hydrogen peroxide reduced the specific viscosity of the solution by 50% in 5 minutes. The addition of hydroxylamine hydrochloride, hydrazine, and phenylhydrazine activated the degradation by peroxide, while only little acceleration of the reaction could be observed with pyrocatechol, hydroquinone, and pyrogallol. Schardinger enzyme,[499] prepared from milk, also showed some activation. Resorcinol, phloroglucinol, cysteine, glutathione, guaiacol, hemoglobin, maleic acid, dihydroxymaleic acid, tannin, and several other compounds tested by Deuel showed no activation whatsoever.

2. Degradation by Ascorbic Acid

Although ascorbic acid is known for its strongly reducing properties, there are many reports in the literature concerning the oxidative effect of ascorbic acid on organic compounds; of these only the degrading effect on starch[500] and mucin[501] will be mentioned here. As stated previously, when ascorbic acid is added to a solution of pectinic acid, it progressively reduces the viscosity and, in general, causes degradation similar to that

[497] C. Neuberg and S. Miura, *Biochem. Z.*, **36**, 37 (1911).
[498] H. J. H. Fenton, *J. Chem. Soc.*, **65**, 899 (1894).
[499] F. Schardinger, *Chem.-Ztg.*, **28**, 1113 (1908).
[500] G. Woker and I. Antener, *Helv. Chim. Acta*, **20**, 144 (1937).
[501] W. B. van Robertson, M. W. Ropes, and W. Bauer, *Biochem. J.*, **35**, 903 (1941).

observed upon the addition of peroxide. An example of the progress of this reaction is shown in Figure 13. Deuel showed that the velocity of this reaction is increased when larger proportions of ascorbic acid are used, but that a maximum rate is soon reached. This limit may be determined by the amount of oxygen dissolved in the solution. Shaking the solution with air or bubbling air or oxygen through it accelerates the reaction and no degradation occurs if the oxidation of the ascorbic acid itself is prevented, as by the addition of hydrogen sulfide, sulfurous acid, or sulfites, for example. An excess of iodine also prevents the reaction, presumably through the immediate complete oxidation of the ascorbic acid. The reaction is very slow at pH 2 or below but proceeds with increasing velocity as the pH approaches 6.3. Simultaneously with the loss of viscosity the amount of ascorbic acid in the solution also decreases. The degradation (and disappearance of ascorbic acid) proceeds more rapidly as the temperature of the mixture is raised, showing (at pH 3.6) an approximate temperature coefficient (Q_{10}) of 1.2 for the range from 0 to 50°C. It is interesting to note that reductones and reductic acid, as well as isoascorbic acid,[502] can act in the same manner as ascorbic acid. Crystalline dehydroascorbic acid[503] causes much slower degradation than does ascorbic acid itself,[502] but the final (irreversible) oxidation products of ascorbic acid have no detectable effect on pectinic acids.[490]

Ascorbic acid is apparently active only in the presence of a suitable hydrogen acceptor. Methylene blue and hydrogen peroxide greatly accelerate the degradation by ascorbic acid, but methylene blue alone has no effect on the pectinic acid.

Solid pectinic acids prepared[502] after extensive interaction of ascorbic and pectinic acids showed properties similar to those of the heat-degraded pectinic acids discussed on previous pages. While the typical high solution viscosity disappears, the optical rotation does not change essentially. When precipitated with ethanol or transformed into calcium pectate, these samples again behaved like heat-degraded pectinic acids. It would be interesting to know whether this similarity is merely an illusion or whether the degradation in these two cases results in a similar manner of destruction of the macromolecular structure.

3. Degradation by Ascorbic Acid and Hydrogen Peroxide

As shown in Figure 13, the degradation of a pectinic acid in the presence of these two reagents proceeds at a rate far in excess of the additive sum of the rates by the two reagents separately. Deuel[490]

[502] A. Collier, A. Rosen, R. J. McColloch, and Z. I. Kertesz, *unpublished work*, 1947–48.

[503] E. M. Crook and E. J. Morgan, *Biochem. J.*, 38, 10 (1944).

demonstrated that the concentrations of both the peroxide and the ascorbic acid diminish during the reaction. The presence of 10% ethanol in the reaction mixture increases the time required for 50% loss of specific viscosity about 10-fold, and even 1% ethanol shows a definite retarding effect. The reaction is virtually prevented by 50% ethanol. Similarly, the addition of sucrose to the reaction mixture reduces the velocity of the reaction. Low concentrations of sucrose show less effect than ethanol but at a 10% level the inhibition is about equal. Although Deuel assumes that part of the peroxide in these cases of inhibition is utilized for the oxidation of the ethanol or sucrose, recent experiments in the author's laboratory[502] indicate that the major effect of sucrose, at least, is to reduce the solubility of oxygen in the solution.

It is impossible to state at this time whether the action of peroxide and ascorbic acid is through primary disaggregation, hydrolysis, or oxidation, but there is considerable likelihood that all these reactions occur during the degradation. The manner of degradation may be different from that found for other polysaccharides since oxidation on carbon atom 6 causes decarboxylation in this case, rather than the formation of carboxyl groups. Oxidation may also occur on carbon atoms 2 and 3, causing cleavage of the pyranoxide ring structure. The peroxide is active whether directly added to the pectinic acid solution or produced in the solution from other reactions.[490] The activation of peroxide oxidation by Fe^{+++} ions, ascorbic acid, and other agents indicates that the oxidation is not a direct function of the peroxide itself but occurs through the transmission of hydrogen atoms or electrons by inductors or activators some of which may always be present. This is well substantiated by the fact that many metal ions which can change their valence activate the reaction. One may assume, therefore, that this is an induced or coupled, rather than a purely catalytic, reaction, since the ascorbic acid is itself oxidized and eventually "inactivated" during the reaction. Apparently ascorbic acid does not occupy a specific place as an inductor.

Woker and Antener[500] described a similar system which acts on starch as possessing "amylase" activity and indeed there is much similarity between the action of peroxide–ascorbic acid on pectinic acids and the decomposition of the latter by hydrolytic enzymes. The reactions, however, are essentially different. As Deuel showed, the present system is not affected by hydrocyanic and tannic acids and heat, while true enzymic hydrolysis is inhibited or entirely prevented by these.

The idea presents itself that reactions of this nature are perhaps responsible for the transformations of pectic substances which occur in plant tissues, especially ripening fruits.[496] This assumption is quite plausible in view of the fact that peroxides do occur among the decomposition products of ascorbic acid.[504] Experiments conducted with apple tissue proved[505] that treatment with peroxide and ascorbic acid reduces the total proportion of pectic constituents in the tissue and diminishes the amount of insoluble pectic constituents (protopectin). It appears, therefore, that protopectin as well as soluble pectic constituents may undergo the type of degradation discussed above.

VII. FRACTIONATION OF PECTINIC ACIDS

The main purpose of this discussion is not to report all available information, but rather to emphasize once again the need for further work on this subject. The separation of homogeneous samples of pectinic acids would be desirable for several reasons. First of all, it would make possible the determination of the properties and behavior of individual pectinic acids rather than of widely heterogeneous mixtures as is now done (see Chapter V). Second, knowledge of the quantitative distribution of different pectinic acids would make possible much more accurate evaluation of the results obtained for the usual mixtures.

A complex pectinic acid sample composed of a variety of different molecules may be segregated according to many different methods. The molecules may be sorted out according to molecular weight or molecular size—in the latter case the emphasis being on molecular asymmetry. Or they may be fractionated on the basis of the proportion of free and esterified carboxyl groups. As noted in Chapter V, many other causes of heterogeneity—and thus bases for fractionation—might exist but the discussion of these is hardly profitable at the present time.

Some degree of fractionation or rather segregation into two groups is usually effected when pectic substances are purified by precipitation. When organic solvents are used, molecular size appears to be the chief governing factor which determines the line of demarcation. When polyvalent ions are used, the extent of esterification also becomes of much importance. Until about 1935, practically all workers used concentrations of 70 to 80% ethanol and it was assumed that a high ethanol concentration would give pectinic acids of increased purity. Schneider and Bock[506] showed that exactly the opposite is true and that the admixed "ballast" materials may be easily removed by using low concentrations of ethanol for the precipitation. As a result, concentrations in the range of 50 to 60% ethanol are now most commonly used for the precipitation

[504] H. G. Steinman and C. R. Dawson, *J. Am. Chem. Soc.*, **64**, 1212 (1942).
[505] J. H. Griffin and Z. I. Kertesz, *Botan. Gaz.*, **108**, 279 (1946).
[506] G. G. Schneider and H. Bock, *Ber.*, **70**, 1617 (1937).

(see Chapter VI). We still lack comprehensive investigations on the fractionation of pectinic acids with ethanol, although such work may give important information on the approximate size distribution.

Precipitation by metallic salts[507] proceeds in a different manner. Aluminum sulfate, for instance, is claimed to cause precipitation by neutralization of the particle charge of the pectinic acid molecules. Whether this is the case or the precipitation proceeds through salt formation, the proportion of free carboxyl groups plays a dominant role.

Mixtures of pectinic acids may also be segregated according to the particle sizes of the component fractions by passing through a series of standardized membranes. Mehlitz[508] fractionated in such manner a sample of impure liquid apple pectin containing about 10% total solids and 3.44% pectinic acid, determined as calcium pectate. Nitrocellulose membranes with average pore sizes of from over 3.0 to 0.2 microns in diameter were used in this test. Quantities ranging from 1 to 17% were retained by the various membranes but 57% did not pass the one with the smallest (0.2 micron) pore size. Mehlitz also measured the acidity, methoxyl content, and "jelly grade" of these fractions. The acidity figures are rather meaningless because of the presence of such a high proportion of other substances. The "jelly grade" of all fractions were of similar orders of magnitude with the exception of the fraction which passed through only the smallest membrane and which showed no jelly-forming ability. This indicates that the average size of the pectinic acid particles of sufficient magnitude for the formation of the customary pectin-sugar-acid jellies was between 0.6 and 3.0 microns. The average methoxyl content of the last smallest particle size fraction was about 3% as compared with about 9% in all the previous fractions. Mehlitz felt that this confirms the hypothesis of Wendelmuth[476] and others that the "jelly grade" depends on the degree of methylation (Section XV). While this low proportion of methyl ester undoubtedly influences the jelly-forming ability, it is more likely that the low methoxyl content was accompanied by reduced molecular or aggregate size, which in reality governs the jelly-forming properties.

Electrophoresis is likely to provide effective means for separating pectinic acids according to particle charges (see Section XIV). This now fashionable method has been applied for the characterization of the distribution patterns in pectinic acids but apparently has not been used as yet for the preparation of homogeneous or at least more homogeneous samples.

There are a number of reports in the literature dealing with the

[507] E. Jameson, F. N. Taylor, and C. P. Wilson, U. S. Pat. 1,417,884 (1924).
[508] A. Mehlitz, *Kolloid Z.*, **41**, 130 (1927).

fractionation of various pectin derivatives, especially of nitrated pectinic acid, usually designated as nitropectin. Results obtained on fractions of such derivatives should be regarded with considerable suspicion as far as drawing conclusions about the state of affairs in the starting material is concerned. The use of strong acids or of alkaline solutions is involved in the preparation of most derivatives of pectinic and pectic acids which have been used for subsequent fractionation. Such treatments are known to cause various types of degradations. If such a degradation occurred uniformly with all components of the heterogeneous sample of pectinic acid, no great distortion of the distribution picture might be caused. It is more likely, however, that the different pectinic and pectic acids resist such destructive influences to different extents, and therefore the composition of the derivative does not truly reflect conditions as they existed in the starting material.[509]

Although the preparation of such derivatives might involve fractionation as well as nonproportional destruction or alteration of pectinic acids, the results may be regarded as indicative of trends. Schneider and Fritschi[510] fractionated a sample of nitropectin by precipitation from acetone solution with water. The percentage distribution of various fractions as determined by osmotic measurements was given previously in Chapter III, Section I-3.

Speiser and Eddy[511] prepared nitropectins from a series of pectinic acids and determined the molecular weight distribution patterns of a series of precipitates formed upon addition of toluene. Viscosity in acetone solutions was then used for the calculation of the molecular weights. These authors note that the first fraction precipitated did not always contain the pectinic acids of the highest (average) molecular weight as judged by the viscosity. Although results such as those reported by Speiser and Eddy are useful in demonstrating trends in the changes which occur, there is considerable uncertainty whether the differences in the viscosities might have been caused by the treatment of the pectinic acid, by the nitration procedure, or by the precipitation. No claims were made by these authors concerning the homogeneity of the various fractions nor did they attempt to fractionate the pectinic acids obtained according to methyl ester content.

Owens, Miers, and Maclay[512] fractionated pectin propionate prepared by the method of Carson and Maclay.[513] The samples were prepared by adding petroleum ether to a solution of the propionate in

[509] T. Svedberg and N. Gralén, *Nature*, 142, 261 (1938).
[510] G. Schneider and U. Fritschi, *Ber.*, 69, 2537 (1936).
[511] R. Speiser and C. R. Eddy, *J. Am. Chem. Soc.*, 68, 287 (1946).
[512] H. S. Owens, J. C. Miers, and W. D. Maclay, *J. Colloid Sci.*, 3, 277 (1948).
[513] J. F. Carson and W. D. Maclay, *J. Am. Chem. Soc.*, 68, 1015 (1946).

dioxane and their viscosities were determined in acetone solutions. The osmotic pressures of these fractions were also determined. Considerable degradation was observed by these authors in the course of preparation and fractionation. The fractionation here was apparently according to molecular sizes since the methoxyl contents of the fractions did not show a definite trend.

With the present keen interest in the characterization of pectinic acids, rapid progress in the development of technics of fractionation and definition can be expected. It would be highly desirable to have such methods available, especially if they could be applied to pectic substances directly rather than to their derivatives.

VIII. VISCOSITY OF PECTINIC ACID SOLUTIONS

Viscosity is the resistance offered by a liquid or solution to flow. It is a characteristic property which results from the friction between adjacent layers of the liquid moving past each other.

The high viscosities of some fruit juices and extracts attracted the attention of chemists some 120 years ago and led to the discovery of the pectic substances. Ever since, the literature abounds in references to this property, and viscous behavior is now regarded as an important and typical characteristic of solutions of pectinic acids. The invention of the capillary viscometer by Graham produced a splendid tool for the investigation of the viscosity relations of colloids in general and of pectinic acids in particular.

Viscosity is often a sensitive indicator of differences or changes in colloidal solutions. It is, moreover, relatively easy to measure and, as a consequence, has been used in colloid investigations more than any other property. Unfortunately, quantitative interpretation of the results is most difficult and often impossible. It would be out of place to enter here into a discussion of the theory of viscosity in colloidal solutions and for such information the reader must be referred to the extensive literature.[514-516] Only some of the highlights will be touched upon in the following discussions.

The only rigorous hydrodynamic analysis of the viscosity of colloidal solutions is that of Einstein.[517] His formula for the variation of viscosity with concentration, however, depends on a number of assumptions and is valid only for an ideal case. It is rather likely that in a

[514] E. O. Kraemer in H. S. Taylor, *A Treatise on Physical Chemistry*. Vol. I, 3rd ed., Van Nostrand, New York, 1942.

[515] E. C. Bingham, *Fluidity and Plasticity*. McGraw-Hill, New York, 1922.

[516] H. Mark in A. Weissberger, *Physical Methods of Organic Chemistry*. Vol. I. 2nd, ed., Interscience, New York, 1949.

[517] A. Einstein, *Ann. Physik,* **19,** 289 (1906); **34,** 591 (1911).

dilute colloidal solution of a pectinic acid, for instance, at least four factors—solvation, electroviscous effects, asymmetrical particle shape, and particle porosity—will operate singly or in concert to cause the relationship to differ materially from the ideal case. From viscosity measurements alone it is not generally possible to determine the importance of each factor in a given colloidal sol. Even with independent information concerning these factors, the interpretations given are usually highly speculative. As stated by Kraemer,[514] the causes for the high viscosities of polymers in general are still the subject of debate. One group of investigators interprets the results in terms of solvation, defending the hypothesis that colloidal particles can attach to themselves hundreds of times their own volume of the solvent. Another group denies this extreme degree of solvation and advocates that the swollen sponge-like particles enclose relatively large quantities of the medium.

Unfortunately, little of the work done until a few years ago on the solution viscosity of pectinic acid proved to be of lasting value. Due to the undeveloped state of pectin chemistry, the preparations which were used in such studies were ill defined and contained in most cases large proportions of nonpectic materials of unspecified nature. Some of these latter materials undoubtedly often "diluted" the effects shown by the true pectic components, while in other cases they masked the viscous behavior of the pectinic acids. Of even greater importance is the fact that the presence of minute proportions of certain elements, especially polyvalent metallic ions, exert pronounced influence on the viscosity of pectic solutions. High methoxyl content seems to enhance the solubility of pectinic acids. As the solubility decreases with lower methoxyl contents, the effect of traces of metals simultaneously becomes increasingly important. The limit is reached upon complete demethylation: pectic acid is soluble in water in the absence of mineral contamination but becomes almost entirely insoluble in the presence of even traces of certain ions. In the past most of the pectinic acid preparations studied contained "ash constituents" and even now the pure preparations often retain a small proportion (0.1 to 0.2%) of ash. This small residual ash content will have little influence on the viscosity of a high methoxyl pectinic acid but may change considerably the viscosity of pectinic acids of low methyl ester contents.

Since there are but few and fragmentary observations on the viscosity characteristics of solutions of pectic acid, the present discussion will be restricted to pectinic acid solutions of more than 50% methylation. The literature on this topic was ably reviewed by Myers and Baker.[518]

[518] P. B. Myers and G. L. Baker, *Univ. Delaware Agr. Expt. Sta.,* Bull. No. 149 (1927).

1. Methods of Measurement

The Ostwald capillary viscosity pipette is the instrument most commonly used for pectinic acid solutions. Contrary to Rosen,[519] the shape and size of the pipette has no influence on the results.[520] The viscosity measurements are usually performed in carefully controlled constant temperature baths at 25 or 30°C., the lower temperature being most commonly used. A constant volume of solution should be used in the pipette to assure a consistent hydrostatic head. Measurements on very viscous solutions (relative viscosities over 10) tend to be unreliable and for this reason dilute solutions (0.5% and less) are usually applied. The Ostwald-Cannon-Fenske[521] and Couette[522] viscometers are also suitable for pectinic acid solutions and are used by some investigators. The Stormer viscometer was found (in the author's laboratory and elsewhere[523]) to be subject to too great experimental errors when used with dilute solutions. The MacMichael viscometer has been used successfully for pectinic acid solutions and is especially useful when the purpose of the investigation is to follow changes in the viscosity as they occur. The Höppler falling-ball viscometer has also been used for pectinic acid solutions, especially in Europe.

Freshly made pectinic acid solutions should be allowed to stand for several hours before starting any viscosity measurements. An apparent increase in the viscosity during the first few hours, as reported by Sauer and Sanzenbacher,[470] for instance, may be observed unless this precaution is taken.

2. Relationship between Methyl Ester Content and Viscosity

Fellenberg,[524] Wendelmuth,[476] and many later workers reported that the viscosity of a pectinic acid solution decreases upon progressive demethylation. It is now clear, however, that the viscosity is not governed by the methyl ester content but rather by the average molecular weight or size of the pectinic acid. Naturally, the viscosity may drop if the acid or alkali used for the removal of ester groups causes, in addition, degradation of the molecular size. An experiment of Myers and Baker[518] which illustrates how markedly the viscosity of a pectinic acid solution may change without an appreciable change in the methyl ester content was described previously.

[519] K. B. Rosen, *Bull. Natl. Formulary Comm.*, 9, 35 (1940).
[520] H. S. Owens, H. Lotzkar, R. C. Merrill, and M. Peterson, *J. Am. Chem. Soc.*, 66, 1178 (1944).
[521] M. R. Cannon and M. R. Fenske, *Ind. Eng. Chem., Anal. Ed.*, 10, 297 (1938).
[522] M. Couette, *Ann. chim. phys.*, 21, 433 (1890).
[523] E. Ott, ed., *Cellulose and Cellulose Derivatives*. Interscience, New York, 1943.
[524] T. Fellenberg, *Mitt. Lebensm. Hyg.*, 4, 122 (1913).

3. Effect of Concentration on Viscosity

Although some of the early work on crude pectin solutions indicated a straight-line relationship between concentration and viscosity, there is good agreement at present among various authors[519,525-527] to the effect that typical viscosity–concentration curves, as shown in Figure 14, appear to have three distinct regions. In very dilute solutions (up

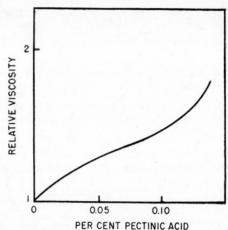

Fig. 14. Schematic illustration of the effect of concentration on the viscosity of a pectin solution.

to 0.01%) the relation is almost constant and the slope of the curve is unexpectedly steep. Owens, Lotzkar, Merrill, and Peterson[520] state that in such solutions pectinic acid is highly ionized and that a number of possible factors may increase the viscosity of the solution above that expected for an un-ionized solute. Some of these factors are: (*1*) interaction between solute and solvent, (*2*) extension or unfolding of the molecules,[528] (*3*) increase in the amount of work to move one ion relative to another, and (*4*) factors comprising the electroviscous effect. In the next region of concentration (up to 0.1%) the slope of the curve decreases. At concentrations above 0.1% the slope again increases. The latter is likely to be due to the formation of aggregates which may enclose some of the solvent. The curves become increasingly steep until the limit

[525] H. P. Kortschak, *J. Am. Chem. Soc.*, **61**, 681, 2313 (1939).

[526] G. L. Baker and M. W. Goodwin, *Delaware Agr. Expt. Sta.*, Bull. No. 216 (1939).

[527] S. Säverborn, "A Contribution to the Knowledge of the Acid Polyuronides," *Dissertation*, Univ. of Uppsala, 1945.

[528] H. Meyer and H. Mark, *Der Aufbau der hochmolekularen Naturstoffe.* Akadem. Verlagsgesellschaft, Leipzig, 1930.

of usefulness of the method of determining viscosity is reached. The nature of the curve will depend on the character of the pectinic acids and in those of highly colloidal nature the initial hump as well as the rapidly increasing slope at higher concentrations is very pronounced. In the case of pectinic acids of comparatively low viscosities or those which were artificially degraded by heating (see Section IV, this chapter), the curve may approximate a straight line for a considerable range of intermediate concentrations.

4. Influence of Changes in the pH

The changes which occur in the viscosities of solutions of pectinic acids (over 50% methylation) upon the addition of an acid or alkali were observed by many early workers. Edson[529] in 1928 made a systematic study of this point using a 0.25% solution of a low-ash (0.18%) pectinic acid prepared from apple pomace. Several later investigators confirmed Edson's results.[520-526] The general shape of pH-viscosity curves is shown in Figure 15. The pH of dilute (1.0 to 0.01%) solutions of high-ester pectinic acids is usually between 3 and 4. Upon lowering the pH of the solution by the addition of an acid the viscosity drops until at below 2.2 or 2.4 a range is reached where it shows no further change. The results obtained with different acids are identical. The value at which the viscosity curve reaches this almost horizontal region depends on the viscous character of the pectinic acid and may be used for the characterization of pectinic acid preparations. Even more important is the fact that, when the concentration–viscosity relationship is determined at low pH values, such as 1.5, for instance, the log viscosity–concentration relationship is linear and may thus serve as the basis for further calculations. This behavior is also utilized in the approximate determination of jellying properties by viscosity measurements which will be discussed later (see Chapter XXIII, Section IV-1).

Upon the addition of sodium hydroxide the viscosity of low-ash pectinic acids increases and reaches a maximum at around pH 6. This may be caused by the fact that sodium hydroxide reacts to form with pectinic acid a highly ionized pectinate.[530] Further additions of the alkali reduce the viscosity. Beyond pH 8 the values become meaningless because of the demethylation and other changes caused by the alkali.

Some authors, such as Myers and Baker[518] and Glückman,[531] found that various pectinic acid preparations have pH maxima at different pH

[529] L. E. Edson, "A Physico-Chemical Study of Pectin." *Dissertation*, Columbia Univ., 1928.
[530] R. F. Stuewer, *J. Phys. Chem.*, **42**, 305 (1938).
[531] S. Glückman, *Kolloid Z.*, **55**, 65 (1931).

values. Owens, Lotzkar, Merrill, and Peterson[520] attribute this either to the presence of mineral constituents in the pectinic acids used or to the fact that sufficient time may not have been allowed for the solutions to reach equilibrium before the determinations were made.

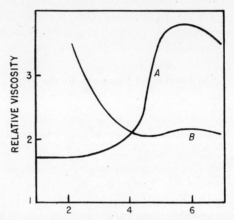

Fig. 15. Schematic illustration of the effect of pH (abscissa) on the viscosity of a high-ester (*A*), and of a low-ester (*B*) pectinic acid solution.

The pH relations of pectinic acids with less than 50% methyl ester content are entirely different. As shown by Olsen, Stuewer, Fehlberg, and Beach,[532] Baker and Goodwin,[533] and Speiser, Eddy, and Hills,[534] the maximum viscosity of a pectinic acid solution will occur at a progressively lower pH value as more and more of the methyl ester is removed. This is illustrated for one specific case in Figure 15. The presence of minute quantities of polyvalent ions such as calcium, insignificant at higher methyl ester contents, will also have an increasing effect on viscosity as the proportion of free carboxyl groups increases with demethylation. Even salts such as sodium chloride (0.1 N) will cause great differences in the viscosity–pH relationship with low-methoxyl pectinic acids. In addition to the drift in the optimum pH range, the maximum attainable viscosity may also increase to well over the values which may be obtained with pectinic acids of higher degrees of esterification. The pH optimum for highest viscosity can be at 2.2 (5.2% methoxyl),[533] at 2.0 (4.5% methoxyl),[534] or actually at any value

[532] A. G. Olsen, R. F. Stuewer, E. R. Fehlberg, and N. M. Beach, *Ind. Eng. Chem.*, 31, 1015 (1939).

[533] G. L. Baker and M. W. Goodwin, *Univ. Delaware Agr. Expt. Sta.*, Bull. No. 246 (1944).

[534] R. Speiser, C. R. Eddy, and C. H. Hills, *J. Phys. Chem.*, 49, 563 (1945).

between pH 6 and 2, depending on the degree of esterification and on the presence of minute quantities of "ash constituents."

5. Effect of Temperature

Temperature has two distinct effects on the viscosity of a pectinic acid solution. As the temperature is elevated the viscosity of the solution is reversibly reduced. Elevated temperatures (especially above 50°C.) will cause, in addition, an irreversible reduction in the viscosity due to degradation of the pectinic acid. Only the reversible changes caused by temperature variations will be discussed here since irreversible heat degradation was dealt with in Section IV of this chapter.

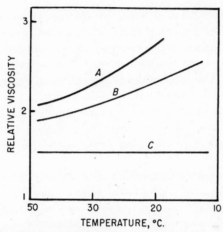

Fig. 16. Schematic illustration of effect of temperature on viscosity of a (high-ester) pectinic acid solution.

Curves *A* and *C* were obtained on a pectinic acid in 0.5 and 0.05% solutions, respectively. Curve *B* was obtained on a pectinic acid of lower "colloidality" in 1.0% solution. (Adapted from Owens, Lotzkar, Merrill and Peterson.)

There are numerous observations in the literature concerning the effect of temperature on the viscosity of pectinic acid solutions. In Figure 16 this relationship is shown[520] for the range from 0 to 50°C. The viscosity of the more viscous (or more concentrated) solutions increases as the temperature is lowered. The shape of the viscosity–temperature curve varies somewhat with the nature of the pectinic acid. The interesting fact is that, as the concentration of the pectinic acid is reduced, temperature changes have less significance[535] until—at 0.1% concen-

---

[535] K. Smolenski, W. Wlostowska, and A. Mlynarski, *Roczniki Chemji*, **10**, 328 (1930); through *C. A.*, **24**, 4309 (1930).

tration and below—the relative viscosity does not change with variations in the temperature within the range shown in Figure 16. The limit value at which sensitivity toward temperature ceases depends on the colloidal nature of the pectinic acid. Low-viscosity pectinic acids or those artificially degraded will show this lack of sensitivity toward temperature even at higher concentrations.

6. Effect of Addition of Various Compounds on Viscosity

The effect of added compounds on the viscosity of pectinic acid solutions is a complicated affair. There are so many factors which do or may influence the reaction that it is utterly impossible to present a simple and unified picture.

It is clear, however, that at least two distinct types of influences may be differentiated. Certain compounds, when added to a solution of a pectinic acid, cause changes in the viscosity of the solution without entering into the formation of any compounds with the pectinic acid. Such effects were observed by Owens, Lotzkar, Merrill, and Peterson[520] and, with various other organic compounds, by Glückman.[531] The change in viscosity in this case is either the result of an effect on the solvent or caused by some change in the colloid chemical state of the solution. On the other hand, changes in the viscosity may occur upon the addition of certain compounds, especially ionized salts, as the result of the formation of chemical compounds with the pectinic acid. In this latter relationship the free carboxyl groups play a prominent role. It may be mentioned, finally, that complex compounds may also be formed in certain cases. The proportion of free carboxyl groups or, stating the matter otherwise, the equivalent weight of the pectinic acid, is an important factor in determining the sensitivity toward such additions. The heterogeneity emphasized previously also plays its confounding role.

Most compounds which, when present in small concentrations increase the viscosity of a solution of pectinic acid, precipitate it upon further addition. In the present discussion only concentrations will be considered which do not effect actual precipitation of the pectinic acid. The precipitability and precipitation of pectinic acids will be discussed later in Section XIII.

Glückman[531,536] studied the effect of low concentrations (4%) of various alcohols, glycerol, sucrose, and other organic compounds on the viscosity of dilute solutions of pectinic acids. Most of these caused a slight but definite increase in the viscosity. In all these determinations a simple relationship was observed: The relative viscosity of the pectinic acid solu-

[536] S. Glückman, *Kolloid Z.,* **57,** 330 (1931).

tion containing the addition was equal to the relative viscosity of the solvent (in similar concentration in water) multiplied by the relative viscosity of the pectinic acid solution alone. In other words, the addition of the organic compound increased the viscosity of the solution to the same extent as it would have increased the viscosity of water. This was still true with higher concentrations (up to 35%) of glycerol and with 8% methanol, ethanol, and propanol, throughout the temperature range from 10 to 40°C., and was taken by Glückman as an indication of the fact that no reaction occurred between the added compounds and the pectinic acid.

Baker and Goodwin[526] used a 0.125% solution of a pectinic acid containing 10.11% methoxyl and 0.76% ash and studied the effect on the viscosity of a number of salts at various pH values. Copper sulfate, even in minute quantities, greatly increased the viscosity. Other salts which caused increases in the viscosity of pectinic acid solutions were aluminum sulfate, ferric chloride, lead nitrate, and arsenous oxide. The increase in the viscosity was most pronounced between pH 5 and 6, but no noticeable influence was found at values below pH 2.5. The effect of the salts diminished as the pH of the solution approached alkalinity, and became negligible as it approached pH 8. Results at higher values are meaningless because of demethylation. Since the strongest effect occurred at acidities at which these metallic ions are normally precipitated, Baker and Goodwin assumed that the increased viscosity resulted from the formation of complex hydroxides with the salts of these metals.

Contrary to the action of these metallic salts, calcium chloride, ferrous sulfate, magnesium sulfate, manganous sulfate, nickel sulfate, potassium citrate, sodium chloride, and zinc chloride depressed the viscosity of the pectinic acid solution used by Baker and Goodwin. It is noteworthy that the hydroxides of these cations are not precipitated in the range from pH 3 to 7. Again, there was no noticeable effect on the viscosity under pH 2.5. On the other hand, Sauer and Sanzenbacher[470] observed that in two solutions of pectinic acids (0.5%, pH 3.8 and 3.2, methoxyl contents not given but presumably high) the addition of sodium chloride and calcium chloride up to 0.5 N concentration in the mixtures caused no change whatsoever in the viscosities. Owens, Lotzkar, Merrill, and Peterson[520] found that 0.9% sodium chloride caused a depression in the viscosity of dilute, ash-free pectinic acid solutions. As mentioned before, Olsen, Stuewer, Fehlberg, and Beach[532] found that 0.1 N sodium chloride increased the viscosity of pectinic acid solutions with low ester contents.

It is apparent from these few observations that the viscosity of pectinic acid solutions may respond in various ways to the addition of salts and other compounds. The effect will depend on the factors discussed on previous pages and is, thus far, not entirely clear. A point of paramount interest is the proportion of free carboxyl groups of the pectinic acid because this characteristic, together with the pH of the solution, will be of governing importance. An increase in the proportion of free carboxyl groups will rapidly increase the sensitivity to polyvalent ions. This point has been made quite clear by recent work on the behavior of low-ester pectins. Unfortunately, most of the low-ester pectin preparations studied by various workers were far from free from "ash constituents," which probably influenced the behavior of the pectinic acid. The commercial application of low-ester pectinic acids depends on their reaction with added polyvalent ions, usually calcium salts. For further observations on the solution viscosities of low-ester pectins the reader is referred to the articles of Hills, White, and Baker,[537] Baker and Goodwin[533,538] Olsen, Stuewer, Fehlberg, and Beach,[532] and others.

The fact that at low pH values the presence of moderate proportions of salts has no effect on the viscosity of solutions of pectinic acids with over 50% esterification, provides a simple means for the measurement of the viscosity of the pectinic acid solution with the exclusion of the effect of ash constituents, etc. The same is accomplished by the addition of small proportions of sodium chloride. The presence of sodium chloride or the low pH of the solution will also alter the concentration–viscosity relationship in a manner which makes the calculation of certain constants possible. We shall return to this point below.

7. Interpretation of Results of Viscosity Measurements

The calculation of molecular weight and other properties of high polymers from the viscosities of their solutions is a science in itself and can be only touched upon here. Let it be said at the outset that most of the calculations made from viscosity values involve certain important assumptions. Although some workers accept the results of such calculations at face value, it is much more desirable to regard them with some reservation. This is especially desirable in view of the great differences among the basic assumptions which are made to permit such calculations and on account of the great volume of more or less contradictory results which have been obtained by such means.

We have stated before that viscosity has been extensively used in the study of various macromolecular compounds. Although some connection was for a time assumed to exist between viscosity and molecular weight

[537] C. H. Hills, J. H. White, Jr., and G. L. Baker, *Proc. Inst. Food Technol.*, 1942, 47.
[538] G. L. Baker and M. W. Goodwin, *Univ. Delaware Agr. Expt. Sta.*, Bull. No. 234 (1941).

of high polymers, no mathematical formulation of this relationship was given until Staudinger[539] proposed his viscosity rule. This postulates a direct relationship between the specific viscosity (relative viscosity — 1) of a dilute solution of a high polymer and its molecular weight:

$$\text{specific viscosity/concentration} = KM$$

where K is a constant. At infinite dilution the equation reduces to:

$$\text{specific viscosity} = KM$$

More recent systematic studies by many workers make it clear that several changes in this formula must be made to establish the quantitative relationship between intrinsic viscosity (specific viscosity extrapolated to zero concentration)[540] and molecular weight. This topic was recently discussed by Mark,[516] and by Bawn.[541] Of the various improved formulas developed for such calculations, reference is made to those suggested by Simha[542] and Huggins.[543]

The use of the results of viscosity measurements on pectic substances dissolved (dispersed) in water for such calculations is open to criticism on account of charge and hydration effects. However, Malsch[544] suggested that upon the addition of some salts the viscosity–concentration relationship of pectinic acid solutions satisfies the Staudinger equation. It is now believed that such charge and hydration effects are considerably reduced by the use of 1% sodium chloride and low pH values (± 1.5) for the measurements. In the comparison of pectinic acids of widely differing degrees of esterification this method offers little help because at low pH values low-ester pectinic acids show such great sensitivity toward traces of various ions. The customary method of obtaining comparative viscosity values is still through the preparation of derivatives which are soluble in nonpolar organic solvents. The objections to the use of such derivatives were already discussed.

Using water solutions at pH 1.5 in the presence of 0.9% sodium chloride, Owens, Lotzkar, Merrill, and Peterson[520] measured viscosities at various concentrations and calculated the following values for the pectinic acids used:

[539] H. Staudinger, *Die hochmolekularen organischen Verbindungen*. Springer, Berlin, 1932.
[540] W. E. Davis and J. H. Elliot, *J. Colloid Sci.*, 4, 313 (1949).
[541] C. E. H. Bawn, *Research*, 1, 343 (1948).
[542] R. Simha, *J. Phys. Chem.*, 44, 25 (1940).
[543] M. L. Huggins, *J. Am. Chem. Soc.*, 64, 2716 (1942).
[544] L. Malsch, *Biochem. Z.*, 309, 283 (1941).

Sample	Intrinsic viscosity
De-ashed apple pectinic acid..........................	6.4
De-ashed citrus pectinic acid..........................	4.2
Autoclaved de-ashed citrus pectinic acid..............	1.2

Baker and Goodwin[526] used the following formula:

$$2.3 \times (\log \text{ relative viscosity/concentration})$$

and obtained the value of 18 for the intrinsic viscosity of a lemon pectin in very dilute solutions. This latter value, according to Kraemer,[545] is higher than the values for starches and raw cellulose dissolved in cuprammonium, and several times higher than those for rayon, cellulose acetate, and nitrocellulose as used in plastics and lacquers. Kraemer suggests that solutions of pectinic acids with such high intrinsic viscosities might not be molecular solutions.

Baker and Goodwin[526] also determined the specific viscosity—concentration relationship of an apple pectin at low pH values and calculated the approximate molecular weight of 280,000. Schneider and Bock[506] reported the comparative molecular weights of several samples of pectinic acids determined in this manner and gave the comparative values of 56 to 190 for lemon, orange, and apple pectinic acids, 25 for a pectinic acid from fermented pomace, and 17 for a sample of beet pectinic acid.

An interesting field, still unexploited, is the possible viscosity behavior of pectic solutions under high pressure. Ebbecke and Haubrich[546] found that information relative to the molecular shape may be gained by this method. These authors measured the viscosity of "spheric colloids" such as proteins, and of linear polymers under pressures up to 800 atmospheres. When the results of such determinations are compared with data obtained under normal pressures, important conclusions can be drawn concerning the shape of the molecule. The ratio between the two viscosities is high for linear polymer compounds, while it is low for proteins and other compounds of compact molecules. This method may yield interesting results with pectinic acids, especially when the molecular size or shape is changed due to heat or other effects.

Only reference is made here to the measurements of the viscosities of various derivatives of pectinic acids.[510-512,547] Most of these results were discussed previously. The effect of heating on the viscosities of pectinic acid solutions was already discussed in Section IV of this Chapter. The

---

[545] E. O. Kraemer, personal communication cited in reference 526.
[546] U. Ebbecke and R. Haubrich, *Biochem. Z.*, 303, 242 (1939).
[547] S. Morell, L. Baur, and K. P. Link, *J. Biol. Chem.*, 105, 1 (1934).

use of viscosity determinations for establishing the jelly-forming ability ("grade") of pectins will be dealt with in Chapter XXIII, Section IV.

IX. OPTICAL PROPERTIES OF PECTIC SUBSTANCES

1. Double Refraction

If light passes through a substance with the same velocity along all axes, the material is isotropic. If the velocity of light differs along different axes, the substance is anisotropic and will exhibit double refraction (birefringence). Until about a decade ago it was generally assumed that pectic substances are isotropic since they are derived from the isotropic cell wall. This contention was in harmony with the prevalent opinion, based almost entirely on Ehrlich's investigations, that the pectic substances are composed of small, compact basic units ("tetragalacturonic acids") not showing orientation and double refraction. It is now clear, however, that under suitable conditions pectic substances show definite double refraction.

Iterson[548] in 1933 reported some optical observations on thread-like pectinic acid coagulums prepared by the injection of dissolved pectinic acid into ethanol and ether. These threads showed negative uniaxial double refraction in air, while in water, shortly before their dissolution, they showed positive uniaxial double refraction. Iterson concluded that the rod-shaped particles of pectinic acid in these threads must be oriented in the direction of the thread. This anisotropy was later confirmed by Henglein and Schneider[549] for various pectic derivatives. Results obtained by x-ray technic also confirm the anisotropic nature of pectinic acids in films and threads. Observations quoted below on the streaming double refraction of pectinic acid solutions further strengthen this view. On the other hand, Snellman[550] states that "pectins do not show double refraction as may be easily understood on theoretical grounds."

2. Streaming Double Refraction

Streaming double refraction (streaming birefringence) is the double refraction observed in an anisotropic substance under kinetic conditions. It is now evident that streaming birefringence is a typical property of many asymmetric molecules and that a quantitative relationship should exist between particle asymmetry and the extent of streaming birefringence. The relationship, however, seems to be as complicated as re-

[548] G. van Iterson, Jr., *Chem. Weekblad* **30**, 2 (1933).
[549] F. A. Henglein and G. G. Schneider, *Ber.*, **69**, 309 (1936).
[550] O. Snellman, *Acta Chem. Scand.*, **1**, 291 (1947).

lationships between solution viscosity, molecular asymmetry, and molecular weight.

Boehm[551] measured the streaming birefringence of pectinic acid solutions by the rotating concentric cylinder method.[552] In a stationary hollow cylinder a smaller coaxial cylinder rotates. The experimental solution is placed in the annular space between the two cylinders. Streaming birefringence is exhibited by the rotating solution when observed between a pair of Nicol prisms. The very viscous apple pectin used by Boehm showed a larger positive angle of extinction than a less viscous beet pectinic acid. Nitropectin behaves similarly to nitrocellulose and shows strong negative birefringence. Boehm concludes that the pectinic acid molecules must be rod-shaped and anisotropic.

Einsele[553] and Horn[554] also made observations on the streaming birefringence of pectinic acid solutions. Snellman and Säverborn[555] studied the streaming birefringence of apple pectinic acid solutions prepared by precipitation with ethanol, followed by redissolution and dialysis. A pectinic acid extracted from lemon albedo with water at 30°C. and then precipitated, redissolved, and dialyzed was also tested. Snellman and Säverborn state that the shapes of the curves indicate heterogeneity and that it is impossible to reach any exact conclusions from the results. These authors also made determinations on acetone and amyl acetate solutions of nitropectin prepared by the method of Schneider and Bock[506] and found that the various constants which they calculated were similar to those of pectinic acids obtained by acid extraction. The average molecular weights calculated for lemon and apple pectinic acids were 136,000 and 96,000, respectively.

By far the most complete study of the streaming birefringence of pectic substances in water solutions was reported by Pilnik,[552] who worked with well-defined preparations. Using the technic noted above, he determined the influence of various factors on streaming birefringence. The results obtained by Pilnik may be summarized as follows: While pectinic acids (in water) show positive double refraction, they exhibit negative streaming birefringence. In harmony with previous observations, the measurements indicate elongated thread-like molecules. The "specific birefringence" as defined by Signer[556] is not constant when the measurements are made on pectinic acid solutions of different concentrations;

[551] G. Boehm, *Arch. exptl. Zellforsch.*. 22, 520 (1938–1939).

[552] This method and apparatus are discussed in detail by W. Pilnik, *Ber. schweiz. botan. Ges.*, 56, 208 (1946).

[553] R. Einsele, *Dissertation*, Techn. Hochschule, Karlsruhe, 1939.

[554] J. T. Horn, *Dissertation*, Bern, 1940.

[555] O. Snellman and S. Säverborn, *Kolloidchem. Beihefte*, 52, 467 (1941).

[556] R. Signer, *Helv. Chim. Acta*, 19, 897 (1936).

Pilnik explains this on the basis of differences which exist in the extent of aggregation at different concentrations. Electrodialysis of a pectinic acid solution increases the streaming birefringence as well as the viscosity and decreases the electrical conductivity and ash content. Addition of thiourea or hexamethylenetetramine has no essential effect.

Measurements of streaming birefringence during enzymic decomposition indicate that the measurement of this property cannot be used as a direct indication of changes in the chain length of the pectinic acid molecule. Thus, such measurements would not be applicable to the evaluation of the commercial usefulness of pectin preparations where the molecular size apparently plays a dominant role.

Partial neutralization causes an increase in both viscosity and streaming birefringence, but the effect is eliminated by the addition of sodium chloride prior to neutralization. As alkalinity is attained with continued addition of alkali and deesterification of the pectinic acid commences, both the streaming birefringence and the viscosity drop in the absence of sodium chloride. However, when sodium chloride is added to the solution before deesterification, the viscosity decreases but the streaming birefringence increases during the progressive saponification. Pilnik explains this by the assumption that during deesterification partial coagulation occurs which reduces the effect of disoriented Brownian movement of the particles and this results in an increase in the streaming birefringence. Simultaneously, the axial ratio of the pectinic acid molecules is decreased due to the effect of the alkali and thus the viscosity decreases. The hypothesis is claimed to be supported by the behavior of pectinic acid solutions upon the addition of larger concentrations of sodium chloride. The extent of esterification does not directly influence the streaming birefringence. For details of these experiments the reader must be referred to the original article.

It is interesting to note that the work of Snellman and Säverborn and of Pilnik indicate behavior of the pectic acids which apparently can be explained by the existence of aggregates of the simpler units. This is in harmony with views expressed on previous pages, that the structure of the pectin macromolecule involves some kind of association in addition to the main valence "primary" polymers formed through 1,4 glycosidic linkages.

3. Index of Refraction

Refractive index is the ratio of the velocity of light in a vacuum to the velocity in a medium. In water solutions of equal strengths the refractive indices of most sugars are about the same.[557] Dilute dextrin solu-

[557] C. A. Browne and F. W. Zerban, *Physical and Chemical Methods of Sugar Analysis*. 3rd ed., Wiley, New York, 1941.

tions have a similar refractive index which becomes only slightly different (4%) as the concentration is raised to 30%. One may assume that the refractive index of pectic substances may not be too different, but unfortunately no results are available in the literature to confirm or refute this supposition. Gaponenkov[558] studied the refractive indices of some solutions of crude pectinic acids ("Hydrato-Pektin") made from apple pomace and beets and found that the ratio of the difference between the index of refraction of the solution and that of the water to the concentration of pectinic acid was a constant and thus satisfied the formula of Dumanski.[559] Sodium ions caused an increase in the constant, calcium caused no change, while barium ions reduced it. Unfortunately, this report can be quoted only indirectly and it is difficult, therefore, to evaluate the significance of the results. Gaponenkov adhered strictly to the methods and terminology of Ehrlich and therefore the "Hydrato-Pektin" used may have been a preparation greatly diluted by other components. Ehrlich's similar preparations often contained less than 50% polygalacturonic acid.

A few values of the refractive indices of commercial pectin extracts are given in the older literature, but most of these contained overwhelming proportions (50 to 95%) of other solids and these results are therefore of little value.

4. Optical Rotation

Optical rotation is the ability of the solutions of certain substances to rotate to the right or left the plane of polarization of a beam of light passing through them. The optical rotation of a solution is proportional to the concentration and to the length of the path of light in the liquid.

Ever since it became certain that the pectic substances are related to the carbohydrates, much attention was given to their optical rotation. It is useless to discuss here the older literature on this subject since most pectinic and pectic acids were very impure. Furthermore, the araban which often accompanies pectic substances in plant tissues and in preparations is strongly levorotatory $[a]_{20}^D = -123°$ to $-176°$), while the pectinic acids themselves are dextrorotatory. Therefore, the presence of even small proportions of arabans has a considerable effect on the observed optical rotation of pectinic acid preparations.

Ehrlich's pectinic acids (*Pektinsäure*), obtained with hot water, had specific rotations from $+160°$ to $+240°$, depending on the source and

[558] T. K. Gaponenkov, *J. Gen. Chem. U. S. S. R.*, **5**, 185 (1935); quoted from R. Ripa, *Die Pektinstoffe*, Serger und Hempel, Braunschweig, **1937**.
[559] A. Dumanski, *Kolloid Z.*, **65**, 178 (1933).

method of preparation. The observations of other authors were within the same range. Highly purified citrus pectinic acids prepared in the author's laboratory showed specific rotations ranging from 237° to 250°.

The specific rotation of pectic acid appears to be somewhat higher. Ehrlich's various partly degenerated polygalacturonic acids (*Tetragalacturonsäure*) showed an $[\alpha]_{20}^{D} = +250°$ to $+285°$. Polygalacturonic acids prepared by Hirst[560] and collaborators ranged from $+170°$ to $+230°$. These latter products may have been degraded during the tedious steps of purification. Baur and Link[561] prepared a series of pectic acids (*Pektolsäure* and *Pektolaktonsäure*) by Ehrlich's methods and observed specific rotations in the range from $+237°$ to $+286°$. Ehrlich's own values for these compounds were $+250°$ to $+290°$.

The specific rotation of pectinic or pectic acid solutions is constant in the pH range of 3.0 to 6.5. The optical rotation decreases rapidly during enzymic hydrolysis (see Chapter XIV). On the other hand, degraded pectinic acids prepared by heating may show the same specific rotation as the parent pectinic acid (see Section IV above). Heating with acid, as used by Ehrlich in the preparation of his partially degraded pectic compounds, seems to cause little change in rotation. In fact, at times the specific rotation increases, perhaps due to the hydrolysis and subsequent removal of inert or perhaps even levorotatory impurities. This is especially noticeable in preparations having originally low polygalacturonide contents. Prolonged heating with acid causes a drop in the specific rotation. In the preparation of Ehrlich's *Pektolaktonsäure* (a degraded polygalacturonic acid) from *Pektolsäure* (a polygalacturonic acid obtained by milder treatment) the average drop in the case of five different preparations was about 20%.

There is some indication, especially from the results obtained by thermal degradation, that the specific rotation is either the property of the main valence component units which compose the pectinic acids or that a maximum optical rotation is reached at a comparatively low degree of polymerization.

X. SEDIMENTATION VELOCITY MEASUREMENTS AND THE ULTRACENTRIFUGE

Stokes' law defines the rate of sedimentation of solid particles suspended in a liquid in a gravitational field. The size and shape of the particles may be calculated from measurements of the sedimentation rate. When the particles are of colloidal size, the rate of sedimentation is very low

[560] E. L. Hirst, *J. Chem. Soc.*, 1942, 70.
[561] L. Baur and K. P. Link, *J. Biol. Chem.*, 109, 293 (1935).

and, in order to make measurements, it is necessary to use field intensities much greater than that of gravity. The high-speed ultracentrifuge developed by Svedberg[562] and his collaborators produces field intensities up to a million times that of gravity and uses photographic observations and records of sedimentation equilibrium or velocity in a centrifugal field obtained from up to 150,000 revolutions per minute. Kraemer and Lansing[563] state that the values obtained by this method are comparable in reliability to those obtained by the classical methods for substances of low molecular weights.

The first observations on the behavior of pectic solutions in the ultracentrifuge were reported by Svedberg and Gralén,[509] who used juices expressed from various fruits and lily (*Lilium*) bulbs without further purification and definition. The results indicated molecules of asymmetrical shapes or strong hydration. The approximate molecular weights of the pectinic acids contained in the juices from apples, pears, and plums were in the range 25,000–35,000, while the range for pectinic acids extracted from orange albedo was 40,000–50,000. Later Säverborn[564] reported a series of observations on apple, lemon, and currant pectinic acids prepared by a number of different methods. The methoxyl contents of the hot water-extracted apple pectinic acid was 10.5%, whereas that of the cold water-extracted preparations from lemon albedo was 12.0%. No further definition of purity was given for these pectinic acids. Some of these pectinic acids were dissolved and subjected to heating for two hours at 94°C. in 0.05 N sulfuric acid to observe the effect of partial hydrolytic degradation.

The measurements were made in solutions containing 0.2 N sodium chloride. Concerning the shape of the sedimentation curves, Säverborn remarks that the curve for lemon pectin is unusually pointed, indicating the presence of great cohesion among the structural components of the macromolecule, and that this also prevents the occurrence of normal diffusion. This is also indicated by the steadily increasing values of the sedimentation constants upon decreasing the pectinic acid concentration. The diffusion constants calculated from the averages of the sedimentation constants for the various preparations of Säverborn and the molecular weight computed therefrom are summarized in Table 20.

Säverborn emphasizes the fact that these results should be regarded as being merely indicative and that the molecular weights calculated are comparative values. The difference in behavior between the water- and

[562] T. Svedberg and K. O. Peterson, *The Ultracentrifuge*. Oxford Univ. Press, London (1940).
[563] E. O. Kraemer and W. D. Lansing, *J. Phys. Chem.*, 39, 153 (1935).
[564] S. Säverborn, *Kolloid Z.*, 90, 41 (1940).

acid-extracted samples is rather striking. The slight degradation caused by heating with 0.05 N acid is remarkable and indicates the acid resistance of polygalacturonic acids. One may note, however, that no analyses are given for these latter preparations which were made by precipitation

TABLE 20

DIFFUSION CONSTANTS AND CALCULATED MOLECULAR WEIGHTS OF SÄVERBORN'S PECTINIC ACIDS

Preparation	Diffusion constant $(D \times 10^{-7})$	Molecular weight
Apple pectinic acid (from juice)................	0.8–1.4	99,000–117,000
Apple pectinic acid (acid extracted)............	2.0	55,000
Same, heated with acid........................	2.1	47,000
Lemon pectinic acid (water extracted)..........	0.65	271,000
Lemon pectinic acid (acid extracted)...........	2.4	43,000
Same, heated with acid........................	2.2–2.5	39,000–45,000
Currant pectinic acid (water extracted)........	2.9	33,000

with ethanol after the acid treatment. It is possible, therefore, that during the acid treatment some of the "ballast" hemicelluloses were hydrolyzed and then subsequently removed by the ethanol, thus increasing the true pectinic acid content of the preparations. The determinations made by Säverborn on nitropectins prepared from these pectinic acids indicate a molecular weight range of 50,000–100,000.

Tiselius and Ingelman[565,566] reported some observations on the behavior of beet pectinic acid solutions in the ultracentrifuge. The pectinic acid preparation contained only 58.6% galacturonic acid anhydride and 8.2% methoxyl. This would indicate 14% methoxyl on the polygalacturonic acid basis, or 86% esterification. However, this figure may be too high (see Chap. VIII, Sect. VI-3'). The behavior of the pectinic acid in the ultracentrifuge indicates elongated molecules. The calculated approximate molecular weight, 90,000, is in the same range as the values given by Säverborn for apple and lemon albedo pectinic acids. This is rather remarkable in view of the impure preparation used and is contrary to the generally accepted opinion that the pectinic acids of beets are of lower colloidality (and molecular weights) than those obtained from fruits.

By far the most complete discussion of the behavior of pectic substances in the ultracentrifuge is contained in a more recent treatise of Säverborn.[527] In this work efforts were made to define the various pectic mate-

[565] A. Tiselius and B. Ingelman, *Förh. Svenska Socker.*, 1942, II, 16 pp.
[566] B. Ingelman and A. Tiselius, *Förh. Svenska Socker.*, 1943, II, 16 pp.

rials used by both analytical data and jellying ability. This author shows the sedimentation diagrams of a number of different pectic substances and of other polyuronides. Säverborn states that, on account of charge effects, at concentrations of 0.3% pectinic acids will hardly sediment, and that in some cases, such as with acid and neutral apple pectin, the substance "had not come off the meniscus" even after four hours' run at the highest speed of the rotor. The sedimentation velocity is greater in the presence of electrolytes. At lower concentrations (0.05%) the sedimentation becomes measurable even in water. Säverborn discusses in detail the effect of electrical charge and its influence on sedimentation velocity. From these observations and additional diffusion measurements he then calculates various molecular constants, such as particle dimensions and molecular weights. Some of these were discussed previously in Chapter III. Säverborn also made sedimentation equilibrium measurements at 18,000 r.p.m. By choosing a suitable low revolution a state of equilibrium is eventually attained when the amount of substance sedimenting through a unit area at any point of the cell is equal to that diffusing in the opposite direction. From such measurements average molecular weights in the range 40,000–93,000 for the various samples of apple, citrus, and beet pectin were calculated. These values agree quite well with those calculated from sedimentation velocity and diffusion measurements. In some cases, however, there are discrepancies, the reason for which is not clear. Säverborn states that it is probable that pectin particles are made up of single-chain molecules. To quote directly: "too much importance should not be attached to such a statement, however, as the particles dealt with here are no doubt hydrated, a fact the importance of which in this connection is at present unknown."

It would indeed be undesirable to accept such results of molecular weight calculations without reservation, since here again many assumptions must be made to make such computations possible. Nevertheless, this method has already yielded much information on the physical changes which occur in pectic substances under certain conditions. There is little doubt that the trends and differences shown by sedimentation velocity and equilibrium measurements have a real significance, even if the full meaning of some observations is not clear at the present time. It is hoped that such precise measurements will be applied increasingly in connection with chemical studies of the structure of pectic substances.

XI. OSMOTIC PRESSURE AND OTHER COLLIGATIVE PROPERTIES

Osmotic pressure is exhibited by molecules diffusing through a membrane and is usually measured by the pressure required to counteract the transfer of fluid from one side of the membrane to the other. The osmotic pressure which can be expected from solutions of high molecular compounds is very small. In contrast to phenomena like viscosity and sedimentation velocity, all molecules present, irrespective of size, play an equal role in causing the osmotic pressure. The value obtained will therefore, be a number average, and thus will not emphasize the dominant role played by large molecules in producing the important colloid-chemical properties such as hydration, viscosity, and gel and jelly formation. Apart from the slightness of the effect to be measured, there are other difficulties in the experimental determination of the osmotic pressure of pectinic acids. Colloidal solutions, even when carefully purified, contain dissolved impurities, usually electrolytes. These—even if present in small concentration—may possibly account for the greater part of the observed osmotic pressure. The removal of the last traces of ash constituents from pectinic acid preparations has been found to be very difficult on account of the extreme tenacity with which these adhere to the pectinic acid. By using a membrane which is permeable not only to the dispersion medium but also to the dissolved impurities, the error due to the latter can be diminished but not eliminated. Only passing reference can be made here to further complications caused by dissociation and by the phenomenon usually designated as Donnan equilibrium.[567]

Edson[568] used small collodion bags to measure the osmotic pressure of purified apple pectinic acid at different pH values. The osmotic pressure, observed after equilibrium was reached, increased from pH 2.2 to a maximum at neutrality. On the alkaline side the osmotic pressure values dropped rapidly. The significance of these latter readings is questionable in view of the changes effected in pectinic acids by alkaline solutions. Edson used various acids to adjust the pH values and found that the pH, rather than the kind of acid, governed the osmotic pressure. When glucose is added to the pectinic acid contained by the collodion bag, the osmotic pressure is lowered. Edson interpreted this as an indication of association of pectinic acid with the sugar. The numerical values obtained will not be quoted here since even Edson considered them "quantitatively unsatisfactory." Schneider and Fritschi[569] made osmotic measurements on dialyzed sterile solutions of pectinic acids and obtained values corresponding to molecular weights in the range 30,000–40,000. These authors also place little faith in these values because of the possible association of the pectinic acid molecules in water solution. On the other hand, they feel that the values obtained by osmotic measurements on nitropectin and

[567] R. H. Wagner, in A. Weissberger, *Physical Methods of Organic Chemistry*. Vol. I, 2nd Ed., Interscience, New York, 1949.
[568] L. E. Edson, *Dissertation*, Columbia Univ., 1928.
[569] G. Schneider and U. Fritschi, *Ber.*, **69**, 2537 (1936).

acetylpectin represent true molecular weights. These range from 30,000–100,000, depending on the source of pectinic acid and the derivative used. These authors also determined the molecular weights of two samples of nitropectin by the osmotic method and found that the values did not change upon the transformation of the nitropectin into acetylpectin. Schneider and Fritschi have also determined the changes in osmotic pressure which occur upon heating the pectinic acid esters under pressure or with dilute acids; insufficient details of these experiments are given to warrant a detailed discussion here. The major conclusion of these authors is that the pectin macromolecule is not an aggregate but a polymer involving only primary valences through the 1,4 glycosidic linkages.

More recently Owens, Lotzkar, Schultz, and Maclay[570] and Owens, Miers, and Maclay[512] reported osmotic pressure measurements on both pectinic acids and pectin propionates. In contrast to Schneider and Fritschi, the latter authors describe in detail the technic used in these measurements. Lucite or stainless steel cells with concentric rings were used with membranes prepared from Cellophanes 300, 450, and 600 PT. The membranes were first allowed to swell in $7 N$ ammonium hydroxide for one hour, followed by washing in water. This method was slightly modified for the work on the propionates. In order to reduce electroviscous effects, $0.155 M$ sodium chloride was used for dissolving the pectinic acid. For the pectinic acids the pressure–concentration curves measured for concentrations up to 0.55% gave straight horizontal lines. The number-average molecular weights calculated from the values obtained were in the range 18,000–39,000. However, little relationship could be observed between the intrinsic viscosity and these number-average molecular weights except that they both followed the same trends. Owens, Lotzkar, Schultz, and Maclay state that variations in the distribution of pectinic acids of different sizes in the samples might account for this observation. It is noteworthy that, in spite of the high quality and purity of the pectinic acids used, these values are lower than those reported by Schneider and Fritschi.

The measurements on the propionates were made in acetone solutions. Owens, Miers, and Maclay state that an assumption that propionation does not degrade pectinic acid is unwarranted. The osmotic pressure–concentration relationship gave straight lines but some of these showed regular increases, while others showed decreases for the ratio. The number-average molecular weights calculated from the observed osmotic pressures ranged from 55,000 to 100,000. For a detailed evaluation of these results in comparison with calculations made from the measurements of the viscosities of these solutions, the reader must be referred to

[570] H. S. Owens, H. Lotzkar, T. H. Schultz, and W. D. Maclay, *J. Am. Chem. Soc.*, **68**, 1628 (1946).

the original article. Jansen, MacDonnell, and Ward[571] recently reported some osmotic pressure measurements on the methyl glycoside of polygalacturonic acid methyl ester.

While these measurements are important in investigations of pectic substances and are no doubt suitable for detecting and following certain changes, it would be a mistake to accept at face value the numerical values for molecular weights obtained by such means. To repeat, there are too many assumptions which must be made in these calculations and too many irregularities in the results which are not clearly understood.

There is little to be said here about the results obtained on pectinic acids by freezing point depression. As mentioned earlier, Ehrlich and Kosmahly[572] claimed to have obtained molecular weight values in the neighborhood of 1300 by the cryoscopic method. Gaponenkov,[573] using the same technic, obtained the value of 720 for a pectic acid. It is now obvious that these results are either altogether erroneous or that they were obtained in the presence of low-molecular weight impurities, such as occluding electrolytes, etc.

XII. WATER RELATIONS: HYDRATION, IMBIBITION, WATER-HOLDING CAPACITY, AND "BOUND" WATER

Both in the plant tissue and in commercial application of isolated pectic substances, the most important characteristics of these compounds depend on their water relations. The high viscosities of pectic solutions and the formation of gels and of jellies with sugar and acid demonstrate an intricate relationship between this group of colloidal materials and water. We shall deal here briefly with the water relations of isolated pectic substances. The formation of jellies in mixtures of pectins with sugar and acid and of gels upon the addition of polyvalent ions to low-ester pectinic acids and pectic acid will be discussed in Section XV below as well as in Chapter XXVII, Section I.

It would be out of place at this time to engage in a detailed discussion of the water relations of biocolloids. The reader is referred to the splendid chapter on this topic in Gortner's[574] book. Although there is disheartening little information on the water relations of the pectic substances, we have reasons to assume that they would behave similarly in some respects to dextrins and hemicelluloses such as arabans, for instance.

The pectic substances are strongly hydrophilic colloids. Protopectin

[571] E. F. Jansen, L. R. MacDonnell, and W. H. Ward, *Arch. Biochem.*, 21, 149 (1949).
[572] F. Ehrlich and A. Kosmahly, *Biochem. Z.*, 212, 162 (1929).
[573] T. K. Gaponenkov, *Colloid J., U. S. S. R.*, 3, 439 (1937); through *C. A.*, 32, 6229 (1938).
[574] R. A. Gortner, *Outlines of Biochemistry.* 3rd ed., Wiley, New York, 1949.

can take up and retain several times its weight of water. When a dry preparation of protopectin is suspended in water, it swells up gradually until a maximum degree of imbibition has occurred. Partial hydrolysis of the protopectin into pectinic acid may further increase the degree of hydration. In the case of protopectin a part of the water-holding capacity may be attributed to the cellulose which either occurs with or is a component of protopectin. The effect of the polyuronide fraction, however, may be easily ascertained by digesting the preparation with a commercial pectinase.[575]   The cellulose of the protopectin is not affected by this enzyme. The difference between the water held by the untreated protopectin and that held after digestion gives an indication of the degree of hydration caused by the pectinic acid component of the protopectin. The water-holding capacity may be conveniently measured by pouring the mixture onto moist filter paper placed in a funnel and determining the proportion of liquid retained by the preparation. The extent of imbibition or hydration as determined in such tests varies widely for different protopectin preparations which at times are able to hold a thousand times their own weight of water.

Similar tests may be made on other insoluble pectic constituents. As shown earlier in Table 18, when calcium pectate is permitted to settle in dilute acetic acid after precipitation, it may occupy a volume of 2400 cc. per gram of dry calcium pectate. Thermal degradation or enzymic hydrolysis rapidly reduces the water-holding capacity of pectic substances.

The measurement of the imbibition or hydration of the soluble pectic compounds is somewhat more complicated. Romeo[576] states that pectinic acid absorbs 15-fold its weight of water. The degree of imbibition can be measured by the use of semipermeable membranes, but due to many interfering reactions, only approximate results can be expected from this method. The usual approach, therefore, is to use mixtures of water and some solvent such as ethanol for the hydration. Stuewer[577] reported such measurements on apple pectin, and on pectinic acid, pectic acids, and salts prepared therefrom. Stuewer's pectinic acid had a combining weight of 425, corresponding to an approximate methoxyl content of 9%. The thoroughly dried preparations were immersed for 24 hours in ethanol–water mixtures of different concentrations and the increase in the ethanol concentration in the supernatant liquid was determined. With initial ethanol concentrations below 80% the plots of ethanol concentration against per cent of hydration approximated straight lines. Ex-

[575] Z. I. Kertesz and B. R. Nebel, *Plant Physiol.*, 10, 763 (1935).
[576] G. Romeo, *Rivital. essenze e profumi offic.*, 24, 12 (1930).
[577] R. F. Stuewer, *J. Phys. Chem.*, 42, 305 (1938).

trapolation to zero ethanol concentration gave values in the range of 25 to 38%. Some of the materials tested were partially dispersed at the low ethanol concentration and therefore a better comparison may be made of data obtained with 50% ethanol. Some of these are shown in Table 21.

Pectic acid and pectates seem to be less hydrated than the parent pectinic acid and its salts. This, however, could also be the result of partial degradation caused by the alkali used in the demethylation. Since an increase in acidic properties (demethylation) seems to decrease the degree of hydration, it would be of interest to establish whether such a relationship exists in series of pectinic acids with decreasing methyl ester contents. Deuel and Huber[578] have found that the removal of the ester groups from the propylene oxide derivative of pectic acid[579] resulted in the loss of about 60% of the swelling power.

To be sure, a degree of hydration in the range given by Stuewer is much lower than what would be expected from the general behavior of various pectic substances, especially in plants. This can be attributed at

TABLE 21

HYDRATION OF SOME PECTIC SUBSTANCES IN 50% ETHANOL–WATER MIXTURE (ADAPTED FROM STUEWER)

| | Per cent hydration of | | | |
Sample	Acid	Sodium salt	Magnesium salt	Calcium salt
1. Original apple pectin..............	25	33	33	—
2. Purified pectinic acid from 1........	26	34	37	30
3. Pectic acid prepared from 2........	19	33	33	27

least partly to the presence in the plant tissue of other compounds with which the pectic substances associate in a wide variety of different reactions. One may also question whether Stuewer's results are of more than comparative value since ethanol, even in insufficient concentrations to cause outright precipitation, is apt to affect physical properties of the pectinic acids.

Gaponenkov and Mymrikova[580] determined the water-holding capacity of beet and apple pectinic acids and found that the hydration of the latter was higher. Gaponenkov[581] also determined the swelling and heat of swelling of beet pectinic acid.

[578] H. Deuel and G. Huber, *Helv. Chim. Acta*, 33, 10 (1950).

[579] H. Deuel, *Helv. Chim. Acta*, 30, 1523 (1947).

[580] T. K. Gaponenkov and V. N. Mymrikova, *Izvestiya Gosudarst. Nauch.-Issledovatel. Inst. Kolloid. Khim.*, No. 2, 117 (1934); through *C. A.*, 34, 5722 (1940).

[581] T. K. Gaponenkov, *Colloid J., U. S. S. R.*, 4, 641 (1938); through *C. A.*, 33, 6121 (1939).

Although such data may be of great interest, there are no reports of measurements of the force of imbibition in the case of any pectic substances. Similarly, we lack reports on the existence and quantitative variation of "bound" water[574] in water solutions and suspensions of pectic substances. One may safely assume, however, that a portion of the water in both solutions and suspensions is "bound." It is likely that the pectic substances are at least in part responsible for the "bound" water in succulent plant tissues and cell saps. Investigations of the water relations of pectic substances both *in vitro* and *in vivo* would be likely to yield important information concerning the factors governing water relations of plants.

Palmer, Merrill, and Ballantyne[582] determined the equilibrium moisture contents at 25°C. of some pectinic acids containing from 0.2 to 10.9% methoxyl. In the range from 0 to 95% relative humidity the equilibrium moisture content is independent of the methyl ester content of the pectinic acid, with the possible exception of the highest (95%) humidity used.

XIII. SOLUBILITY RELATIONS AND PRECIPITABILITY OF PECTIC SUBSTANCES

The solubility relations of pectic substances are very complicated. Besides being colloidal in nature, pectic substances may undergo such a variety of transformations that it is difficult indeed to make statements which hold true under all conditions. No discussion of the properties of pectic substances, however, can be complete without some observations concerning their solubility behavior[583]; for this reason a short summary of the most important characteristics will be given below. The solubility relations of protopectin do not require any discussion. According to our present definition (see Chapter III) protopectin is insoluble in water and we may assume that if and when it becomes soluble it has already been altered and thus should not be regarded as "true" protopectin. Sucharipa[584] claimed to have dissolved protopectin in Schweitzer reagent, but there seems to be some doubt concerning the validity of this observation. This point was discussed earlier.

Pectinic acids, according to the definition, are soluble in water. Generally speaking, the solubility decreases with increased molecular size, as indicated by colloidality or viscosity, for instance. This is actually implied by comparison of different pectinic acid preparations, as well as from the solubility changes which occur during degradation and decom-

---

[582] K. J. Palmer, R. C. Merrill, and M. Ballantyne, *J. Am. Chem. Soc.*, **70**, 570 (1948).
[583] On the use of the term "solubility," see footnote 14, page 7.
[584] R. Sucharipa, *J. Am. Chem. Soc.*, **46**, 145 (1924).

position. Since pectinic acids which are isolated from various sources and by different methods show variations in many respects, it is difficult to give any definite ranges of solubilities. One may state arbitrarily that it is difficult to make—at room temperatures—solutions containing more than 2 or 3% pectinic acid. With pectinic acids of low colloidality, as measured by viscosity, jelly grade, or other properties, higher concentrations may be reached.

The solubility of a dry pectinic acid increases when the particle size is reduced. However, grinding in itself may have a detrimental effect on the colloidal properties of a pectinic acid.[585] The method of dissolution has a profound effect on the concentration attained in the solution. Speiser, Copley, and Nutting[586] have shown that when "saturated" solutions of pectinic acids are obtained by shaking, and the solutions are then diluted and shaken again with the undissolved pectinic acids, the amount of pectinic acid in the solution increases very slightly. These authors discuss in detail the solubility behavior of various pectinic acids and the apparent reasons for their abnormal behavior under such conditions. They state that the solubility of a pectinic acid is an index of its gel-forming ability.

A decrease in the proportion of esterified carboxyl groups reduces the solubility of pectinic acids, although little quantitative information is available on this point. Pectic acid, the end product reached upon complete demethylation, has often been regarded as insoluble in water. This alleged insolubility of pectic acids is probably due to the presence of electrolytes, which may easily render pectic acid insoluble in water. When the ash content of a pectic acid is reduced to 0.1% or below, a definite change in the solubility is noticeable inasmuch as it becomes dispersible in water. The exact limit of ash content will naturally depend on the characteristics of the pectic acid, as well as on the kind of impurities present.

Potassium, sodium, or ammonium salts of both pectinic and pectic acids are easily dispersible in water. The solubility of acid calcium pectinates will depend on the relative proportions of carboxyl groups which are free, esterified, or engaged in salt formation. This point is discussed in several other places in this volume. Calcium acid pectates are quite insoluble, while (normal) calcium pectate is sufficiently insoluble to permit repeated washing with boiling water during its quantitative estimation. The solubility of calcium pectate, by the way,

[585] L. H. Lampitt, R. W. Money, B. E. Judge, and A. Urie, *J. Soc. Chem. Ind.*, **66**, 157 (1947).

[586] R. Speiser, M. J. Copley, and G. C. Nutting, *J. Phys. & Colloid Chem.*, **51**, 117 (1947).

is a very interesting and—from the standpoint of plant chemistry—very important matter. Calcium pectate is insoluble in 0.1 N sodium hydroxide.[587] As it is treated with successive portions of the sodium hydroxide solution, some of the calcium is replaced by sodium and the insoluble material becomes dispersible. Similarly, calcium pectate is insoluble in 0.1 N hydrochloric acid. But when it is washed with successive portions, the calcium is removed and the material becomes dispersible in sodium hydroxide solution or even in water.

Pectinic acids dissolve easily in liquid ammonia to form 2% solutions.[588] It seems, however, that with de-esterification compounds other than ammonium salts may also be formed (see Chapter VI, Section V-3 (b)).

When placed in water, protopectin preparations take up water, and the whole mass shows uniform "swelling." Unless precautions are taken, pectinic acid and, to a lesser degree, pectic acid will "lump" or "clump" when put into water. The formation of a hard gelatinous shell prevents the entrance of water into the mass so completely that the center may remain dry. There are several commonly used methods to prevent the occurrence of "clumping" which, once it occurs, may make subsequent dispersion of the preparation impossible: (1) The pectinic acid may be wetted by a small quantity of ethanol or glycerol[589] before the water is added. (2) The preparation may be mixed with a small quantity of dry sugar or other water-soluble substance and then added to water with thorough stirring.[590]   (3) A small quantity of an effervescent mixture[591,592] is added which, in most cases, assures easy and rapid dispersion. A fourth possible method is coating of the outside of the pectinic or pectic acid particles with some compounds or salts which enhance the dispersibility in water. Of these latter treatments, coating with an outside layer of aluminum salts[593] and by higher fatty acids and their derivatives[594] are noted here.

In research work it is often desirable to dissolve pectins or pectinic acids without the addition of even minute quantities of any foreign compounds. In such cases the best method is to use water at 60 to 80°C. and introduce the pectinic acid very slowly on the surface of the water during vigorous stirring with a mechanical stirrer. No pectinic acid should be placed on the surface until

[587] J. D. Loconti and Z. I. Kertesz, *Food Research,* 6, 499 (1941).
[588] R. Raft, *Trans. Kansas Acad. Sci.,* 32, 38 (1929).
[589] A. K. Epstein, U. S. Pat. 1,995.281 (1935).
[590] H. T. Leo, U. S. Pat. 1,646,157 (1927); etc.
[591] E. Jameson, U. S. Pat. 1,611,528 (1926).
[592] W. E. Baier and R. E. Harris, U. S. Pat. 1,945,963 (1934).
[593] A. G. Olsen, U. S. Pat. 2,261,858 (1942).
[594] R. C. Nelson, U. S. Pat. 2,412,282 (1946).

that which was put on previously has become completely wetted. The solution is stirred for a few minutes after all the pectinic acid is introduced and is then filtered with suction while hot, and cooled at once. Depending on the colloidality of the pectinic acid, solutions of concentrations up to 3% may be prepared in this manner. In the case of high-quality preparations and careful operation, the filter paper retains practically no solid particles.

The soluble pectic compounds form opalescent colloidal solutions which show the Tyndall effect and other typical colloidal properties. Pectinic acid solutions do not exhibit sol–gel transformations as the result of temperature changes as do sols of gelatin or agar.

The particles in a pectinic acid solution carry a high negative charge which varies with the proportion of free carboxyl groups. This negative charge is apparently responsible for the ready precipitation of the pectic substances by electrolytes, with variations in the charge causing variations in the precipitability. Fellenberg,[595] in very thorough studies of the precipitability of pectinic acids by metallic ions, observed that pectinic acids containing a small proportion of methoxyl groups show increased sensitivity toward metallic ions. Many salts, such as silver nitrate, zinc sulfate, chlorides of calcium, barium, strontium, cadmium, as well as sodium and potassium salts, do not precipitate a pectinic acid of fairly high methoxyl content. Upon lowering the ester content, however, all metallic salts will precipitate pectinic acids but higher concentrations of univalent than of multivalent cations are tolerated. Stuewer and Olsen[596] state that pectinic acids having equivalent weights of 475 and less are precipitable with calcium. However, experimental conditions like the pH of the solution also influence the precipitability.

A number of other authors, especially Glückman[531,536,597] and Gaponenkov,[573,580,581] made extensive studies of the precipitability of pectinic acids by various salts. Most of these tests were performed on pectinic acid preparations which were not up to our present standards of purity and contained considerable proportions of "ash constituents." The definition of methyl ester content was also incomplete since, as a rule, the methyl ester content of the preparation, but not the proportion of esterified carboxyl groups, was given. We know now, furthermore, that the distribution pattern of pectinic acid molecules of different degrees of methylation is also of importance in such reactions.

Solutions of pectinic acids are readily precipitated by small quantities of dehydrating agents, which is in sharp distinction to the behavior of

[595] T. Fellenberg, *Biochem. Z.*, **85**, 118 (1918).
[596] R. F. Stuewer and A. G. Olsen, *J. Am. Pharm. Assoc.*, **29**, 303 (1940).
[597] S. A. Glückman, *Acta Physicochim.*, *U. S. S. R.*, **13**, 379 (1940); through *C. A.*, **35**, 2052 (1941).

solutions of most other gums and hemicelluloses. The latter need, as a rule, twice their own volume of 95% ethanol for precipitation.

The precipitation of pectinic acids from solutions by various miscible organic solvents, which may be regarded as dehydrating agents, also attracted the attention of investigators. Purification by ethanol precipitation has been described by Braconnot.[598] This method of precipitation is discussed in several other places in this volume. As a comparison of the amounts of organic compounds, especially so-called solvents, needed for the precipitation of a pectinic acid from a 0.8% solution, some observations given by Glückman,[599] may be quoted. Unfortunately, the methyl ester content of this pectinic acid was not given but may be assumed to have been fairly high. The concentrations needed to obtain the first signs of precipitation and for complete precipitation are given in Table 22. The concentrations required seem surprisingly low.

TABLE 22

QUANTITIES OF VARIOUS ORGANIC CHEMICALS NEEDED TO PRECIPITATE A PECTINIC ACID FROM 0.8% SOLUTION (ADAPTED FROM GLÜCKMAN)

Chemical	To give first signs of precipitation, g./100 cc.	For complete precipitation, g./100 cc.
Sucrose	—	60
Glycerol	46	50
Methanol	15	17
Ethanol	16	17
Propanol	18	21
Acetone	18	23
Ethylene glycol	—	41

According to the theory advanced by Kurbatow[600] the precipitating effect of these chemicals is the result of the decreased ionization of the water caused by the addition of such less associated compounds. This change in the ionization reaches a point where the relation between the water and pectinic acid is disturbed and as a consequence the pectinic acid is precipitated.

Glückman[531] noted that the concentration of ethanol necessary for the precipitation of a pectinic acid from solution is greater in the presence of potassium, sodium, lithium, manganese, and magnesium ions, the same with calcium ions, and less in the presence of barium or aluminum

[598] H. Braconnot, Ann. chim. phys., 47, 266 (1831).
[599] S. A. Glückman, Colloid J., U. S. S. R., 6, 925 (1940); through C. A., 35, 7796 (1941).
[600] W. Kurbatow, Kolloid Z., 55, 70 (1931).

ions. The pectinic acid used in this test was obviously one with a comparatively low proportion of free carboxyl groups.

Pectinic acids in solution may be affected by other hydrophilic colloids.[601] A solution consisting of 8% pectinic acid and 8% gum arabic separates into two layers, one which contains principally pectinic acid, the other mostly gum arabic. The same reaction occurs when other hydrophilic colloids are used, although the concentrations required to cause separation vary. Under certain conditions pectinic acids also form coacervates with other colloids such as gelatin.[602] Sodium caseinate is precipitated from solution in the presence of traces of calcium ions upon the addition of a pectinic acid solution.[603] The casein of fresh milk is also coagulated by pectinic acid solutions (see Chapter XXVII, Section VIII).

XIV. ELECTROPHORESIS

Electrophoresis is the migration of charged particles in an electrical field. The mobility of the molecules depends mostly upon the charges they carry and, in the case of pectinic acids, is governed mainly by the degree of esterification or, more exactly, the proportion of free carboxyl groups. Some time ago Bonner[602] made a study of the particle charges of pectinic acid, sodium pectinate, and sodium pectate. Using the method of Bungenberg de Jong and van der Linde[604] Bonner applied various amounts of "hexol nitrate" and measured the electrophoretic activity under an applied potential of 150 volts. The results, expressed in "reciprocal hexol numbers" gave a measure of the charge of the particles. The reciprocal hexol number of sodium pectate has been found to be a reproducible quantity giving, on three different preparations, values of 201, 202, and 204. This value is essentially the "equivalent weight" per equivalent particle charge in the sol and it is not surprising, therefore, that it is close to the mean equivalent weight of 229, calculated for sodium pectate from the sodium content. The reciprocal hexol numbers for pectinic acid and sodium pectinate were 582 and 603, respectively. These higher values are in harmony with the more difficult precipitabilities of these latter compounds from sols by electrolytes.

In a preliminary report, Tiselius and Ingelman[565] state that the pectic substances show "very great velocity in electrophoresis." Of course, with the preparations of comparatively low purity used by these authors the significance of such measurements is limited because of the possible

[601] J. Bonner, *Botan. Rev.*, 2, 475 (1936).
[602] J. Bonner, *Proc. Roy. Acad. Amsterdam*, 38, 346 (1935).
[603] G. H. Joseph, *Bull. Natl. Formulary Comm.*, 9, 2, 18 (1940).
[604] H. Bungenberg de Jong and P. van der Linde, *Biochem. Z.*, 262, 162 (1933).

effect of electrolytic impurities. Their statement, however, may be taken as a further indication of the strong negative charge of pectinic acid particles. More recently Speiser, Copley, and Nutting[586] reported electrophoretic measurements conducted by the moving boundary method on various pectinic acid preparations. On the basis of the sharpness of the patterns obtained with various low-ester pectins which were de-esterified by acid, alkali, and enzyme, these authors state that the removal of methoxyl groups by the enzymic method produces an ordered arrangement of methoxyl-free points on the molecules, whereas such removal by acid and alkali produces a random de-esterification. They then explain the greater gel strength of low-ester pectins produced by acid and alkali on the basis that the resulting random distribution of free carboxyl groups offers a greater probability for calcium cross linkages. In a later study, Ward, Swenson, and Owens[605] found that although the electrophoretic mobility of sodium pectinate is inversely related to the degree of esterification, the relation is not a linear one as suggested by Speiser, Copley, and Nutting. Ward, Swenson, and Owens discuss in detail the conclusions which might be drawn concerning the type of de-esterification obtained in the preparation of low-ester pectins by various methods. It is clear that there is still little unanimity in the interpretation of results obtained by such measurements.

Säverborn[527] studied the conductivity, electrical transport, and electrophoretic mobility of pectin solutions, and found that in solutions of the pectinic acid, the conductance is due almost entirely to hydrogen ions. Increasing the concentration of pectin causes a decrease in conductivity which is attributed to a decrease in the mobility of the hydrogen ion. Titration of the solutions with sodium hydroxide results in an increase in the conductivity in which the pectin anions now take a part in current transport. This is attributed to an increase in ionization due to salt formation and a consequent decrease in intermolecular forces between the pectin molecules themselves. This is in agreement with the fact that pectin forms sugar jellies only at acid pH values at which intermolecular forces are strong and the mobility is low. Säverborn found that the pectin molecules in general have a relatively high mobility typical of a strongly negative electrolyte. The mobility increases markedly with decreasing ionic strength reaching a value of about 40×10^{-5} cm.^{2}/sec.-volt in neutral solution at 0.01 to 0.001 ionic strength. The mobility approaches zero at a pH of about 2.0 and increases with increasing pH with a sharp break in the slope of the mobility curve occurring at pH 3.5. Thus the mobility of pectin solutions in general follows

[605] W. H. Ward, H. A. Swenson, and H. S. Owens, *J. Phys. & Colloid Chem.*, 51, 1137 (1947).

and agrees with the conductivity data obtained and with the work of previous authors.

XV. PECTINIC ACID JELLIES AND GELS

The formation of jellies and gels from pectic substances is a complex phenomenon the exact nature of which is still in dispute. Inasmuch as the major use to which manufactured pectic materials are put is the production of jams, jellies, and similar products, it is desirable to discuss briefly what is known concerning the structure of pectin gels and jellies. Unfortunately, there is little unanimity on this subject[606] among various workers and it would be grossly misleading to state that the views given below are generally accepted. Indeed, one may say that it is unreasonable to expect that the matter of gel and jelly structure be clear at this time when the macromolecular structure of pectic substances themselves is still a subject of debate. Any complete presentation of the subject of gel and jelly structure would inevitably involve a presentation and defense of the fundamental principles of colloid chemistry. It must, therefore, be left to someone else to present a detailed review of this intriguing subject, while an attempt will be made to present the most widely accepted views on this topic.

When a polymer solution gels, a liquid solution incapable of withstanding shear stress is transformed into a "solid" solution which is rigid and elastic.[586] Such a rigid structure must be bonded in all three directions lest neighboring layers slide apart. In the case of pectinic acids, two distinct types of such products exist. The first type is the conventional pectin-sugar-acid-water jelly containing 50% or more of sugar and now generally recognized as being formed predominantly through hydrogen bonding. The second type is the ion-bonded gel, produced from low-ester pectinic acids or pectic acids with the aid of calcium or other multivalent ions. Let us first discuss the specific case of gelling with sugar and acid which we call jelly formation.

1. Pectin-Sugar-Acid-Water Jelly

There are two major groups of factors determining the firmness and other properties of a jelly. The first consists of inherent properties of the pectinic acids. It is known, for instance, that apple pectins form jellies of more elastic texture than citrus pectin; jellies made from beet pectin again seem to be different in rheological characteristics. The reason for such differences is not clearly understood. The second group of factors

[606] R Ripa, *Die Pektinstoffe*. 2nd ed., Serger und Hempel, Braunschweig, 1937.

consists of the conditions under which the jelly is prepared and obviously includes a great many variants.

There is general agreement that a gel or jelly is composed of some kind of semirigid structure which enmeshes the liquid phase. On the other hand, there is considerable disagreement on how such a structure is formed and of what kind of structural elements it is actually built. Let us consider some of the conditions which lead to the formation of a pectin-sugar-acid-water jelly.

The stability factors operating in a system containing agar-agar have been outlined by Kruyt[607] and, according to Olsen,[608] they may also apply in the case of a pectin-sugar-acid-water jelly as follows:

(a) The sugar functions as a dehydrating agent.

(b) The hydrogen ion concentration functions by reducing the negative charge of the pectin, thereby permitting the pectin to precipitate and coalesce in the form of a network of insoluble fibers, providing the concentration of the sugar is sufficiently great.

(c) The dehydration of the pectin by the sugar requires time to come to an equilibrium.

(d) The rate of dehydration and precipitation increases with an increase in the hydrogen ion concentration.

(e) The maximum jelly strength is reached when the system comes to equilibrium and depends upon the position of the equilibrium.

(f) Any foreign components such as salts added to the system function either by changing the rate of gelation, by affecting the ultimate equilibrium of the system, or by a combination of both effects.

Thus jelly formation might be regarded as unsuccessful precipitation. When pectin is in the "sol" state, it is stabilized by water layers probably held to it by electrical attraction between the negative charge of the pectin and the unbalanced positive charges of the water dipoles. The dehydrating influence of added sugar (or of other polyhydroxy compounds) decreases the stability of the pectin by disturbing the water balance. With high sugar concentrations the dehydration is sufficiently complete so that, when acid is added, the hydrogen ions complete the destabilization and a jelly forms as the result of an unsuccessful attempt to precipitate.[609] The pectin in a jelly may be present in large independent units, in a superstructure involving large volumes, or in the form of ordered aggregates or as loose and irregular micelles.[610]

Speiser, Copley, and Nutting[586] state that it is unlikely that the jelly

[607] H. R. Kruyt, *Colloids.* Wiley, New York, 1927.

[608] A. G. Olsen, *J. Phys. Chem.,* 38, 919 (1934).

[609] G. H. Joseph, *J. Phys. Chem.,* 44, 409 (1940).

[610] G. Testoni, *Boll. sci. facoltà chim. ind. Bologna,* 1941, 62; through *C. A.,* 37, 6050 (1943).

formation is the result of dehydration alone. It is more likely that poly-hydroxy compounds like sugars, glycerol, or glycol form bridges between the rather stiff pectin molecules and stabilize the structure by means of the large number of hydrogen-bonding groups they present. As the extent of esterification decreases (and the proportion of free carboxyl groups increases) the number of groups that can contribute to hydrogen bonding also increases, thus enhancing the effectiveness of the added hydrogen-bonding agents and therefore less sugar is needed to form jelly.

While this seems to be the most generally accepted theory of jelly formation at present, it is by no means shared by all workers in this field. Bonner,[601] for instance, questions the dominant role played by charge effects, and Testoni[610] doubts that the function of sugar consists in its dehydrating effect. The latter author suggests that jellying is brought about by the formation of adsorption complexes between the pectin and the sugar to form aggregates.

Many factors will influence jelly formation and most of these factors will naturally influence each other. This leads to a reaction system in which almost endless variations are possible. Of the many investigations of the principles involved in jelly formation, only the sustained and systematic efforts of workers at the Delaware Agricultural Experiment Station will be noted here.[611-616] References to other investigations of this topic will be found in the following paragraphs and dispersed throughout this volume.

The jelly- or gel-forming ability of a pectinic acid will depend pre-dominantly on the length of the macromolecular polygalacturonic acid chains. In other words, the molecular size and weight and the resulting "colloidality" of the pectinic acids—whatever means are used to measure and express these characteristics—will show good correlation to jelly-forming ability. Yet, at the present time, it is not possible to state pre-cisely the extent of polymerization (or minimum molecular size or weight) which will enable a pectinic acid to form a jelly of "desirable firmness." It is clear, furthermore, that two pectin preparations of identical (aver-age) molecular weights might behave quite differently on account of the differences in their kind and extent of heterogeneity (see Chapter V).

[611] L. W. Tarr, *Delaware Agr. Expt. Sta.*, Bull. No. 134 (1923); No. 142 (1926).

[612] L. W. Tarr and G. L. Baker, *Delaware Agr. Expt. Sta.*, Bull. No. 136 (1924).

[613] P. B. Myers and G. L. Baker, *Delaware Agr. Expt. Sta.*, Bull. No. 144 (1926); No. 149 (1927); No. 160 (1929); No. 168 (1931); No. 187 (1934).

[614] G. L. Baker, *Delaware Agr. Expt. Sta.*, Bull. No. 204 (1936).

[615] G. L. Baker and M. W. Goodwin, *Delaware Agr. Expt. Sta.*, Bull. No. 216 (1939); No. 234 (1941); No. 246 (1944).

[616] G. L. Baker and C. W. Woodmansee, *Delaware Agr. Expt. Sta.*, Bull. No. 272 (1948).

However, the general relationship between molecular size and jellying power is well established. Whether the "molecular weight" is determined by osmosis, sedimentation velocity, viscosity measurements, or other methods, a preparation or a fraction of a preparation showing higher (average) molecular weight will, as a rule, give a firmer jelly. We have noted this correlation a number of times on previous pages.

Naturally, a minimum proportion of pectin is required for the formation of a jelly. This minimum amount required to make a jelly of a certain strength is used in the definition of the commercial usefulness of a pectin (see Chapter XXIII). When the logarithm of the pectin concentration in a series of jellies is plotted against the logarithm of numerical expressions of jelly firmness, a straight line is obtained.[608,617,618] The slope of this line is characteristic of any given pectin preparation. The concentration of pectin required for jelly formation will depend on the firmness required and will vary widely in pectin preparations isolated from various sources. Commercial pectin preparations are standardized in this respect.

We have already discussed the role of methyl ester (methoxyl) groups in pectinic acids and therefore this factor will be noted here only briefly. Fellenberg[595] at one time believed that jelly formation results from the splitting off of these groups and Ripa[606] and Lüers and Lochmüller[619] stated that the methyl ester content governs the jelly formation and thus is a measure of the usefulness of a pectin preparation. Later work[613] made it clear that this is not the case and that jellies of desirable firmness might be made with pectinic acids of a wide range of methyl ester content. The jelly-forming ability of pectins will actually tend to increase as the methoxyl content is reduced to about 8% (50% esterification).[615] The ester content is also of much importance for the "time of set," a subject to be discussed in Chapter XXII.

The presence of acetyl groups in beet pectin is claimed by some investigators to prevent jelly formation. This subject was discussed in Chapter IV, Section V.

The effect of nonpolyuronide substances, as arabans and galactans ("ballast," see Chapter IV), might under certain conditions influence jelly formation, but the situation is not entirely clear. It is quite well established, however, that the polygalacturonic acid portion of pectin preparations is of governing importance in jelly formation, and therefore one might state that pectins will show increased ability to form jellies as the ballast in a given preparation is decreased, provided, of course, that there are no other changes introduced.

[617] A. G. Olsen, *Ind. Eng. Chem.*, **25**, 699 (1933).
[618] L. H. Lampit and R. W. Money, *J. Soc. Chem. Ind.*, **56**, 290 (1937); **58**, 29 (1939).
[619] H. Lüers and K. Lochmüller, *Kolloid Z.*, **42**, 154 (1927).

The importance of acidity in jelly formation[619a] was recognized ever since pectins were first used for making jellies over a hundred years ago. The relationship between acidity and jelly formation was first stated by Goldthwaite[620] in exact terms. The later development of the concept of hydrogen ion concentration and the now general use of the term "pH" aided in better understanding and application of acidity effects.[611,621]

The addition of acids will suppress the dissociation of pectinic acids in solution and this will reduce the particle charge and increase the tendency of the molecules for association. According to Hinton,[622] only the undissociated carboxyl groups are capable of jelly formation. As a result, jelly formation usually becomes possible only below pH 3.5. As the pH is further lowered, the firmness of the jelly obtained with the same amount of pectin will increase and, conversely, the amount of pectin required to obtain a jelly of standard strength will decrease. After a usually sharp optimum, further decreasing of the pH below the range of 2.8–3.4 will result in jellies of decreased firmness. In such jellies made with too high acid contents, syneresis or "weeping" is frequent. The location of the pH optimum of a pectin preparation with respect to jelly formation will depend on a number of factors. Higher proportions of sugar will usually increase, lower pectin concentrations decrease, the pH optimum. By the use of buffer salts, the pH optimum can be raised as high as 4.5.

Deuel, Huber, and Leuenberg[622a] found that a pectinic acid completely methylated by the diazomethane method gave firm jellies at pH 5.8, without the addition of any acid. It is not clear just where this interesting observation fits in (if it does) with our present ideas of the mechanism of jelly formation.

Cole, Cox, and Joseph[623] showed that the drop in jelly strength with increased acidity at pH values below the optimum might be the result of the more rapid formation of jellies, which as a result might start to form before pouring ("pan gelation," "premature setting," or "curdling"). Because of the too rapid jelly formation the development of a proper structure is prevented. Olliver[624] recently emphasized that, in addition to pH, the rate of cooling and the temperature of aging may also significantly affect jelly formation, especially under pH 3.0–3.2.

[619a] F. A. Henglein, *Z. Lebensm.-Unters. Forschung,* **90,** 417 (1950).

[620] N. E. Goldthwaite, *Ind. Eng. Chem.,* **1,** 333, 457 (1909).

[621] W. G. Ogg, *Dissertation,* Cambridge, 1924, cited from T. N. Morris, *Principles of Fruit Preservation,* Van Nostrand, New York, 1933.

[622] C. L. Hinton, *Biochem. J.,* **34,** 1211 (1940).

[622a] H. Deuel, G. Huber, and R. Leuenberg, *Helv. Chim. Acta,* **33,** 1226 (1950).

[623] G. M. Cole, R. E. Cox, and G. H. Joseph, *Food Inds.,* **2,** 219 (1930).

[624] M. Olliver, *Food Technol.,* **4,** 370 (1950).

McDowell[625] observed that, over a limited range, the formation (setting) of a jelly is more rapid at a higher temperature.

The amount of sugar required to give a jelly of a certain firmness will depend on the characteristics of the pectin used. This relationship is used in the definition of the commercial value of pectins (see Chapter XXIII). A certain weight of pectin will be able to form a given quantity of sugar into a jelly of minimum firmness. When the sugar content of the mixture is increased or the pectin content decreased, a weaker jelly will result.

The importance of the sugar concentration in jelly formation had already been observed by Goldthwaite,[620] who also noted that excessive amounts of sugar will flocculate the pectin from solution. In addition to sugars, many other polyhydroxy compounds will behave similarly in forming a jelly with acid and pectin. Of such polyhydroxy compounds other than sugars, glycerol has been most often used by research workers. We have noted earlier in this Chapter the theory that the role of sugar in jelly formation is to effect a partial and gradual precipitation of pectin. Neutral salts may accomplish the same, as shown by Neukom,[626] who made jellies with pectin and 25% ammonium sulfate. The latter product, however, does not come within the definition used here for jellies.

Ullrich[627] states that freezing followed by thawing causes pectin-sugar-acid jellies to liquefy.

2. Low-Ester Pectin-Calcium (Acid Calcium Pectinate) Gels

It is interesting to note that, although the subject of low-ester pectins did not come to the fore until about ten years ago,[628] a great quantity of work has already been done on the formation of gels from this group of pectinic acids. Actually, the recent intense interest in this subject proved a bonanza for pectin chemistry in general.

We have stated repeatedly that the addition of calcium to a pectinic acid of more than 50% esterification does not cause precipitation. As the methyl ester content is lowered, a range is reached within which firm gels may be obtained with minute quantities of calcium (or other polyvalent ions). The best range of ester content is 30–50% esterification. In most cases such gels are made in the presence of 35% sugar. Such a product might be designated as an acid calcium pectinate and is both a gel and a jelly. Most workers believe that the formation of low-ester gels is de-

[625] R. McDowell, *Nature*, 148, 780 (1941).
[626] H. Neukom, *Dissertation*, Zürich, 1949.
[627] H. Ullrich, *Kolloid Z.*, 96, 348 (1941).
[628] G. L. Baker, in E. M. Mrak and G. F. Stewart, *Advances in Food Research*, 1, 395 (1948).

pendent on the formation of ionic bonds between pectinic acid macro-molecules. The strength of a pectin-sugar-acid-water jelly depends mostly on the molecular weight and is influenced slightly by the extent of esterification. Contrariwise, the strength of an ion-bonded acid calcium pectinate gel depends both on the extent of esterification (or, rather, proportion of free carboxyl groups) and the distribution of these on the pectinic acid molecules. However, some investigators believe that such ion bridges are not likely to participate in the formation of three-dimensional pectinate gel structures from low-ester pectins and polyvalent ions.[629]

The methyl ester (methoxyl) content of a low-ester pectin will be an important factor in determining the amount of pectin and sugar needed for forming a satisfactory pectinate gel. Baker and Goodwin[615] demonstrated that, as the sugar concentration is diminished to below 50%, the pectin requirements rise rapidly in pectinic acids of 7.1% methoxyl content. In pectinic acids of lower ester content the increase is less rapid, while in a low-ester pectin of 4.5% methoxyl the decrease in sugar concentration caused no change in the amount of pectin required.

The calcium requirement for the formation of a gel of optimum strength from a low-ester pectin must be determined for each sample and might vary considerably. It is usually in the range of about 0.10 to 0.01% (as calcium).

Low-ester gels will form over a wide range of pH values, from about 2.5 to 6.5.[630] These gels are quite dependent upon the temperature of gelation and are heat reversible. The "melting point" of the gel may be shifted somewhat by altering the composition of gel mixtures.[630] Changes in pectinate gels occur during aging, and at least some of these are due to the loss of ester in the pectinic acids in the gel during storage.[631]

The distribution of free carboxyl groups may be the main reason for the differences shown by low-ester pectinic acids prepared from high-ester pectinic acids by different methods, such as by the use of acid, alkali, or enzymes. Although this subject is still under intense investigation in several laboratories, it is already clear that the "rhythm" of de-esterification and the resulting distribution of free carboxyl groups has a marked effect on the bonding abilities and thus on the strength of the gel produced. The differences observed in acid-, alkali-, and enzyme-deesterified low-ester pectins were discussed in Chapter VI, while their use will be dealt with in Chapter XXVII.

[629] H. Deuel, G. Huber, and L. Anyas-Weisz, *Helv. Chim. Acta*, 33, 563 (1950).

[630] "Exchange Pectin L-M," California Fruit Growers Exchange, Ontario, California, 1947.

[631] G. L. Baker, C. W. Woodmansee, and E. E. Meschter, *Food Technol.*, 1, 11 (1947).

XVI. MISCELLANEOUS OBSERVATIONS

The turbidity of aqueous solutions of pectinic acids was measured by Speiser, Copley, and Nutting.[586] Palmer and Lotzkar[632] prepared x-ray diffraction photographs of sodium pectate fibers. Palmer, Merrill, and Ballantyne[582] investigated the x-ray diffraction of a series of pectinic acids from 0.2 to 10.9% methoxyl contents. Dwight and Kersten[633] found that irradiation of apple pectin with soft x-rays caused rapid degradation as measured by solution viscosities. The destructive effect was irreversible. Wuhrmann and Pilnik[634] investigated the x-ray diffraction of pectinic acid and of pectic acid prepared therefrom and state that the calculations made support the hypothesis that these compounds occur in folded chains.

In contrast to mannan and alginic acid, aqueous solutions of the methyl and monoglycol esters of pectic acid do not jellify when borax is added.[635]

Acetylpectin causes noticeable lowering of the surface tension, even in dilute solutions.[636] The interfacial tension in solutions of citrus and apple pectin was measured by Matthews.[637] The partial specific volume of a series of pectinic acid preparations was determined by Säverborn.[527] The values obtained decreased with decreasing pH values in the solutions. Becher and Leya[637a] reported that pectin powder will absorb aniline from benzol or ethanol solution. Anyas-Weisz and Deuel[637b] studied the coagulation by electrolytes and ethanol of artificially esterified pectinic acid (sodium oxyethylene pectinate). See also Chapters XXVII and XXVIII for some of the useful properties of pectic substances.

[632] K. J. Palmer and H. Lotzkar, *J. Am. Chem. Soc.*, **67**, 884 (1945).
[633] C. H. Dwight and H. Kersten, *J. Phys. Chem.*, **42**, 1168 (1938).
[634] K. Wuhrmann and W. Pilnik, *Experientia*, **1** (9), 1 (1945).
[635] H. Deuel, H. Neukom, and F. Weber, *Nature*, **161**, 96 (1948).
[636] K. Smolenski and W. Pardo, *Chem. Listy*, **25**, 446 (1932); through *C. A.*, **27**, 707 (1933).
[637] J. B. Matthews, *Trans. Faraday Soc.*, **35**, 1113 (1939).
[637a] R. Becher and S. Leya, *Experientia*, **3**, 282 (1947).
[637b] L. Anyas-Weisz and H. Deuel, *Helv. Chim. Acta*, **33**, 559 (1950).

CHAPTER VIII

Detection, Determination, and Characterization of Pectic Substances

The method used for the detection, estimation, or characterization of any given pectic substance depends on the type of information which is sought. In accordance with the great variety of scientific and technical interests in these compounds, many entirely different approaches must be used in such work. The chief interest of the botanist, for instance, consists in the location of the pectic substance in the tissue. The physiologist and plant biochemist, on the other hand, are more likely to seek knowledge concerning the proportions and behavior of these materials in plants. The chemist and technologist, again, are principally interested in the composition, structure, and useful properties of pectic substances. As a rule, a variety of methods must be used in most cases to obtain sufficient characterization of the pectic substance in question.

Many of the methods for the detection, determination, and characterization of pectic substances are comparatively recent, but most of them are modernized versions of procedures which were developed some time ago. It should always be remembered that there is still no unanimity of opinion concerning the structure—and even the composition—of pectic substances and that the views on the structural peculiarities responsible for many of the typical characteristics are still subjects of controversy. Such differences in viewpoint also influence the degree of confidence placed in any given method or, indeed, the application or distrust of determinations based on certain properties.

I. DETECTION OF PECTIC SUBSTANCES IN PLANT TISSUES

The whole course of development of the science of pectic substances during the nineteenth century was intimately related to the development of plant morphology and histological technics. As a result, much attention was paid to the location of pectic substances in plant tissues. The historical background of the methods of detection, determination, and characterization will not be discussed here. For these the reader is referred to Branfoot's[638] pamphlet which contains a splendid summary of the literature of histological methods dealing with the pectic constituents of plants.

Unlimited variations occur in the composition, structure, and, consequently, the behavior of plant tissues. In addition to these variations, the pectic constituents themselves vary widely in characteristics. It is impossible, therefore, to give any universally applicable procedures for the microscopic detection of pectic substances and a discussion of some of the principles followed is all that can be offered.

The methods used in histological investigations of the pectic constituents of plants may be grouped in the following two classes: (a) those which apply selective and specific solvents for the stepwise removal of certain types of plant constituents, including pectic substances, and (b) those which apply more-or-less specific stains to show the presence or absence of pectic constituents. The most satisfactory approach, however, is the use of combinations of selective removal and staining.

1. Removal of Various Structural Constituents to Show Presence and Location of Pectic Substances in Tissue

The cellulose occurring in plants may be removed by Schweitzer reagent.[639] Frémy,[640] who introduced this method, recommended that the slices of plant tissue be immersed in this reagent for several hours. The removal of the cellulose is usually complete, especially if sufficiently thin sections are applied. In the case of fruit tissues, microscopic examination of the treated sections reveals that the cellular structure has been retained, although the outlines of the cell walls may not be very distinct. It is generally assumed that this treatment with alkaline Schweitzer reagent transforms all pectic compounds of the tissue into copper pectate. By careful treatment of the slide with dilute (3 to 5%) acetic acid, the copper may be entirely removed. The remaining pectic acid is soluble in dilute alkali and may be gradually dissolved. The thin-walled structure observed after the removal of the pectic components is usually assumed to be the cellulose component of protopectin. Subsequent treatment with Schweitzer reagent now dissolves this cellulose. Unfortunately, a description of this method is more impressive than the results which are usually obtained by its use. The prolonged treatment with the strongly

[638] M. H. Branfoot (neé M. H. Carré), "A Critical and Historical Study of the Pectic Substances of Plants," Dept. of Sci. and Ind. Research, Special Report No. 33, H. M. Stationery Office, London (1929).

[639] E. Schweitzer, *J. prakt. Chem.*, **56**, 109 (1859).

[640] E. Frémy, *J. pharm. chim.*, **35**, 81 (1859).

alkaline reagent causes many alterations in the tissue. In addition, copper salts are formed by other compounds than the pectic substances and these may obscure the results. But at times—especially with tissues rich in pectic constituents—the results obtained by this method are quite satisfactory.

Cellulose is difficult to dissolve without the use of strong reagents. Pectic substances, on the other hand, may be easily solubilized, dissolved, and removed by successive treatments with acid and alkali. Microscopic observations on tissues from which the pectic components rather than cellulose have been removed are, therefore, much more satisfactory. Such methods, as described by Mangin,[641] for instance, often give good results and make a certain degree of differentiation between various pectic compounds possible. The essence of these procedures is as follows:

(1) The tissue sections are boiled with water. This treatment is very unspecific since it removes only some of the pectic components and simultaneously dissolves many other water-soluble nonpectic compounds.

(2) The tissue sections are boiled with 5% hydrochloric acid, followed by treatment with a warm 2–5% solution of potassium hydroxide. The hot acid affects solubilization of the pectic constituents. The tissue is thoroughly washed with water after the treatment. The protopectin is hydrolyzed and insoluble constituents such as calcium pectate, etc., are rendered soluble in alkali by the removal of the calcium (or other polyvalent ions) by the acid. The alkali, however, causes disintegration of the tissue owing to the decomposition of the middle lamella. After thorough washing, the tissue usually gives a positive reaction for cellulose but both staining and microchemical tests show the absence of pectic compounds.

(3) The sections are treated with acid ethanol. The great advantage in using the ethanol with the acid lies in the fact that the tissues do not disintegrate and, therefore, better microscopic observation is possible. After treatment with acid ethanol and washing with water, the tissue is treated with dilute ammonium hydroxide, alkali carbonates, or ammonium oxalate to dissolve the solubilized pectic constituents. The pectic constituents solubilized by the acid ethanol treatment will remain undissolved *in situ* and thus may be subsequently stained for observation. Thereafter the tissue may be treated with alkali and then stained again.

(4) The tissue slice is treated with Schweitzer's cellulose solvent as given above. Mangin also boiled sections with alkali, omitting the preliminary treatment with acid. The protopectin of the cell wall regions is largely unaffected by this treatment.

By using combinations of these methods a considerable amount of information may be gained concerning the presence, location, and types of pectic constituents in plant tissues. A more elegant approach is based on

[641] L. Mangin, *Compt. rend.*, 110, 295, 644 (1890).

the application of enzymes for the decomposition of tissue constituents. The use of enzymes for this purpose depends on their specificity toward certain compounds. By application of various enzyme mixtures, obtained chiefly from microorganisms, practically all constituents with the exception of cellulose and lignin may be digested with comparative ease. Although the specificity of commercial enzymes which act upon pectic substances has not been clearly established as yet, they have already been applied in such tests (see Chapter XIV). Certain pectic constituents may be distinguished at present by the use of commercial pectinases.[642] Calcium pectate, for instance, seems to be entirely unaffected even by prolonged treatment. There is much interest both in the specificity of pectic enzymes and in their application to histological investigations and important developments may be expected along these lines in the near future. Other enzymes such as amylases and proteolytic enzymes may also be applied for similar purposes. Unfortunately, complications often arise due to the insufficient specificity of such amylolytic and proteolytic enzymes and even more so because of the inaccessibility of the substrate in the plant tissue.[643]

2. Use of Stains for Observation of Pectic Constituents in Plant Tissues

Mangin[644] observed that the pectic constituents of plants behave as acidic substances, and are consequently not colored by the acid stains which are fixed by cellulose. He introduced a number of basic stains which can be used with some degree of success to distinguish the pectic compounds from cellulose, nitrogenous compounds, and other common plant constituents. These stains include safranin, night blue, methylene blue, and naphthalene blue. Safranin stains pectic compounds an orange-yellow color, while nitrogenous substances show cherry-red coloration. Methylene blue and night blue stain pectic substances violet blue, while nitrogenous substances appear a brighter blue, the difference being enhanced by examination of the stained sections in yellow light. Mangin also found that acidification of the stained sections on the slide causes decolorization of the pectic constituents whereas the remaining components remain unaffected. Double staining with naphthalene B.R. and acid green (Poirier), according to Mangin, gives excellent results; the pectic substances stain a violet color, while lignin, cutin, and nitrogenous substances are colored green. Branfoot[638] considers all these stains grossly unspecific and thus unreliable.

[642] J. D. Loconti and Z. I. Kertesz, *Food Research*, 6, 499 (1941).
[643] Z. I. Kertesz, *Plant Physiol.*, 12, 845 (1937).
[644] L. Mangin, *Compt. rend.*, 111, 120 (1890).

Use of ruthenium red (dilute ammoniacal solution of ruthenium oxychloride) as a stain for pectic compounds was introduced by Mangin[645] in 1893. It was first assumed to be entirely specific for the pectic substances, with the only exception of callose,[646] a still ill-defined constituent of the cell wall of root hairs. The latter substance may be easily differentiated from pectic substances by its solubility in acid. Some gums and hemicelluloses also show staining with ruthenium red. This, of course, may be caused at times by admixed pectic substances. Further limitations of the specificity of ruthenium red were discovered by Tobler[647] who states that glycogen and isolichenin also stain with this dye. Meyer[648] found that chromatin, nuclei, and coagulated or granular protoplasm are also colored by ruthenium red, and Priestley[649] pointed out that, in addition, the presence of fatty acids and lipides makes staining with ruthenium red unreliable.

In spite of the extensive use of ruthenium red, little is known about the mode of action of this stain beyond the fact that it is taken up by the cell walls in which (by other chemical methods) pectinic acid is known to be present. As Tetley[650] states, pectinic acids themselves do not take up stain until they have been treated with alkali. Demethylation by enzyme action also results in the formation (in slightly acid solution) of gellike precipitates which take up ruthenium red.[651] These observations may indicate that staining with ruthenium red shows the presence of pectic acid, pectates, or low-ester pectinic acids rather than of pectinic acids of a higher degree of (over 50%) methylation. Harlow[652] further warns that the differences in stainability of various cell constituents are quantitative rather than qualitative. In spite of these limitations, ruthenium red is still the best stain recommended for the observation of pectic constituents of plants under the microscope.

Branfoot[638,653] gives the following method for the preparation of ruthenium red-stained sections for microscopic examination:

Sections of the tissue are washed with water to remove sugars, acids, and other easily soluble compounds. They are then immediately stained with a freshly prepared dilute (0.02%) solution of ruthenium red. The stain is removed from the

[645] L. Mangin, *Compt. rend.*, 116, 653 (1893).
[646] E. C. Miller, *Plant Physiology*. 2nd ed., McGraw-Hill, New York, 1938.
[647] F. Tobler, *Z. wiss. Bot.*, 23, 182 (1906); through *Chem. Zentr.*, 2, 1020 (1906).
[648] A. Meyer, *Botan. Ztg.*, 62, 113 (1904); quoted in reference 638.
[649] J. H. Priestley, *New Phytologist*, 23, 1 (1924).
[650] U. Tetley, *J. Pomol. Hort. Sci.*, 8, 153 (1930).
[651] Z. I. Kertesz and J. D. Loconti, *New York State Agr. Expt. Sta.*, Tech. Bull. No. 272 (1944).
[652] W. M. Harlow, *New York State College of Forestry*, Tech. Bull. No. 24 (1928).
[653] M. H. Carré and A. S. Horne, *Ann. Botany*, 41, 1 (1927).

nonpectic structures by warming the section in water for a few minutes. After washing with water the pectic bodies are distinctly stained while the remainder of the cell structure is practically unstained. The sections are then examined and treated, in turn, with various reagents known to effect the decomposition of pectic compounds as given above. Such digestions are followed by further examinations under the microscope. Ammonium oxalate is recommended by Branfoot as a good general solvent for the removal of all pectic substances contained by the tissues.

Devaux[654] prefers ruthenium red in ethanol because none of the soluble pectin is lost from the tissue and the observations may thus also be made *in situ*. The insolubility of pectic substances in ethanol also facilitates subsequent separation of the various pectic compounds by the successive action of acid or alkali. Devaux emphasizes the necessity of avoiding prolonged heating with acid and other reagents since the decomposition products formed are no longer stainable with ruthenium red. He found that cold acid is just as suitable for the hydrolysis of protopectin as hot acid although the reaction is more rapid in the latter case.

Actually, in any systematic research on the pectic constituents of a given plant tissue, combinations of all these methods must be applied to show the presence and distribution of pectic compounds. Apparently little work along such lines has been done for a number of years, although there is great need for systematic investigation of the histological methodology of the detection of pectic substances.

II. DETECTION OF PECTIC SUBSTANCES IN SOLID MIXTURES

It is often desirable to ascertain whether pectic substances are present in a solid or liquid mixture. The tests which may be used for this purpose can be grouped according to whether they are designed to show the presence of: (a) pectic substances directly, or (b) (after decomposition of the pectic material) galacturonic acid and, in the case of pectinic acids, methanol. Microscopic examination of solid preparations has been claimed by Casavecchia[655] to give valuable information on the presence of pectic substances in solid mixtures. It is rather likely, however, that the usefulness of such tests is restricted to showing the presence of foreign materials (especially starches and gums) which are added to pectic preparations as adulterants. Staining with ruthenium red may also give some, although often none too conclusive, information on the possible presence of pectic materials. The best and most common procedure is to dissolve

---

[654] H. Devaux, *Mem. soc. sci. phys. natl. Bordeaux*, 3 (6), 89 (1903); quoted in reference 638.
[655] E. S. di Casavecchia, *Chim. ind. agr. biol.*, 15, 322 (1939).

the dry preparation in hot water and make the tests in solution as described below. If some of the material is insoluble in water and if there is some suspicion that water-insoluble pectic materials may be present, one or both of the procedures given below should be used in the preparation of the test solution:

(1) If protopectin is present, heating of the finely pulverized material in 0.1 N hydrochloric acid (1:50) for 1 hour at 80°C. renders a sufficient proportion of it soluble for dissolution in hot water.

(2) If insoluble pectinates or pectates are present, the dry powder should be extracted with several successive portions of a fairly large (1:100) volume of 90% ethanol containing 0.1 N hydrochloric acid. This solution removes calcium or other ions which render the salts insoluble and, after the washings with acid ethanol, they dissolve in water or very dilute alkali.

If there is need to detect the presence of pectic substances in a solid mixture, without or after the application of these two methods of solubilization, the procedure described in Section III-9 should be applied. These tests can be performed by starting with a suspension of the material in question and then proceeding as outlined.

III. TESTS FOR PECTIC MATERIALS IN SOLUTION

The aim of the analyst should be to obtain a solution containing 0.1 to 1.0% of pectic substances. The tests which show the presence of pectic substances as such (without necessity of decomposition) will be described first. The methods for the detection of components will be listed under Sections 8 and 9.

1. Detection by Viscosity

Pectinic acids and most other pectic compounds in water solution show a typical high viscosity. With pectinic acids of high degrees of methylation the highest viscosity usually occurs around pH 6. However, in the case of low-ester pectins the maximum viscosity is observable at lower pH values. This method has been extensively used for the detection of pectinic acids. Letzig[656] recommended viscometric observation for the detection of added pectinic acids in the case of milk and milk products.

Detection by the abnormal viscosity is comparatively simple with milk but in the case of milk products there is a considerable increase in the viscosity of the serum due to the ripening process even without added pectinic acid. In such cases and, as a matter of fact, in most cases, pectic enzymes may be used to advantage. The viscosity of the (filtered) solution or extract is determined at some pH value between 3 and 4 and then 0.05% of a highly active commercial pectinase (see

[656] E. Letzig, Z. Untersuch. Lebensm., 84, 289 (1942).

Chapter XV) is added together with a small crystal of thymol. After keeping the mixture at temperatures between 30 and 40°C. for at least 4 hours but prefer-ably overnight, the viscosity is again determined. A control determination is run in the same manner but with the enzyme previously heated to 100°C. for 10 minutes. If pectic substances are present and responsible for the high viscosity of the solution, they are decomposed by the enzyme and the viscosity of the solu-tion is reduced to a value caused by the nonpectic constituents in the solution. The limited specificity of commercial pectinases should not be overlooked, how-ever, especially if the presence of hemicelluloses or gums is suspected.

2. Detection by Precipitation with Ethanol

All pectic substances are precipitated from solution by the addition of 2 volumes of ethanol. In the case of solutions of about 1% the addition of equal volumes of 95% ethanol is sufficient to produce a translucent gelatinous precipitate. With more dilute solutions or pectinic acids which are partially degraded or have a low ester content, the precipitate is less gelatinous. In the case of ash-free pectinic acids precipitation from dilute solution is again somewhat more difficult. Solutions of Irish moss, agar, gum arabic, and karaya gum are not precipitated with 50% ethanol. In addition, the polyose of tamarind seed (see Chapter XVIII, Section IV), quince seed and locust bean gums also give such precipitates[657] with ethanol at this low concentration. The occurrence of a precipitate on the addition of ethanol, therefore, is by no means evidence that pectic sub-stances are present. On the other hand, if there is no precipitate whatso-ever (even after standing for a few hours), it may be concluded that pectic compounds are absent from the solution. Starch and many other compounds common in plant tissues also precipitate with ethanol, especi-ally as the ethanol concentration is increased from 50 to 70 or 80%. In the case of solutions containing small proportions of dissolved pectic substances together with large quantities of other materials, precipitation with 2 volumes of ethanol (giving a final concentration of about 60% in the mixture) should always be performed as a preliminary step of puri-fication for both qualitative tests and quantitatives estimation.

Balavoine[658] described a procedure for the detection of pectic sub-stances in solid mixtures. The material is first extracted with ether and dried and then treated with water at room temperature. The extract is centrifuged and the residue is then extracted with hot 2% hydrochloric acid. The presence of pectinic acids in the combined extracts is then as-certained by viscosity determinations used in combination with precipita-tion with ethanol, tannin, and various other reagents.

[657] E. F. Bryant, Ind. Eng. Chem., Anal. Ed., 13, 103 (1941).
[658] P. Balavoine, Mitt. Lebensm. Hyg., 36, 274 (1945).

3. Detection by Flocculation with Alkaline Earth Bases

Pectinic and pectic acids are precipitated on being boiled with calcium hydroxide. The reaction depends on the demethylation of pectinic acids, followed by the precipitation of the pectic acid as calcium pectate. The precipitate is insoluble in an excess of the reagent. Flocculation is retarded by the presence of sucrose and partially prevented by the presence of more than small proportions of sodium, potassium, and ammonium salts. Barium hydroxide causes even more rapid flocculation and is affected in a similar manner by the presence of the above salts.

4. Use of Fruit Juices Rich in Tannin as Reagents

The dilute extract or expressed juice of a number of tannin-rich fruits may be used as a very sensitive reagent for pectic substances. Griebel,[659] who describes this method in detail, attributes the action to some compounds which occur, in addition to tannin, in these fruit extracts. The sloe fruit (*Prunus spinosa*), the berry of the service tree (*Sorbus domestica*), wild apples, field pears, and lotus plums, as well as Cornelian cherries (*Cornus mascula*) and several other fruits may be used for this purpose.

The ripe fruit is peeled rapidly with a brass knife, and the juice is removed by pressure, boiled, and filtered while hot. The reagent is stable for several years when kept at ice-box temperatures and covered with a layer of toluene. For the test 0.2 cc. of the extract is added in small drops to 1 cc. of the sample in a test tube. A solution of pectin as dilute as 0.01% first produces a haze, soon followed by the occurrence of a precipitate. This method of testing for pectic substances has never attained any wide degree of popularity, perhaps because most investigators prefer to use better understood reactions.

5. Use of Thorium Nitrate and Neutral Lead Acetate to Identify Pectin and Differentiate It from Gums and Hemicelluloses

These tests are useful for the identification of pectinic acids in mixtures with hemicelluloses and gums.

The mixture should first be purified by precipitation with ethanol as described under Section 2 above. The solid material is then dissolved in water to make an approximately 1% solution. As stated before, quince seed and locust bean gums are also precipitated by 50% ethanol, as are most other gums, as the ethanol concentration is raised above 60%. Bryant[657] recommends the following procedure: To 10 cc. of the approximately 1% solution containing the mixture of gums (already purified by ethanol precipitation), 1 cc. of 10% thorium nitrate solution is added; the mixture is stirred and allowed to stand for 2 minutes. If a gel re-

[659] C. Griebel, *Z. Untersuch. Lebensm.*, **63**, 291 (1932).

sults, either pectinic acids or quince seed gum or both are present. If there is no precipitate, there are no pectic substances present. By the addition of 1 cc. of 5 N acetic acid before the thorium nitrate solution or the use of neutral lead acetate the presence of pectinic acids or gums may be ascertained. The reactions of the most common gums and pectinic acid with thorium nitrate and neutral lead acetate are summarized in Table 23. Balavoine[658] also described tests to differentiate pectic substances from various gums, gelatin, agar, proteins, etc.

TABLE 23

REACTIONS OF PECTINIC ACID, GUMS, AND HEMICELLULOSES WITH THORIUM NITRATE AND NEUTRAL LEAD ACETATE (ADAPTED FROM BRYANT)

Material used	Thorium nitrate alone	Thorium nitrate and acetic acid	Neutral lead acetate alone	Neutral lead acetate and acetic acid
Pectinic acid	Firm, transparent gel	Very weak gel, a thickening	Firm, transparent gel	Firm, brittle, clear gel
Quince seed gum	Firm, opaque gel	Firm gel	Fairly firm gel	Very weak gel, a thickening
Locust bean gum	0[a]	0	Slight thickening	0
Irish moss	Stringy white precipitate	White granular precipitate	Cloudy	Cloudy
Agar	Slight haze	0	0	0

[a] The 0 denotes no apparent reaction. Gum arabic, gum tragacanth, karaya gum, methyl cellulose, and starch give no reactions under these conditions.

6. Color Formation and Fluorescence with Potassium Permanganate

According to Savini and Gianferrara[660] pectic substances in solution may be detected and in addition distinguished from gum tragacanth, gum arabic, lichen, and agar by their reaction with 0.25% potassium permanganate solution. When a mixture with the reagent is heated to the boiling point, intense malaga coloration with slight greenish fluorescence is obtained. The various other compounds listed above give a reddish coloration with no fluorescence. The nature of the reaction which occurs and its sensitiveness and specificity are not well established.

7. Formation of Yellow Color with Alkali

A typical reaction for pectic substances in solution is the yellow color formed upon the addition of strong alkali. To 0.5 cc. of solution, which should contain at least 0.5% pectic material, a few drops of 2% potassium hydroxide are added. A strong yellow coloration occurs. The color may be best observed after about 15 minutes' standing at room tempera-

[660] G. Savini and S. Gianferrara, *Ann. chim. applicata*, **29**, 111 (1939); through *C. A.*, **33**, 8528 (1939).

ture. Upon subsequent acidification, a white, flocculent precipitate, consisting of pectic acid, appears in the mixture. In more concentrated solutions solid, yellow-colored gels may form. The reaction does not occur in dilute solutions and is also given by alginic and ascorbic acids. See also Chapter VII, Section II-2, on this reaction.

8. Detection of Pectinic Acids through Methanol Split Off from Ester Groups

This test depends on the detection of methanol after alkaline saponification and distillation of the methanol formed. As a preliminary step the precipitation of the test material from solution with 2 volumes of acetone is recommended. Ethanol is not suitable in the present case because it adheres tenaciously to the precipitate (see Section VII-2 below). If there is suspicion that the sample has been previously precipitated with ethanol (or if acetone is not available) the adhering ethanol should be removed by one of the several procedures described for this purpose. Stone and Rohner[661] describe the following procedure for the determination:

The mixture (1 g.) to be tested for the presence of pectinic acid is dissolved in 50 cc. of boiling water in a small Erlenmeyer flask. The solution is cooled to about 70°C. and 5 cc. of 5 N sodium hydroxide solution is added. The mixture is permitted to stand, after thorough stirring, for 10 minutes. Dilute sulfuric acid is then added until the solution becomes slightly acid and the mixture is distilled and 5 cc. distillate collected by using any standard equipment or, in the absence of such, a bent glass tube reaching into a test tube. The latter is surrounded with ice water. The methanol split off from the pectinic acid and distilled over is then detected by any of the common tests as described in the recent editions of the U. S. Pharmacopeia or in *Methods of Analysis* of the A. O. A. C.,[662] for instance. The latter employs a modification of Denigè's method, and recommends that the unknown solution (0.25 cc.) be mixed in a Nessler tube, with 4.75 cc. of water and 2 cc. of a 3% potassium permanganate solution containing 15% sirupy phosphoric acid. After 10 minutes of standing with occasional shaking (without inverting the tube), 2 cc. of a mixture of oxalic and sulfuric acids (5 g. of oxalic acid dissolved in 100 cc. of 1:1 sulfuric acid) is added. Thereupon 5 cc. of modified Schiff reagent is added, the tube is inverted 3 times, stoppered, and allowed to stand for 1 hour. The Schiff reagent is prepared by dissolving 0.2 g. of rosaniline hydrochloride of sufficient purity in about 120 cc. of hot water. The solution is cooled and 2 g. of sodium sulfite, dissolved in 20 cc. of water, and 2 cc. of hydrochloric acid are added; the mixture is diluted to 200 cc. and kept in the refrigerator for at least 24 hours before use. The color in the Nessler tube

[661] I. Stone and R. Rohner, *Chemist-Analyst*, **21**, 10 (1932).
[662] *Official and Tentative Methods of Analysis*. 6th ed., Association of Official Agricultural Chemists, Washington, D. C., 1945.

is compared with a control mixture prepared from the reagents only. If the test mixture shows a deeper color than the control, the methanol may be quantitatively determined by comparison with standards containing 22% ethanol and different quantities of methanol. Stone and Rohner[661] recommend that in this test the whole 5 cc. distillate and no water be used, that only 0.5 cc. of potassium permanganate solution be used in the oxidation, and that 5 drops of 5% manganese sulfate be added to the test solution after the addition of the oxalic acid reagent in order to speed up the reduction of the unused permanganate.

The sensitivity of the test naturally depends on the sensitivity of the method for detecting the methanol: 10 mg. of commercial pectin shows definite coloration in the test in 30 minutes, 25 mg. in 10 minutes. The test, obviously, is of more limited use on pectinic acids of low ester content. Stone and Rohner found that commercial samples of agar, gum arabic, gum karaya, quince seed gum, locust bean gum, Irish moss, dextrin, starch, and Galagum give negative results, indicating the expected absence of methyl ester groups. Gum tragacanth, on the other hand, gives a strong reaction, caused by the methanol derived from the pectinic acids admixed to this gum. Janot and Gonnard[663] found 1.9–3.8% methoxyl in a series of samples of this gum obtained from different sources.

9. Detection of Galacturonic Acid Obtained by Hydrolysis of Pectic Substances

The detection of galacturonic acid in hydrolyzates of pectic substances is a convenient method of identification.

In order to remove nonpectic polygalacturonic acids, galacturonic acid, and the bulk of accompanying sugars, hemicelluloses, etc., the sample is either dissolved and precipitated with a final concentration of 60% acid ethanol, or finely ground and extracted with this solvent. The precipitate or extracted sample is then dissolved in water and either digested with a commercial pectinase as outlined before, or hydrolyzed by refluxing for 1 hour with 0.5 N hydrochloric acid. The digest should be filtered and then used for any of the tests for galacturonic acid described in Chapter II. Some specific test for galacturonic acid should always be used in conjunction with the tests listed above under Sections 1 to 8. If it is of great importance to obtain absolute proof of the presence of pectic substances in a mixture, many of the tests listed here may be applied in succession to the unknown for the detection of the presence of pectic substances. Intonti and Giacometti[664] describe a scheme in which a whole series of tests for pectic substances and galacturonic acid are used on the same sample.

[663] M. M. Janot and P. Gonnard, *Compt. rend.*, 207, 549 (1938).
[664] R. Intonti and T. Giacometti, *Ann. chim. applicata*, 32, 297 (1942); through *C. A.*, 38, 4712 (1944).

IV. QUANTITATIVE DETERMINATION OF PECTIC SUBSTANCES

The uncertainties of definition at times cause considerable trouble in the quantitative determination of pectic substances. Even if protopectin, which we can estimate by difference only, is overlooked, the line of demarcation between nonpectic polygalacturonic acids and those which we regard as "typical" pectic substances is hazy indeed. This shows up in the discrepancies between various methods of determination, especially where the separation of the pectic substances depends on precipitation. As shown before, the ethanol precipitates (see Table 13) and calcium pectate yields obtained during the degradation or decomposition of pectinic acids will depend on the average molecular size and on the distribution patterns of various polygalacturonic acids in the sample. It is for this reason that: (*1*) one should always adhere exactly to the procedures given; and (*2*) the method by which any given set of results has been obtained should always be specified.

Quantitative Estimation of Protopectin

As was indicated in the discussion of protopectin (Chapter III, Section III), little is known about this compound. It is even possible that protopectin is not a separate chemical entity but rather a specifically immobilized pectinic acid. The only method which was ever claimed to separate protopectin[665] in the pure form has been found unreliable by many workers. As a matter of fact, this method would be unsuitable for the quantitative estimation of protopectin even if it could always be carried out successfully. The definition of protopectin states that it is "a substance which occurs in plants and which upon restricted hydrolysis yields pectin or pectinic acids." In harmony with this indirect definition, protopectin is always determined by difference. From the tissue or other sample the "soluble" or "water-soluble" pectic constituents are extracted by any of the methods given in Chapter VI. This is followed by treatments which cause the solubilization of protopectin. The line of demarcation between "soluble" and "insoluble" pectic substances (protopectin) is ill defined and arbitrary. Practically every author prefers and describes a different method. This is understandable because most source materials require specific procedures in order to attain efficiency and accuracy in the determination.

For these reasons only a short discussion of the methods which may be used for the quantitative estimation of protopectin will be presented here. In the author's laboratory the "soluble" pectic constituents are removed from the

[665] R. Sucharipa, *J. Am. Chem. Soc.*, **46**, 145 (1924).

well-ground tissue or sample by extractions for 2 hours each with 3 successive portions of cold (20–25°C.) distilled water used in the ratio of approximately 100 cc. per gram of sample. The separation is either accomplished by filtration on fast filter paper[666] or by centrifuging, or a combination of both. As a rule, after three such extractions followed by rinsing at least 98% of the "soluble" pectic substances is removed, although small quantities will be found in the extract even after repeating the extraction many times. The method used by Carré and Haynes,[667] which involves sixty to eighty extractions with water, is hardly practical and perhaps not even more exact. The pectic constituents which remain in the sample can be regarded (especially in the case of plant tissues) as "protopectin." These pectic constituents may then be solubilized by any of a number of methods described in Chapter VI, washed out of the sample, and determined by the procedures given below for pectinic acids or pectic acids. Of the methods of extraction, treatment with subsequent portions of 0.5% ammonium oxalate at 85°C. for 2 hours or with 0.05 N hydrochloric acid in the same manner are the most common. Three extractions followed by rinsing are usually sufficient to obtain at least 99% of the total pectic substances present.

If the sample contains plant tissues which have been treated in such a manner that transformations resulting in the insolubilization of the pectic substances are suspected, the progress of extraction must be checked by analyzing the subsequent extracts. This is a common difficulty when plant tissues are treated with calcium or other polyvalent ions, especially salts of heavy metals. In such cases it is necessary to treat the sample before extraction with 95% ethanol containing 0.05 N hydrochloric acid.

At times considerable difficulty may be encountered in the extraction of pectic constituents from some plant materials, especially woody tissues. A further difficulty is that, with the small proportion of pectic material, in such tissues, relatively large proportions of various hemicelluloses will be present in the extracts. These difficulties were reviewed by Anderson and Sands.[668] Wurz and Swoboda[669] recommend treatment of the tissue with 1% hydrochloric acid for 30 hours at 20°C., followed by extraction with 0.2% ammonium hydroxide for 3 hours at the same temperature. Lüdtke[670] and Lüdtke and Felsner[671] also describe various methods for the extraction of pectic substances from flax stems and wood.

[666] See footnote 334, p. 101.

[667] M. H. Carré and D. Haynes, *Biochem. J.*, 16, 60 (1922).

[668] E. Anderson and L. Sands, in W. W. Pigman and M. L. Wolfrom, *Advances in Carbohydrate Chemistry*. Vol. I, Academic Press, New York, p. 329.

[669] O. Wurz and O. Swoboda, *Papier-Fabrikant*, 37, 125 (1939); through *Analyst*, 73, 350 (1948).

[670] M. Lüdtke, *Holz als Roh-und Werkstoff*, 5, 338 (1942); through *C. A.*, 38, 1635 (1944).

[671] M. Lüdtke and H. Felsner, *Cellulosechemie*, 21, 86 (1943).

V. QUANTITATIVE DETERMINATION OF TOTAL PECTIC SUBSTANCES

The term "total pectic substances" covers all polygalacturonides, whether originally soluble in water or not, which when brought into solution will satisfy the criteria given in Chapter I. Thus "total pectic substances" will include protopectin, pectinic, and pectic acids, as well as pectates and pectinates. It will also be obvious to the reader that the numerical figure denoting the total proportion of pectic substances in a given sample of plant tissue will depend (1) on the method of extraction and (2) on the method of estimation.

Obviously, many of the methods given in Chapter VI and especially combinations of several methods will be suitable for the extraction of all pectic substances from a tissue sample. The merits and disadvantages of these extraction procedures have been discussed in detail.

When the purpose of an investigation is to obtain the proportion of total pectic substances without an attempt to preserve these as intact as possible, the procedure is quite simple. The ground tissue is extracted in the Weihe-Phillips apparatus shown in Figure 8 (Chapter VI) with successive portions of 0.05 N hydrochloric acid at 80°C., using 30 minutes for every extraction. After 3 to 5 extractions using 50 cc. of acid per gram of (dry) tissue, the bulk of all pectic substances will have been extracted. The completeness of the extraction can be easily ascertained by mixing a small amount of the cooled extract with ethanol in a 1:2 ratio.

Ammonium oxalate (0.5%) and many other agents have been also used for the determination of the total pectic substances in plant tissues. However, it seems from experiences in the author's laboratory that multiple extraction with acid is more desirable and is less likely to cause subsequent difficulties. The acid extraction procedure was described in detail in Chapter VI, Section II. Experience has also shown that, although some degradation of the extracted pectins may occur during the heating, this would cause no significant differences in the quantity of pectin found by any of the methods given later in this chapter.

The combined extracts are filtered clear of suspended particles and then the solution is used for the determination of pectic substances by any of the methods given below, preferably by ethanol precipitation followed by estimation of the calcium pectate yield. For details see the following pages.

VI. QUANTITATIVE ESTIMATION OF PECTINIC AND PECTIC ACIDS

In this section methods for the quantitative estimation of pectinic and pectic acids will be described. It will be assumed that the sample or material in which the proportion of pectic constituents is to be ascertained is already in solution or that it can be dissolved in water without difficulty. Boiling water and vigorous stirring should be used in making the solution. In the case of high-grade pectins precautions should be taken to prevent "clumping" (see p. 188). Fresh extracts from plant tissues show a sediment upon prolonged standing which, however, is rarely composed of pectic materials. Solutions should be kept at ice-box temperatures and in the presence of some toluene or thymol to prevent bacterial infection. Once a solution is visibly invaded by microorganisms, the addition of these preservatives is of little help since the enzymes present might proceed with hydrolysis. It is safest to make the solutions in boiled water by dispersing the sample as described previously, followed by cooling and the immediate addition of a preservative.

1. Determination of Pectinic Acids without Demethylation

(a) Precipitation with Ethanol

The earliest analytical method for the determination of dissolved pectic substances consisted of precipitation with two volumes of ethanol, filtration, and drying and weighing of the precipitate. This method is useful in the case of pure pectic substances but has many faults when used on unknown mixtures, especially plant extracts. Proteins, starch, dextrins, hemicelluloses, and many other common plant constituents are also precipitated by ethanol. Furthermore, as we have seen earlier, pectinic acids may fail to precipitate under certain conditions from solutions containing less than 0.05% pectinic acid.[672] Until 1922 there was no standard method for the determination of pectinic acids as ethanol precipitate. In that year Wichmann[673] described a method which with slight modifications is still given as a "tentative" procedure for "alcohol precipitate" in the *Official and Tentative Methods of Analysis*.[662]

To 100 cc. of the (prepared) solution, in a beaker, 4–8 g. of sucrose (1 or 2 lumps of cube sugar) is added (if sugar is not already present) and the mixture evaporated to a volume of 20–25 cc. If water-insoluble matter separates during evaporation more sucrose is added. The solution is then cooled to room temperature and 200 cc. of 95% ethanol is introduced slowly and with constant stirring. The mixture is allowed to stand for at least 1 hour, filtered on 15-cm. qualitative filter paper, and the precipitate is washed with ethanol. The precipitate should not be permitted to dry on the paper. The precipitate is then washed back into the original beaker with hot water and the filter paper rinsed thoroughly. The solution is evaporated to about 20 cc. and 5 cc. of (1:2.5) hydrochloric acid is added. If water-insoluble matter separates, the mixture is stirred well and, if necessary, warmed slightly. Again 200 cc. ethanol is added, the mixture is allowed to stand for 1 hour, and filtered through paper. The precipitate and paper are

[672] M. H. Carré, *Biochem. J.*, **16**, 704 (1922).
[673] H. J. Wichmann, *J. Assoc. Offic. Agr. Chemists*, **6**, 35 (1922).

washed thoroughly with ethanol to remove all hydrochloric acid. The precipitate is then rinsed from the paper with hot water into a platinum dish, evaporated to dryness on a steam bath, dried to constant weight in a water oven, and weighed, ignited, and weighed again. The loss of weight is the "alcohol precipitate." As the precipitate is often colorless and almost invisible, care must be exercised that none is lost in the transferring and dissolving operations. If the quantity of the ethanol precipitate, as indicated by its volume in the first precipitation, is not excessive, the second filtration may be made through a Gooch crucible containing a thin asbestos mat. If the quantity of the precipitate is very small it may not be visible at all. In this case a small amount of sodium chloride should be added to the solution. This will flocculate the precipitate and render it visible.

While the ethanol precipitate determined in this manner includes all pectic substances, it may also contain many of the other previously mentioned plant constituents. As we have seen, the concentration of ethanol used in the precipitation will influence the purity of the pectic material precipitated and, contrary to earlier belief, more dilute ethanol yields a purer pectic precipitate. The following procedure is used in the author's laboratory for the determination of soluble pectic substances as ethanol precipitate.

To 50 cc. of the solution, preferably containing about 0.1–0.25 g. of pectic substances, enough concentrated hydrochloric acid is added to render it 0.15 N. After mixing, 100 cc. of 95% ethanol is introduced dropwise and with constant stirring. After standing for at least 1 hour, the precipitate is filtered off on a fast paper, washed with a mixture of water and ethanol (1:2) containing 0.05 N hydrochloric acid, and dissolved through the paper with hot water to give a total volume of 50 cc. If difficulties are encountered in dissolving the precipitate a few drops of dilute alkali may be added to the hot water. The filtrate is neutralized and made up to 50 cc. Hydrochloric acid and ethanol are again added as described above. The precipitate is filtered off, washed with an ethanol–water mixture until the filtrate is free from acid, then rinsed with 95% ethanol, transferred into a platinum dish, with hot water, evaporated, dried, weighed, ignited, and weighed again. In the absence of interesting foreign materials the difference is the quantity of pectic substances present; in the presence of interfering materials (as in plant extracts, etc.) it gives the maximum value for the pectic substances in the solution.

Tests for starch and dextrins in plant extracts should always be made before precipitation. If starch is present in the solution this may be digested first as described in Chapter VI, Section III-1.

(b) Precipitation with Acetone

Acetone, like ethanol, precipitates pectic substances from water solutions. Hinton[674] compared the merits of ethanol and acetone precipita-

[674] C. L. Hinton, Fruit Pectins, Their Chemical Behaviour, and Jellying Properties. Chem. Publishing Co., New York, 1940.

tion and prefers the latter since it gives a firmer coagulum and acetone is easier to recover. Acetone, however, must be used at a lower concentration than ethanol because at higher strengths it precipitates more non-pectic materials than does ethanol. Hinton recommends the following procedure for the determination of pectinic acids by acetone precipitation.

The quantity of dilute solution used should contain about 0.1 g. of pectinic acid. Sufficient acetone is stirred in slowly to make the final concentration of acetone about 50%. The mixture is allowed to stand for a few minutes and poured through a 15-cm. filter paper. When the precipitate has drained fairly free from liquid, it is washed back into the beaker with cold water. The volume is adjusted to 100 cc. with water and, if necessary, warmed to dissolve the precipitate. It is then cooled and precipitated with acetone as before. If necessary, a little sodium chloride solution may be added to assist coagulation. The precipitate is filtered off on a tared ashless 15-cm. filter paper, washed with 60% acetone, and dried to constant weight, which is conveniently done at 100°C. over-night. For more exact results the dried filter paper and precipitate are ashed after weighing and half of the weight of the ash is deducted from the weight of the acetone precipitate. This correction for the ash is only an approximate one, and when the proportion of ash is high, the determination is less accurate. Results by this method may be occasionally high, owing to the inclusion of non-pectic materials precipitated by the acetone.

(c) Determination of Soluble Pectic Substances by Electrodeposition

Soluble pectic substances are negatively charged and therefore may be collected on the anode of a suitably arranged electrolysis system. Brown[675] attempted the deposition of pectinic acid electrolytically but was unsuccessful because the aqueous solutions contained large amounts of electrolytes. Griggs and Johnstin[676] observed that pectinic acid is flocculated at the anode upon electrolysis with 110-volt direct current. More recently Williams and Johnson[677] described a complete procedure for the determination of soluble pectic compounds by electrolysis preceded by removal of most of the electrolytes from the solution. The details of the method are as follows:

A conventional electrolysis apparatus supplied with 220-v. direct current from a rectifier-transformer unit is used. The mercury cathode cell may be easily constructed from a 250-cc. Griffin-type beaker into the side of which a platinum wire is fused. A side arm, filled with clean mercury, is added on the outside of the beaker to provide a convenient connection to the cathode. For the anode a 45-mesh platinum gauze disc, 6.25 mm. in diameter, is used. This is edged with 0.75-mm. platinum wire to give rigidity, and is supported with a 15-cm. long

[675] J. C. Brown, *Am. Vinegar Ind.*, 2, 14 (1923).
[676] M. A. Griggs and R. Johnstin, *Ind. Eng. Chem.*, 18, 623 (1926).
[677] K. T. Williams and C. M. Johnson, *Ind. Eng. Chem., Anal. Ed.*, 16, 23 (1944).

piece of 1.25-mm. platinum wire attached to the center. Such disc-shaped electrodes have proved to be more practical than the usual cylindrical or spiral electrodes, since the disc anode–mercury cathode system makes it possible to have most of the solution under the influence of the field without stirring. An aliquot of the aqueous solution containing approximately 5 to 50 mg. of pectinic acid is placed in the electrolysis vessel and diluted to 50 cc. with distilled water. Thereupon 24 cc. of 95% ethanol is added with stirring. In order to obtain quantitative deposition in the shortest time, the ethanol concentration must be close to 40% by volume. Any precipitation of the pectinic acid by this concentration of ethanol indicates that the electrolyte content of the solution is too high and that these must be removed. This is best accomplished by the use of ion-exchange resin columns as described in Chapter VI, Section III-2. During the electrolysis the vessel is immersed in a water–ice bath to prevent any undue rise in the temperature of the solution. The weighed anode is lowered into the solution so that the gauze is barely covered and the current is connected. The current may vary between 5 and 20 milliamperes, depending on the electrolyte content and temperature of the solution. Occasionally it is necessary to adjust the level of the anode disc as the level of the solution changes as a result of changes in temperature. At the end of 5 hours the anode is withdrawn from the vessel, and immersed in 99% ethanol for 3 minutes and then in anhydrous ether for 3 minutes. The alcohol–ether treatment enables the precipitate to dry completely after one hour of heating at 105°C. The cooled electrode is then weighed again. The electrodes are cleaned by immersion in boiling water to which a little dilute alkali may be added. Removal of the deposit by ignition in a flame is undesirable because it may change the electrode surface.

In a series of analyses by this method, Williams and Johnson obtained results 9 to 13% higher than by the determination of the pectinic acid as calcium pectate by the procedure of Emmett and Carré.[678] On pectic acid solutions the results were practically identical with the calcium pectate values. These authors claim that the procedure is preferable to the calcium pectate method (see below) since it is less time consuming and needs less of the analyst's attention.

It may be added that the differences between results of the electrolytic and calcium pectate methods for pectinic acids are likely to be caused by the fractionation which occurs during the calcium pectate precipitation but not in the electrolytic procedure.

(d) Some Other Possible Methods for Determination of Pectinic Acids

A variety of other methods may be suggested for the determination of pectinic acids but only turbidimetric measurements and the estimation on the basis of optical rotation will be noted here.

The turbidity of a solution of pectinic or pectic acids will vary with

[678] A. M. Emmett and M. H. Carré, Biochem. J., 20, 6 (1926).

conditions. Turbidity caused by the addition of mineral acids will increase with decreasing ester content and increasing electrolyte concentrations. The turbidity upon acidification will also markedly increase during degradation by heat. There is no evidence at the present time that turbidimetric measurements are suitable for the determination of pectic substances.

The optical rotation of any given solution of pectinic or pectic acids is a function of concentration and the length of the solution through which the polarized light passes. As we have seen in Chapter VII (Section IX), various conditions of observation, e.g., the pH of the solution, will also have an influence. Inasmuch as there is no evidence at the present time that pectinic or pectic acids have a constant specific rotation, this method of determination is useful only when the specific rotation of the preparation on hand is established. Thus optical rotation may be applied for the determination of the concentration of pectinic or pectic acid in a solution of a given preparation of defined optical rotation but not as a general method for the estimation of pectinic and pectic acids not already characterized.

2. Determination of Pectic Substances as Pectic Acid

(a) Precipitation with Hydrochloric Acid

Pectic acids are precipitated from solution by strong mineral acids. Since, under certain conditions, the solubility of pectic acids even in hot water is very low, this method may well be applied to the quantitative estimation of pectic substances. The procedure given below is directly applicable in the case of dissolved pectic acid (acid pectates). When it is certain that no methyl ester groups are present in the pectic material used, the first step of saponification may be omitted, although no harm will be done by carrying out the entire procedure just as given below for pectinic acid. As with the ethanol precipitation, most workers until about 1922 used a variety of methods for the quantitative precipitation of pectic acids by mineral acid. Wichmann,[673] in that year, published a method for the determination of soluble pectic substances in the form of pectic acid. The pectic acid precipitate formed during this procedure has been assumed by Nelson[679] to be identical with the hypothetical "digalacturonic acid" of Ehrlich and Sommerfeld.[680] Subsequently the Official and Tentative Methods of Analysis of the A. O. A. C. adopted the term "pectic acid (di-galacturonic acid)" and this archaic term still appeared in the most recent (1950) edition of this handbook. Of course

[679] E. K. Nelson, J. Am. Chem. Soc., 48, 2412 (1926).
[680] F. Ehrlich and R. Sommerfeld, Biochem. Z., 168, 2519 (1926).

it is now clear that the pectic acid obtained by this procedure is not a digalacturonic acid. Up to the present time (1950), this latter compound has not been isolated and described. The essence of Wichmann's procedure is as follows:

To 25 cc. of a fairly concentrated (1%) solution or to a more dilute solution evaporated to this volume, 8–12 g. of sucrose and 200 cc. of 95% ethanol are added with constant and vigorous stirring and the precipitate is allowed to settle. The precipitate is filtered off on 15-cm. qualitative filter paper, washed with ethanol, and transferred to the original beaker with hot water. The solution is evaporated to about 40 cc. and cooled to below 25°C. If water-insoluble material separates during evaporation, the mixture is stirred vigorously and, if necessary, a few drops of hydrochloric acid (1:2.5) are added and the solution is first warmed, and then cooled again. Now 50 cc. of 0.2–1% sodium hydroxide (depending on the amount of precipitate) is added, and the solution is mixed and allowed to stand for 15 minutes. Then 40 cc. of water and 10 cc. of the above hydrochloric acid solution are added and the mixture is boiled for 5 minutes. Afterward the precipitate is filtered off and washed with hot water. The filtration should be rapid and the filtrate should be clear. If this is not the case, the determination should be repeated because either insufficient alkali was used or the temperature of saponification was too high, or both. In such cases the determination must be repeated with more concentrated alkali and the temperature kept lower. The precipitate is washed back into the beaker, the volume is adjusted to 40 cc. and cooled below 25°C., and the steps of saponification with alkali, boiling, and precipitation with acid are repeated. The precipitate is filtered and washed with hot water but only to the point where a test filtrate shows only a negligible quantity of acid. (Not more than 500 cc. of total filtrate should be necessary.) The pectic acid precipitate is then washed into a platinum dish, and dried on the steam bath and finally in a water jacketed oven (98°C.) to constant weight. After weighing the precipitate is ashed, cooled, and weighed again. The loss in weight is pectic acid.

This method gives reproducible results with even small quantities of pectinic acid and, of course, is likewise applicable to the determination of pectic acid. It is of interest to note that the quantity of pectic acid obtained from even highly purified pectins seems to be lower than what one would expect from considerations of the structure and polygalacturonide content of the pectinic acids. Wichmann[681] reported results in the range of 60–75% on purified pectinic acids; in the author's laboratory values in the neighborhood of 80% have been obtained on highly purified preparations almost exclusively (98%) composed of pectinic acid. The reason for this discrepancy is not clear but some degradation may occur during the heating, especially with the acid. In a discussion of the precipitation of pectic acid by hydrochloric acid, Hinton[674] remarks that

[681] H. J. Wichmann, *J. Assoc. Offic. Agr. Chemists*, **7**, 107 (1923).

the filtrate from the pectic acid almost invariably shows—upon the addition of acetone (to a final concentration of 75%)—some precipitate. This fraction of polygalacturonic acids represents, in Hinton's tests, up to 8% of the total pectinic acid (as defined by calcium pectate determination).

For some reason the Wichmann method has never attained wide popularity and most workers in the field prefer the calcium pectate method of Carré and Haynes[667] which will be described later.

(b) Volumetric Measurement of Pectic Acid Precipitate

Fellers and Rice[682] describe a simple method which, at certain times, is very useful. In the procedure pectic acid is prepared under specified conditions and then centrifuged under standardized circumstances. The method, however, must be calibrated by some more exact method of estimation such as, for example, the Carré-Haynes method, and may be used only to obtain comparative values on pectinic acids or pectic acids of similar origin and history. The details of the procedure are as follows:

It is best to perform all operations in 15-cc. graduated, tapered glass centrifuge tubes. Depending on the concentration of pectinic or pectic acid in solution, a clear filtered sample is diluted to 10 cc. and 1 cc. of 10% sodium hydroxide solution is added. After 15 minutes 2 cc. of 10% hydrochloric acid is added and mixed with the contents of the tube. The latter is then placed (in a wire basket) in a boiling water bath for 8–15 minutes or until the flocculation is complete. (It is advisable to standardize this step to 15 minutes of heating and regulate the flocculation by proper choice of the size of sample.) The tube and its contents are then cooled to 20–25°C. and centrifuged at 2400–2500 r.p.m. for exactly 15 minutes on a 14-inch head. The volume of the precipitate is then read immediately. (Naturally, any other type of centrifuge of good efficiency may be used.) The reading should be at least 0.7 cc. on the aliquot used and not much in excess of 2.5 cc.

The relation between the volume of the precipitate and its weight is established by running a series of determinations on various dilutions by both the present method and by any other accepted method. Fellers and Rice used the Wichmann[673] pectic acid method for calibration but calcium pectate procedures[667] seem to be favored by most workers. The relationship between the volume and weight of the pectic acid precipitate is linear.

According to Fellers and Rice, the average deviation in a 16-fold variation of the quantity of pectinic acid was 7.1%. In a set of tests with 10-fold variation of currant juice, the mean deviation was only 5.4%.

The volume of the precipitate depends not only on the quantity but also on the molecular size of the pectinic acid, and therefore caution

---

[682] C. R. Fellers and C. C. Rice, *Ind. Eng. Chem., Anal. Ed.,* **4**, 268 (1932).

should be exercised in using this method. It is suitable to show the concentration of a given preparation of pectinic or pectic acid in solution, or to indicate the progress of changes in a series of determinations starting with the same pectinic acid, as during enzymic hydrolysis, for instance. It may also be applied to the approximate determination of the pectic constituents in fruits or in fruit juices, assuming that the variations are limited. The difficulty faced in most cases is that there is no assurance that a larger volume of precipitate actually represents a larger quantity (weight) of pectic acid. A larger volume of precipitate may be caused by a higher average molecular weight in the sample, or, loosely speaking, by higher "colloidality" and consequent water-holding capacity per weight unit of dry pectic acid. The volume of the precipitate is, in a way, a weight-average property, and therefore little variation in the proportion and characteristics of the fraction of highest molecular weight may cause considerable changes in the volume of the precipitate.

(c) Determination of Pectinic and Pectic Acids by Titration of Pectic Acid

The polygalacturonic acid, which is the basic skeleton of all pectic substances, can be isolated and titrated in such a manner as to give information of fair accuracy with regard to the amount of pectinic or pectic acids in a solution or extract. This idea has reoccurred periodically in pectin chemistry but Ahmann and Hooker[683] first described a complete method of determination based on this principle. The titration method of Ahmann and Hooker gives results on fruit juices and other similar materials which appear to be more accurate than direct determination by the calcium pectate method. If, however, the latter method is used after a preliminary precipitation from acid ethanol as now recommended, the advantages of the titration method vanish. Recently Hinton[674] investigated the titration method for the determination of pectinic and pectic acids. Since this procedure finds occasional application, it is given below in detail.

In applying the method to fruit juices and plant extracts, it is necessary to precipitate the pectinic acids with acetone before carrying out the determination. Sufficient acetone is stirred into the solution to bring the strength up to about 60% ; the mixture is then allowed to stand for a few minutes and filtered through a large fluted filter paper. The precipitate is washed moderately with 60% acetone, then rinsed back into the original vessel with cold water. The solution is boiled to remove most of the acetone and to reduce the volume to 40 cc., transferred to a 200-cc. graduated flask, and cooled. It is then carefully titrated with 0.1 N sodium hydroxide using pH 7.5 as the end point. Hinton's indicator

---

[683] C. F. Ahmann and H. D. Hooker, *Ind. Eng. Chem.*, **18**, 412 (1926).

mixture (see Section VII-2b below) or electrometric titration may be used. After the titration is completed, 10 cc. more alkali is added. The flask is stoppered and allowed to stand for 30 minutes at room temperature. The excess of alkali is titrated with 0.1 N hydrochloric acid, taking care that the end point is not overrun. Thereupon exactly 50 cc. of 0.1 N hydrochloric acid is added, the contents of the flask are swirled around, and the flask is placed in the boiling water bath for 10 minutes, being shaken once again during that time. The flask and contents are then cooled, made up to the 200-cc. mark, mixed, and filtered. A large aliquot (say 150 cc.) of the filtrate is titrated with 0.1 N sodium hydroxide, the end point used being the same as in the preliminary titration of the free acidity. A blank experiment is treated in the same way throughout, and the difference between the final titrations is calculated to the full 200 cc. of mixture (neglecting the volume occupied by the precipitate of pectic acid). The average value of 16% for the titration equivalent, expressed as sodium hydroxide, is used for the calculation of the acid groups:

$$\text{cc. 0.1 } N \text{ NaOH used by the precipitated pectic acid} \times 0.004 \times \frac{100}{16} =$$
$$\text{grams pectinic acid in the sample}$$

Theoretically 1 cc. of 0.1 N NaOH equals 0.177 g. of pure polygalacturonic acid or pectic acid.

Hinton points out that there are at least two sources of error in this method: (1) the retention by the carboxyl groups of the precipitated pectic acid of small quantities (0.50–1.30%) of sodium; and (2) the apparent slight solubility of pectic acid in water. This volumetric method gives results as accurate as calcium pectate determinations without purification and it shows, for most practical purposes, sufficient accuracy. It is also suitable for routine determinations on large numbers of samples.

Deuel[684] described a similar titrimetric method in which 25 cc. of an approximately 0.5% solution of the pectinic acid is titrated with 0.05 N sodium hydroxide from a microburette, using methyl red indicator. Thereupon 25 cc. of the same alkali is added and the solution is allowed to stand in a stoppered flask for 30 minutes. Now 25 cc. of 0.05 N sulfuric acid is added and the mixture is then titrated with alkali. If x designates the volume of alkali used in the first titration and y that consumed in the final titration, the sample contains $0.176x + (0.190y/2)$ pectinic acid, expressed in grams.

Pectic acids, in addition to being directly titratable, may also be estimated by the calcium acetate method developed by Lüdtke[685] for oxidized cellulose. Yackel and Kenyon[686] have described in detail a modification of this method in which the carboxyl groups react with salts of a weaker acid such as calcium acetate, forming a salt and releasing an equivalent amount of the weaker acid. McGee, Fowler, and Kenyon[687]

[684] H. Deuel, *Mitt. Gebiete Lebensm. Hyg.*, **34**, 41 (1943).
[685] M. Lüdtke, *Biochem. Z.*, **233**, 25 (1931); **268**, 372 (1934); **285**, 78 (1936).
[686] E. C. Yackel and W. O. Kenyon, *J. Am. Chem. Soc.*, **64**, 121 (1942).

reported some results obtained by this procedure on a sample of pectic acid but the general usefulness of the method is not clear at the present time.

Such titration methods have been extensively used in industrial control work. For the determination of pectin in a jam,[688] the sample is boiled with water and filtered. The residue is washed on the paper with hot water and the collected filtrates are reduced in volume by evaporation, cooled, and precipitated with acetone or alcohol. Thereupon the titration is performed as described above.[674]

3. Determination of Pectic Substances as Calcium Pectate

There are many observations in the literature on the extreme insolubility of calcium pectate in water. Carré and Haynes[667] developed a method for the quantitative estimation of dissolved pectic and pectinic acids in the form of calcium pectate. This procedure, with some modifications, has become one of the few standard methods used in pectin research.[689,690] Similarly to those obtained by pectic acid methods, the values found by the calcium pectate procedure indicate the proportion of polygalacturonic acids above the threshold of precipitability as a neutral calcium salt. Therefore, the frequently used terms "pectic substances as calcium pectate" or "pectinic acids (or pectin) as calcium pectate" do not give the weight of the original compound but that of the calcium pectate derived therefrom, independently of its original degree of esterification. Such results are also often designated as "calcium pectate numbers," "calcium pectate values," or "calcium pectate yields."

The method, in the modification recommended below, gives fairly sharp separation of different pectinic acids at an arbitrary line defined by the solubility of calcium pectates in the reaction mixture. Since both the ester groups and the major proportion of accompanying ions are removed during the preliminary operations, the precipitation is normally governed by the molecular size of the polygalacturonic acid. It may be assumed that the molecular size at which calcium pectates representing a whole range of molecular sizes are soluble or insoluble in the reaction mixture is a definite and reproducible value.

(a) Original Method of Carré and Haynes

By the use of carefully standardized manipulations, calcium pectate can be made to flocculate, even from very dilute solutions, as a product

[667] P. A. McGee, W. F. Fowler, Jr., and W. O. Kenyon, J. Am. Chem. Soc., 69, 348 (1947).
[688] C. L. Hinton, Food Manuf., 23, 364 (1948).
[689] R. Ripa, Die Pektinstoffe. Serger und Hempel, Braunschweig, 1937.
[690] Y. N. Trehan and B. Ahmad, J. Sci. Ind. Research (India), (1B), 6, 16 (1947).

of fairly definite chemical composition. There are three main steps involved in the precipitation: (1) saponification, (2) acidification with acetic acid, and (3) formation of the calcium salt. Carrè and Haynes conducted extensive investigations in order to ascertain the best conditions for the precipitation and recommend the following procedure.

A quantity of the unknown sufficient to yield approximately 20 to 30 mg. of calcium pectate should be used. The solution is neutralized and diluted to about 300 cc. Now 100 cc. of 0.1 N sodium hydroxide is added and the mixture is allowed to stand for at least 1 hour but preferably overnight. After standing, 50 cc. of 0.1 N acetic acid is added, followed after 5 minutes by 50 cc. of a 1 M solution of calcium chloride. The mixture is allowed to stand for about 1 hour, boiled for a few minutes, and filtered through a large fluted filter paper. If the precipitation has been properly carried out, the filtration is rapid. The precipitate is washed with boiling water until a sample of the filtrate is free from chloride, after which the precipitate is washed back into the beaker, boiled, and filtered again. The filtrate is tested for chloride and this process is repeated until the first filtrate after boiling shows no chloride when tested with silver nitrate. It is then filtered into a small fluted filter paper, from which it is transferred to a dish and finally to a Gooch crucible which has been previously dried at 100°C. and weighed. The precipitate is dried to constant weight at 100°; this usually requires about 12 hours.

Emmett and Carré[678] changed the procedure somewhat by recommending only two boilings. Even so, the procedure is very tedious and the manipulations required to transfer the precipitate from the filter paper to a dish and then to the Gooch crucible call for considerable skill. The final filtration usually takes a long time, and at times several days are required to collect and wash all the precipitate in the crucible. The results are quite reproducible even with quantities as low as 5 mg. of calcium pectate. For such small quantities the calcium pectate method is superior to all the pectic acid methods and also to direct precipitation methods using ethanol or acetone.

Carré and Haynes found a rather constant calcium content in calcium pectate prepared in this manner, namely, 7.6%. This value agreed well with the theoretical value of 7.66% calculated from the now abandoned Fellenberg[691] formula for pectic substances. The present polymolecular conception of the structure of linear polygalacturonic acids, however, requires 10.2% calcium in the calcium pectate. The discrepancy between this latter theoretical value and the 7.6% of calcium usually found in calcium pectates is likely to be caused either by the presence of carboxyl groups, which for some reason are not available for the formation of calcium salts, or by the presence of other ions as salts which are not replaced by calcium during the precipitation.

[691] T. Fellenberg, *Biochem. Z.*, **85**, 45 (1918).

Several workers criticized this method. Wichmann[692] found that continued washing, boiling, and filtration eventually reduce the calcium content and cause partial dissolution of the precipitate. Tutin[693] stated that the procedure gives the calcium salts of any acids which may be present in the sample and which may be insoluble in dilute acetic acid. Both criticisms are correct and subsequent modifications of the method aimed at the elimination of these possible sources of errors.

(b) Modifications of Calcium Pectate Method

Mehlitz[694] collected the precipitate after only a single boiling. He also attempted to use the calcium pectate yield to express the commercial usefulness of a pectin preparation or extract. As Ripa[689] stated, the calcium pectate yield is no indication of commercial value and pectinic acids may also be degraded to lose their jelly-forming value with only slight changes in calcium pectate yield (see Chapter VII). Mehlitz corrected the values obtained by his modification of the calcium pectate method by subtracting 8% from the weight of the precipitate for the average amount of calcium which he has found to be present.

In response to some of these criticisms Emmett and Carré[678] undertook further detailed investigation of the effect of various conditions on the precipitation of calcium pectate. To avoid the precipitation of insoluble calcium salts other than pectate, they recommended that, as a preliminary step, the pectinic acids (or pectinates) should be precipitated by four volumes of 95% ethanol containing 0.1 N hydrochloric acid. The precipitate is allowed to stand in the acid ethanol overnight, filtered off, dissolved in hot water, and used for the determination of the calcium pectate yield. This is indeed a very important step and has been incorporated, with some modifications, in the method recommended below.

Appleman and Conrad[695] found that calcium pectate precipitated directly from an extract from tomatoes contained a great deal of nonpectic material. These authors purified the previously precipitated calcium pectate by digestion for 45 minutes with a boiling 1% solution of ammonium citrate. The residue left after filtering and washing was dried and weighed. This weight was subtracted from the weight of the original "unpurified" calcium pectate to give the "true" calcium pectate figure. Later Heinze and Appleman[696] corrected for coprecipitated nonpectic materials by determining the nitrogen content of the precipitates, multiplying the weight of nitrogen found by the usual factor of 6.25, and

[692] H. J. Wichmann, *J. Assoc. Offic. Agr. Chemists*, **8**, 23 (1924).
[693] F. Tutin, *Biochem. J.*, **15**, 494 (1921).
[694] A. Mehlitz, *Konserven-Ind.*, **12**, 229 (1925); **13**, 149 (1926).
[695] C. O. Appleman and C. M. Conrad, *Maryland Agr. Expt. Sta.*, Bull. No. 291 (1927).
[696] P. H. Heinze and C. O. Appleman, *Plant Physiol.*, **18**, 548 (1943).

subtracting this weight as a correction. The application of such corrections may be justified under certain specific conditions but is, generally speaking, a dangerous practice. Preliminary purification of the pectinic acid solution is definitely preferred to the use of such corrections.

Poore[697] described a simplified calcium pectate procedure. This modification is much less time consuming than the original method and gives very reliable values. It has been used for several years in the author's laboratory and has been, in essence, incorporated into the method described below.

(c) Recommended Procedure for Determination of Pectic Substances as Calcium Pectate

The method described here is a combination of the desirable features of procedures of several different authors. It has been found universally applicable and is simple enough for serial determinations by technicians. It will be assumed that the unknown pectic materials are in solution. If they are not, any of the methods described earlier may be used to dissolve them. Needless to say, the solution should be clear and entirely void of suspended particles.

The solution is first tested for the presence of starch. If any blue or purple coloration is obtained with iodine, the starch (or dextrin) is digested by any of the methods already given. An aliquot is then used for the determination which will give approximately 25 mg. of calcium pectate, but the weight may be within the range of 10 to 50 mg. of calcium pectate. With small amounts the accuracy decreases, with larger amounts the filtrations are tedious. The solution is first neutralized (using phenolphthalein indicator) and then 5 cc. of 10% hydrochloric acid is added and the mixture is at once made up in a beaker to a volume of 100 cc. Now 200 cc. of 95% ethanol is added dropwise with vigorous stirring and the mixture allowed to stand overnight. Next day it is filtered on a fast filter paper and washed, first three times with a water–ethanol mixture (1:2), and then with 95% ethanol. The precipitate should not be allowed to dry on the paper. After the last of the ethanol has drained off, the precipitate is dissolved through the paper with hot water. After the precipitate is completely dissolved, the paper is washed three more times with hot water.

The collected filtrate is made up to a volume of 200 cc., then 150 cc. of 0.2 N sodium hydroxide is added, and the mixture is allowed to stand for at least 1 hour or preferably overnight. Now 60 cc. of 1 N acetic acid is added and the solution is mixed and allowed to stand for a few minutes. Thereupon, first 25 cc. of 0.1 M, then 25 cc. of 2 M, calcium chloride solutions are added dropwise and with constant vigorous stirring. The mixture is boiled for exactly 2 minutes, filtered through a hard, fast (preferably shark skin) filter paper and washed three times with boiling water. The precipitate is washed back into the beaker with

[697] H. D. Poore, Ind. Eng. Chem., 26, 637 (1934).

at least 100, but not more than 200, cc. of water and boiled again for 2 minutes. It is then filtered through a glass crucible with a fritted glass bottom (medium porosity) which has been dried and weighed previously. Little suction should be applied at first; this will shorten the length of time required for the whole filtration. After all the calcium pectate has been transferred from the beaker the precipitate is washed, on the crucible, three times with hot water, followed by three washings with 95% ethanol. During these latter washings it is advisable to stir up the precipitate with a small glass rod (which has a fire-polished end) and rinse any calcium pectate attached to the rod into the crucible with some ethanol. Finally the precipitate is washed twice with ether and the crucible dried overnight at 95° or 100°C.

Apparently the calcium pectate yield is changed little if the duration of saponification is shortened to 30 minutes, although the rate of filtration may be unfavorably influenced. Täufel and Just[698] recommend saponification for 10–15 minutes only, but it is doubtful whether the small saving in time would be worth the possible difficulties during filtration. In purified preparations of pectinic acids the calcium pectate yield is usually between 105 and 110% of the weight of the pectinic acid used in the determination.

Determinations of the polyuronide content of calcium pectates prepared by this method from commercial pectins and pectinic acids indicated sufficient purity. However, this is not always the case with samples prepared directly from plant material, even from such rich sources as unripe apples. Corrections which have been previously described[695,696] might be applied in such cases. Current practice in the author's laboratory is to determine the polyuronide content of the final calcium pectate precipitate by the methods described in Chapter II and designate this as pectic acid or as "pectic polyuronide" content. The precipitation methods used in the above procedure exclude nonpectic polygalacturonic acids. There is little doubt that with the availability of more expedient methods for the determination of the polyuronide content[699] such a combination of methods of precipitation and chemical analysis for the basic constituent will be increasingly used.

The pectinic acid content of a solution when determined by ethanol or acetone precipitation is usually higher than when the calcium pectate method is used. A higher true calcium pectate content is only possible in preparations of very high purity. Thus any reports of determinations on a plant extract in which higher results were obtained by the calcium pectate method than by ethanol precipitation[700] should be regarded with suspicion.[701] There are many reports in the literature on the pectic

[698] K. Täufel and E. Just, Z. Untersuch. Lebensm., 82, 504 (1941).
[699] R. M. McCready, H. A. Swenson, and W. D. Maclay, Ind. Eng. Chem., Anal. Ed., 18, 290 (1946).
[700] W. E. Elwell and W. M. Dehn, Plant Physiol., 14, 809 (1939).
[701] Z. I. Kertesz, Plant Physiol., 15, 565 (1940).

contents of plant tissues as estimated by the ethanol precipitate and calcium pectate methods, but only the papers of Hardy,[702] Savur and Sreenivasan,[703] and Money and Christian[704] will be noted here.

VII. DETERMINATION OF VARIOUS CONSTITUENTS OF PECTINIC AND PECTIC ACIDS

1. Determination of Uronide Content

Determination of the polygalacturonic acid content is perhaps the most reliable method for the determination of the proportion of pectic materials in a preparation. Precautions should be taken, however, to have the polygalacturonic acids defined in some manner by separation from lower polymers which may occur in plant tissues. This can be accomplished by precipitation with ethanol or precipitation as pectic acid or calcium pectate. Purification before the determination of the uronide content by removing excessive proportions of sugars and other foreign materials is also desirable. Fortunately, glucuronic and mannuronic acids are (with the exception of a few species) not very common in the plant world, at least not in proportions comparable to those in which pectic substances are found and thus it can normally be safely assumed that the uronide found was galacturonic acid.

(a) Lefèvre-Tollens Carbon Dioxide Method

This very dependable method, modified by Whistler, Martin, and Harris,[705] McCready, Swenson, and Maclay,[706] and others, has been previously described in detail in Chapter II. In the presence of large proportions of carbohydrates and other materials which also give carbon dioxide, even if only at a very low rate, the method of Whistler, Martin, and Harris should be used. The curves obtained by this procedure make a correction for the nonuronide carbon dioxide possible. It should be noted that ascorbic acid gives carbon dioxide in about the same proportions as does galacturonic acid and therefore care should be taken to remove this constituent (and its immediate decomposition products) from any sample to be used for the determination of uronide carbon dioxide. This can be easily accomplished either by precipitation with ethanol from a solution or extraction with 80% ethanol of a dry powdered sample.

[702] F. Hardy, *Biochem. J.*, 18, 283 (1924).
[703] G. R. Savur and A. Sreenivasan, *J. Sci. Ind. Research (India)*, 5, (3), 41 (1946).
[704] R. W. Money and W. A. Christian, *J. Sci. Food Agr.*, 1, 8 (1950).
[705] R. L. Whistler, A. R. Martin, and M. Harris, *J. Research Natl. Bur. Standards*, 24, 13 (1940).
[706] R. M. McCready, H. A. Swenson, and W. D. Maclay, *Ind. Eng. Chem., Anal. Ed.*, 18, 290 (1946).

A micromethod for uronic acids was described by Tracey.[707]   Vollmert[708] recently described a method for the simultaneous determination of both the uronide and methoxyl contents on 0.1 g. samples of pectinic acids, either titrimetrically or gravimetrically. This author claims that, in spite of the fact that the carbon dioxide yield by this method is 7.3% below the theoretical value, the method is better than digestion with 12 or 19% hydrochloric acid because it gives a sharper end point with impure preparations. Vollmert uses hydriodic acid for the digestion.

(b)   Applicability of Naphthoresorcinol, Cysteine, and Carbazole Methods

These methods, discussed previously in Chapter II, cannot be considered at the present time as useful for the determination of pectic substances. They may be applied in the analysis of highly purified preparations but even then only after complete hydrolysis. The only dependable means to accomplish such hydrolysis is by using enzymes (see Chapter XIV) because acid hydrolysis usually causes some destruction of the galacturonic acid (see Chapter II). All these methods are unreliable in presence of more than equal proportions of other carbohydrates, especially pentoses.

(c)   Determination by Production of Furfural

This method, already discussed in detail in Chapter II, may be applied to pectic substances. In the presence of pentoses either these must be removed before the determination or the values obtained by the furfural method must be corrected in some other manner as described in Chapter II.

2. Determination of Methyl Ester Content of Pectinic Acids

In the past results obtained by the Zeisel[709] method and its modifications for the proportion of methyl ester in pectinic acids have been accepted at face value. Recent reports,[710,711] however, make it clear that some of the older results are probably unreliable because solvents capable of forming volatile iodides in the Zeisel determination are often strongly adsorbed by pectic preparations; these, in turn, increase the apparent methoxyl content of the preparations. It is now known that such retained solvents may be easily removed (see below). In addition to the

[707] M. V. Tracey, Biochem. J., 43, 185 (1948).
[708] B. Vollmert, Z. Lebensm.-Untersuch. u. Forsch., 89, 347 (1949).
[709] S. Zeisel, Monatsh., 6, 989 (1885); 7, 406 (1886).
[710] C. H. Hills, C. L. Ogg, and R. Speiser, Ind. Eng. Chem., Anal. Ed., 17, 507 (1945).
[711] E. F. Jansen, S. W. Waisbrot, and E. Rietz, Ind. Eng. Chem., Anal. Ed., 16, 523 (1944)

modifications of the Zeisel method, deesterification with alkali or enzymes or the estimation of the methanol produced upon deesterification may also be used for the determination of the methyl ester content of pectinic acids.

(a) Zeisel Method and Its Modifications

When an organic compound containing methyl or methoxyl groups is refluxed with hydriodic acid, methyl iodide is formed. This may be determined gravimetrically as silver iodide or volumetrically as the iodate. The method has many modifications[712] which will not be discussed here. Micromethods are also available[662,713] and have been described in the splendid handbook written by Niederl and Niederl.[714] In recent years the semimicro modification described by Clark[715] has found wide application in pectin research and for this reason this method will be described in detail.

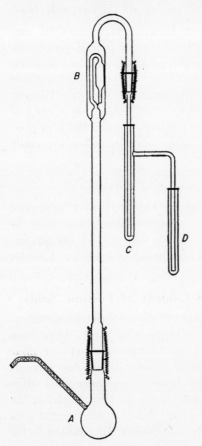

The apparatus employed in the determination is shown in Figure 17. 20 to 30 mg. of the dry pectic preparation (previously treated to remove adsorbed ethanol) is weighed on a counterpoised 2 × 3 cm. piece of cigarette paper. The paper containing the sample is placed in the bottom of the boiling flask, A. A boiling rod, 2.5 cc. of melted analytical quality phenol, and 5 cc. of constant boiling hydriodic acid are added. The boiling rod used here is a glass tube approximately 60 mm. long and with a 3.5 mm. outside diameter and a 1 mm. bore. It is sealed at one end and also closed about 10 mm. from the other. The open end is fire-polished. When this is placed in the flask with the open end down, it induces uniform boiling as long as sufficient heat is applied constantly to the liquid. The hydriodic acid often contains more or less

Fig. 17. Clark's modification of the apparatus for the determination of methoxyl groups by Zeisel's method.

[712] H. Meyer, Analyse und Konstitutionsermittlung organischer Verbindungen. 5th ed., Springer, Berlin, 1931.

[713] F. Pregl, Die quantitative organische Mikroanalyse. 3rd ed., Springer, Berlin, 1930.

[714] J. B. Niederl and V. Niederl, Micromethods of Quantitative Analysis. Wiley, New York, 1938.

[715] E. P. Clark, J. Am. Chem. Soc., 51, 1480 (1929); J. Offic. Agr. Chemists, 15, 136 (1932).

free iodine resulting from the decomposition of the acid. A permanently colorless solution of hydriodic acid may be obtained if the liquid, heated to approximately 100°C., is treated with slightly more than the necessary quantity of 50% hypophosphorous acid. When a hydriodic acid solution thus treated is used for alkoxyl determinations no free iodine is evolved, and consequently no phosphorus need be employed in the scrubber, *B*.

The flask is connected with the remainder of the apparatus, which consists of the scrubber, *B*, containing a little water, and the receivers, *C* and *D*. The receivers contain 10 cc. of a 10% glacial acetic acid solution of potassium acetate, to which 6 drops of bromine has been added. Approximately 6 cc. of the solution is placed in *C* and 4 cc. in *D*. A slow, uniform stream of carbon dioxide is passed through the capillary side arm of the boiling flask. The liquid is gently heated by means of a mantled microburner, or better by an oil bath with automatic temperature control, at such a rate that the vapors of the boiling liquid rise half way up the condenser. For most substances 30 minutes is sufficient to complete the reaction and sweep out the apparatus. The contents of both receivers are then washed into a 250-cc. Erlenmeyer flask which contains 5 cc. of a 25% aqueous sodium acetate solution. The volume of the liquid is adjusted to approximately 125 cc., and 6 drops of 90% formic acid is added. The flask is rotated until the color due to the bromine is discharged, then 12 more drops of formic acid is added, and the solution is allowed to stand for from 1 to 2 minutes. 1 g. of potassium iodide and a few cc. of 10% sulfuric acid are added next and the free iodine is titrated with 0.1 *N* sodium thiosulfate. A control should be run on the reagents as phenol often contains substances which give a small blank. For the quantity of phenol used in a determination the blank usually amounts to 0.06 cc. of 0.1 *N* sodium thiosulfate. 1 cc. of 0.1 *N* thiosulfate equals 0.517 mg. of methoxyl (CH_3O).

Care should be taken to heat up the reaction mixture slowly and to avoid overheating since this may cause lower results due to resinification.[716] Only reference is made here to Vollmert's recently published method for the simultaneous determination of methoxyl and uronide contents.[708]

(b) *Determination of Methyl Ester Content by Saponification*

The methyl ester in pectinic acids is easily saponified by alkali. The ester content of a pectinic acid may either be calculated from the amount of alkali consumed or the methanol produced can be separated and determined. The latter method will be discussed in Section *d*.

Determination of the amount of alkali required to accomplish the saponification of an ester is one of the classical methods of organic chemistry. It has been applied to pectinic acids by Ehrlich and Kos-

[716] F. Neumann, *Ber.*, **70**, 734 (1937).

mahly,[717] Romeo,[718] Myers and Baker,[719] Olsen, Stuewer, Fehlberg, and Beach,[720] Hinton,[674] and many other workers. Most of these authors also described procedures for the saponification but unfortunately these were always based on control results obtained by the Zeisel method and its modifications. As stated before, it may now be assumed that most figures reported in the past for the methyl ester contents of pectinic acids by the Zeisel method were high and therefore little reliance can be placed on older results obtained by saponification.

The saponification method is often useful for obtaining comparative and approximate results. One of the most frequently used procedures is that given by Myers and Baker,[719] the essence of which may be described as follows.

A 1-g. sample of the pectinic acid is dissolved in carbon dioxide-free water and diluted to 200 cc. in a large flask, care being taken to protect the solution from air. The solution is exactly neutralized with carbon dioxide-free sodium hydroxide solution, using phenolphthalein indicator. Then an excess of 20 cc. of 0.5 N sodium hydroxide is added and the solution is allowed to stand, in a well-stoppered flask, for 2 hours at room temperature. Afterward the excess of alkali is determined by titration with 0.5 N sulfuric acid. 1 cc. of 0.5 N alkali equals 15.52 mg. of methoxyl (CH_3O).

The procedure described more recently by Hinton[674] has several advantages over the above method and is now preferred by most workers. This author uses an indicator mixture composed of 1 volume each of 0.4% bromothymol blue, 0.4% cresol red, and distilled water, and three volumes of 0.4% phenol red. The procedure is as follows.

About 40 cc. of a solution containing about 0.4 g. of pectinic acid is placed in a 200-cc. volumetric flask, two or three drops of the indicator is added, and the solution is neutralized by the cautious addition of 0.1 N sodium hydroxide. The end point is taken when the red color, indicating pH 7.5, persists for one half minute. Now 10 cc. of 0.5 N sodium hydroxide is added and the flask is stoppered and allowed to stand for one half hour at room temperature. Then the excess of the alkali is titrated by 0.1 N hydrochloric acid, care being taken to avoid overrunning of the end point. A blank experiment is conducted in exactly the same manner but without the pectinic acid. The difference between the two titrations gives the amount of alkali used for the saponification.

Hinton expresses his results as grams of sodium hydroxide per 100 g. of dry, ash-free pectinic acid. It seems more logical to use the methoxyl

[717] F. Ehrlich and A. Kosmahly, *Biochem. Z.*, 212, 162 (1939).
[718] G. Romeo, *Ann. chim. applicata*, 23, 530 (1933); through *C. A.*, 28, 1955 (1934).
[719] P. B. Myers and G. L. Baker, *Univ. Delaware Agr. Expt. Sta.*, Bull. No. 187 (1934).
[720] A. G. Olsen, R. F. Stuewer, E. R. Fehlberg, and N. M. Beach, *Ind. Eng. Chem.*, 31, 1015 (1939).

equivalent calculated in the manner described above. In the author's laboratory the results of methoxyl determinations are expressed on the basis of the calcium pectate yield obtained from the preparation. From the weight of the calcium pectate precipitate 8% is subtracted to correct for the calcium content. To the weight of the "pectic acid" thus obtained $^{17}/_{31}$ of the weight of methoxyl (obtained from the same size of sample as was the calcium pectate) is added.[721] The methoxyl content is then expressed on the basis of this "pectinic acid."

Recently Hills, Ogg, and Speiser[710] studied the applicability of saponification methods to the determination of the methyl ester contents of low-ester pectins and found that different procedures must be applied in the case of acid-demethylated pectins and those which have been partially demethylated by other methods. Their recommendations are as follows.

For the determination of the methyl ester content of all but acid-demethylated pectins, a 2-g. sample is weighed into a 600-cc. beaker, moistened with ethanol, and dissolved in 400 cc. of distilled water, using a mechanical stirrer. The solution is titrated to pH 7.5 by adding 0.5 N sodium hydroxide. The exact end point is determined by a pH meter equipped with extension glass electrodes. The neutralized solution is transferred to a 500-cc. Erlenmeyer flask and the temperature is adjusted to 25°C. An amount of 0.5 N sodium hydroxide (x) is now added which is 5.0 cc. ($\pm$ 0.5 cc.) in excess of the amount equivalent to the methyl ester content of the sample. This may have to be determined in a preliminary run. The solution is allowed to stand for 30 minutes and then 0.5 N sulfuric acid, equivalent to the amount of sodium hydroxide used (x), is added. Thereupon the mixture is again titrated with sodium hydroxide to pH 7.5 as described above. The amount of alkali used in the final titration (y) subtracted from that originally added (x) should equal 5.0 cc. ($\pm$0.5 cc.). If the difference is either larger or smaller, the determination should be repeated with corrected amounts of alkali. After correcting for the blank the methoxyl content is calculated as described above.

In the case of acid-demethylated pectins the saponification is carried out in the same manner except that 40 cc. of alkali is used for the saponification and the time is increased to 40 minutes. Hinton's indicator may also be used instead of electrometric determination of the pH but the precision of the method is thereby decreased.

When carefully executed, any of the above saponification methods can be expected to give results within about 5% of the methoxyl content. The error is likely to be larger when the degree of esterification of the pectinic acid is low (3–6%) or when the proportion of nonpectic constituents in the preparation is high.

The calculated maximum methoxyl content of a pectinic acid is 16.34%

[721] Z. I. Kertesz and R. J. McColloch, *New York State Agr. Expt. Sta.*, Bull. No. 745 (1950).

(see Table 14). The saponification method for determination of the ester content should always be used with discretion since there are many possible interfering factors (see Table 16).

(c) Determination by Use of Enzymes

Hills, White, and Baker[722] employed the enzyme pectin-methylesterase (pectase) (see Chapter XIV) for the deesterification of pectinic acids. Since the hydrolysis of each methyl ester group liberates one carboxyl group, it is possible to follow the reaction by simple titration. Tomatoes contain a very active enzyme which may be applied for the purpose of demethylation. The preparation of an active extract from tomatoes is described in Chapter XIV. Hills, Ogg, and Speiser[710] give a complete procedure for the determination of methyl ester groups in pectinic acids by the use of an enzyme. The essence of the method is as follows.

2 g. of the pectinic acid is weighed into a 600-cc. beaker, moistened with ethanol, and dissolved in 400 cc. of distilled water, using a mechanical stirrer. The solution is neutralized to pH 7.5 with 0.5 N sodium hydroxide, using a pH meter with extension electrodes. The neutralized solution is transferred to a 500-cc. Erlenmeyer flask; 5 cc. of 3 N sodium acetate solution and 5 cc. of 2% sodium oxalate solution, both adjusted to pH 7.5, are added. Then 20 cc. of tomato extract (adjusted to pH 7.5 immediately before use) is added and the contents of the flask are mixed by rotation. The flask is allowed to stand at room temperature for 2 hours. Afterward the solution is transferred to a 600-cc. beaker and titrated to pH 7.50 with alkali. If the pH of the solution after the standing with the enzyme is below 5, the analysis should be repeated using double amounts of sodium acetate solution. If the solution has formed a gel, the determination should be repeated using more oxalate. A blank determination is made in the same manner and the result subtracted from that found for the complete reaction mixture. The methyl ester content of the sample (calculated as per cent of CH_3O) is (cc. of 0.5 N alkali $\times$ 0.0155 + 0.70% of CH_3O.

Under these conditions the enzyme does not hydrolyze the pectinic acid completely; fortunately, however, the residual ester content is a fairly low and reproducible figure and contributes (according to Hills, Ogg, and Speiser) only a negligible error if the indicated correction is applied. In the case of low-methoxyl pectins, however, the enzymic method is not entirely satisfactory, and lower corrections than 0.70% must be applied.

In summary, it may be stated that for exact determination of the methyl ester content of pectinic acids the Zeisel method or any of its modern modifications should be used, after careful removal of any

[722] C. H. Hills, J. W. White, and G. L. Baker, *Proc. Inst. Food Technol.*, 1942, 47.

ethanol possibly adsorbed by the preparation. For routine work or where no great accuracy is required, any of the saponification methods may be applied. The use of electric pH meters is always preferable to indicators, but if an indicator must be used, it should be Hinton's mixture which gives a fairly sharp end point at pH 7.5.

(d) Determination of Amount of Methanol Produced by Saponification and Use of Such Results to Estimate Pectinic Acids

There are several reports in the literature dealing with so-called quantitative methods of estimation of pectinic acids based on the amount of methanol which may be recovered from the pectinic acid. All these procedures are based either on assumed "theoretical" methyl ester contents or on ill-defined average methyl ester contents.[691,723-726] They are mentioned here only to make it clear that such methods are considered to be untrustworthy and should never be applied for even approximate quantitative estimation of pectinic acids.

3. Removal of Retained Solvents, Especially Ethanol, from Pectic Preparations

At some time it was believed that some of the methyl groups in pectinic acids might be attached by other than ester linkages.[727] The reason for this assumption was that even prolonged saponification with alkali did not appear to remove the methyl groups completely. The Zeisel method and its modifications gave results in the range of 0.1 to 1% for most pectic acid preparations. This phenomenon has recently been studied by Jansen, Waisbrot, and Rietz,[711] and independently and simultaneously by Hills, Ogg, and Speiser.[710] The latter workers determined the "methoxyl" content of a sample of apple pectinic acid and found 12.0%. When the analysis was repeated and the volatile iodides subjected to the trimethylamine separation method,[728] it was found that the sample contained only 9.0% methoxyl and 4.5% ethoxyl (or 3.1% calculated as methoxyl). The pectinic acid was originally prepared by precipitation with ethanol and it was apparent that some of the ethanol was retained in spite of the drying. In fact, even two hours of drying at 80°C. in the Abderhalden dryer failed to remove the ethanol. After treatment with water vapor and drying, the methoxyl content was found to be 9.35% which is in

[723] A. Romeo, Ann. chim. applicata. 27, 304 (1937); through C. A., 31, 8731 (1937).
[724] S. M. Strepkov, Botan. Arch., 38, 399 (1937); through C. A., 31, 4233 (1937).
[725] W. Strubczewski, Przemysl Chem., 16, 135 (1932); through C. A., 26, 6031 (1932).
[726] A. J. W. Hornby, J. Soc. Chem. Ind., 39, 246 (1920).
[727] Z. I. Kertesz, New York State Agr. Expt. Sta., 56th Annual Report (1937).
[728] L. M. Cooke and H. Hibbert. Ind. Eng. Chem., Anal Ed., 15, 24 (1943).

good agreement with the originally found methoxyl content (9.0%), recalculated on an ethanol-free basis, which is 9.43%. The close agreement indicates that the treatment removed all adsorbed ethanol. The removal of such retained ethanol is accomplished in the following manner.

The pectic preparation is placed in a thin layer in a shallow dish and the dish placed in a vacuum desiccator in which the drying agent has been replaced by water. Toluene is kept on the surface of the water to prevent mold growth. The desiccator is then evacuated and the sample allowed to stand overnight. Afterward the sample is removed and dried in an Abderhalden dryer under vacuum over phosphorus pentoxide at 80°C. for 2 hours.

Similar tenacious retention of ethanol by cotton[729] and glucosidocytosine[730] was previously observed and in turn overcome by similar treatment with water vapor.

VIII. DETERMINATION OF COMPOUNDS COMMONLY ACCOMPANYING PECTIC SUBSTANCES

Reliable methods are available for the determination of pectic substances. On the other hand, the analytical methods which may be applied for the determination of the most common accompanying carbohydrates such as arabinose, and especially xylose and galactose, are none too satisfactory. For this reason it is, as a rule, advantageous to determine the pectic substances in a given preparation and obtain the proportion of admixed "ballast" by difference. The situation is different, of course, when the interest of the worker is in the accompanying carbohydrates or when a complete analysis of the preparation or plant tissue is required.

1. Arabinose and Araban

The arabans and galactans which often accompany pectic substances may be removed for the most part by extraction with 55–60% ethanol, or even better by precipitation with this concentration of ethanol. As noted before, such treatment also causes fractionation of the various polygalacturonic acids present. The customary method for the determination of arabinose in pectic preparations is to determine the furfural yield, which may be obtained by boiling with hydrochloric acid, and then to correct this for the amount of uronide material present on the basis of the amount of carbon dioxide obtained. The methods for the determination of pentoses from the furfural yield and for the determination of the uronide content from the amount of carbon dioxide evolved were described in Chapter II, Section IV-4 and 5. These methods are far from

[729] R. T. Mease, *Ind. Eng. Chem.*, *Anal. Ed.*, **5**, 317 (1933).
[730] G. E. Hilbert and E. F. Jansen, *J. Am. Chem. Soc.*, **58**, 60 (1936).

perfect and, as was mentioned previously, disagreement exists concerning the methods of calculation which give the most exact results.

From other possible methods which may be applied for the determination of arabinose and araban in pectic preparations the following scheme has been applied with some success.

It is desirable for the determination of carbohydrates in pectic preparations to hydrolyze the various polysaccharides which they contain. Until recently this was accomplished with hot acid, but there is little doubt that many other changes occurred in addition to hydrolysis due to the severe treatment required to hydrolyze the fairly acid-resistant polygalacturonic acids. It is, therefore, preferable to accomplish hydrolysis by means of enzymes as described in Chapter XIV.

The pectic preparation is dissolved or suspended in water and the pH is adjusted to 3.5. Now a filtered solution of the purified pectinase is added in the proportions of 0.5 g. of solid enzyme to every 10 g. of pectic preparation. Some toluol is added and the mixture kept at 30°C. for 3 days. The addition of enzyme is repeated on the third and sixth days and, if needed, the pH is also adjusted to 3.2–3.5. Simultaneously, a blank determination is carried out in which the successive portions of the enzyme are added to some water and the mixture incubated, in the presence of toluol, in the same manner as the other digests. On the tenth day the mixture, which contains the hydrolyzed polysaccharides, is treated with a slight excess of barium carbonate[731] and evaporated to dryness on the steam bath or preferably under vacuum. The dry residue is then extracted several times with boiling 90% ethanol, always followed by filtration with suction. The combined extracts contain the arabinose and other monosaccharides, while the residue contains the barium salt of galacturonic acid. In the case of partially purified pectic preparations the extract contains arabinose and galactose, in rare instances xylose, and perhaps small quantities of galacturonic acid. The galactose may be removed from the mixture by the fermentation method described below and the arabinose determined either by estimating its reducing power or from the furfural yield. The readings obtained on the blank containing only the enzyme and handled in exactly the same manner should be subtracted from the results.

Unfortunately, this method is not altogether satisfactory and its thorough revaluation and refinement are sorely needed. Meanwhile, it is essential that the assumption that the major portion of the residual carbohydrate is actually arabinose be confirmed by qualitative tests. Additional tests should be made to disclose the presence of galacturonic acid, galactose, or xylose in the ethanol extract. For details of such tests reference is made to the handbooks mentioned on earlier pages.[731,732] A

[731] A. W. van der Haar, *Anleitung zum Nachweis, zur Trennung und Bestimmung der Monosaccharide und Aldehydsäuren.* Borntraeger, Berlin, 1920.
[732] C. A. Browne and F. W. Zerban, *Physical and Chemical Methods of Sugar Analysis.* 3rd ed., Wiley, New York, 1941.

titrimetric method which shows promise of being applicable to the determination of pentoses occurring in pectic preparations has recently been described by Meissner.[733]   Tracey[733a] recently described a colorimetric method for the quantitative determination of pentoses in the presence of hexoses and uronic acids.

2. Galactose and Galactan

Pectic preparations have been reported to contain up to 10% galactose in the form of galactans or "arabino-galactans." The determination of the galactose component should be performed after hydrolysis, preferably by an enzymic method as described above. Commercial pectinase preparations seem to contain active enzymes digesting both arabans and galactans (see Chapter XV).

The galactose may be determined, together with galacturonic acid, by oxidation to mucic acid.[731]   Since the quantity of galacturonic acid in the mixture may be determined by the carbon dioxide method, the mucic acid yield can be corrected for the portion of mucic acid derived from the galacturonic acid. This method, even in its modification by van der Haar,[731] is far from reliable. In the case of purified pectic preparation the proportion of galactose is often very low and thus, when determined together with galacturonic acid (which may make up 80 or 90% of the preparation), the results are of little value.

The customary method used for the determination of galactose is that described by Kluyver[734] and is based on the selective fermentation of carbohydrates by pure yeast cultures. The yeast used most frequently for this purpose, *Saccharomyces cerevisiae*, may be isolated from fresh yeast cake in the following manner.[719]

Two sets of test tubes containing sterile galactose agar (2.3% nutrient agar and 1% galactose) at 50°C. are inoculated from a fresh yeast cake and plated out. The second tube is inoculated from the first tube, the third from the second, etc., so that a dilution series is obtained. The pure culture is isolated from colonies from the more dilute plates incubated at 32°C. Afterward it is kept virulent on galactose-agar by frequent transfer.

For the determination of galactose the pH of the enzyme digest (see above) is adjusted to between 5 and 6, and 1 cc. of this solution is added to the van Iterson-Kluyver fermentation apparatus together with 1 cc. of sugar-free broth and 1 cc. of galactose solution containing 0.075 g. of galactose. The apparatus must be previously sterilized and filled with mercury. The sample is then inoculated with the yeast by means of a platinum needle, care being taken

[733] R. Meissner, *Biochem. Z.*, **317**, 17 (1944).
[733a] M. V. Tracey, *Biochem. J.*, **47**, 433 (1950).
[734] A. J. Kluyver, *Dissertation*, Delft, 1914; quoted from reference **732**.

to prevent contamination. After thorough mixing, exactly 1 cc. of the mixture is run into the apparatus by withdrawing some of the mercury from the stopcock in the bottom of the tube. The apparatus is now put into an incubator kept at 32°C. and, as the gas evolves, the mercury is withdrawn through the lower arm of the stopcock to prevent pressure in the apparatus. Occasionally the apparatus is carefully shaken to distribute the yeast and prevent supersaturation with carbon dioxide. When the fermentation is completed (usually within 60 or 65 hours) the apparatus is removed from the incubator and allowed to reach equilibrium at room temperature. The mercury is then adjusted to the same level in the two arms of the U-tubes and the volume of carbon dioxide, the temperature, and the barometric pressure are noted. The volume of carbon dioxide is corrected to 0°C. and 760 mm. pressure by means of the values shown in Table 24. The quantity of dissolved carbon dioxide is added and the corrected volume of carbon dioxide converted to galactose. According to Kluyver 1 cc. of carbon dioxide under normal conditions equals 4.3 mg. of galactose.

Kluyver states that, when using pure galactose, the amount of carbon dioxide dissolved in 1 cc. of fermented solution is 1.2 cc. Ehrlich and Sommerfeld[735] found that a fermented solution of pectinic acids, which contains salts from the pectic material as well as those due to the neutralization, contained only 0.6 to 0.9 cc. of carbon dioxide. In the work of Myers and Baker the fermentation was always carried out with 0.0238 or 0.0250 g. of galactose added; the dissolved carbon dioxide under such conditions proved to be 0.9 to 1.1 cc. Therefore, the average correction of 1.0 cc. was used by the latter authors.

Wise and Appling[736] studied the determination of galactose in plant mucilages by selective fermentation with two yeasts, *Saccharomyces*

TABLE 24
PERCENTAGE CORRECTION TO REDUCE CARBON DIOXIDE READ IN THE VAN ITERSON-KLUYVER APPARATUS TO NORMAL CONDITIONS (ADAPTED FROM KLUYVER)

Temp., °C.	Barometric pressure in mm. mercury					
	730	740	750	760	770	780
15	8.9	7.7	6.4	5.2	3.9	2.7
16	9.3	8.0	6.8	5.5	4.3	3.0
17	9.6	8.3	7.1	5.9	4.6	3.4
18	9.9	8.6	7.4	6.2	4.9	3.7
19	10.2	9.0	7.7	6.5	5.3	4.0
20	10.5	9.3	8.0	6.8	5.6	4.4
21	10.8	9.6	8.3	7.1	5.9	4.7
22	11.0	9.8	8.6	7.4	6.2	4.9

carlsbergensis, which ferments galactose, and *S. bayanus*, which leaves galactose unfermented. The yeasts have little action on arabinose, xylose,

[735] F. Ehrlich and R. Sommerfeld, *Biochem. Z.*, **168**, 263 (1926).
[736] L. E. Wise and J. W. Appling, *Ind. Eng. Chem., Anal. Ed.*, **16**, 28 (1944).

and glucuronic and galacturonic acids. The method has a fair degree of accuracy in the presence of an excess of galacturonic acid, but has not been applied as yet to mixtures containing as large quantities of galacturonic acid and small proportions of galactose as digests of purified pectic preparations contain. Wise and Appling measure the galactose by determinations of the reducing power of the fermented mixtures.

3. Xylose and Xylan

Pectic preparations derived from plant tissues rich in cellulose and lignin and of insufficient purity often contain xylans. The determination of xylose in a digest from such preparations is rather complicated since no direct chemical method for the determination of xylan in the presence of galacturonic acid, arabinose, and galactose is available. The furfural method gives information on the combined proportions of galacturonic acid, arabinose, and xylose. As shown before, the furfural yield may be corrected for the galacturonic acid present. It is also possible to remove the galacturonic acid from the mixture by the barium carbonate method, the galactose by fermentation, and then determine the proportions of arabinose and xylose by the method of Browne[737] on the basis of determinations of the optical rotation and reducing power. The determination is, at best, an approximation. Recently, Wise and Appling[738] published a method based on selective fermentation by two organisms. A quantity of 12–50 mg. of xylose can be estimated by this procedure in the presence of glucose, arabinose, mannose, and glucuronic acid. It remains to be seen how useful the method is when used on mixtures of the types obtained in the enzymic digestion of pectic substances. Since the occurrence of xylose in pectic preparations is comparatively rare, the reader is referred for the details of analytical methods to the original articles and handbooks.[731,732]

4. Determination of Acetyl Groups

It should be clear from the discussion in Chapter IV that there is considerable doubt at the present time whether the acetyl groups found in beet pectin are *de facto* attached to the pectinic acid molecule. Some references have already been made to the methodological difficulties which are encountered in attempts to determine acetyl groups.

The method used by most workers is identical with or similar to that described by Myers and Baker.[719] The essence of this procedure is as follows.

[737] C. A. Browne, Jr., *J. Am. Chem. Soc.*, **28**, 439 (1906).
[738] L. E. Wise and J. W. Appling, *Ind. Eng. Chem., Anal. Ed.*, **17**, 182 (1945).

First of all, the methyl ester groups are saponified in the manner described previously. Thereafter the solution is neutralized and sufficient carbon dioxide-free sodium hydroxide is added to make the solution contain 0.2% free alkali. The contents of the flask are now refluxed on the steam bath for 5 hours with the top of the condenser protected against entrance of carbon dioxide. The flask containing the digest is then connected to a steam-distilling apparatus which consists of a steam-generating flask containing distilled water to which barium hydroxide has been added. The steam is directly conducted into the bottom of the flask containing the sample which has previously been neutralized with sulfuric acid and to which an excess of this acid has been added to contain 2% free acid. The 2-liter flask used to collect the distillate is also protected from the entrance of carbon dioxide.

Each liter of distillate is titrated with carbon dioxide-free 0.1 N sodium hydroxide. The distillation is stopped when a liter of distillate consumes less than 1.0 cc. of the alkali. The combined distillates are made alkaline and evaporated on the steam bath to about 15 cc. The formic acid is then determined by the mercuric chloride method[662] and from the weight of the precipitate the equivalent amount of formic acid is calculated, which in turn is expressed by its equivalents of 0.1 N sodium hydroxide. This is subtracted from the total titration giving the net titration equivalent of the acetic acid.

This method has been found reliable in the author's laboratory for mixtures of acetic and formic acids and using a stream of nitrogen to exclude carbon dioxide.[739] Citrus pectin gives no acetyl groups, a beet pectin preparation gave values around 2%. Under the same conditions glucose gives 4% acetic acid and 1.7% formic acid; galacturonic acid yields 6.4% acetic acid and 2.2% formic acid. The pitfalls in this method are obvious. Ehrlich and Kosmahly[717] used a similar method but determined the formic acid by oxidation with potassium dichromate and redistilling the acetic acid formed. Neither Myers and Baker nor the author found the latter of satisfactory accuracy on pure mixtures.

For further information on acetyl determinations in pectic substances, see the articles of Henglein and Vollmert[740] and of Pippen, McCready, and Owens.[741] It is clear that both the occurrence of acetyl groups in pectic substances and the methods of quantitative estimation of acetyl groups in pectic materials are in dire need of thorough revaluation.

IX. CHARACTERIZATION OF PECTIC SUBSTANCES

1. Characterization of Protopectin Preparations

Little is known about the composition and structure of protopectin and it is therefore difficult to go much beyond the implications of its defi-

[739] B. Crowley and Z. I. Kertesz, *unpublished work*, 1948.
[740] F. A. Henglein and B. Vollmert, *Makromol. Chemie*, 2, 1 (1948).
[741] E. L. Pippen, R. M. McCready, and H. S. Owens, *Anal. Chem.*, 22, 1457 (1950).

nition that: (1) protopectin is insoluble in (cold) water; and (2) that it may be transformed by a number of means (see Chapter VI, Section I) into pectinic acids of colloidal characteristics.

Protopectin preparations should contain at least 30 to 40% polygalacturonic acid (as determined by the carbon dioxide method) and at least a few per cent of methoxyl and some cellulose. The usual method for crude fiber[662] may be used to approximate the proportion of cellulose in a preparation.

2. Characterization of Pectinic Acids

For practical purposes the information which may be used to characterize a preparation of pectic acid can be divided into those dealing with its chemical and physical characteristics and behavior.

The following chemical characteristics of pectinic acid preparations may be used for their characterization.

(1) The preparation should be characterized as a pectic polyuronide by determination of the calcium pectate yield (Section VI-3) after purification by precipitation with ethanol or acetone. Crude pectic preparations have, as a rule, calcium pectate numbers not lower than 60, while purified preparations of pectinic and pectic acids should give values in the neighborhood and slightly above 100.

(2) It is usually desirable to ascertain that the precipitate obtained is indeed a polyuronide. This should be done by the carbon dioxide method and the results should be expressed as polygalacturonic acid. Crude preparations should contain at least 50%, purified preparation over 80% polyuronide. It is recommended that this uronide determination be performed on the calcium pectate in order to exclude nonpectic polyuronides. This will also demonstrate the purity of the calcium pectate precipitates.

(3) It is, furthermore, desirable to establish that the polyuronide in question is composed of galacturonic acid units. This may be done directly by the thorium nitrate test (Section III-5) or by the various tests for galacturonic acid after enzymic hydrolysis. Usually the Ehrlich color test is used for this purpose.

(4) Having characterized the material in question as a pectic polyuronide, the next question is the extent of esterification of the carboxyl groups. For this purpose the total carboxyl groups and those esterified should be determined by any of the methods described previously. Both can be determined with fair accuracy from titration values as given above. The results should be expressed in two ways. First, the contents of total acid groups should be defined; this should agree with the results obtained under (2) and, in many cases, may be used instead of the carbon dioxide method to state the total polyuronide content. Secondly, the methyl ester content should be expressed on the basis of the pectinic acid content of the preparation, calculated as described

in Section VII-2*b*. It is now also customary to express the ester content by the fraction or percentage of all carboxyl groups esterified.[742] Some workers prefer to state this as a percentage, others use 1.00 as the total and express the extent of esterification as a fraction. Thus, 50% and 0.5 esterification both mean that half of the carboxyl groups are free, and half of them in the form of the methyl ester. Such characterization is especially important in the case of low-ester pectinic acids. Unless one deals with a highly purified pectinic acid, expression of the methyl ester (methoxyl) content on the basis of the preparation is usually meaningless.

(*5*) It is often desirable to state the pH of a 0.5% solution of the preparation at room temperature.

(*6*) The proportion of nonuronide components ("ballast") should be determined either directly or indirectly. This value, of course, is the difference between the pectinic acid content and 100.

(*7*) The proportion of inorganic constituents is customarily expressed as per cent of ash. This information is of importance for all pectic preparations but especially in the case of low-ester pectinic acids and pectic acids. The composition of the ash, if more than a trace is present, should also be ascertained. Specific attention should be given to the presence of heavy metals and to cations of the alkaline earth metal group. Defining the alkalinity of the ash has also been suggested.[742a]

Physical measurements should be used to supplement the data obtained by chemical methods. This is most essential in view of the lack of chemical methods for the determination of the average molecular size. Attention is called to the fact that highly degraded pectinic acids may have high uronide and methoxyl contents as well as show high calcium pectate yields, yet be beyond the definition of pectinic acids for lack of colloidal characteristics.

At the present time there is little unanimity among the methods which may be applied for the colloidal characterization of various pectic substances. Considerable effort is being extended (1949) by various committees to reach some agreement on this point. For the present, two methods may be used.[742a] The intrinsic viscosity (see Chapter VII, Section VIII-7) seems to be a characteristic suitable for this purpose. However, there are now no generally accepted conditions for the determination of the intrinsic viscosity and for this reason only reference is made to the discussions of this point.

Even more important is the jelly grade of the pectinic acid since the major proportion of the pectin now manufactured is used under conditions where this characteristic is of dominant importance. The methods for the evaluation of the jelly strength of pectin preparations are given and dis-

[742] C. H. Hills and R. Speiser, *Science*, **103**, 166 (1946).
[743a] D. T. Berglund, *Socker Handlingar*, **6**, 219 (1950).

cussed in Chapter XXIII, Section IV. There is still little agreement as to the methods which may be applied for the evaluation of low-ester pectinic acids inasmuch as the conditions under which they will be most useful are still not clearly defined. There is little likelihood that an agreement will be reached on this point within the next few years on account of the widely different conditions under which low-ester pectins may be used.

Henglein[743] suggested that pectin preparations be characterized by a combination of four numbers giving: (1) the average molecular weight calculated from the viscosity of the nitrated sample; (2) the extent of esterification as expressed by a fraction of 1.0 (on the basis of the total carboxyl content); (3) the purity expressed as per cent pectinic acid in the preparation; and (4) the jelly grade. Thus the definition of a given preparation might read:

$$^P180,000; 0.71; 85\%; 220.$$

There is as yet little unanimity in the interpretation of molecular weight determinations as recommended by Henglein and there is as yet no standard method for the determination of the jelly grade (see Chapter XXIII). However, any attempt to define pectin preparations in a more exact manner is a step in the right direction.

In closing this discussion two further remarks must be made in connection with the characterization of pectinic acids. First of all, as we have seen there is some tendency in certain groups of workers to obtain a definition of pectinic acids with regard to molecular size, for instance, by determinations on various derivatives such as nitropectins. For the present this cannot be considered as an entirely legitimate approach since the relationship between the structure and characteristics of pectinic acids and their nitro derivatives is not sufficiently established. Secondly it should be emphasized again that all pectinic acid preparations described thus far are heterogeneous in several respects (see Chapt. V). Any definition which may be given of the degree of heterogeneity will be of great importance since it is known that pectinic acids of identical average properties (methyl ester content, "molecular weight," etc.), but differing in the proportions of the various pectinic acids, may show great differences in behavior. Unfortunately, the degree of heterogeneity is not yet even generally appreciated and, as shown on previous pages, means for its determination and expression are still in their infancy.

Pectinic acids may also be characterized by the scheme described in the *National Formulary*[744] for pectins to be used for pharmaceutical

[743] F. A. Henglein, *Z. Lebensm. Untersuch. Forsch.*, **90**, 417 (1950).
[744] *National Formulary VIII.* American Pharmaceutical Assoc., Washington, D. C.. 1943.

purposes. The criteria used in the N. F. definitions are mostly similar to those given here except that for pharmaceutical uses generally purity requirements had to be agreed upon (see Chapter XIII for details of these definitions).

3. Characterization of Pectic Acids

All colloidal polygalacturonic acids or pectic acids are precipitable as acid calcium salts and, therefore, the calcium pectate yield should be, in the case of purified preparations, more than 100% of the pectic acid applied in the determination. The presence of various inorganic constituents (ash content) is of great importance to the behavior of pectic acids and should always be given in the definition of a preparation. With the exception of the methyl ester content, the same criteria as described above for pectinic acid may be used in the case of pectic acid.

The physical characteristics of pectic acids are even more difficult to define than those of pectinic acids. There is no agreement at this time on methods of viscosity measurements which may be used to indicate the colloidal properties of pectic acid solutions, although such should be applied if possible. The apearance of the pectic acid when precipitated by ethanol, mineral acids, or as a calcium salt (calcium pectate) is as good an indication of its nature as we have at the present time. There is little doubt that the increasing commercial application of pectic acids will necessitate a better definition of this compound and it may be hoped that such will be soon developed.

CHAPTER IX

Some Derivatives of the Pectic Substances

Pectic and pectinic acids form many derivatives which may be grossly classified into the following groups: (*1*) Esters may be formed by the carboxyl groups of the galacturonic acid residues; pectinic acid is a natural acid methyl ester of polygalacturonic acid. (*2*) The carboxyl groups form salts in the manner which is normal for organic acids. (*3*) Polygalacturonides are also capable of forming compounds through the attachment of various groups to the hydrogen atoms of the hydroxyl groups at carbon atoms 2 and 3; these compounds are usually esters of mineral and organic acids and have commanded considerable attention in recent years. (*4*) Substitution may occur at carbon atom 1 of the anhydrogalacturonic acid unit at the end of the polygalacturonic acid chain, at the so-called "reducing end group" of polygalacturonic acid.

The terminology of many of these derivatives is not clear at this time due to uncertainties in structure. It is for this reason that, in most cases, the orginal designation given by the workers who prepared the derivatives will be given, as well as the terms which are considered to be more correct and are, therefore, applied in the text.

It should be stated, in addition, that clear distinctions are made in the present discussion between derivatives obtained in the four ways mentioned above and pectic compounds which are obtained by partial degradation of the polygalacturonic structure. As indicated earlier, there are a great many such partial decomposition products described in the literature under an unfortunate conglomeration of terms, now mostly meaningless. Ehrlich alone describes several score partial decomposition products of this nature. Such products will not be considered as derivatives and will not be discussed in this chapter.

I. PECTINIC ACIDS AND OTHER DERIVATIVES OF PECTIC ACIDS OBTAINED BY METHYLATION AND ETHYLATION

The methylation of pectic acid to form pectinic acids is a means of demonstrating the interrelation of these substances. While demethylation is easily accomplished by a number of different methods (see Chapter VI), methylation is much more difficult. Buston and Nanji[745] could not attain definite methylation with methyl oxalate and methyl sulfate. Treatment of silver pectate with methyl iodide, however, gave preparations in which about 64% of the carboxyl groups were esterified. These authors heated 1–2 g. of silver pectate (containing 30–32% silver) with 10–15 g. of methyl iodide in 25 cc. of methanol. The most successful preparations contained about 10.5% methoxyl with a yield of 47% of the theoretical. The methyl derivatives of Buston and Nanji resembled natural pectinic acids, and their rate of deesterification with alkali was comparable to that of the natural pectinic acids. There is no certainty from the description of Buston and Nanji whether methyl groups were introduced at the "reducing end groups" of the polygalacturonic acids.

Morell and Link[746] used the method of Fischer and Speier[747] for the methylation of pectic acid.

The commercial pectic acid was first purified by extraction with 10% ethanol and some 150 g. of this material was refluxed for 24 hours with 1500 cc. of absolute methanol containing 3% hydrochloric acid. Thereupon the hydrochloric acid concentration was elevated to 50% by the addition of 500 cc. of methanol containing 10% hydrochloric acid and the refluxing was continued for 66 hours, after which the cooled mixture was centrifuged. The liquid portion contained 1-methyl D-galacturonic acid methyl ester and other soluble products. Morell, Baur, and Link[748] further investigated the portion which resisted solution and which contained the methyl derivative of polygalacturonic acid. This was washed with absolute methanol, dried, and ground. The yield was 55% and the crude preparation contained 17.5% methoxyl. It was purified by pouring its water solution into 5 volumes of 95% ethanol. The mixture was allowed to stand overnight at 4°C. and then centrifuged, washed with ethanol, and dried in vacuo at 80°C. The average methoxyl content of 15 such preparations was 18.0%, the polygalacturonic acid content 90%, and the saponification equivalent (per gram) 48.6 cc. of 0.1 N sodium hydroxide. It showed only a negligible reducing power toward hypoiodite and a specific rotation of +198° (1 to 1.5% solution in water).

The importance of these results in the evolution of the polymolecular conception of the structure of pectic substances was discussed in Chapter III, and reference is made here only to Table 6 which compares the analytical results obtained for these preparations. Morrell, Baur, and Link also investigated the physicochemical characteristics of this de-

[745] H. W. Buston and H. R. Nanji, Biochem. J., 26, 2090 (1932).
[746] S. Morell and K. P. Link, J. Biol. Chem., 100, 385 (1933).
[747] E. Fischer and A. Speier, Ber., 28, 3252 (1895).
[748] S. Morell, L. Baur, and K. P. Link, J. Biol. Chem., 105, 1 (1934).

rivative as well as the kinetics of its hydrolysis by hydrochloric acid. As was stated earlier, there is little doubt that the polygalacturonic acid suffered considerable degradation during the preparation of this derivative and for this reason there is no need to deal extensively with its properties.

Hinton[749] used dimethyl sulfate for the esterification. Jansen and Jang[750] have shown that at 25°C. polygalacturonic acids (pectic acids) are esterified much more slowly by methanol–hydrochloric acid than is galacturonic acid.

The synthetic methyl glycoside of polygalacturonic acid methyl ester may be easily saponified with alkali to give the methyl glycoside of polygalacturonic acid (pectic acid). The sodium and barium salts of the methyl glycoside of polygalacturonic acid have been prepared by treatment of the polyester with a slight excess of the corresponding alkali and precipitation with ethanol.[748,751]

Luckett and Smith[752] converted citrus pectinic acid into pectic acid and treated the latter repeatedly with methyl sulfate and sodium hydroxide. The partially methylated derivative was transformed into the thallium salt and further methylated with methyl iodide and methanol and again with silver oxide and methyl iodide. This derivative was hydrolyzed by Luckett and Smith and the derived methylated galacturonic acids were studied with the aim of obtaining information on the types of linkages which occur in the natural pectinic and pectic acids. This work was discussed previously in Chapter III.

Schneider and Ziervogel[753] methylated purified nitropectin by refluxing it with absolute methanol containing 1% hydrochloric acid for 48 hours. The methoxyl content of the preparation increased from 5 to 9.3%. Further heating for 8 hours in a sealed tube at 100°C. elevated the methoxyl content to 11.2–11.8%. Due to the presence of the nitrous oxide groups, the calculated maximum (ester) methoxyl content of a nitropectin is 13.2%; consequently these values represent 91–95% methylation and show the complete absence of free acid (COOH) groups. The pH of solutions of these products was also unusually high, about 4.2. Schneider and Fritschi[754] state that the products obtained by this prolonged methylation indicate complete esterification with the exception of methylation at the end group.

[749] C. L. Hinton, *Fruits Pectins, Their Chemical Behaviour and Jellying Properties.* Chem. Publishing Co., New York, 1940.
[750] E. F. Jansen and R. Jang, *J. Am. Chem. Soc.*, **68**, 1475 (1946).
[751] L. Baur and K. P. Link, *J. Biol. Chem.*, **109**, 293 (1935).
[752] S. Luckett and F. Smith, *J. Chem. Soc.*, **1940**, 1106.
[753] G. Schneider and M. Ziervogel, *Ber.*, **69**, 2530 (1936).
[754] G. Schneider and U. Fritschi, *Ber.*, **69**, 2537 (1936).

Buston and Nanji[745] also made unsuccessful attempts to form ethyl esters of pectic acid under similar conditions. They believe that the use of ethyl iodide under identical conditions does actually result in the momentary ethylation of the pectic acid, but that this ethyl ester is immediately decomposed in a radical manner, destroying—in addition to the ester linkages—the polygalacturonide structure. However, recently MacDonnell, Jang, Jansen, and Lineweaver[755] mentioned a polyethyl ester made by the method of Morell and Link[746] but at 65°C. This derivative contained 11.7% ethoxyl, indicating about 50% esterification. The properties of this compound have not yet been described.

II. NITROPECTIN

Both Braconnot[756] and Smolenski and Pardo[757] have prepared and identified the pectic and pectinic acid esters of nitric and acetic acids. In these derivatives the nitrous oxide, acetyl, etc., radicals are attached to carbon atoms 2 and 3 of the anhydrogalacturonic acid units of the polygalacturonic acids. The terminology of these compounds is confused at the present time. In the commonly used name *nitropectin* the use of both terms *nitro* and *pectin* is incorrect since this is not a true nitro compound but rather a nitric acid ester. Again, the term *pectin* is used here in a loose generic sense as it was applied before the reintroduction of the name *pectinic acids*. Of course, pectic acids (polygalacturonic acids) are just as capable of forming nitropectin as are pectinic acids in which the methyl ester groups occur. The chief reason for the use of the name *nitropectin* is—in addition to simplicity—the overwhelming resemblance of these compounds to nitrocellulose. As our knowledge of nitropectins develops, it may become desirable to formulate a more logical terminology for these derivatives.

Smolenski and Pardo introduced, with constant stirring and cooling, 10 g. of finely powdered polygalacturonic acid into 45 cc. of fuming nitric acid. After constant mixing at room temperature for several hours, the solution was decanted from the sediment and poured on 200 g. of ice. The precipitated nitropectin was dissolved in acetone and reprecipitated with water, washed with 80% ethanol, and dried at 35°C. under vacuum. The light gray powder dissolved in acetone showed a specific rotation of +295°. Upon ignition it burned vigorously, almost explosively. Due to this fact, Smolenski and Pardo experienced some difficulty in determining its composition and found it neces-

[755] L. R. MacDonnell, R. Jang, E. F. Jansen, and H. Lineweaver, *Arch. Biochem.*, 28, 260 (1950).

[756] H. Braconnot, *Ann. chim. phys.*, 30, 96 (1825).

[757] K. Smolenski and W. Pardo, *Chem. Listy*, 25, 446 (1932); through *C. A.*, 27, 707 (1933).

sary to ignite nitropectin only after it was mixed with large amounts of lead chromate. Its nitrogen content (10.3%) indicated the presence of two nitrous oxide, NO_2, groups. They state that, in behavior and properties, nitropectin shows great similarity to nitrocellulose.

The most thorough investigation of nitropectin to date was reported by a group of German workers during the years 1935–38. Henglein and Schneider[758,759] studied the conditions most suitable for the formation of nitropectin. These authors nitrated purified pectinic acid and crude pectinic acid and also prepared nitropectin from pectin-containing raw materials, such as apple pomace, citrus peel, and extracted sugar beet slices, without previous isolation and purification of the pectic and pectinic acids. In the case of the latter raw materials, the nitration and dissolution of the pectic constituents occur simultaneously and the nitropectin thus formed is dissolved in the nitrating agent.

Just as in the case of cellulose, the nitrating mixture must contain as little water as possible so that the polygalacturonic acid is not extensively hydrolyzed during nitration. When a mixture of nitric and sulfuric acids is used for nitration, the concentration of sulfuric acid must be below 25%. The nitration should preferably be performed at 0°C. Henglein and Schneider state that nitric acid which contains nitrous acid seems to be more suitable for nitration because the nitrous acid apparently inhibits hydrolysis. A mixture of 18.4% nitrous acid (as NO_2) and 78.0% nitric acid gives better results than a mixture of 96.3% nitric acid and only 0.15% nitrous acid. The exact conditions which were found by these authors to be most suitable are likely to have little general meaning because the process of nitration depends on the starting materials. In these tests a comparatively short nitration (1–3 hours) has been found to introduce the maximum proportion of nitrogen oxide groups. The nitropectin which is formed is always dissolved in the nitrating mixture and may be precipitated by simply pouring this in a large volume of water. Nitropectin is soluble in acetone and may be further purified by being dissolved in this solvent and reprecipitated with water.

The composition of some nitropectin preparations, as given by Schneider and Fritschi,[754,760] is shown in Table 25. The polyuronide contents have been calculated from the carbon dioxide contents given by these authors with the use of the factor 4.0.

These results indicate that, just as in the case of the nitropectin of Smolenski and Pardo, the nitropectins prepared by the German authors probably contained two nitrous oxide groups in every anhydrogalacturonic acid unit. The nitrogen contents of the preparations are somewhat lower

[758] F. A. Henglein and G. Schneider, Ber., 69, 309 (1936).
[759] F. A. Henglein and G. Schneider, German Pat. 680,396 (1942).
[760] G. Schneider and U. Fritschi, Ber., 70, 1611 (1937).

than that required by the theory for two NO_2 groups. However, nitropectins, like other pectic preparations, represent heterogeneous mixtures of various compounds, some of which may be more readily nitrated than others. Assuming the presence of a small proportion of foreign material in the preparations, some of the values (9.5–9.7%) are very close to the calculated (10.0%) proportion of nitrogen.

TABLE 25

POLYGALACTURONIC ACID, NITROGEN, AND METHOXYL CONTENT AND SOLUTION VISCOSITIES (IN ACETONE) OF SOME NITROPECTIN PREPARATIONS (ADAPTED FROM SCHNEIDER AND FRITSCHI)

Preparation	Sp. visc. Concn.	N, %	CH₂O, %	Polygalacturonic acid, %
A. Directly from extracted beet slices..........	100	9.58	4.51	66.0
	145	9.72	3.46	67.0
	180	8.05	4.26	71.6
	85	8.24	9.72	69.6
B. From pectinic acid......	45	8.06	6.99	68.8
	42	7.46	3.94	74.4
Calculated Values				
C. For pectic acid with 2 NO₂ groups in the anhydrogalacturonic acid units	—	10.5	0.0	66.1
D. For a fully methylated pectinic acid ("ideal ester").............	—	0.0	16.3	92.6
E. Compound as in (D) but with 1 NO₂ group per basic unit...........	—	5.9	13.2	74.8
F. Compound as in (D) with 2 NO₂ groups per basic unit...............	—	10.0	11.1	62.8

Henglein and Schneider made an extensive study of the viscosity of acetone solutions of nitropectin preparations. The nitropectin should not be completely dried lest its solubility in acetone be decreased. During the nitration there is a short initial increase in the viscosity, after which the viscosity decreases steadily. The maximum viscosity is much higher with nitration at 0°C. than at 20°, and the subsequent loss of viscosity is also slower at the lower temperature.

Like nitrocelluloses, nitropectins can form films and threads under the same conditions. In the preparation of such products plasticizers and, probably, stabilizers must be used. Henglein and Schneider state that plasticizers commonly used for nitrocellulose also seem to be applicable to nitropectin. They report a series of tensile strength measurements made on nitropectin films prepared by the use of glycerol, tributyl phosphate, and other plasticizers. The values are in the range of 1.6 to 6.2 kg. per mm.[3]. The wet strength of the films is about one third lower than that of the dry films. The nitropectin films resist dilute acids very well and, to some extent, even concentrated acids, but alkalis cause the films to swell and, in turn, to dissolve.

In contrast to nitrocellulose, nitropectin seems to swell in water to a limited extent.[761] Henglein and Schneider investigated the behavior under x-rays of nitropectin threads similar to viscose. The investigation indicated weak orientation of the molecules in the crystallite in the direction of the thread. Although this is in harmony with the elongated shape of the molecule, it does not exclude the possibility of branching chains in the molecule or other aberrations which would invalidate the relationship which, according to Staudinger, exists between the viscosity and molecular weight of linear polymers (see Chapter VII, Section VIII-7).

For further information on nitropectin see the previously discussed article of Speiser and Eddy[762] and the more recent report of Schlubach and Hoffmann-Walbeck.[763] The latter workers used the nitration procedure of Caesar and Goldfrank[764] and found that, in contrast to the 30% loss of methoxyl found by Speiser and Eddy, this more protective method resulted in the loss of only 4–7% methoxyl.

III. SOME FURTHER DERIVATIVES OF PECTIC SUBSTANCES

Schneider and Ziervogel[753] found that during direct formylation of pectic acids and pectinic acids with formic acid the product is greatly degraded. On the other hand, formylation of nitropectin in the presence of 1% sulfuric acid as catalyst gives very good results. The nitrous oxide groups are progressively replaced by formyl groups until the nitrogen content is reduced from the original 9.5% to about 2.5%. The maximum formyl content (15.0%) is reached in three days at 20°C. at a time when the nitrogen content is 3%. The mixed formyl-nitro ester of pectinic acid is similar in its physical properties to the acetyl-nitro pectinic acid described below.

Smolenski and Pardo[757] prepared the acetyl derivative (pectic acid ester of acetic acid) in the following manner.

With constant and vigorous stirring 10 g. of purified polygalacturonic acid was slowly introduced into a mixture of 35 g. of anhydrous acetic acid and 1 g. of sulfuric acid. The mixture was refluxed on the steam bath for 9–10 hours. The acetyl ester solidified after cooling and was washed with 300 cc. of anhydrous ether. It was then repeatedly dissolved in acetone, precipitated by the

[761] B. Eriksson and S. Säverborn, *Acta Agr. Suecana*, **2**, 233 (1946).
[762] R. Speiser and C. R. Eddy, *J. Am. Chem. Soc.*, **68**, 287 (1946).
[763] H. H. Schlubach and H. P. Hoffmann-Walbeck, *Makromol. Chem.*, **4**, 5 (1949).
[764] G. V. Caesar and M. G. Goldfrank, *J. Am. Chem. Soc.*, **68**, 372 (1946).

addition of ether, and finally dried at 50°C. under vacuum. The preparation, which shows a reducing power of 7–8% (calculated as galactose), is the diacetate. The alkali consumption per 100 grams of 385.4 cc. of 1 N sodium hydroxide about equals that calculated for an "octagalacturonic acid" (see Chapter III). The acetyl groups may be removed by saponification with an excess of alkali and the pectic acid precipitated by acid ethanol. The yield in this latter operation is about 90%.

A more detailed study of the acetyl derivatives of pectinic acid and of nitropectin has been reported by Schneider and Ziervogel[753] who describe the difficulties experienced during the acetylation and state that the introduction of acetyl groups may be best performed on gel-like pectinic acid. The latter is prepared by precipitation of purified pectinic acid with ethanol in the form of threads. These are dehydrated with ether and then used without complete drying. The threads are first pre-treated with glacial acetic acid, followed by acetylation with a mixture of about 90–95% acetic anhydride and 5–10% glacial acetic acid. The maximum acetylation obtained with different catalysts is shown in Table 26. This is in harmony with the statement of Smolenski and Pardo that 1%

TABLE 26

EFFECT OF KIND OF CATALYST ON MAXIMUM EXTENT OF ACETYLATION (ADAPTED FROM SCHNEIDER AND ZIERVOGEL)

Catalyst (1%)	Temp., °C.	Acetyl in ester, %
Sulfuric acid	20	39.5
	40	43.0
Pyridine	20	36.4
	40	39.2
Zinc chloride	20	25.5
Perchloric acid	20	33.0

sulfuric acid is an effective catalyst. From the properties of the acetyl derivatives it is apparent that all samples are degraded during acetylation. The chief reason for hydrolysis appears to be the insolubility of pectic or pectinic acids in the acetylating mixtures. Several days are required under these conditions to attain the maximum extent of acetylation. Schneider and Ziervogel also acetylated nitropectin. Nitropectin is soluble in acetic anhydride and thus the reaction proceeds entirely in the liquid phase. During the acetylation (lasting 4 to 6 days) the nitrous oxide groups are replaced by the acetyl groups until the nitrogen content is reduced to values around 2% and the proportion of acetyl groups increases to a maximum between 30 to 40%, and then decreases. However, in none of the experiments with various catalysts are the nitrous oxide groups completely removed. After the completion of acetylation the mixture is diluted with some glacial acetic acid and poured into water. The nitro-acetyl derivative of pectinic acid separates as a curd-like precipitate.

The mixed nitro-acetyl esters prepared by Schneider and Ziervogel are soluble in acetone, and show (by the osmotic pressure method) molecular weights of the same order of magnitude as those found for the starting material, namely, nitropectin. During the acetylation of nitropectin the viscosity (as measured in acetone solution) decreases considerably. The tensile strengths of films formed from this derivative are somewhat lower than of films made from the parent nitropectins. The preparations of Schneider and Ziervogel are assumed to contain two acetyl groups per anhydrogalacturonic acid residue. The methyl ester groups present in nitropectin, usually in the neighborhood of 5% (as methoxyl, CH_3O), are not affected by acetylation and the acetyl-nitro pectinic acids still contain this proportion of methyl ester groups.

Carson and Maclay[765] described a method of preparation of a series of esters of pectinic acid, including the diacetate.

First a pectinic acid–water paste is partially dehydrated with acetone. The water and acetone are then gradually replaced with pyridine to give pectinic acid in a highly swollen gelatinous state. The freshly precipitated pectinic acid may also be directly swollen in pyridine. The acetylation is accomplished by heating with acetic anhydride at 45–50°C. for 3–5 hours with vigorous stirring. The ester is precipitated by pouring the reaction mixture into a large volume of cold water containing 3% hydrochloric acid. After separation by centrifuging, the product is further washed in turn with 3% hydrochloric acid, water, 95% ethanol and ether. A second acetylation at room temperature for two days is usually performed to insure maximum acetylation. The diacetate ester contains about the same proportion of methoxyl (7%) as the original pectinic acid and shows an ester content nearly as large as that required by theory (32.0%). The ester prepared in this manner is insoluble in water and is only partly soluble in chloroform, tetrachloroethane, pyridine, and acetic acid, but is insoluble in ethanol, acetone, ether, and benzene. In spite of some efforts, the cause of the partial solubility could not be satisfactorily explained by Carson and Maclay. The suggestion is inescapable that the partial solubility represents fractionation according to molecular size. Films made from this diacetate are very weak.

The dipropionate, dibutyrate, laurate, myristate, palmitate, and benzoate esters of pectinic acid have also been prepared by Carson and Maclay. For the synthesis of the propionate and dibutyrate the corresponding anhydrides were used in a manner similar to that employed

[765] J. F. Carson and W. D. Maclay, *J. Am. Chem. Soc.*, **67**, 787 (1945); **68**, 1015 (1946).

in the preparation of the diacetate. They contained almost the theoretically required acyl groups calculated for the diesters.

The laurate, myristate, and palmitate have been prepared by reaction with the corresponding acid chloride in pyridine. They have acyl contents indicating the esterification of 1.0–1.6 hydroxyl groups per anhydrogalacturonic acid unit. Repeated acylation did not essentially increase the ester content. The latter three esters were soft, waxy solids only partially soluble in ether, acetone, dioxane, and benzene. The original proportion of methyl ester content (methoxyl) is only slightly reduced during preparation of the esters. The benzoate was prepared by these authors in the same manner as the three esters just discussed. It showed the presence of 1.6 esterified hydroxyl groups per anhydrogalacturonic acid unit and is a horny, resinous material.

Micheel and Dörner[766] prepared a series of derivatives of pectinic acids for immunological tests.

As starting material apple pectin purified by extraction with 70% ethanol was used. This material was first methylated with 3% hydrochloric acid in absolute methanol but it appears, from the low methoxyl content (13.18%), that either the preparation was impure or the methylation was far from complete. The yield was 50%. Some 185 g. of this ester was suspended in absolute methanol together with 1.5 g. of hydrazine hydrate and the mixture kept at 38°C. for 2–3 days. The hydrazide was washed with absolute methanol saturated with carbon dioxide or purified by dialysis. It contained 11.3–13.5% nitrogen and, at the most, traces of methoxyl. The azide was prepared from the hydrazide by suspending the latter in 2% hydrochloric acid and then mixing it with a slight excess of a solution of 30% sodium nitrite. The reaction mixture was cooled in an ice bath. The azide was precipitated from the mixture with dioxane. The hydrazide and azide were not further characterized.

The N-tyrosyl ethyl ester, N-tyrosyl hydrazide, N-glucosaminic acid ethyl ester, and D-glucosaminic acid hydrazide of polygalacturonic acid were prepared by Micheel and Dörner from the hydrazide described above. It is more than likely that considerable degradation and hydrolysis occurred during the synthesis of these compounds, but the extent is not discernible from the article of these authors.

Gelatin and globulin compounds of polygalacturonic acids obtained from the azide derivatives have also been prepared by Micheel and Dörner. The polygalacturonic acid–gelatin contained 26–42% polygalacturonic acid, the polygalacturonic acid–globulin about 15%. They contained 14% and 12% nitrogen, respectively. Gelatin and globulin derivatives of a number of the compounds mentioned above were also prepared by these authors. Only the analyses but no description of the properties and of colloidal characteristics are given.

[766] F. Micheel and H. Dörner, Z. physiol. Chem., 280, 92 (1944).

Carson[767] described the preparation of some polygalacturonide n-alkyl amides. Deuel[768] described the action of formaldehyde on pectic substances, leading to the formation of semiacetals. Deuel and Neukom[769] prepared an amide of pectic acid by the action of ethylenediamine on the glycol ester of pectic acid and discussed the similarity between the behavior of this compound and proteins. The preparation and properties of the glycol ester of pectic acid were described by Deuel.[770] Steiner and Miller[770a] obtained a patent on the manufacture of glycol pectates and pectinates. Bergström[770b] and Karrer, König, and Usteri[770c] prepared sulfuric acid esters of pectin. Dryden, Wrigley, and Willaman[771] prepared the allyl ether of pectinic acid.

IV. SALTS OF PECTINIC AND PECTIC ACIDS

Pectic and pectinic acids are typical organic acids of high molecular weight and there is no limit, therefore, to the number of salts which they may form. The salts, as stated in the definition in Chapter I, may be neutral or acid pectates, depending on whether all or only a fraction of the carboxyl groups in pectic acid have been engaged in salt formation. Similarly, pectinic acids, which are known thus far to occur always with some free acid groups, may form neutral or acid salts.

A great many such salts have been prepared and described in the literature. The researches of early workers placed considerable stress on the preparation of such salts and attempts were made to gain insight into the composition and structure of the molecule through knowledge of the proportion of cation which may be attached to various pectic derivatives. Fellenberg,[772] Bonner,[773] Deuel,[774] Wlostowska,[775] and others described sodium pectates and pectinates; Myers[776] and Myers and Rouse[777] described cobalt, manganese, lead, zinc, copper, silver, etc., salts, the latter all containing only about 0.5% metallic component. In addition, many other salts have been described.[778]

[767] J. F. Carson, *J. Am. Chem. Soc.*, 68, 2723 (1947).
[768] H. Deuel, *Helv. Chim. Acta*, 30, 1269 (1947).
[769] H. Deuel and H. Neukom, *Nature*, 159, 882 (1947).
[770] H. Deuel, *Helv. Chim. Acta*, 30, 1523 (1947).
[770a] A. B. Steiner and A. Miller, U. S. Pat. 2,522,970 (1950).
[770b] S. Bergström, *Z. physiol. Chem.*, 238, 163 (1936).
[770c] P. Karrer, H. König, and E. Usteri, *Helv. Chim. Acta*, 26, 1296 (1943).
[771] E. C. Dryden, A. W. Wrigley, and J. J. Willaman, personal communication, 1950.
[772] T. Fellenberg, *Biochem. Z.*, 85, 45 (1918).
[773] J. Bonner, *Proc. Roy. Soc. Amsterdam*, 38, 346 (1935).
[774] H. Deuel, *Mitt. Lebensm. Hyg.*, 34, 41 (1943).
[775] W. Wlostowska, *Roczniki Chemji*, 10, 342 (1930).
[776] P. B. Myers, U. S. Pat. 2,259,767 (1942).
[777] P. B. Myers and A. H. Rouse, U. S. Pat. 2,323,483 (1943).
[778] T. H. Schultz, H. S. Owens, and W. D. Maclay, *J. Colloid Sci.*, 3, 53 (1948).

The preparation of the insoluble salts of pectinic and pectic acids is simple and obvious. The water-soluble salts of pectinic acid may be most conveniently obtained by adding the calculated amounts of the ions in the forms of salts of weak acids to a suspension of the pure pectinic acid in dilute ethanol.[779] For this purpose the carbonates are very suitable. In 50% ethanol the particles swell sufficiently so that rapid reaction occurs. After the reaction is complete the pectinate is removed by filtration, followed by dehydration with 95% ethanol and drying.

Stuewer and Olsen[779] prepared a series of organic base derivatives of pectinic and pectic acids.

In general, the organic bases suitable for reaction with pectinic or pectic acids fall between the limits of $K = 1 \times 10^{-3}$ to 1×10^{-10}. Some substituted ammonium hydroxides are even stronger than $K = 1 \times 10^{-3}$ and, of course, react with either pectinic or pectic acid. The reactivity of these bases may be readily demonstrated by their ability to disperse pectic acid. In the preparation of pectinates, care must be taken not to use too great an excess of the base because this results in demethylation and eventually in the formation of neutral or acid pectates. While pectic acid is quite insoluble in water, nearly all the organic derivatives are very soluble and the solubilization of the pectic acid is therefore a definite indication that the reaction has taken place. There are some derivatives, such as with quinine and cinchonine, which are not soluble in water. Stuewer and Olsen described the following: simple aliphatic amines—the N-propylamine, n-butylamine, di-n-butylamine, tri-n-butylamine, and tri-isoamylamine; substituted aliphatic amines—the diethanolamine, triethanolamine, ephedrine, benzylamine, and methylglucamine derivatives. The preparation of three aromatic amine derivatives, namely, with aniline, o-anisidine, and p-toluidine, and three heterocyclic base derivatives, with pyridine, piperidine, and quinine, were also described together with the diphenylguanidine and phenylhydrazine derivatives. Stuewer and Olsen note that some of the organic base derivatives have interesting properties. The maximum concentration of ethanol in which neutral sodium pectate may be dispersed to form a clear solution is 6–8%. Clear solutions of the triethanolamine pectate may be formed with up to 60% ethanol, of propylamine pectate up to about 75% ethanol.

We have noted in Chapter VI that, upon treatment of pectinic acids with ammonia, some amide groups are introduced in addition to the formation of the ammonium salt.[780,781] Deuel and Neukom[782] and Deuel, Neukom, and Weber[783] have studied the formation of a complex between pectinic acids and sodium tetraborate (borax).

[779] R. F. Stuewer and A. G. Olsen, *J. Am. Pharm. Assoc.*, **29**, 303 (1940).
[780] G. H. Joseph, A. H. Kieser, and E. F. Bryant, *Food Technol.*, **3**, 85 (1949).
[781] W. A. Mitchell, *Food Technol.*, **4**, 135 (1950).
[782] H. Deuel and H. Neukom, *Makromol. Chem.*, **3**, 13 (1949).
[783] H. Deuel, H. Neukom, and F. Weber, *Nature*, **161**, 96 (1948).

PART TWO
THE BOTANY OF PECTIC SUBSTANCES

CHAPTER X

Occurrence and Distribution of Pectic Substances in Plants

Pectic substances occur in most, perhaps in all, plant tissues. Generally speaking, they are found in relatively large amounts in succulent, soft tissues composed chiefly of primary walls, and under conditions of rapid growth and high water content. During the process of lignification the content of pectic materials in plants usually decreases and in hard tissues such as wood they constitute only a negligible fraction of the total plant substances. In the present chapter the occurrence of pectic substances in plants will be discussed from the morphologic point of view, without regard to the amounts which may be found by chemical analysis. The results of investigations in which the pectic substances of various tissues were quantitatively estimated without regard to their location in the plant tissue will be dealt with in Chapter XIII.

It is not clear at this time whether pectic substances are formed by microorganisms although there is much information in the literature concerning various polysaccharides formed by molds and bacteria.[784,785] In a recent study of the effect of boron on plant metabolism, Winfield[786] reported that under certain conditions the mold *Aspergillus niger* is capable of synthesizing galacturonic acid and that *Penicillium glaucum* can form a polyuronide resembling pectic substances. It is postulated from these tests that the presence of boron and the formation of pectic materials are in some manner related. The tests made by Winfield were of such unsatisfactory specificity that the drawing of the above conclusion seems to be unwarranted; this is essentially admitted by Winfield. The occurrence of pectic substances in the soil-inhabiting fungus *Phymatotrichum omnivorum* was recently noted by Ergle and Blank,[787] but there is some

[784] A. G. Norman, *Biochemistry of Cellulose, the Polyuronides, Lignin, etc.* Clarendon Press, Oxford, 1937.
[785] B. S. Gould, "Chemical Compounds Formed from Sugar by Molds," Sugar Research Foundation, New York, *Sci. Rept.*, No. 7 (1947).
[786] M. E. Winfield, *Australian J. Exptl. Biol. Med. Sci.*, 23, 267 (1945).
[787] D. R. Ergle and L. M. Blank, *Phytopathology*, 37, 153 (1947).

doubt about the true pectic nature of their "pectin" even if it was determined as calcium pectate. As shown in Chapter VIII (Section VI-3), this method is not entirely specific in the presence of other polysaccharides and for this reason a further examination of the calcium pectate precipitates obtained would be desirable before final conclusions are drawn. There are some old and usually very general statements concerning the presence of pectic substances in microorganisms but these are not likely to stand critical revaluation. A recent review of the literature on polysaccharides formed by bacteria, molds, and yeasts by Evans and Hibbert[788] also fails to reveal any instance of the formation of pectic substances by microorganisms.

In spite of the efforts of many investigators, the morphologic relations of pectic substances in plants are still not clear. Several factors are responsible for this situation. First, the chemical nature of the most important building block of the pectic substances was unknown until 1917. The confusion in general terminology, as well as concerning the definition of a "pure" pectic compound, made the evaluation and harmonization of the experimental observations of various workers difficult and often impossible. Even after the discovery of galacturonic acid, the confusion in nomenclature prevailed, although the definition of pectic substances became somewhat sharper. With disagreement among the chemists themselves on the topic of pectin terminology, they were of little help to the botanists who tried to pry into the occurrence, role, characteristics, and transformations of the pectic substances in plant tissues.

The botanists, however, were not much better off with regard to nomenclature than were the chemists. The heterogeneous character of cell membranes was not universally accepted until Mangin published his important series of memoirs during the years 1888–1894.[789] The morphology and taxonomy of certain cell structures (and especially of the cell membranes in which our chief interest lies) remained confused until recent years.[790] There is still no unanimity in this matter, although the situation has been considerably clarified by the efforts of Kerr and Bailey[791] and others. The botanist is compelled to use chemical treatments in his work to produce satisfactory staining for the observation of various

[788] T. H. Evans and H. Hibbert, "Bacterial Polysaccharides," Sugar Research Foundation, New York, Sci. Rept., No. 6 (1947). Also T. H. Evans and H. Hibbert, in W. W. Pigman and M. L. Wolfrom, Advances in Carbohydrate Chemistry, Vol. II, Academic Press, New York, 1946, p. 204.

[789] L. Mangin, Compt. rend., 107, 144 (1888); 109, 579 (1889); 110, 295 (1890); 111, 120 (1890); 113, 1069 (1891); etc.

[790] M. H. Branfoot (neé M. H. Carré), "A Critical and Historical Study of the Pectic Substances of Plants," Dept. of Sci. and Ind. Research, Food Investigation Special Rept. No. 33, H. M. Stationery Office (1929).

[791] T. Kerr and I. W. Bailey, J. Arnold Arboretum (Harvard Univ.), 15, 327 (1934).

tissue components. These often result in distortion of the conditions as they originally existed in the living plant. Tests made on extracted or isolated materials are of doubtful significance from the morphologic standpoint. Finally, it may be added that ruthenium red, the most commonly used stain in such work,[792] is now known not to be specific for pectic substances (Chapter VIII, Section I-b). The most suitable method for the investigation of the distribution and chemical characteristics of tissue components may be the actual separation of the various structural elements. A further elaboration and perfection of the technic used by Bailey,[793] for example, who applied micromanipulators for the segregation of cell structures for subsequent microchemical analysis, may lead to information which is morphologically and chemically more dependable. It is more than likely that the electron microscope will eventually open up further possibilities along such lines.

Of the many complicated structural components of plant cells, our interest is limited to a few. The bulk of the interior of mature cells is occupied by a single large cavity, the vacuole. This is filled with water in which a great variety of substances are dissolved or dispersed. Although the occurrence of pectic substances in the cell sap has been observed by many workers, such as Nanji and Norman,[794] some authors doubt whether such dissolved pectic substances are common. The rather sensible postulation of Kizel and Yatsyna,[795] that the pectic components of the cell wall are formed in the cell itself and are only later deposited, makes the cell sap the primary source of pectic substances in the plant tissue. There is no doubt, however, that some of the dissolved pectic substances may at times originate from the insoluble pectic constituents of the cell walls and the middle lamella. There is ample evidence that such dissolution takes place, especially as the tissue matures and disintegrates. As a consequence, pectic materials in the state of transition can also be found in plant tissues. The solubility of pectic substances in the cell sap might be governed, at least partly, by the degree of methylation. The presence of dissolved pectinic acids of a high degree of methylation in the cell sap of strawberries and raspberries[796] is in harmony with such an assumption.

Griebel[797] described a striking form of semifluid pectic material which appears in sections of the fruit of the "service tree" (Pirus sorbus domestica) when the tissue is submerged in water. The bubble-like objects

[792] L. Mangin, Compt. rend., 116, 653 (1893).

[793] A. J. Bailey, Ind. Eng. Chem., Anal. Ed., 8, 52 (1936).

[794] D. R. Nanji and A. G. Norman, Biochem. J., 22, 596 (1928).

[795] A. Kizel and R. Yatsyna, Bull. soc. naturalistes Moscou. Sect. biol., 45, 441 (1936); through C. A., 32, 1300 (1938).

[796] L. R. Leinbach, C. G. Seegmiller, and J. S. Wilbur, Food Technol., 5, 51 (1951).

[797] C. Griebel, Z. Untersuch. Nahr. u. Genussmit., 49, 90 (1925).

which arise from the cell wall are apparently pectic bodies between the insoluble and soluble stages. Such pectic compounds with intermediate solubility properties can be observed in many ripe fruits, especially in those very rich in pectic constituents. The behavior of kumquats (Chap. XIII) during ripening is a well-known example of the whole fruit undergoing such transformation.

The serious discrepancies in the use of terms describing cell membranes necessitate a short description of these structures before the occurrence and role of pectic substances are discussed. Of course, it is beyond the scope of this volume even to list the endless variations which may be observed in the appearance of cell membranes.

In young tissues the cell wall consists of a single layer, while in older tissues it is composed of two or more layers. There are great variations in the thickness of the walls of different cells and even greater differences in the physical and chemical properties of cell walls. A well-developed cell wall, according to Kerr and Bailey,[791] is composed of the following three main layers:

(1) The middle lamella or intercellular substance is formed from the cell plate during cell division and is shared by adjacent cells. It is completely isotropic (see Chapter VII) and is composed largely, or entirely, of pectic substances.

(2) The primary wall is developed from the cambial wall; it is composed of cellulose, hemicelluloses, pectic substances, and lignin. In woody tissues the primary wall is heavily lignified.

(3) The secondary wall may be composed of several zones; it is incapable of extension growth and, during growth, is added to by apposition. It is composed of a mixture of cellulose, hemicelluloses, lignins, and pentosans. Some of these structures may not be visibly developed in certain tissues and are often difficult to distinguish.

The pectic substances of the middle lamella are deposited in a single or double layer by the plasma membranes and undergo changes in form, quantity, and characteristics during the development of the plant. Their mass is often increased by the secretion of further pectic materials from adjoining cells into the spaces formed when they are rounding off. The middle lamella may be partially absorbed by the rest of the wall. It has also been suggested by Treub[798] that in cell division the protoplasmic cell plate splits to form the plasma membrane of the two daughter cells. Between these membranes a substance is secreted which becomes the primary layer or middle lamella. Timberlake[799] and Allen[800] later confirmed

---

[798] M. Treub, *Quelques recherches sur la rôle du noyau dans la division des cellules végétales,* Amsterdam, 1878; quoted from A. W. Schorger, *The Chemistry of Cellulose and Wood,* McGraw-Hill, New York, 1926.

[799] H. G. Timberlake, *Botan. Gaz.,* 30, 73, 154 (1900).

[800] C. E. Allen, *Botan. Gaz.,* 32, 1 (1901).

this theory. Figure 18 shows a drawing illustrating pectic substances in the middle lamella of an unripe apple.

It was recognized early that pectic substances occur in the middle lamella. Frémy[801] in 1847 observed them in the cell membranes of walls and considered that the thickening of cell walls was caused by the deposition of an insoluble pectic material together with cellulose. He also observed that, during the ripening of fruits, the cell walls became appreci-

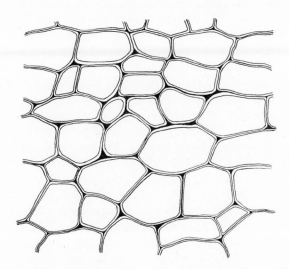

Fig. 18. The middle lamella in an unripe apple (×1350).

This drawing shows only the structures stained by ruthenium red. The solid black masses between the cells represent the middle lamella pectic substances.

ably thinner and attributed this change to the decomposition of the insoluble protopectin and the formation of soluble pectinic acids. Mangin[789] found that the middle lamella contains no cellulose but is composed mostly of a pectic substance different from protopectin; he suggested that it is calcium pectate. Molisch[802] showed that the middle lamella is indeed rich in calcium. Bonner[803] goes one step further and ascribes the occasional differences in the appearance of the middle lamella in different plant tissues to variations in the calcium content. It has been suggested that the middle lamella is composed entirely of protopectin[804]

[801] E. Frémy, *Compt. rend.*, **24**, 1046 (1847).
[802] H. Molisch, *Microchemie der Pflanze*. Fischer, Jena, 1913.
[803] J. Bonner, *Botan. Rev.*, **10**, 475 (1936).
[804] A. C. Sloep, *Dissertation*, Delft (1928).

or of a protein–pectin complex,[805,806] but the overwhelming evidence indicates that it is made up of some water-insoluble pectic substance essentially similar in nature to calcium pectate. The possible role of proteins in forming the insoluble pectic components should not be completely discarded, however, because even fragmentary and very thin coatings enveloping pectic materials may render otherwise soluble substances insoluble. Although the use of solubilities as the only means of characterization is indeed a meager foundation for deciding the nature of the middle lamella, its easy solubility in pectic solvents and the apparent role of calcium seem to indicate that it is composed mostly of protopectin in which the calcium has a definite role or of calcium pectate or pectinates.

The primary cell wall, contrary to the middle lamella, is rich in more typical protopectin.[807] Pectin commercially produced from apple pomace comes mostly from the primary cell walls of the fleshy parenchyma. The white albedo of citrus fruits also consists of parenchymous cells whose primary walls contain a large proportion of protopectin. Just like the pectic substance of the middle lamella, the protopectin of the primary walls may also undergo marked changes. These were observed by many early workers and were thoroughly investigated in apples and other fruits. The most important contributions along these lines were made by Carré and co-workers[807,808] who systematically compared microscopic observations with the results of careful chemical analysis performed with methods which are still among the best. Let us see, as an example, what morphologic changes occur in some of the most common fruits and other plant tissues during growth and maturation.[790]

A stainable middle lamella appears in apples with the first signs of differentiation. Apples only 1.3–1.5 cm. in diameter have been found by Tetley[809] to show the presence of middle lamella on ruthenium red staining. Such young tissues are very resistant to maceration with alcoholic or aqueous potassium hydroxide, hydrochloric acid, and ammonium oxalate. By the time the apples reach a diameter of 3.4 cm., the resistance of the tissues is reduced and boiling with water alone produces maceration in the high acid containing varieties but none in those of low acidity. Such tests show early differences between the cell membranes of sweet and acid varieties of apples.

The cell walls of growing apples stain uniformly with ruthenium red,

[805] R. M. Tupper-Carey and J. H. Priestley, *Proc. Roy. Soc.* (*London*), **95**, 109 (1923–24).
[806] A. Dauphiné, *Compt. rend.*, **196**, 1738 (1933); **199**, 307 (1934).
[807] M. H. Carré, *Biochem. J.*, **16**, 704 (1922); **19**, 256 (1925); *Ann. Botany*, **39**, 811 (1925).
[808] M. H. Carré and A. S. Horne, *Ann. Botany*, **41**, 1 (1927).
[809] U. Tetley, *J. Pomol. Hort. Sci.*, **8**, 153 (1930).

indicating an apparently even distribution of pectic substances. With advanced development unevenly stained, irregular areas appear. Throughout ripening there is no change in the staining of the middle lamella, but when the fruit becomes soft and slightly overripe the pectic compounds diminish. This results in gradual loosening of the cells, causing softening of the tissue, until during senescence the cells become entirely separated from one another owing to the almost complete disappearance of the middle lamella substance. The pectic substances of the cell walls of apples behave similarly to that composing the middle lamella. As the apples grow and mature, the cell walls become thinner and contain less pectic material. With advanced softening and senescence stainable pectic compounds disappear completely.

During these pectic changes in the cell membranes certain apparently typical pectic structures appear.[808] In the decomposing walls of contact some disc-, crescent-, and band-shaped pectic bodies can be found upon staining with ruthenium red. These structures diminish in size and number and eventually disappear during softening and senescence. It has been suggested that the band- and crescent-shaped pectic bodies may be merely sectional views of the disc-shaped formations.

In ripening pears dissolution of the pectic framework has also been observed, but without the appearance of structures described in the previous paragraph. Carré and Horne[808] state that these structures are perhaps of intermediate character and that they do not appear in pears because of the rapid metabolic changes. In the potato both crescent- and disc-like pectic bodies can be observed in the cell wall but these are minute in size and stain only feebly with ruthenium red. On the other hand, the middle lamella of potatoes stains very distinctly. In certain root structures, such as the turnip and carrot, the petiole of the rhubarb, and in many fruits such as the orange, lemon, plum, gooseberry, and red currant, there is an abundance of pectic material in the cell wall and middle lamella which stain deeply with ruthenium red. In the melon short cylindrical connections hold the cells together in the early stages of growth. These pectic structures become constricted during development and are finally ruptured as the cells in the tissue attain maximum expansion. As a result, large globules composed of pectic substances remain on the opposing surfaces of the walls of separated cells.[790]

The majority of root hairs contain an inner membrane composed mostly of cellulose and an outer one consisting of pectic substances. The high efficiency of root hairs as absorbing organs may be attributed to the presence of this membrane apparently composed of calcium pectate.[810]

[810] E. Roberts, *Botan. Gaz.*, **62**, 497 (1916).

It has also been suggested that the acidic properties of root hairs, which play an important part in the solubilization of nutrients in virgin soils, may also come from their pectic constituents.[811]

Considerable attention has been paid in recent years to the occurrence and role of pectic substances in cotton fibers. During the period of elongation the protoplasm of the cotton hair is enclosed only by the thin primary wall which is made up of pectic materials, cellulose, and probably other components. This primary wall stains well with ruthenium red and is insoluble in a typical cellulose solvent such as cuprammonium. When young fibers are treated with hot 0.5% oxalic acid solution followed by hot 0.5% ammonium oxalate solution, the pectic compounds are removed and the walls now dissolve in cuprammonium.[812]   The cell wall of mature cotton fibers consists of a primary and a secondary wall. The secondary wall comprises the bulk of the fiber and is enclosed by a thin primary wall composed of cellulose, wax, and pectic substances. The lumen also contains wax and pectic substances together with degenerated protoplasm.[813]   The opinion has often been voiced that the short pieces of fibrils ("dermatozonics") produced upon the treatment of fibers with acid or by swelling, are joined to the spiral fibrils by a cement of pectic nature.[814]   This pectic substance covers both the dermatozonics and the fibrils and the lamellae. A recent study by Eriksson and Säverborn[815] of the fine structure of the flax fiber by the electron microscope should be noted in this connection. We shall return to a discussion of the importance of the pectic substances of cotton and other plant fibers in Chapter XIII.

Contrary to former belief[816,817] pectic substances are constant components of woody tissues (see Table 58 in this connection). According to Kerr and Bailey[791] the "isotropic middle lamella" of mature woody tissue (xylem) is not a homogeneous layer but consists of two anisotropic lignified cambial walls and an intervening isotropic layer composed of pectic substances and lignin.

Carré and Horne[808] state that the methods used by most investigators for the preparation of plant tissue for microscopic observation are not suitable for the detection of any water-soluble pectic components of the cell structure. Upon treating unwashed sections with stains made up in alcoholic media, they showed that water-soluble pectinic acids may be extracted from the depositions on the cell walls of ripe and overripe fruits

[811] C. G. Howe, *Botan. Gaz.*, **72**, 313 (1921).

[812] D. B. Anderson and T. Kerr, *Ind. Eng. Chem.*, **30**, 48 (1938).

[813] C. W. Hock, R. C. Ramsay, and M. Harris, *J. Research Natl. Bur. Standards*, **26**, 93 (1941).

[814] K. Hess, *Naturwissenschaften*, **22**, 469 (1934).

[815] B. Eriksson and S. Säverborn, *Acta Agr. Suecana*, **2**, 233 (1946)

[816] M. M. Mehta, *Biochem. J.*, **19**, 969 (1925).

[817] G. J. Ritter, *Ind. Eng. Chem.*, **17**, 248 (1928).

and in plant tissues undergoing natural decay. In ripe and overripe fruits the liquid in intercellular spaces may also contain dissolved pectic materials which may be lost in the course of preparation unless specific precautions are taken.

It should be emphasized again that practically all the information mentioned previously on the location of various pectic substances in plant tissue was obtained by using staining technics rather than by actual microchemical tests or analysis of isolated structures. The alarming lack of specificity of ruthenium red, which has been the main tool in all these researches, was also noted. Remarkably enough, the limitations of staining have not always been clearly realized, in spite of the fact that a number of serious warnings have been given on this point.

It would appear that essential progress toward obtaining information on the location of various pectic components in plants can be made only after the technics which are now available have been improved. Certainly, a detailed investigation of the effect of ruthenuim red on a series of chemically well-defined pectic substances is equally desirable.

One of the limitations of the use of ruthenium red consists in the considerable differences in the affinity shown to pectic substances of different degrees of acidity, *i.e.*, proportion of free carboxyl groups.[818] As a result, even transformations in pectic components in the tissues very often cause differences in the extent of staining obtained with ruthenium red, resulting in erroneous conclusions concerning the occurrence and role of pectic substances in the tissues.

Thus our knowledge of the pectic substances as they occur in plants is very meager. Better methods for the histological investigation of plant tissue components, especially of the various pectic substances, should be developed. Perhaps, our chemical knowledge concerning the interrelation of various important cell wall constituents (cellulose, lignin, hemicelluloses, and pectic compounds) and their possible transformations into each other will have to be increased before much progress can be made. But first of all, we will have to know more about the true nature, composition, and structure of protopectin and the other insoluble pectic components of plant tissues.

The limitations of morphologic information obtained through staining technics are well demonstrated in an interesting theory recently advanced by Lutman.[819] Lutman states that the material between plant cell walls is composed of a variety of pectins and gums, cell exudate, and some protein. The intercellular spaces are large in mature tissue, but the cell walls

[818] Z. I. Kertesz and J. D. Loconti, *New York State Agr. Expt. Sta.*, Tech. Bull. No. 272 (1944).

[819] B. F. Lutman, *Vermont Agr. Expt. Sta.*, Bull. No. 522 (1945).

facing these spaces are covered with this heterogeneous mixture. According to this author, actinomyces filaments are imbedded in this mixture in some plants, running through clear tubes which they have apparently formed by dissolving the components listed above. The filaments branch, become more delicate, and fray out, and their general direction is that in which growth had occurred in the tissue. They can be most easily observed, according to Lutman, at the corners or angles of the cells. In sections made of the cell, these filaments appear in part in one section, but are then cut off and reappear in the next section.

According to this theory, the intercellular substances usually designated on the basis of ruthenium red staining as pectic substances would in reality be the actinomyces which have grown within the tissue. This assumption is the opposite of the viewpoint generally accepted at the present time and would, in fact, assume a very wide extent of symbiosis between higher plants and the actinomyces. Lutman maintains that he can demonstrate these structures through the use of a series of stains, but the conclusion is inescapable that he may have dealt with structures of different degrees of acidity and that the differences which he obtained may have been caused by the varying proportions of free acid groups in the pectic substances present in the tissue. Lutman did not support his observations with microchemical tests of significance or by isolation of the actinomyces from the described cell structures. His theory is indeed a serious challenge to morphologists, and it may be said that even if it proves to be erroneous—which is not at all established at the present time—it may be hoped that it will have the merit to catalyze some further thorough investigations of the chemistry of cell wall constituents.

CHAPTER XI

Genesis and Fate of Pectic Substances in Plants: Relation to Hemicelluloses and Lignin

Galactose may be oxidized to galacturonic acid and the latter may be decarboxylated to a pentose. Based on this chain of reactions, a simple genetic relationship was thought to exist between galactans, polygalacturonides (pectic substances), and arabans. This assumed relationship appears reasonable indeed because of the common occurrence of galactans and arabans with pectic substances. Furthermore, these galactans and arabans are actually composed of the sterically corresponding D-galactose and L-arabinose. This scheme has been considered by many workers to be a truthful picture of transformations as they occur in plants.[820,821] Unfortunately, there is no evidence whatsoever that in nature pectic substances are formed directly from galactose or galactan and that eventually they are transformed into arabinose or araban.

A short time ago Hirst[822] examined critically the possible genetic relation between galactans and pectic substances and concluded that the galactans may not be directly transformed to the polygalacturonic acids which form the basic skeleton of pectic substances. Galactans appear to be composed of β-D-galactopyranoside residues, whereas in pectic acid the repeating units of anhydrogalacturonic acid are in the a form. For this reason, if a genetic relation does exist at all between the galactans and pectic compounds, the transformation must proceed through complete hydrolysis into the monomer units and subsequent resynthesis, or through intermediate steps and products still unknown. It is of interest to note in this connection that free D-galactose does not seem to occur in plants and that, as noted previously, there is some doubt whether (mono) D-galacturonic acid as such is present in plant tissues. These observations imply that hydrolysis of galactans to monomers, followed by oxidation

---

[820] F. Ehrlich, *Cellulosechemie*, 11, 161 (1930).
[821] R. Ripa, *Die Pektinstoffet.* 2nd ed., Serger und Hempel, Braunschweig, 1937.
[822] E. L. Hirst, *J. Chem. Soc.*, 1942, 70.

and resynthesis to pectic substances, may not be the usual way in which pectic substances are produced in plants.[823-826]

An interesting observation which may have some bearing on the formation of pectic substances has been reported by Whistler, Martin, and Conrad.[827] They found that in the early phases of development of cotton fiber the total uronide content was about 50% higher than the proportion of pectic substances estimated by the calcium pectate method. This may indicate the presence of nonpectic uronides which perhaps participate in the subsequent formation of true pectic substances.

Unfortunately, the possible enzymic synthesis of pectic substances through the 1-phosphoric acid esters[828-830] has not yet been investigated. This ingenious method of biological synthesis and its possible variations are likely to give important information, not only concerning the synthesis of pectic substances, but also on the interrelation between polygalacturonides and other polysaccharides.

Let us now consider the possibility of direct transformation of pectic substances into arabans. It is generally assumed that pentoses and pentosans are not direct photosynthetic products and that they arise from hexoses, hexosans, and polyuronides by processes of oxidation as indicated above. Neuberg[831] in 1904 reported the formation of a pentose by the oxidation of an uronic acid but there is no evidence that such a reaction actually occurs in plants. Biological means of decarboxylating a glucuronic acid have been studied by Salkowski and Neuberg[832] who used crude cultures of putrefying organisms from decaying meat. By this method the formation of some xylose from glucuronic acid could be demonstrated. However, Conrad[833] in a study of the chemical decarboxylation of galacturonic acid could not find arabinose after the treatment of galacturonic acid or pectinic acid with hot 4% sulfuric acid, while Franken,[834] by lowering the acid concentration to 2% or using oxalic or hydrofluoric acids, succeeded in identifying arabinose among the decom-

[823] E. L. Hirst and J. K. N. Jones, in W. W. Pigman and M. L. Wolfrom, *Advances in Carbohydrate Chemistry*. Vol. II, Academic Press, New York, 1946, p. 235.

[824] E. L. Hirst and J. K. N. Jones, *J. Chem. Soc.*, 1947, 1221.

[825] E. L. Hirst, J. K. N. Jones, and W. O. Walder, *J. Chem. Soc.*, 1947, 1225.

[826] G. H. Beaven and J. K. N. Jones, *J. Chem. Soc.*, 1947, 1218.

[827] R. L. Whistler, A. R. Martin, and C. M. Conrad, *J. Research Natl. Bur. Standards*, 10, 449 (1940).

[828] C. F. Cori, in *Symposium on Respiratory Enzymes*. Univ. Wisconsin Press, Madison, 1942, p. 175.

[829] C. S. Hanes, *Proc. Roy. Soc. (London)*, 128, 421 (1940); 129, 174 (1940).

[830] W. Z. Hassid, M. Doudoroff, and H. A. Barker, *J. Am. Chem. Soc.*, 66, 1416 (1944).

[831] C. Neuberg, *Ergeb. Physiol.*, 3, 373 (1904).

[832] E. Salkowski and C. Neuberg, *Z. physiol. Chem.*, 36, 261 (1902); 37, 464 (1903).

[833] C. M. Conrad, *J. Am. Chem. Soc.*, 53, 2282 (1931).

[834] H. Franken, *Biochem. Z.*, 257, 245 (1933).

position products. Apparently in Conrad's experiments the pentose formed by the decarboxylation was entirely transformed into furfural or other decomposition products by the 4% sulfuric acid. Norman and Norris[885] used oxidation with Fenton reagent[886] (hydrogen peroxide plus ferrous sulfate) and obtained a hemicellulose-like substance from pectinic acid. The material obtained in small yield by such oxidation resembled, to a certain extent, hemicelluloses extracted from wheat bran. It is noteworthy, however, that the substance gave galactose and galacturonic acid upon hydrolysis rather than arabinose as would be the case if the hemicellulose was obtained by decarboxylation.

Investigating the possible formation of hemicelluloses from pectic substances, Candlin and Schryver[887] found that pectic acids also undergo decarboxylation on treatment with weak alkaline solutions even at room temperature. The hemicellulose-like polycarbohydrates formed still contain uronic acid groups. The uronic anhydride content of the product from citrus pectic acid was reduced in this manner from the original 89% to 37%, that of pectic acid from onions from the original 70% to 22%. No additional decarboxylation occurred upon further treatment with boiling 0.5% sodium hydroxide. For comparison these authors isolated polyuronide hemicelluloses from turnips by the method described by Norris, and Schryver[888] and from beech wood by the method of O'Dwyer.[889] The hemicelluloses from turnips were slightly decarboxylated by treatment with hot alkali, while those from beech wood remained intact. Candlin and Schryver conclude from these tests that the hemicelluloses produced from pectic acid, which were shown to resist further decarboxylation, are similar to those found in woody tissues. Actually, these experiments showed that the formation of hemicellulose-like substances from pectic acid is possible but they supplied no evidence whatsoever that such substances are produced in plant tissues by decarboxylation.

Decarboxylation of pectic substances may also be effected by heating with water under pressure in the presence of an absorbing agent for carbon dioxide. A water-insoluble product obtained in this manner by Linggood[840] from citrus pectinic acid contained only 3.6% uronic anhydride as compared with 69.4% in the starting material. The water-soluble fraction contained by the orange-colored liquid gave no precipitate with alcohol and acid alcohol but showed strong reducing action. Uronic acid groups were absent.

It will be noted that in all these experiments in which some hemicellu-

---

[885] A. G. Norman and F. W. Norris, *Biochem J.*, **24**, 402 (1930).
[886] H. J. H. Fenton, *Chem. News*, **43**, 110 (1881).
[887] E. J. Candlin and S. B. Schryver, *Proc. Roy. Soc. (London)*, **103**, 365 (1928).
[888] F. W. Norris and S. B. Schryver, *Biochem. J.*, **19**, 676 (1925).
[889] M. H. O'Dwyer, *Biochem. J.*, **19**, 694 (1925).
[840] F. W. Linggood, *Biochem. J.*, **24**, 262 (1930).

lose-like substances were produced, drastic reagents or heat were employed. There is no guaranty, or even likelihood, that similar reactions occur in nature. Biological reactions are known to take much more subtle paths, and they are apt to be more elaborate. For the present, therefore, the theory of direct formation in plants of pentoses and pentosans from polyuronides must remain purely speculative. It is hoped that the enzyme systems causing the decarboxylation of pectic substances—if such exist—will be soon discovered and investigated to throw light on this reaction. A search conducted recently in the author's laboratory[841] showed the absence of such decarboxylating enzymes in a number of plant samples.

Meanwhile, there is an additional strong argument against such a direct genetic connection between pectic substances and arabans. In certain plant tissues, such as the peanut hull, strawberries, and citrus peel, such a simple relationship between the pectic substances and arabans, occurring side by side, is apparently out of the question. The work of Beaven and Jones[842] and Smith[843] demonstrated that the anhydrogalacturonic acid units in the polygalacturonic acid isolated from these sources possess a pyranose structure, while the arabans isolated from the same sources are composed of arabinofuranoside residues.[823]   Thus, the arabans may not be derived by direct decarboxylation of the polygalacturonic or pectic acids.

Another periodically recurring idea is that pectin is a precursor of lignin. This was first suggested by Fellenberg,[844] who discovered that pectic substances contain methoxyl groups. Although lignin preparations always contain 15–20% methoxyl, the suggested possible relationship between the methoxyl groups of pectin and those in lignin is not too convincing at this time. The methyl groups in pectic substances are present as esters and are easily removed by enzymes, acid, and especially alkali. They would probably be removed under conditions which lead to the decarboxylation of polygalacturonic acid units. On the other hand, the methoxyl groups in lignin are very stable, are not removed by the usual drastic methods of preparation, and are presumed to be present in ether linkages.

Ehrlich[820] was one of the many authors who assumed that the pectic substances are intermediate products in the following chain of transformations: galactans—pectic substances—pentose hemicelluloses (arabans)—lignin. These changes were thought to be brought about by enzymic oxidation, decarboxylation, dehydration, and reduction, respec-

[841] J. D. Lipps and Z. I. Kertesz, *unpublished work*, 1947.
[842] G. H. Beaven and J. K. N. Jones, *Chemistry & Industry*, **58**, 363 (1939).
[843] F. Smith, *Chemistry & Industry*, **58**, 363 (1939).
[844] T. Fellenberg, *Biochem. Z.*, **85**, 118 (1918).

tively. As mentioned before, it has long been observed that nonlignified tissues contain relatively large amounts of pectic substances, small amounts of hemicelluloses, but no lignin. On the other hand, lignified tissues contain large amounts of hemicelluloses and lignin, but hardly any pectic materials. It was a rather obvious suggestion, therefore, that the pectic substances are changed during development into hemicelluloses and that they are transformed into lignin either directly or through hemicelluloses. Fuchs[845] postulated that the primary cell wall constituents such as pectic substances are transformed into phenols, which by further changes, especially condensation, may contribute to the formation of lignin. Let us see if any experimental evidence may be cited for or against the theory that lignin is formed from pectic substances.

O'Dwyer[839] concluded that the hemicelluloses of timber are intermediate products in the transformation of pectic substances into lignin. Buston[846] examined this assumption critically in a series of very thorough experiments and reached the conclusion that, while pectic substances may possibly serve to a limited extent as precursors of hemicelluloses, there is no indication whatsoever that lignin is formed from polygalacturonides. He suggests that lignin may be formed from some carbohydrates of the glucosan-xylan series which usually occur in association with it in plants. Norman, in his book on cellulose, polyuronides, and lignin,[847] considers the formation of lignin from pectic substances to be unproved and unlikely. More recently, Bennett[848] reinvestigated this matter using Kentucky blue grass and red clover at various stages of growth, but again found no direct evidence for the relationship between pectic substances, hemicelluloses, and lignin. It is of interest to note that the balance between the cellulose, lignin, pentosan, and pectin polyuronide contents of certain tissues is influenced by treatment with colchicine.[849]

It must be concluded, therefore, that the origin and the fate of pectic substances in plant tissues are unknown at present. It is possible that, once formed, they are utilized after some transformations in some unknown manner, or that they are, perhaps after hydrolysis, used by a respiratory system. The often reported "decreases" in percentage content of various plant tissues will have to be reconsidered on the basis of the sampling technic used, because a percentage decrease may or may not be a true decrease in absolute quantities. This point will be discussed in Chapter XIII.

[845] W. M. Fuchs, *Paper Trade J.*, **102**, 33 (1936).

[846] H. W. Buston, *Biochem. J.*, **29**, 196 (1935).

[847] A. G. Norman, *The Biochemistry of Cellulose, the Polyuronides, Lignin, etc.* Clarendon Press, Oxford, 1937.

[848] E. Bennett, *Science*, **91**, 95 (1940); *Plant Physiol.*, **15**, 327 (1940).

[849] C. J. Gorter, *Proc. Netherlands Acad. Sci.*, **48**, 326 (1945); through *C. A.*, **40**, 4117 (1946).

CHAPTER XII

Possible Functions of Pectic Substances in Plants

The pectic substances may serve a multitude of different purposes in plants. There is little doubt, however, that the contribution to rigidity of the insoluble pectic compounds in the middle lamella is one of the most important known functions. As Allen[850] emphasized, the middle lamella should not be regarded merely as an intercellular cement or wall of partition in the sense stated by Mangin.[851] It is rather a plastic region adaptable to the changing size and shape of the protoplast itself. Its pliability is of great importance in giving the plant tissue its rigidity during the period of growth and expansion. The great advantage of pectic substances as structural components over cellulose and lignin is that the latter materials, once formed in the plant, cannot be removed. On the other hand, the pectic substances give the tissues the required firmness while this is needed but may be subsequently changed in such a manner that their contribution to rigidity (firmness, etc.) is greatly reduced. As was noted in Chapter XI, during the ripening of many fruits the pectic substances of the middle lamella which are responsible for the cementing together of the adjacent cells undergo transformations which cause the softening and eventual "maceration" of the tissue.

There is no such obvious explanation of the functions of the insoluble pectic substances of the primary cell wall. It is likely that they have an important role in the imbibition of the tissue—the ability to take up and hold water. Pectic substances are hydrophilic in nature and can hold quantities of water several times their own weight; they may therefore be necessary for the proper hydration of young growing cell walls. Reed[852] goes one step further and proposes that all hydrophilic colloids of the middle lamella and the cell wall serve as means of water translocation. The movement of water, accordingly, is governed by differences in water-absorbing capacity. Thus, changes which may occur in the quantity and

---

[850] C. E. Allen, *Botan. Gaz.,* **32,** 1 (1901).
[851] L. Mangin, *Compt. rend.,* **110,** 295 (1890).
[852] H. S. Reed, *Am. J. Botany,* **17,** 971 (1930).

character of pectic substances would have a direct bearing on the direction and rate of translocation. While there is no direct and conclusive evidence that this is the case, there is little doubt that the pectic compounds play some role in water relations. They are formed in largest proportions in the tissue during rapid growth and copious water supply and may well provide some of the forces necessary for water movement. It has also been suggested that the cracking of certain fruits under conditions of plentiful water supply and rapid growth may be the result of the rapidly increased rate of formation or swelling or of the formation and swelling of colloidal constituents such as pectic substances. Cherries which are likely to crack have a higher proportion of pectic substances than those which do not crack.[853]

The premature dropping of apples seems to be directly caused by dissolution of the middle lamella in the abscission layer. McCown,[854] who studied the anatomical and chemical aspects of this problem, states that the rapidly progressing pectic changes in the middle lamella play a dominant role in lowering the cohesion of the cells to the point at which abscission results.

Like all colloids, pectic substances may also have a role in the winter hardiness of plants.[855-857] According to Kobel[858] they may play an especially significant role when dissolved in the cell sap. The drought resistance of sugar beets has also been said to be influenced by their content of pectic substances.[859] It seems that in certain seeds the pectic substances may have an important role in influencing the rate of drying and the injury which may result from it. The slow, uniform drying caused by the high water-holding capacity of the Malpighian coating, due to the pectic constituents in it, prevents its cracking and forms, upon the completion of the drying, a continuous and water-impervious coating. In the case studied by Raleigh[860] the Malpighian layer of *Gymnocladus dioicus* (coffeetree) seeds was found to contain 22% pectic substances.

The role of pectic substances in cellulose fibers may consist in: (*1*) providing some of the colloidal forces necessary for water movements in the plant during the early part of growth; (*2*) cementing the individual fibers; or (*3*) both. There are two facts worth noting in this connection. The pectin appears in the primary wall of cotton fiber[861] which must pro-

[853] Z. I. Kertesz and B. R. Nebel, *Plant Physiol.*, **10,** 763 (1935).
[854] M. McCown, *Botan. Gaz.*, **105,** 233 (1943).
[855] R. Newton and R. A. Gortner, *Botan. Gaz.*, **74,** 442 (1922).
[856] R. Newton, *Alberta Univ. College Agr.*, Research Bull. No. 1 (1924).
[857] R. Newton and W. M. Martin, *Can. J. Research*, **3,** 336 (1930).
[858] F. Kobel, *Lehrbuch des Obstbaus.* Springer, Berlin, 1931.
[859] T. K. Gaponenkov, *Colloid J., U. S. S. R.*, **6,** 541 (1940); through *C. A.*, **35,** 7004 (1941).
[860] G. J. Raleigh, *Botan. Gaz.*, **89,** 273 (1930).
[861] W. K. Farr, *Am. J. Bot.*, **33,** 229 (1946).

vide protection for the fiber itself. The pectic substances, furthermore, are deposited mostly during the early growth of young tissues. In both cotton fibers and woody tissues the deposition seems to cease after the very early period of development. This may indicate that the role of the pectic substances is associated with the mechanism of growth of young tissues.

One of the provisions in nature to prevent the accumulation of the remains of annual and perennial plant tissues is the fact that these are rich in pectic substances. These compounds are easily attacked by the microorganisms present in the soil.[862]   The number of microorganisms in any sample of soil ranges from one hundred million to over one billion per gram, depending on a number of conditions,[863] and will as a rule contain many organisms which are capable of attacking pectic materials.[864]   The decomposition of cellulose and lignin by microorganisms is much slower than that of pectic substances. The easy decomposition of pectic substances by microorganisms may also play a role in releasing seeds imbedded in fruit tissues supported by these materials rather than the more resistant structures rich in cellulose and lignin.

The role of pectic substances in plant tissues will be discussed further in Chapter XXVII.

[862] S. A. Waksman and M. C. Allen, *J. Am. Chem. Soc.*, **56**, 2701 (1934).
[863] C. Rouschal and S. Strugger, *Naturwissenschaften*, **31**, 300 (1943).
[864] A. G. Norman and W. V. Bartholomew, *Soil Sci.*, **56**, 143 (1943).

CHAPTER XIII

Proportions of and Changes in Pectic Components in Some Plants

There have been reports that pectic substances are absent from certain plant tissues such as cereals and wood. Improved analytical methods have proved, however, that apparently pectic materials occur in all plant tissues, although at times, as in the cases noted above, they may be present in very small quantities and be extracted only with considerable difficulty.

In this chapter the proportions of pectic substances in some plants will be discussed. In the few cases in which such information is available, the changes which occur during growth, maturation, storage, handling, etc., will also be described.

The literature abounds in reports giving the pectin content of plant material. However, in the majority of cases either the description of the plant tissue is insufficient or the methods of analysis which were used cannot be considered sufficiently accurate and specific. It is because of such considerations that the quantitative data on the proportions of pectic substances in Wehmer's monumental *Die Pflanzenstoffe*[865] are practically useless. The information on the following pages has been obtained from reports which have withstood scrutiny on these two points. In a few cases data obtained by methods not entirely free from objection on some more important plants are included for lack of more reliable information. This is done in order to cover the whole range of various types of changes which occur in the pectic components of plants. Naturally, it will always be noted in the text if the data should be regarded as expressing trends rather than actual quantities of the pectic substances.

As was shown in Chapter VIII, determination of pectic constituents in a plant extract by direct precipitation with ethanol or acetone may include so many nonpectic materials that values obtained in this manner are in most cases worthless. On the other hand, at times some authors

---

[865] C. Wehmer, *Die Pflanzenstoffe*. 2nd ed., Fischer, Jena, 1929–31.

determined the uronic acid contents of such alcohol precipitates by the Lefèvre-Tollens method and its modifications discussed in Chapter VII. If the uronic acid analysis indicates that the ethanol precipitate contained at least 75% polygalacturonic acid, the value obtained by the determination has been included. Care has been taken to indicate the analytical procedure which was used, together with as much information as could be gathered on the variety, maturity, etc., of the plant tissue analyzed.

It is a mistake to assume that such unreliable reports of determinations of pectic substances are not still appearing with disheartening periodicity in the literature. Reference may be made to the survey of Elwell and Dehn,[866] for instance, in which obviously erroneous data have been reported,[867] or to the reports on "tamarind seed pectin"[868] which, after receiving wide publicity even in the daily press, turned out not to be a pectic substance at all.[869,870]

In connection with the determination of changes which occur during growth, maturation, storage, etc., it must be noted that proper sampling has often been neglected. Most plant tissues contain a high proportion of water, and at times changes in the water content occur rapidly, altering both the weight of the tissue and the relative proportions of its various constituents. Often the difficulty is eliminated simply by basing calculations on the dry material content of the tissue, although the true water content of a plant tissue is not an obvious and well-defined matter. Some of the water is easily removed, while some of it appears to be held more strongly by various forces. Therefore, the final figure for water content depends on the method of estimation employed.[871] The efficiency of the very same method, furthermore, is influenced by the condition and past history of the tissue.

During the development and growth of plant tissues, certain constituents are often formed and others disappear. Consequently, the percentage content of any one component may change merely because the proportions of accompanying materials change without any actual gain or loss of the component itself.[872] The literature of plant chemistry, as well as that of animal biochemistry, contains numerous references to alleged increases and decreases which apparently occur in the proportions of certain constituents. In reality, often no such changes occurred at all; what does occur is "dilution" by newly formed components of the tissue. On the

[866] W. E. Elwell and W. M. Dehn, *Plant Physiol.*, 14, 809 (1939).

[867] Z. I. Kertesz, *Plant Physiol.*, 15, 565 (1940).

[868] T. P. Ghose and S. Krishna, *J. Indian Chem. Soc., Ind. Eng. News Ed.*, 5, 114 (1942).

[869] H. R. Nanji, G. R. Savur, and A. Sreenivasan, *Current Sci.*, 14, 129 (1945).

[870] H. R. Pithawala, *Dissertation*, University of Bombay, 1949.

[871] C. W. Schroeder and J. H. Nair, *Anal. Chem.*, 20, 452 (1948).

[872] Z. I. Kertesz, *New York State Agr. Expt. Sta.*, Bull. No. 622 (1933).

other hand, increases were at times observed when other components were lost, such as water and sugars in transpiration and respiration of the tissue. The simplest method of overcoming these effects is to express the analytical results on the *single unit* basis. In following the changes in growing and storing apples or peas, the results should be expressed, not only on the percentage basis, but also as the absolute weight per single apple or pea.[873] Often plant parts of a certain length serve as a suitable basis for the expression of such changes.[874] Certain reference components known to be constant in the tissue may also be used as the basis for such calculations.[875]

All numerical results reported in this section will refer to the pectic substances determined as calcium pectate by the Carré-Haynes method and its modifications as given in Chapter VIII unless specific mention of some other method is made.

There are a number of surveys of the pectin contents of plant materials of which those by Rongo and Quiatson,[876] Savur and Sreenivasan,[877] Trehan and Ahmad,[878] Bennett,[879] Lampitt and Hughes,[880] and Money and Christian[881] may be noted here.

1. Apples

The pectic constituents of apples attracted more attention in the past than those of any other plant. Many of the early workers observed the occurrence of pectic compounds in apples as well as the transformations which take place during growth, maturation, and decay. Quantitative studies, however, were greatly handicapped by lack of exact quantitative methods. As was noted in Chapter VIII, such methods were developed during the early twenties, mostly by a group of workers under the aegis of the British Food Investigation Board.

(a) Changes in Apples on the Tree

During the period of growth on the tree, there is an initial rapid decrease in the percentage of total pectic substances of very small apples. As an illustration, the results obtained by Widdowson[882] on apples (grown in England) are given in Table 27. This table also includes a

---

[873] Z. I. Kertesz and E. L. Green, *J. Agr. Research,* **45,** 361 (1932).
[874] H. W. Buston, *Biochem. J.,* **29,** 196 (1935).
[875] F. A. Lee, *Ind. Eng. Chem., Anal. Ed.,* **17,** 719 (1945).
[876] V. Rongo and S. L. Quiatson, *Philippine Agr.,* **29,** 1 (1940).
[877] G. R. Savur and A. Sreenivasan, *J. Sci. Ind. Research (India),* **5,** 41 (1946).
[878] Y. N. Trehan and B. Ahmad, *J. Sci. Ind. Research (India),* **6,** 16 (1947).
[879] E. Bennett, *Food Research.* **9,** 462 (1944).
[880] L. H. Lampitt and E. B. Hughes, *Analyst,* **53,** 32 (1928).
[881] R. W. Money and W. A. Christian, *J. Sci. Food Agr.,* **1,** 8 (1950).
[882] E. M. Widdowson, *Ann. Botany,* **46,** 597 (1932).

column giving the total pectic substance content per apple, calculated from Widdowson's data. The results illustrate the point discussed above that, while the proportion of pectic substances first decreases and later tends to be constant, such compounds are in reality continually formed in growing apples.

TABLE 27

CHANGES IN PECTIC SUBSTANCES OF GROWING BRAMLEY'S SEEDLING APPLES (ADAPTED FROM WIDDOWSON)

Date	Total pectic substances on fresh wt. basis (as Ca pectate), %	Av. wt. of one apple, g.	Pectic substances per apple, mg.
May 26	2.27	0.15	3
June 5	1.14	0.47	5
June 16	0.68	2.66	18
June 27	0.60	7.69	46
July 20	0.58	39.0	228
Aug. 14	0.55	61.2	335
Sept. 26	0.52	94.1	490
Oct. 22	0.50	118.5	597
Nov. 5	0.52	118.5	616

One of the most important changes which occurs in apples is the progressive softening of the flesh. As Frémy[883] observed over one hundred years ago, this softening is at times closely associated with changes in the pectic constituents, although changes in the firmness of growing apples cannot be entirely accounted for by the transformations which occur in these components.[884]   In growing apples still attached to the tree a multitude of morphologic and chemical changes occur,[885] many of which may directly or indirectly influence the firmness of the fruit. Perhaps the most important one of these is the increase in size of the individual cells and the consequent changes in size and shape of the intercellular spaces. Alterations in the thickness and firmness of the cell wall and of the cementing substance of the middle lamella have a pronounced effect on the firmness which, in most methods of measurement, seems to depend predominantly on the force required to push the cells apart. All these morphologic changes are closely associated with varietal characteristics of the fruit and cultural conditions. Consequently, numerical figures for the firmness, such as those given in Tables 28 and 29, are typical only

[883] E. Frémy, *Compt. rend.*, **83**, 1136 (1876), etc.
[884] M. H. Haller, *J. Agr. Research*, **39**, 739 (1931).
[885] R. M. Smock and A. M. Neubert, *Apples and Apple Products*. Interscience, New York, 1950.

for the variety for which these data were obtained, and even for the same variety the relation between pectic constituents and firmness may be different in another lot or in apples grown in another year.

The firmness of apples and many other fruits may be conveniently measured by the *pressure tester*[886, 887] shown in Figure 19. This instru-

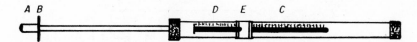

Fig. 19. Schematic illustration of one type of pressure tester.

A plunger head, *B* guard disk, *C* spring housing, *D* scale, and *E* moving indicator which shows maximum pressure exerted before puncture.

ment records the pressure required to force a plunger 11.1 mm. ($^7/_{16}$ inch) in diameter into the fruit for a distance of 7.9 mm. ($^5/_{16}$ inch). Such measurements of the firmness of fruits have often been applied in studies of the interrelation of pectic changes and softening. Another method of following changes in the texture of apples is the measurement of the force required to break apart a dumbbell-shaped piece of apple tissue.[888]

In a lot of Jonathan apples Haller[884] found that the proportion of total pectic substances was constant until the fruit started to soften enough to require only 6.8 kg. (15 pounds) of pressure to puncture. Afterward the total pectic compounds decreased. In Ben Davis apples the total percentage of pectic substances decreased throughout growth, a behavior different from that of Jonathan apples and of the varieties studied by Widdowson.[882] Haller's determinations of the proportions of insoluble and soluble pectic substances indicated that the changes occur in the insoluble fraction, while during this period of growth on the tree the soluble fraction was constant in both varieties of apples. No figures are given in Haller's article on the growth of the fruit throughout this period, but he suggests that the observed decrease in the percentage of insoluble pectic constituents may have been caused by dilution by newly formed components.

(b) Changes in Apples after Picking

The pectic changes which occur in stored apples have been the subject of many investigations, of which those of Carré and collaborators[889]

[886] J. R. Magness and G. F. Taylor, *U. S. Dept. Agr.*, Circ. No. 350 (1925).

[887] M. H. Haller, *U. S. Dept. Agr.*, Circ. No. 627 (1941).

[888] J. H. Griffin and Z. I. Kertesz, *Botan. Gaz.*, **108**, 279 (1946).

[889] M. H. Branfoot (Carré), "A Critical and Historical Study of the Pectic Substances of Plants," *Dept. Sci. Ind. Research Brit. Food Invest.*, Special Rept. No. 33 (1929).

were perhaps the most extensive. A typical set of results showing the nature of these changes in apples stored at 1°C. (33°F.) is shown in Figure 20. In these analyses, the insoluble pectic compounds have been determined in two fractions, namely as protopectin and as calcium pectate. For the significance of such a separation the reader is referred to

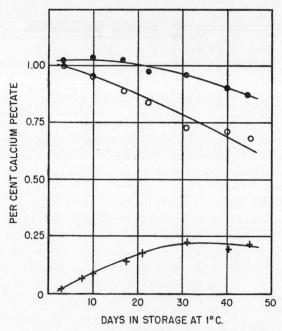

Fig. 20. Pectic changes in stored Bramley's Seedling apples (adapted from Branfoot).

On fresh weight basis. Dots, circles, and crosses represent total, insoluble, and soluble pectic substances, respectively.

the earlier discussion in Chapter VIII. The protopectin decreased in the apples during storage, first rapidly and later slowly. The insoluble fraction which, according to Carré, mainly represents the insoluble pectic constituents of the middle lamella, was practically constant during the first few months of storage but decreased rapidly thereafter. The percentage of water-soluble pectic materials has been shown to be very low and practically constant in apples growing on the tree. As soon as the apples are placed in storage and the softening of the flesh begins, this fraction shows constant increase until full maturity is attained. As the apples become overripe and "mealy," the proportion of soluble pectic components decreases, assumedly because of the ultimate decomposition into nonpectic substances. The proportion of total pectic substances is usually constant until full maturity is reached, but later it shows a gradual decrease as the apples become overripe and approach senescence. Carré and Horne[590] supplemented these chemical observations with microscopic tests; these were discussed in Chapter X.

The determination of the increase in soluble pectic constituents as the apple ripens may be performed either on the fruit itself or on the juice expressed therefrom.

In apples detached from the tree, the relation between pectic changes and softening is much closer than while the fruit is still on the tree. This fact is of practical importance because most apples are picked in an immature condition and the softness of the apple plays an important role in determining its commercial value. There are several reports in the literature giving the relationship of changes in the texture and pectic transformations of stored apples. Some of these will be discussed below in Section (c). As an example, Table 28 shows the relation of firmness (as determined by the plunger type of instrument) to soluble pectic constituents as calculated from the article of Gerhardt and Smith.[891]

TABLE 28

RELATION OF SOFTENING TO INCREASE IN SOLUBLE PECTIN CONTENT IN DELICIOUS APPLES STORED AT 2.5°C. (36°F.) (ADAPTED FROM GERHARDT AND SMITH)

Days in storage	Firmness, kg. pressure	Soluble pectin on fresh wt. basis, %
0	7.7	0.05
30	6.9	0.05
60	6.3	0.07
90	5.8	0.09
120	5.5	0.11
150	5.4	0.12
180	5.4	0.13

(c) *Effect of Storage Temperature on Ripening and Pectic Changes*

There is ample evidence to show that storage at lower temperatures retards the ripening of apples as well as the formation of soluble pectic components in the fruit.[885] Since the formation of soluble pectic compounds seems to be typical of apples which approach maturity, measurements of this component may give important information at times concerning the condition of the fruit.

[590] M. H. Carré and A. S. Horne, *Ann Botany*, 41, 1 (1927).
[891] F. Gerhardt and E. Smith, *Proc. Washington State Hort. Soc.*, 1946, 1.

TABLE 29

EFFECT OF STORAGE TEMPERATURES ON SOFTENING AND PECTIC CONSTITUENTS OF JONATHAN APPLES (ADAPTED FROM HALLER)

Date	Storage temp., °C.	Pressure test, kg.	Pectic substances on fresh wt. basis, %		
			Soluble	Insoluble	Total
Aug. 22	No storage	6.6	0.04	0.80	0.84
Oct. 3	0	6.1	0.03	0.76	0.79
Nov. 14		5.0	0.17	0.58	0.75
Dec. 21		3.9	0.22	0.56	0.78
Mar. 1		3.4	0.23	0.51	0.74
Sept. 15	4	6.1	0.06	0.71	0.77
Oct. 5		4.4	0.16	0.63	0.79
Oct. 24		3.8	0.23	0.45	0.68
Dec. 17		3.5	0.25	0.44	0.69
Sept. 8	10	6.0	0.05	0.74	0.79
Sept. 26		3.9	0.24	0.45	0.69
Oct. 26		3.3	0.28	0.38	0.66
Aug. 26	15	6.7	0.02	0.73	0.75
Aug. 31		6.4	0.02	0.68	0.70
Sept. 9		4.2	0.19	0.55	0.74
Sept. 30		3.4	0.27	0.41	0.68

TABLE 30

STORAGE CHANGES CALCULATED ON PRESSURE TEST BASIS (ADAPTED FROM HALLER)

Storage temp., °C.	Days in storage required to reach:		
	a pressure test of 4.53 kg.	an insol. pectic substance content of 0.385%	a sol. pectic material content of 0.195%
0	100	100	100
4	42	44	51
10	29	27	31
15	16	15	19

The correlation between the softening of apples in storage at different temperatures and the changes which occur in the pectic constituents has been demonstrated by a number of workers. As an example, Table 29 shows the changes in Jonathan apples stored at different temperatures.

With the possible exception of the first period, the fluctuation in total pectic content of the apples was within the experimental variation. The transformation of insoluble pectic components into soluble ones seems to be closely related to the storage temperature. Haller illuminated this relation between the two factors by interpolating the length of storage required to attain the same softness and the pectic fraction in all lots of the apples. These data are shown in Table 30.

Similarly, good correlation between the changes in firmness and increase in soluble pectic substances was found by Smock and Allen[892] and Fisher.[893]   One experiment of the latter author on the increase in soluble pectic substances during storage is especially illuminating and is shown in Table 31. At 0° and 4°C. the apples became ripe with a soluble pectic substance content of 69 and 67 mg. per 100 cc. of juice; at 15°C. the ripeness occurred at 48 mg. but the changes may have occurred too rapidly (138 mg. one week later!) to permit accurate observation.

Recently Phillips and Poapst[894] reported that the changes in the soluble pectin content of stored apples fall into three distinct phases and that lower levels of soluble pectin concur with higher apple quality and longer storage life. These authors feel that following the soluble pectin trends in a given lot of apples would help getting apples of quality on the market at the proper time.

It is clear from the few observations shown here and from the reports of many other workers that the formation of soluble pectic compounds (produced at the expense of the insoluble pectic constituents of the cell wall and the middle lamella) is profoundly affected by storage temperatures. No definite information is available on the mechanism of these changes. They were for a long time assumed to occur through the action of hydrolytic enzymes present in the tissue,[895,896] but there is no conclusive evidence that this is actually the case. Work at the author's laboratory indicated[897] the absence of pectin-hydrolyzing enzymes in apples[898] and therefore there is a distinct possibility that some essentially nonenzymic mechanism may cause these transformations[899] See Chapter XIV, Section II-4, for further discussion of this point.

Pectic changes retain their close relation to softening during the so-called *residual effect* of low temperature storage of apples. When apples first stored at low temperature are kept afterward at room temperatures, softening occurs with greater rapidity than in apples which were not placed in cold storage. In addition, the effect of certain storage temperatures will also depend on the condition of the fruit entering storage. It is entirely outside of the scope of this discussion even to list the many factors, such as the occurrence of "climacterics," which make the matura-

[892] R. M. Smock and F. W. Allen, *Proc. Am. Soc. Hort. Sci.*, **35**, 184 (1938).
[893] D. V. Fisher, *Sci. Agr.*, **23**, 569 (1943).
[894] W. R. Phillips and P. A. Poapst, *Canada Dept. Agr., Div. of Hort., Progress Report for 1934–48*, p. 163 (1950).
[895] E. Bourquelot, *J. pharm. chim.*, **18**, 241 (1903).
[896] R. W. Thatcher, *J. Agr. Research.*, **5**, 103 (1915).
[897] H. G. Beattie, C. S. Pederson, and Z. I. Kertesz, *unpublished work*, 1944.
[898] Dr. C. H. Hills in a personal communication (Sept. 28, 1948) indicated his belief that enzymes hydrolyzing pectinic acids occur in apples.
[899] Z. I. Kertesz, *Plant. Physiol.*, **18**, 308 (1943).

TABLE 31
INCREASE IN SOLUBLE PECTIC SUBSTANCE CONTENT OF STORED DELICIOUS APPLES
(ADAPTED FROM FISHER)

Storage time, weeks	Soluble pectic substances (as mg. Ca pectate/100 cc. juice)		
	Storage at: 0°C.	4°C.	15°C.
0............	31	31	31
1............	—	—	41
2............	—	—	48 (ripe)
3............	33	50	138
4............	—	—	142
6............	36	67 (ripe)	198 (mealy)
9............	52	74	
12............	69 (ripe)	106	
15............	76	124	
19............	84	149 (mealy)	

tion of fruits in cold storage a very complicated phenomenon. Cold storage may also cause physiological disturbances which result in the breakdown of the tissue. The reader is referred to the excellent volume on apples by Smock and Neubert[885] for further information on this topic.

(d) Effect of Storage in Modified Atmospheres

The storage life of apples may be prolonged by atmospheres containing carbon dioxide or only a reduced proportion of oxygen. On the other hand, ethylene has been found to hasten the ripening of many fruits and vegetables. Since both carbon dioxide and ethylene are given off by apples themselves, care must be exercised in the conduct of storage studies as well as in commercial storage to avoid the possible complicating effect of these gases produced by the apple.[885]

Both the retarding effect of carbon dioxide and nitrogen and the hastening action on maturation of ethylene are closely associated with the pectic transformations which occur in the apples. In other words, the relation between softening and the formation of soluble pectic compounds[892,893,900–902] still holds whether the softening is artificially retarded or enhanced. In cases where nitrogen or carbon dioxide is used, the so-called "residual.effect" is even more pronounced than with apples stored in air. After removal from storage, the apples often soften with such speed, that in a few days out of storage they more than make up for the retarding effect of the gas atmosphere. In such cases again the

[900] A. Van Doren, Proc. Am. Soc. Hort. Sci., 37, 453 (1940).
[901] H. H. Plagge and D. V. Fisher, Proc. Am. Soc. Hort. Sci., 40, 169 (1942).
[902] S. V. Soldatenkov, Compt. rend. acad. sci. U. S. S. R., 2, 318 (1935); through C. A., 30, 7710 (1936).

formation of soluble pectic compounds is closely associated with the softening.[885]

There is no generally accepted theory of the effect of changed atmospheres on the rate of ripening of apples in storage. From the similarity of curves for respiratory activity and ethylene formation and the relation of these activities to ripening, it may seem as if all these factors are intimately connected. Nelson suggests[903] that perhaps the increased formation of ethylene during the *climacteric* plays an essential part in ripening in the apple. It is known that the rate of respiration is reduced by such atmospheres. It has also been suggested,[904] that the ripening effect of ethylene may be the result of the activation of the enzymes acting upon the insoluble pectic substances, but we lack evidence that this is actually the case. Inhibition of these enzymes by carbon dioxide and nitrogen can certainly not be assumed. Considering that there is some doubt at this time concerning the presence in apples of the (assumed) enzymes which hydrolyze pectic materials, it appears as if the pectic changes related to the ripening of apples may be connected to the respiratory enzyme system rather than governed by a more or less independent system of catalysts.

(e) Miscellaneous Further Information on Apples

Nanji and Norman [905] estimated the pectic substances in apple peel and pulp; the results of these determinations are shown in Table 32. The variety and condition of the apples were not specified. Thiocyanate sprays were found to have no effect on the total pectic substances in apples but apparently might cause some differences in the rate of ripening in storage.[906]

The proportions of pectic substances in commercial cooking and eating apples of undesignated varieties (determined by the method of Wichmann—see Chap. VIII) are shown in Table 33. The results represent averages from three samples.[880]   Money and Christian[881] found in the edible portion of 60 samples of eating apples an average of 0.53% and in the edible portion of 40 samples of cooking apples an average of 0.55% calcium pectate.

Savur and Sreenivasan[877] found, in an undefined sample of ripe apples, 13.36% total pectic substances and 14.47% ethanol-precipitable materials on a dry matter basis. A sample of "apple nuggets" was found to con-

---

[903] R. C. Nelson, *Plant Physiol.*, 15, 149 (1940).
[904] E. Hansen, *Science*, 86, 272 (1937).
[905] D. R. Nanji and A. G. Norman, *Biochem. J.*, 22, 596 (1928).
[906] R. B. Dustman, R. C. Meade, and V. B. Fish, *Plant Physiol.*, 23, 142 (1948).

TABLE 32

PECTIC CONSTITUENTS IN APPLE PEEL AND PULP (FROM NANJI AND NORMAN)

Sample	Dry matter, %	Soluble pectic substances (as Ca pectate) on dry matter basis, %	Total pectic substances (as Ca pectate) on dry matter basis, %
Peel....................	19.3	9.15	17.44
Pulp....................	12.0	8.92	17.63
Av. section..............	12.2	8.96	17.60

TABLE 33

PECTIC SUBSTANCES IN EATING AND COOKING APPLES (ADAPTED FROM LAMPITT AND HUGHES)

	Pectic acid (fresh basis), %		
Apples	Average	Maximum	Minimum
Cooking................	1.29	1.60	0.84
Eating..................	0.82	0.93	0.71

tain 8.9% pectic substances on the dry matter basis.[907] According to Baker and Murray,[908] the grade calculated from viscosity (Chap. XXIII) of pectinic acids present in dehydrated apples is a good index of their quality. During storage of dehydrated apples both the methoxyl content and the grade of the pectinic acids decrease. Schlubach and Hoffmann-Walbeck[909] found that the methoxyl content of apple pectin is the highest very early in the development of the fruit and that later it drops gradually. The maximum methoxyl content found was 14.9%.

The pectic constituents of the apple juice and of the apple pomace left over from the pressing of the juice will be discussed in Chapters XXVII and XIX, respectively.

2. Apricots

In five samples of apricots[880] an average of 1.03% (0.71–1.32%) total pectic substances as pectic acid (fresh weight basis), and in the edible portion of 44 samples of apricots an average of 0.99% calcium pectate were reported.[881]

[907] C. Gavrilova, *Canner*, 100 (20), 16 (1945).
[908] G. L. Baker and W. G. Murray, *Food Research*, 12, 129 (1947).
[909] H. H. Schlubach and H. P. Hoffmann-Walbeck, *Makromol. Chem.*, 4, 5 (1949).

3. Asparagus

In an unspecified variety of asparagus of eating maturity, Bennett[879] found only a trace of pectic materials.

4. Avocado

Healthy leaves of avocado were found to contain 4.3–16.2% pectic materials (dry matter basis).[910] "Tip burned" leaves had 13.7–21.3%.

5. Bananas

The softening of the pulp of bananas is characterized not only by the conversion of starch to sugars, but also by the transformation of insoluble pectic substances into soluble ones.[911] Barnell[912] found that in green Gros Michel bananas (grown in Trinidad) there is only a negligible proportion of water-soluble pectic substances (extracted at 80°C. overnight). A rapid increase in the water-soluble pectic constituents occurs as soon as the fruit turns yellow and the increase continues throughout ripening. Simultaneously, there is a rapid decrease in the proportion of total pectic substances from an initial content of 0.50% to 0.07% on a fresh weight basis. Bourdouil[913] found a decrease from 1.93 to 0.87% in 27 days of ripening. Conrad,[914] in a study of methods, found 2.24% total pectic substances in bananas on the dry matter basis, and no pectic acid.

The pectic changes which occur in the pulp of five varieties of stored bananas[915] are shown in Table 34.

The progressive transformation of insoluble pectic substances into soluble ones and the subsequent decrease in total pectic substances is quite noticeable. This loss of pectic substances is even more apparent if the loss of weight of the bananas in storage is taken into consideration. Conrad[916] determined the storage changes in bananas and found that in 11 days at 30°C. there was a decrease in total pectic substances in spite of the 31% loss in weight. These results are shown in Table 35.

[910] A. R. C. Haas, California Avocado Association, *Yearbook*, 1936, p. 72.

[911] H. W. von Loesecke, *Bananas*. Second ed., Interscience, New York, 1950.

[912] H. R. Barnell, *Ann. Botany*, **7**, 297 (1944).

[913] C. Bourdouil, *Bull. soc. chim. biol.*, **11**, 1130 (1929); through *C. A.*, **24**, 3064 (1930).

[914] C. M. Conrad, *Am. J. Botany*, **13**, 531 (1926).

[915] F. C. Stratton and H. W. von Loesecke, United Fruit Co., Research Dept. Bulletin No. 32 (1930); quoted in reference 911.

[916] C. M. Conrad, *Plant Physiol.*, **5**, 93 (1930).

TABLE 34

PECTIC CONSTITUENTS IN PULP OF STORED BANANAS (ADAPTED FROM STRATTON AND VON LOESECKE)

Variety	Days in ripening room									
	0		5		9		14		17	
	Pectic substances (as Ca pectate), on fresh wt. basis, %									
	Sol.	Tot.	Sol.	Tot.	Sol.	Tot.	Sol.	Tot.	Sol.	Tot.
Gros Michel....	—	—	0.36	0.67	0.37	0.58	—	—	—	—
Lady Finger....	0.21	0.71	0.52	0.79	0.58	0.89	—	—	—	—
Lacatan........	Trace	0.59	0.13	1.28	0.31	0.71	0.46	0.80	—	—
Plantain........	0.12	0.60	0.14	1.10	0.19	1.22	0.43	0.80	0.33	0.90
Red banana....	0.04	0.91	0.55	1.07	0.62	1.05	—	—	—	—

TABLE 35

CHANGES IN PECTIC CONSTITUENTS OF BANANA PULP AT 30 °C. (ADAPTED FROM CONRAD)

Condition	Days in storage	Loss in weight, %	Pectic substances (fresh wt. basis), %	
			Soluble	Total
Green, no storage...............	0	0	0.11	0.31
"Yellowed skin".................	2	5.1	0.30	0.36
"Table ripe"....................	7	15.9	0.39	0.39
"Dark skin, overripe"...........	11	31.7	0.29	0.32

Von Loesecke[917] found in the peels of green, yellow, and brown bananas 0.51, 0.38, and 0.46% soluble pectic substances and 1.28, 1.02, and 0.81% total pectic substances, respectively. In Barnell's analyses of the peel, the pectic substances showed no regular trends during ripening (0.37–0.91%). One sample of the parenchyma adhering to the pulp of the peeled fruit showed 0.93% soluble and 1.14% total pectic substances on a fresh basis.[912]

Dehydrated banana flakes made in Brazil by the Sardik process[918] contain, according to the label on the can, 0.09% insoluble and 0.92% water-soluble pectic substances.

6. Beans

In a study of the interrelation of various carbohydrate constituents and lignin in bean pods, Buston[874] determined the total pectic substance content of the pods of two varieties of beans. The pods of different sizes were all picked on the same date. Since, at least until full length is approached, the length of the pod is closely related to its age, the series of samples may be regarded as representing pods of different ages. For

[917] H. W. von Loesecke, *Fruit Products J.*, 6, 17 (1928); 8, 6, 14 (1929).
[918] W. W. Cowgill, U. S. Pat. 1,973,613 (1934); 1,973,614 (1934); 2,140,788 (1938).

analysis the dried, ground pods were extracted three times for six hours at 95°C. (203°F.) with 0.5% ammonium oxalate, the extracts precipitated with ethanol, and this precipitate used for the determination of pectic compounds as calcium pectate. The results of these determinations are given in Table 36.

TABLE 36

CHANGES IN TOTAL PECTIC SUBSTANCE CONTENT OF DRY MATTER OF BEAN (*Phaseolus vulgaris*) PODS (ADAPTED FROM BUSTON)

"Tall variety"		"Little Gem variety"	
Length of pod, cm.	Total pectic substances, %[a]	Length of pod, cm.	Total pectic substances, %[a]
2.5	9.8	4	11.1
5.0	9.5	7	11.4
7.5	10.3	9	14.4
10.0	14.1	11	15.4
21.0	15.0	13	13.1

[a] As calcium pectate.

TABLE 37

PECTIC CHANGES IN BEANS STORED AT ROOM TEMPERATURE (17–25°C., 63–77°F.) (ADAPTED FROM PARKER AND STUART)

	Pectic substances, %			
	On dry matter basis		Grams per 100 snap beans	
Sample	Soluble	Total	Soluble	Total
Fresh pods..............	3.17	9.05	2.38	6.79
Fresh beans..............	0.25	0.74	0.09	0.27
Stored 58.5 hrs., pods......	1.84	10.33	1.23	6.88
Stored 58.5 hrs., beans.....	0.24	1.11	0.09	0.42

The dry matter content of bean pods increases rapidly with advancing maturity and, therefore, an increase in the content of pectic substances would be more striking when shown on the fresh material basis. Unfortunately, no dry matter percentages are given by Buston for these pods in the fresh condition. Parker and Stuart[919] determined the pectic changes in Giant Stringless Green Pod variety snap beans during prolonged storage at room temperature. These results are shown in Table 37. Here once again the matter of sampling makes a major difference in the results. During storage the weights of the pods and beans decreased 25.6 and 12.6%, respectively, and therefore recalculation of the results to express the changes which occurred in 100 snap beans shows that, con-

[919] M. W. Parker and N. W. Stuart, *Univ. Maryland Agr. Expt. Sta.*, Bull. No. 383 (1935).

trary to the results expressed on a percentage basis, the total proportion of pectic substances remains constant during storage.

In string beans of an unspecified variety, Bennett[879] found 5.0% total pectic substances on a dry matter basis.

7. Beets

Although the presence of pectic substances in beets was observed over one hundred years ago,[883] there is little systematic information available on this subject. In connection with the manufacture of beet pectin in recent years (to be discussed in Chap. XXI), a great deal of information must have been collected on the effect of various factors on the pectic constituents of beets; as yet such information is not available. Conrad[914] and Savur and Sreenivasan[877] both found 4.8% total pectic constituents in the dry matter of beets not otherwise identified. Gaponenkov[920] made numerous reports on this topic but, unfortunately, most of his work can be studied only in abstracts and these are so contradictory that no purpose would be served by discussing them here. Both dry growing seasons and the application of fertilizers affect the percentage of pectic substances in sugar beets.[921]

Ingelman and Tiselius[922] found in press juice from sugar beets 0.008–0.015% soluble pectic substances. In the dry matter of red beets (*Beta vulgaris* var. *cruenta*)Conrad[914] found 3.8% total pectic substances.

Apparently the proportion of pectic substances in dehydrated beet roots decreases considerably during storage, especially when held at comparatively high temperatures.[923] Neish and Hibbert[924] found that crown gall infection changes the proportion of pectic constituents in beets. In the normal tissue of infected beets they found 8.0% total pectic constituents (on the dry matter basis), in the tumorous tissue 13.2%. The normal beet sample used for control contained 9.7% total pectic substances.

We shall return in Chapter XXI to the pectic constituents of sugar beets in later discussions of the manufacture of beet pectin and resulting difficulties in the manufacture of sugar.

[920] T. K. Gaponenkov, *Colloid J., U. S. S. R.,* **6,** 541 (1940); through *C. A.,* **35,** 7004 (1941). See also *C. A.,* **31,** 1649 (1937); **33,** 6121 (1939); etc.

[921] T. K. Gaponenkov, *Zapinski Voronezh. Sel'ski-Khoz. Inst.,* **18,** 65 (1940); through *C. A.,* **37,** 1469 (1943).

[922] B. Ingelman and A. Tiselius, *Förh. Svenska Socker.,* **1943,** II, 16.

[923] E. M. Aronoff and S. Aronoff, *Food Research,* **13,** 44 (1948).

[924] A. C. Neish and H. Hibbert, *Can. J. Research,* **C18,** 613 (1940).

8. Cabbages

Two analyses of the inner leaves of cabbages give the proportion of total pectic substances as 4.6%[879] and 7.4%[925] on the dry matter basis.

9. Blackberries

In five samples of blackberries Lampitt and Hughes[880] found an average of 0.94% (0.68–1.19%) total pectic substances as pectic acid (on a fresh weight basis). More recent results[881] from 19 samples of wild and 30 samples of cultivated blackberries gave averages of 0.70% and 0.63% calcium pectate, respectively.

10. Cacao

In dried cacao shells Winkler[926] found 3.6–3.9% and Knapp and Churchman[927] found 8.0% pectic substances in samples of fermented and roasted shells. Knapp[928] reported 2.25% total pectic substances in the cotyledon of unfermented West African cacao beans, or 5.20% on the dry, fat-free basis. The corresponding figures in the fermented cotyledons were 4.11 and 9.52%, respectively. This increase during fermentation is somewhat puzzling. Knapp notes the absence of pectinases during fermentation. It is more than likely that some of this increase is due to "concentration" by the removal of other constituents. See also Chapter XXIX, Section V.

11. Carrots

Buston and Kirkpatrick[929] determined the distribution of various pectic substances in carrot roots. The carrots used were "fairly old" and the variety is not given. No cold water soluble pectic compounds were found. The protopectin was extracted by repeated boiling with 0.13 N hydrochloric acid, the total pectic substances with 0.5% ammonium oxalate at 85°C. for 24 hours. The pectic constituents of the "middle lamella" were obtained by difference. The results, given as calcium pectate on a fresh weight basis, are summarized in Table 38.

[925] H. W. Buston, *Biochem. J.,* 29, 196 (1935).
[926] W. O. Winkler, *J. Assoc. Offic. Agr. Chemists,* 20, 415 (1937).
[927] A. W. Knapp and A. Churchman, *J. Soc. Chem. Ind.,* 56, 29 (1937).
[928] A. W. Knapp, *Cacao Fermentation.* Staples Press, London, 1937.
[929] H. W. Buston and H. F. Kirkpatrick, *Ann. Botany,* 45, 519 (1931).

TABLE 38

Pectic Substances in Carrots (Adapted from Buston and Kirkpatrick)

Pectic substance	In cortex, %	In stele, %
Total pectic substances	2.92	1.26
"Protopectin"	2.82	1.17
"Pectic substances of the middle lamella"	0.10	0.09

More recently Simpson and Halliday[930] determined the various pectic fractions in carrots by essentially similar methods. These authors found, on the dry matter basis, 3.7% soluble pectic substances and 18.6% total pectic constituents. The dry matter content of the carrots is not given in either of these papers, and therefore a direct comparison of the results is impossible. Steaming for 20 and 45 minutes increased the proportion of soluble pectic constituents to 6.0 and 8.8%, while during this treatment the proportion of total pectic substances decreased to 16.1 and 13.7%. It is not clear whether the samples were weighed before or after steaming and therefore this apparent loss might be due, in part at least, to an increase in weight of the carrots caused by water uptake.

Baker and Murray[908] state that the grade of pectinic acids extracted from dehydrated carrots is a fair indication of the quality of the product.

Savur and Sreenivasan[877] found 6.9%, and Bennett[879] 7.4%, total pectic substances on the dry matter basis in various samples of carrots.

12. Celery

White-Stevens[931] attempted to correlate the changes which occur in the crispness of celery (Golden Self Blanching variety) in storage at 1°C. with the changes in the various pectic constituents. The proportion of soluble pectic substances in the dry matter fluctuated between 0.1 and 1.0% during 126 days of storage, while the total content of pectic materials ranged from 5.3 to 8.9%. The proportion of pectic constituents did not show any definite trend. White-Stevens concludes that no dissolution of cell wall constituents occurs in stored celery until pathogenic microorganisms infest the tissue. This is also indicated by the observation that the dry matter of a diseased sample still contains a very high proportion (5.5%) of soluble pectic substances.

Bennett[879] found 7.4% total pectic substances in the dry matter of celery.

[930] J. I. Simpson and E. G. Halliday, *Food Research*, 6, 189 (1941).
[931] R. H. White-Stevens, *Sci. Agr.*, 17, 128 (1936).

13. Cereals

Nanji and Norman[905] determined various pectic fractions in a number of cereals. The results, recalculated to show the water-soluble and total pectic substances, are given in Table 39.

The bulk of the pectic materials extracted from cereals was insoluble in water and oxalic acid but soluble in ammonium oxalate. It is likely,

TABLE 39

PECTIC SUBSTANCES IN SOME CEREALS (ADAPTED FROM NANJI AND NORMAN)

| Cereal | Pectic substances (dry matter basis), % | |
	Water soluble	Total
Barley	0.07	2.19
Malt	0.09	0.56
Wheat	0.00	1.01
Rye	0.00	1.13
Corn	0.00	0.59
Oats	0.00	1.08
Rice	0.00	1.13

therefore, that they are present mostly as pectic acid or acid pectates.

Adams and Castagne[932] reported some approximate data on the pectic contents of cereal straws.

14. Cherries

In an unripe sample of cherries, not otherwise described, Conrad[914] found 11.4% pectic substances (on the dry matter basis); pectic acid was absent. The corresponding ripe sample contained 4.3% pectic constituents. Lampitt and Hughes[880] give the average pectic content of four samples of (stone-free) cherries as 0.35% (0.24–0.54%). These latter results are expressed as pectic acid on a fresh weight basis.

Money and Christian[881] found in 6 samples of Morella cherries an average of 0.16% calcium pectate, while in 15 samples of red and 14 samples of white cherries the contents were 0.28% and 0.31%, respectively.

15. Chicory

As calculated from an analysis reported by Aizenberg,[933] the proportion

[932] G. A. Adams and A. E. Castagne, *Can. J. Research,* B27, 924 (1949).

[933] L. N. Aizenberg, *Applied Chem., U. S. S. R.,* 13, 275 (1940); through *C. A.,* 34, 8095 (1940).

of pectic substances in the dry matter of a sample of chicory root was 7.4%.

16. Coffee

A sample of the pulp of the fresh coffee fruit was reported by Teixera[934] to contain 2.8% water-extractable pectic substances. On the other hand, Savur and Sreenivasan[877] found no pectic substances in the sample of "coffee seed." For the role of pectic constituents in coffee fermentation, see Chapter XXIX, Section V.

17. Cotton

Although the presence of pectic substances in cotton fibers was noted a long time ago,[935] only in recent years were methods sufficiently developed to obtain dependable information on the location, occurrence, and proportion of the pectic substances. Nickerson and Leape[936] reviewed the literature of this topic recently. They also reported that seven American-grown mature cottons contained an average of 0.65% (0.43–0.76%) pectic acid (calculated from calcium pectate yields by subtracting 7.5% and expressed on a wax-free, dry matter basis). The pectic substances are surface constituents and there does not appear to be an appreciable quantity of them in the internal structure of the fibers. Whistler, Martin, and Harris[937] were able to show that, contrary to previous postulations,[938] the pectic compounds present in the fiber do not occur as a cellulose–pectic complex ("protopectin") but rather as an insoluble salt (acid pectate?) of polyvalent ions.

The changes in the proportion of pectic substances in growing cotton fibers have been investigated by several authors. The results[939,940] indicate that the proportion of total pectic substances in cotton is about 4.0–6.5% on the tenth day after flowering and that there is a rapid subsequent decrease until a practically constant range (0.7–0.8%) is reached on about the fortieth day. Actually, as Compton demonstrated,[939] this decrease is mostly due to "dilution." The absolute quantity of pectic material per boll about doubles during this period.

[934] W. A. Teixera de Carvalho, *Rev. alimentar Rio de Janeiro*, **2**, 223 (1938).

[935] E. Schunk, *Mem. Manchester Lit. Phil. Soc.*, **24**, 95 (1871).

[936] R. F. Nickerson and C. B. Leape, *Ind. Eng. Chem.*, **33**, 83 (1941).

[937] R. L. Whistler, A. R. Martin, and M. Harris, *J. Research Natl. Bur. Standards.* **24**, 13 (1940).

[938] W. K. Farr and S. H. Eckerson, *Contrib. Boyce Thompson Inst.*, **6**, 189 (1934).

[939] J. Compton, *Contrib. Boyce Thompson Inst.*, **11**, 403 (1941).

[940] R. L. Whistler, A. R. Martin, and C. M. Conrad, *J. Research Natl. Bur. Standards*, **25**, 305 (1940).

During various treatments customary in the commercial utilization of cotton, the proportion of pectic substances is greatly reduced.[941] The relation of the presence of pectic substances to the physical properties of cotton fibers and to the characteristics of solutions made from these has been extensively investigated.[942] The pectic substances are chiefly responsible for the presence of acid groups in cotton and have, therefore, considerable influence on the dyeing properties. The removal of pectic constituents from cotton apparently increases the affinity for direct dyes but lessens its affinity for basic dyes.[943]

18. Currants

Lampitt and Hughes[944] reported that four samples of red currants contained an average of 1.16% (0.91–1.50%), while four samples of black currants gave an average of 1.52% (1.37–1.79%), total pectic substances, determined as pectic acid.

19. Dewberries

In a sample of unripe dewberries which were still hard, Conrad[914] found 0.15% soluble and 1.00% total pectic substances (on a fresh weight basis). The figures for the ripe berries from the same source were 0.51% soluble and 0.70% total pectic substances.

20. Eggplant

A sample of the edible part of the eggplant was found to contain 11.0% total pectic substances on the dry matter basis.[879]

21. Flax

Unretted flax fibers were reported to contain 3–4% pectic substances.[945] During retting at 33°C. for 7 days the proportion of total pectic substances decreased in a sample of flax straw from 2.2 to 0.8%, most of the loss occurring during the first 3 days of retting.[946]

[941] F. Leger and P. Larose, *Can. J. Research*, **B19**, 61 (1941).

[942] R. L. Whistler, A. R. Martin, and M. Harris, *J. Research Natl. Bur. Standards*, **24**, 555 (1940).

[943] S. M. Edelstein, *Am. Dyestuff Reptr.*, **26**, 427 (1937).

[944] L. H. Lampitt and E. B. Hughes, *Analyst*, **53**, 32 (1928).

[945] M. Lüdtke and H. Felsner, *Ann.*, **549**, 1 (1941); *Bastfaser*, **1**, 141 (1941), through *C. A.*, **37**, 4368 (1943); *Cellulosechemie*, **21**, 86 (1943), through *C. A.*, **38**. 5489 (1944).

[946] J. F. Couchman, *J. Council Sci. Ind. Research*, **12**, 183 (1939).

22. Gooseberries

In five samples of gooseberries Lampitt and Hughes[944] found an average of 9.5% total pectic substances (as pectic acid, on the dry matter basis).

23. Grapes

In spite of their great importance, the pectic changes in grapes are little known. Most reports in the literature refer to determinations made

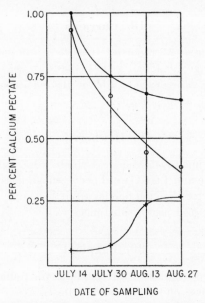

JULY 14 JULY 30 AUG. 13   AUG. 27

DATE OF SAMPLING

Fig. 21. Pectic changes in growing Concord grapes (adapted from Hopkins and Gourley).

On fresh weight basis. Dots, circles, and crosses represent total, insoluble, and soluble pectic substances, respectively.

on expressed juices and are likely to represent only a part of the water-soluble pectic constituents. Determinations made on grape pomace are also of little value here. In addition, most of these determinations were performed by methods now considered obsolete. The pectic constituents of grape pomace will be discussed in Chapter XVII, Section V.

The two sets of data in the literature which were obtained by modern methods are somewhat contradictory. In a study of three varieties of grapes (Tokay, Zinfandel, and Alicante) Marsh and Pitman[947] found

[947] G. Marsh and G. A. Pitman, *Fruit Products J.*, **9**, 187 (1930).

that the proportion of soluble pectic constituents decreased during ripening of the first two varieties from 0.28 to 0.14% and from 0.14 to 0.09%. The Alicante grapes showed 0.11% water-soluble pectic substances in August and 0.13% in September as determined by the Wichmann method.

A much more complete study of the changes which occur in Concord grapes was reported by Hopkins and Gourley.[948] Using the technic developed by Carré,[949] the various pectic fractions were determined for a six-week period; the results are shown in Figure 21.

The trend in proportions of soluble pectic constituents was quite different from that observed by Marsh and Pitman. In general, the changes resemble those which occur in apples in storage. Mehlitz[950] found that in ripening grapes the total pectic constituents increase somewhat at first, after which they decrease continuously. The orchard use of manure or nitrogen fertilizer had no noticeable effect on the pectic constituents.

24. Grapefruit

Grapefruit peel is very rich in pectic constituents and is one of the best sources of commercial pectin. For the discussion of pectin manufacture from citrus peel see Chapter XX. Poore[951] found in the peel (both flavedo and albedo) of some California Marsh Seedless grapefruit 3.3–4.5% pectic substances, and in the peel of some Florida-grown grapefruit 3.2%, and in the rag 3.6%, total pectic substances.

The proportions of pectic constituents change comparatively little during the growth of the grapefruit. Table 40 shows analyses of some California-grown grapefruit flavedo and albedo.[952]

The slight increase is somewhat counterbalanced by the simultaneous decrease in the dry matter content of the samples. The albedo contains far more soluble pectic materials than the flavedo. There is a tendency toward minimum contents of insoluble pectic constituents in midseason. Samples of the same lots of grapefruit were also stored at temperatures ranging from 7° to 20°C. (44° to 68°F.) for six weeks, without any appreciable change in the ratio of the soluble to the insoluble pectic constituents. The surprising observation was that the total proportion of pectic substances increased in all stored lots and there was a tendency to have the greatest increase (from 15.5 to 18.3%) in the lot stored at the highest

[948] E. F. Hopkins and J. H. Gourley, *Proc. Am. Soc. Hort. Sci.*, **1930**, 164.

[949] M. H. Branfoot (Carré), "A Critical and Historical Study of the Pectic Substances of Plants," *Dept. Sci. Ind. Research Brit. Food Invest.*, Special Rept. No. 33 (1929).

[950] A. Mehlitz, *Allgem. deut. Konserven-Ztg.*, **20**, 113 (1933).

[951] H. D. Poore, *Ind. Eng. Chem.*, **26**, 637 (1934).

[952] G. L. Rygg and E. M. Harvey, *Plant Physiol.*, **13**, 571 (1938).

temperature. The samples showed very little variation in dry matter content and therefore loss of water was not the cause of this increase. The fruit may have lost enough solid constituents due to respiration to explain this increase. Rygg and Harvey do not offer an explanation of the phenomenon.

In another study of the conditions leading to the "spotting" of grapefruit in storage, Harvey and Rygg[953] determined the pectic substances in the flavedo and albedo of Marsh grapefruit held in storage for 39 days.

TABLE 40

CHANGES IN PECTIC CONSTITUENTS OF GROWING MARSH GRAPEFRUIT (ADAPTED FROM RYGG AND HARVEY)

| | | Pectic substances (dry matter basis), % | | | |
| | | Flavedo | | Albedo | |
	Date	Soluble	Total	Soluble	Total
		Grown at Oasis, California			
1935	Oct. 29	1.5	14.2	2.5	16.4
	Dec. 10	1.6	14.2	3.1	15.7
1936	Jan. 21	1.9	13.2	3.5	14.5
	Mar. 4	1.7	14.2	5.7	17.0
	Apr. 4	1.7	13.6	6.1	17.7
		Grown at Corona, California			
1936	Mar. 10	1.4	12.0	6.0	15.8
	Apr. 20	1.4	11.3	5.6	16.0
	June 4	1.5	12.0	5.9	14.5
	July 13	1.6	13.2	6.3	17.0
	Aug. 24	1.3	14.1	5.7	17.4
	Oct. 6	2.5	16.8	7.4	19.0

The results were essentially the same as those quoted above and showed no relation to the appearance of "spotting."

In an investigation of Philippine fruits, Rongo and Quiatson[954] found in the albedo of different varieties of grapefruit of eating maturity 8.9–14.9% pectic substances (as pectic acid on the dry matter basis).

25. Guavas

In a sample of the peel of Philippine-grown guavas Rongo and Quiatson[954] found 3.4% total pectic substances (as pectic acid in the dry matter).

[953] E. M. Harvey and G. L. Rygg, *J. Agr. Research,* **52,** 747 (1936).
[954] V. Rongo and S. L. Quiatson, *Philippine Agr.,* **29,** 1 (1940).

26. Hops

Fink and Just[955] report that a sample of hops contained 12% pectic substances, estimated by carbon dioxide evolution from a purified sample. In four samples of hops analyzed in the author's laboratory, the proportion of total pectic substances ranged from 0.60 to 1.84% with an average of 1.36% (on dry basis). As noted in Chapter XXVII, Section III, the pectic substances in hops may play a significant role in brewing.

27. Kumquats

In most citrus fruits a considerable proportion of the white albedo remains at the time they reach full maturity. In kumquats the albedo is gradually solubilized until it becomes gelatinous in texture; at full maturity it completely disappears. These visual changes were shown by Gaddum[956] to be well supported by the transformations in the pectic constituents as followed by analysis. The progress of these changes is shown in Table 41. Since the results are expressed on the ash-free basis, they should be increased by 7.5% for comparison with other determinations made by the calcium pectate method. The total pectic substance con-

TABLE 41

PECTIC CHANGES IN RIPENING NAGAMI KUMQUATS (DRY MATTER BASIS) (ADAPTED FROM GADDUM)

| Date | In albedo | | | In pulp | | |
| | Dry matter, % | Pectic substances, % | | Dry matter, % | Pectic substances, % | |
		Soluble	Total		Soluble	Total
Sept. 6	39.9	7.5	20.5	21.7	6.6	24.6
Oct. 12	31.7	11.2	28.3	19.8	11.0	25.3
Nov. 2	35.3	19.1	29.5	20.6	16.3	25.0
Dec. 18	30.9	25.5	30.0	18.7	15.3	21.9
Jan. 12	31.3	23.1	29.5	17.0	15.8	18.4
Feb. 4	28.8	22.0	28.2	17.6	13.8	15.8
Mar. 10	26.9	19.1	24.1	17.3	12.2	13.6
Apr. 7[a]	15.4	13.4	13.5	14.9	9.4	10.9
May 10	(albedo vanished)			15.7	10.4	11.1

[a] Albedo gelatinous.

tent of the albedo reaches, on the fresh material basis, about 10% and diminishes afterward. The pectic constituents of the "pulp" behave similarly, although the maximum pectin content reached is only about half that of the albedo.

[955] H. Fink and F. Just, *Wochschr. Brauerei*, **52**, 341 (1935).
[956] L. W. Gaddum, *Florida Agr. Expt. Sta.*, Bull. No. 268 (1934).

28. Leaves

The information which may be found in the literature concerning the proportion of pectic substances in various leaves is summarized in

TABLE 42

PECTIC SUBSTANCES IN VARIOUS LEAVES (AS CALCIUM PECTATE ON DRY MATTER BASIS)

Plant	Pectic substances, %		Author
	Soluble	Total	
Alder....................	1.63	4.83	Nanji and Norman[905]
Avocado			
Healthy................	—	4.3–16.2	Haas[910]
Tip-burned leaves.......	—	13.7–21.3	Haas[910]
Bean.....................	—	6.6–9.0	Buston[957]
Cabbage.................	—	4.57	Bennett[958]
Corn.....................	—	1.0–1.7	Buston[957]
Dandelion...............	—	7.81	Bennett[958]
Grape vine..............	—	6.90	Buston[957]
Grass ("Cocksfoot").......	—	2.0	Buston[957]
Grass (Kentucky Blue)....	—	6.5	Bennett[958]
Hyacinth................	—	9.2	Buston[957]
Ivy.....................	3.41	7.46	Nanji and Norman[905]
Kale....................	—	4.55	Bennett[958]
Laurel..................	2.87	4.95	Nanji and Norman[905]
Lemon..................	—	14.6	Haas[910]
Lettuce (head)...........	—	4.00	Bennett[958]
Lime....................	—	20.2	Haas[910]
Lilac....................	2.51	6.11	Nanji and Norman[905]
Narcissus................	—	10.3	Buston[957]
Orange..................	—	16.8	Haas[910]
Potato..................	2.10	7.32	Nanji and Norman[905]
Red clover..............	—	2.5	Greathouse and Stuart[959]
Spinach.................	—	11.58	Bennett[958]
Sumac..................	1.82	5.52	Nanji and Norman[905]
Sycamore...............	3.87	7.90	Nanji and Norman[905]
Tea (green leaf)...........	1.65	4.91	Shaw[960]
Tobacco................	—	13–20[a]	Gabel and Kiprianoff[961]
Walnut			
Healthy................	—	9.0–20.2	Haas[910]
Mottled................	—	9.7–18.9	Haas[910]

[a] As pectic acid, calculated from carbon dioxide evolution.

[957] H. W. Buston, *Biochem. J.,* **29,** 196 (1935).
[958] E. Bennett, *Food Research,* **9,** 462 (1944).
[959] G. A. Greathouse and N. W. Stuart, *Univ. Maryland Agr. Expt. Sta.,* Bull. No. 391 (1936).
[960] W. S. Shaw, *United Planters' Assoc. S. India,* Bull. No. 6 (1934); through *C. A.,* 30, 7236 (1936).
[961] G. Gabel and G. Kiprianoff, *Biochem. Z.,* **212,** 337 (1929).

Table 42. Various leaves seem to contain up to 21% pectic substances. Needless to say, the age, size, and position of the leaves, as well as many additional factors, such as variety, cultural conditions, etc., are likely to have great influence on this matter.

29. Lemons

Lemon peel is an excellent source of pectin and is used in its commercial production (see Chap. XX). The proportions of pectic constituents in lemon peel and pulp were determined by Nanji and Norman[905] and are shown in Table 43.

TABLE 43

PECTIC SUBSTANCES (ON DRY BASIS) IN LEMON PEEL AND PULP (NANJI AND NORMAN)

Sample	Soluble, %	Total, %
Peel....................	15.9	35.5
Pulp....................	11.3	14.1
Av. section...............	14.9	23.3

TABLE 44

EFFECT OF ETHYLENE TREATMENT ON PECTIC SUBSTANCES IN LEMON PEEL (HANSEN)

	Pectic substances (on fresh wt. basis), %			
	Control		Treated	
Time	Soluble	Total	Soluble	Total
At start................	0.10	2.99	0.05	2.99
After 14 days............	0.11	2.80	0.35	1.90

Rongo and Quiatson[954] determined the proportion of pectic substances in the peel of Philippine-grown Hung lemons and Rough lemons and found 22.1 and 7.8%, respectively (as pectic acid on dry matter basis). Savur and Sreenivasan[962] found in the albedo of India-grown lemons 8.1% free (soluble) pectin and 10.6% insoluble pectic constituents. Investigating the chemical changes accompanying the ripening of various fruits with ethylene, Hansen[904] found in lemon peel the proportions of pectic substances shown in Table 44. Morris[963] found pectin more abundant in the yellow than in the white portion of the rind. Sinclair and Crandall,[964] in a study of the carbohydrate changes in lemons, found that the sum of water-soluble and ammonium citrate-soluble pectic constituents accounted

[962] G. R. Savur and A. Sreenivasan, *J. Sci. Ind. Research (India)*, **5**, 41 (1946).

[963] T. N. Morris, *Dept. Sci. Ind. Research, Rept. of Food Investigation Board*, 1936, 207.

[964] W. B. Sinclair and P. R. Crandall, *Plant Physiol.*, **24**, 681 (1949).

for an average of 35% of the alcohol-insoluble solids of lemon peel. Cultrera and de Luca[965] found that the insoluble pectic constituents in lemons during growth were fairly constant around 12% but that with full maturity this fraction dropped to 8%.

30. Loganberries

In two samples of loganberries Lampitt and Hughes[944] found an average of 3.8% total pectic substances (as pectic acid on the dry matter basis). Money and Christian[966] reported an average of 0.59% total pectic substances as calcium pectate, on fresh basis, for eleven samples of loganberries.   ▪

31. Onions

Conrad[914] found in a sample of onion 4.8% total pectic substances (on the dry matter basis). Here again the changes which occur in the pectic constituents during the storage of dehydrated onions might be used as indications of changes in quality.

32. Oranges

Orange peel is one of the raw materials used in the commercial production of pectin (see Chap. XX). Gaddum[956] made a systematic study of the changes in the pectic constituents of Florida-grown Valencia oranges. A summary of his results is presented in Table 45.

TABLE 45

PECTIC CONSTITUENTS IN GROWING ORANGES (ADAPTED FROM GADDUM)

| | As pectic acid on dry matter basis, % | | | |
| | Albedo | | Pulp | |
Date	Soluble	Total	Soluble	Total
Nov. 15	8.1	27.5	9.3	27.6
Dec. 21	13.1	27.8	12.6	26.0
Jan. 14	16.1	28.6	18.9	28.7
Feb. 21	20.4	28.8	18.3	27.6
Mar. 16	19.3	27.8	16.0	19.7
Apr. 7	18.9	28.3	13.7	17.1
May 1	17.8	25.1	15.4	14.5
May 18	14.1	19.6	10.0	15.4
June 5	12.7	17.6	9.5	13.3

[965] R. Cultrera and G. de Luca. *Ann. Chim. Appl.*, **37** (2), 75 (1947).
[966] R. W. Money and W. A. Christian, *J. Sci. Food Agr.*, **1**, 8 (1950).

In the dry matter of the albedo, the proportion of pectic substances is almost constant until advanced maturity (May) when it commences to decrease. The proportion of water-soluble pectic substances in the albedo increases rapidly during the period of rapid growth but decreases as the fruit ripens. The pectic constituents in the dry matter of the pulp show essentially the same trends, except that the decrease in both soluble and total pectic constituents starts some 60 days sooner, before the fruit matures. During the whole period shown in Table 45, the dry matter content of the peel gradually decreases from 35 to 27%, and increases in the pulp from 20 to 27%.

TABLE 46

PECTIC CONSTITUENTS OF ORANGE (ADAPTED FROM NANJI AND NORMAN)

| | | Pectic substances (on dry matter basis) | |
Sample	Dry matter, %	Soluble, %	Total, %
Flavedo...........	26.8	7.54	15.92
Albedo...........	23.7	18.53	38.75
Pulp..............	10.9	10.45	12.40
Av. section........	15.4	14.35	24.53

Nanji and Norman[905] also reported some analyses of oranges of an unspecified variety for pectic materials. A summary of their results is shown in Table 46. The pectin content of the dry matter of the albedo exceeds that of both the flavedo and pulp by a considerable amount.

Heid[967] made a study of the effect of ethylene treatment on the pectin produced from orange peel. Although analyses were not performed by methods now considered sufficiently specific, his results indicate that the ethylene treatment accelerates the disappearance of insoluble pectic constituents. Money and Christian[966] found an average of 0.86% total pectic substances as calcium pectate in the edible portion of 13 samples of oranges. A sample of fresh ground "pear orange," deprived of juice and seeds, was reported to have contained 4.17% pectic substances.[934]

The pectic constituents of orange juice will be dealt with in Chapter XXVII.

33. Parsnips

In a study of extraction methods, Conrad[914] found 10.7% total pectic substances in parsnips. In another set of experiments, the same author determined the effect of the method of preparation on the pectic com-

[967] J. L. Heid, *Fruit Products J.*, 21, 100 (1941).

position of the preserved sample and found the results shown in Table 47.

These results indicate that pectic acid does not occur normally in parsnips, but that it may be produced during heating of the tissue. The importance of rapid inactivation of the pectin-destroying enzymes in the

TABLE 47

EFFECT OF VARIOUS TREATMENTS ON PECTIC COMPOSITION OF PARSNIPS
(ADAPTED FROM CONRAD)

| | Pectic substances (on dry matter basis), % | |
Condition	Protopectin	Pectic acid
Dried at 98°C. in air oven................	6.83	3.95
Dried at 70°C. under vacuum.............	3.83	9.61
Preserved in boiling ethanol................	10.69	0.00
Sun dried................................	7.36	5.26

preservation of plant material for pectic analysis was discussed previously.

Simpson and Halliday[930] found 4.7% soluble and 16.4% total pectic substances in the dry matter of a sample of parsnips. In harmony with the results of Conrad, the amount of pectic acid found was very low (1.6%). Steaming for 20 and 45 minutes increased the amount of soluble pectic substances to 6.1 and 7.9% at the expense of insoluble pectic constituents.

34. Peaches

Appleman and Conrad[968] made a thorough study of the pectic changes in Crawford peaches. The proportions of water-soluble pectic substances in the "green" and "hard ripe" fruits were low (0.19% and 0.24%), while the total pectic substances at the same two stages were 0.87 and 0.78%, respectively. The pectic changes which occurred in the fruit in three or four days on the tree were barely in excess of the experimental variation. On the other hand, when the picked fruit was kept at room temperature for three or four days, the proportion of soluble pectin trebled in the case of both "green" and "hard ripe" fruit. The proportion of total pectic substances showed a slight increase in the fruit held at room temperature, probably not representing a true increase but rather the result of loss of water (and sugar?) during the storage period. Fruit picked and stored for three days at 3.5°C. (39°F.) showed no changes in the pectic components during this period. Conrad[916] reported the changes in the

[968] C. O. Appleman and C. M. Conrad, *Univ. Maryland Agr. Expt. Sta.*, Bull. No. 283 (1926).

)ectic composition of some Early Georgia peaches held in storage. The
oss of weight which occurred during the 72 hours of storage was only
5%. These results are shown in Table 48.

The percentage of soluble pectic substances in both immature and ma-
ure fruit was quite different in several varieties investigated by Fisher,
3ritton, and O'Reilly[969] who made determinations of the soluble pectin
:raction in the expressed juice. Table 49 summarizes this information.
These authors observed a very close correlation between the maturity,

TABLE 48

Pectic Changes in Peaches Held at 30°C. (86°F.) (Adapted from Conrad)

Sample	Hours in storage	Pectic substances (fresh wt. basis), %	
		Soluble	Total
Green, firm........................	0	0.32	0.66
Softer............................	19	0.40	0.66
Quite soft........................	46	0.56	0.74
Soft, yellow, marked aroma.........	72	0.56	0.69

TABLE 49

Soluble Pectic Substances in Peaches (Adapted from Fisher, Britton, and O'Reilly)

Variety	On fresh wt. basis, %	
	Immature	Mature
Rochester...............	0.006	0.044
Vedette.................	0.019	0.150
J. H. Hale..............	0.056	0.200
Elberta.................	0.031	0.094

as measured by pressure testers, and the percentage of soluble pectin, al-
-hough the relationship between the firmness and the percentage of soluble
)ectin was not the same for the different varieties. They also found that
when the peaches are first exposed for a few days to packing house tem-
)eratures and are then put into cold storage, the softening and formation
of soluble pectin continues rapidly even after placing the fruit in 0°C.
storage.

The effect of carbon dioxide storage or artificial ripening with ethylene[904] is essentially similar in the case of peaches to that described for
apples.

Conrad[914] also reported that some peaches of an unspecified variety
contained, on the dry matter basis, 5.1% total pectic substances but no

⁹⁶⁹ D. V. Fisher, J. E. Britton, and H. J. O'Reilly, Sci. Agr., 24, 1 (1943).

pectic acid. In good agreement with the results of Appleman and Conrad,[968] Money and Christian[966] reported an average of 0.86% total pectic substances in peach flesh. The grade of extracted pectinic acids might be a useful measure of the quality of dehydrated peaches.[908]

35. Pears

The pectic transformations occurring in ripening pears are quite similar to those in apples. Emmett[970] found that while the three varieties of pears studied showed marked differences in their rates of ripening and storage behavior, the changes were closely accompanied by differences in the

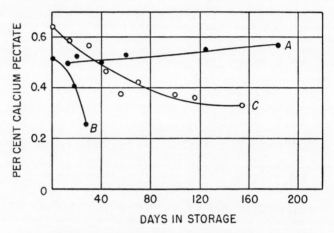

**Fig. 22. Pectic changes in stored Conference pears
(adapted from Emmett).**

On fresh weight basis. Curves *A, B,* and *C* show changes in total pectic substances at 1°C. (34°F.), 12°C. (54°F.), and 4°C. (39°F.), respectively.

pectic constituents. The amount of total pectic substances in Conference pears was in the range of 0.5–0.7% (on the fresh weight basis) at the time the fruit reached full size and was picked for storage. The subsequent changes in total pectin depended on the storage conditions. As shown in Figure 22, the total pectic constituents stayed constant at 1°C. (34°F.) for some time but decreased at 4°C. (39°F.) and even more rapidly at 12°C. (54°F.). No weight losses are given by Emmett for the pears in storage and therefore the slight increase at 1°C. may be more than compensated for by progressive reduction in unit weight.

[970] A. M. Emmett, *Ann. Botany,* **43,** 269 (1929).

The proportion of soluble pectin is very low in unripe pears.[970,971] In
lot of Worcester Pearmain pears the amount was only 0.02% but in-
eased slowly at 1°C. to 0.15% in 50 days and 0.25% in 100 days, show-
g only a very slight further increase up to 217 days (0.28%). At 12°C.
e increase was much more rapid and a maximum of 0.40% was
ached in 50 days, followed by a decrease in the mature fruit. The in-
ease in viscosity due to the increase in soluble pectin in the juice ex-
essed from the pears is quite noticeable.

Emmett believes that the development of soluble pectin in ripening
ars is a chief factor concerned with softening and that the differences
nong varieties may be due to the different rates at which this reaction
curs. He states that the mechanism of pectic changes is apparently
fferent in pears and apples; the higher pH of the pear tissue (about
3 as compared with 3.4 in apples) may be an important factor in this
nnection.

Later work by Gerhardt and Ezell[972] and Smock and Allen[973] estab-
hed that the relation between softening and increase in soluble pectin
so held when carbon dioxide storage was used to retard the maturing
pears. The former authors state that there is a direct relation between
pening and soluble pectin in Bartlett pears and propose the use of
luble pectin as an index of maturity. Gerhardt and Ezell found the
luble pectin content of a lot of Bartlett pears to be 0.025% at the time
picking and 0.815% at the time when the fruit was yellow and in a
irm ripe" state. In overripe fruit and especially during senescence the
rcentage of soluble pectin decreased rapidly. Smock and Allen found
07% soluble pectin in the picked unripe Bartlett pears and about
7–0.8% in the ripe fruit. Hardy pears showed similar trends.

Hansen[974] found that the same relationship still holds when the pears
e ripened by treatment with ethylene. The proportion of soluble pectin
as 0.10–0.19% in the fruit when picked at various times, but it increased
storage to a maximum of 0.7–0.8% in fruit picked in July and was
6% in fruit picked later. The total pectic substances amounted to about
9% in most pickings, except in fruit picked in September.

Savur and Sreenivasan[962] found, in the dry matter of some pears grown
India, 3.07% total pectic substances.

Finally, the more recent and somewhat contrary results of Paech[975]
ould be noted. This author determined the progress of softening and of
ctic changes in pears (*Pastorenbirnen*) in storage at 10°C. (50°F.).

[971] R. Echevin, *Compt. rend.*, **213**, 458 (1941).
[972] F. Gerhardt and B. D. Ezell, *J. Agr. Research*, **56**, 121 (1938).
[973] R. M. Smock and F. W. Allen, *Proc. Am. Soc. Hort. Sci.*, **35**, 184 (1938).
[974] E. Hansen, *Plant Physiol.*, **14**, 145 (1939).
[975] K. Paech, *Landw. Jahrb.*, **85**, 653 (1938).

The results obtained are shown in Figure 23. Except in the overrip
pears, both the decrease of the acid-soluble fraction and the increase c
the water-soluble pectic constituents show a direct relationship to th
progress of softening. Yet, Paech believes that the pectic transformatior
in this case are only incidental or rather co-occurring rather than fur
damentally related to the softening process. His main reason is that i
a different lot of pears stored at 3.5°C. (38°F.) softening occurred in si

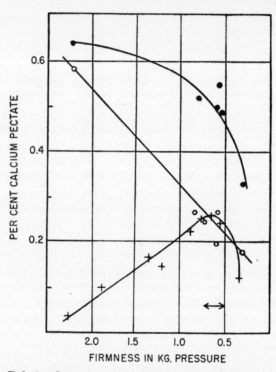

**Fig. 23. Relation between pectic constituents and firmness of "Pas-
torenbirnen" pears (adapted from Paech).**

On fresh weight basis. Dots, circles, and crosses represent total, insoluble, and soluble pectic substances, respectively. Range of eating maturity is indicated by arrow.

months without a simultaneous increase in the water-soluble pectic frac
tion. However, even here the insoluble pectic constituents showed
steady decrease during softening.

Money and Christian[966] found in 31 samples of pears, in the edibl
portion, 0.46% total pectic substances as calcium pectate.

It is clear that many external as well as internal factors, such as th

omposition of the storage atmosphere, the condition of the fruit when
)icked, the period between picking and placing in storage, etc., are likely
o influence the storage behavior of pears. Obviously, more research is
1eeded before we may say that the transformations of the pectic com-
)onents are *de facto* always responsible for softening. It is well estab-
ished, however, that the increase in the soluble fraction at the expense
)f the insoluble pectic constituents does occur in most cases during ripen-
ng.

36. Peas

Bonney and Fischbach[976] reported the proportion of total pectic sub-
tances in 13 varieties of sweet canning peas, as well as in a sample of
Alaska peas. The determination was made on the drained, experimentally
:anned seed peas. The sweet peas showed an average pectic acid content
)f 1.15% (0.94–1.38%), the Alaska peas 1.04%. Mattson[977] found in
ome dry peas grown in Sweden 3.80–3.96% uronides by the carbon
iioxide method.

The pectic constituents of dried peas have received some attention on
account of the alleged relationship between these constituents and "hard-
seededness." The fact that peas (and beans) at times do not soak up water
n the usual manner might cause difficulties in germination tests and in
growing under certain conditions, as well as in cooking. This phenomenon
vas generally assumed to be the result of the formation of calcium–
protein compounds until Shutt[978] showed that this is not the case. Several
nvestigators[979-981] believe that the lack of water uptake is the result of
:he formation of highly insoluble compounds between pectic substances
and polyvalent ions. Recently Mattson[977] reinvestigated this problem
and, while he believes that the pectic constituents are directly responsible
for the resistance to water, he suggested a complex reaction system involving phytin, phytase, low-ester pectinic acids and pectic acid, and
polyvalent ions as responsible for the occurrence of hardseededness. This
whole matter is far from clear at the present time and further work is
needed to elucidate the causes as well as the reactions leading to hard-
seededness.

976 V. B. Bonney and H. Fischbach, *J. Assoc. Offic. Agr. Chem.*, 28, 409 (1945).
977 S. Mattson, *Acta Agr. Suecana*, 2, 185 (1946).
978 F. T. Shutt. *Canada Dept. Agr., Rept. of Dom. Chemist*, 1928–29; through
C. A.. 24, 4100 (1930).
979 J. P. Van Der Marel, *Pharm. Weekblad*, 59, 82 (1922).
980 G. D'Ippolito, *Staz. sper. agrar. ital.*, 58, 128 (1925); through C. A., 20, 2546
(1926).
981 J. Grossfeld, *Naturwissenschaften*, 18, 625 (1930).

37. Plums

Hanes and Morris[982] studied the pectic changes which occur in ripen
ing Victoria plums. With advancing maturity, the proportion of tota
pectic substances decreased only slightly from 0.82 to 0.72%, while the
soluble fraction increased from 0.07 to 0.20%. When the fruit was picked
at three different stages of maturity and placed into 15°C. (59°F.)
storage, the pectic changes were similar to those described previously for
other deciduous fruits. These results are shown in Figure 24. Hanes and
Morris also observed that previous storage at lower temperatures—

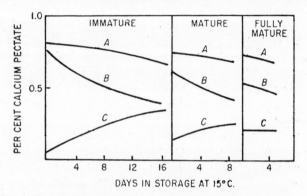

**Fig. 24. Pectic changes in maturing Victoria plums
(adapted from Hanes and Morris).**

On fresh weight basis. Curves *A, B,* and *C* represent total,
insoluble, and soluble pectic substances, respectively.

3°C. and 5°C. (37° and 41°F.)—had considerable influence on the pectic
changes in subsequent storage at 15°C. The ripening was virtually arrested by such treatment and these authors suggest that storage at low
temperatures in some manner injures the mechanism responsible for the
solubilization of insoluble pectic constituents and for ripening. This view
was supported by some observations on the viscosity of the water-soluble
fraction from normally ripened—at 15°C. (59°F.)—and cold-injured
plums. In the normal series the viscosity of the water-soluble fraction decreased rapidly with advancing ripening. The viscosity of the similar
fraction extracted from the cold-injured plums during subsequent storage
at 15°C. was essentially constant. This abnormal viscosity of the pectic
substances in stored plums was previously observed by Smith[983] but the

[982] C. S. Hanes and T. N. Morris, *Dept. Sci. Ind. Research Brit. Rept. Food
Invest. Board,* 1938, 129.

[983] W. H. Smith, *Dept. Sci. Ind. Research Brit. Rept. Food Invest. Board,* 1936, 153.

conditions which cause it are far from clear. Smock and Allen[973] in their work on the carbon dioxide storage of fruit could not establish any definite relationship between the proportion of soluble pectic substances and the state of maturity of plums.

In four samples of greengage plums, Lampitt and Hughes[984] found an average of 8.1% total pectic substances (as pectic acid, on the dry matter basis); and in four samples of otherwise unidentified plums the same authors found 0.96% total pectic substances, on the fresh weight basis. More recently, Money and Christian[966] reported for 18 samples of Damsons an average total pectic substance content of 1.03% (on a fresh basis) while the corresponding values for greengages (43 samples) was 1.11% and for green and yellow, red, and blue plums 0.90%, 0.79%, and 0.86%, respectively. The last three averages were obtained from 19, 61, and 63 samples. The values reported by Money and Christian are in terms of calcium pectate.

38. Potatoes

Conrad[914] found in a sample of potatoes 2.0% total pectic substances (on the dry matter basis) and no pectic acid. Sweetman,[985] in a study of the cooking qualities of potatoes, reported for 24 varieties of potatoes averages of 0.07% (0.05–0.09%) soluble and 4.1% (3.2–5.4%) total pectic constituents (on the dry matter basis). In a later study, Freeman and Ritchie[986] found in some 16 varieties of potatoes an average of about 2.5% (1.8–3.3%) total pectic substances (on the dry matter basis). These authors also used a variety of methods for the determination of water-soluble pectic substances and found, by the customary cold-water extraction, only traces of these in their samples.

Coudon and Bussard[987] recognized over 40 years ago that the development of mealiness in potatoes might be the result of pectic changes. Later work by Davison and Willaman[988] with pectic enzymes increased the likelihood that this might be the case. However, Sweetman[985] could not find any definite relationship between changes in pectic constituents and mealiness.

In 1940 Freeman and Ritchie[986] reexamined this problem. Using a variety of sampling and extraction methods, they found that the pectic constituents of potatoes consist partly of a fraction insoluble in cold water but easily soluble in hot water and a second fraction which is insoluble

[984] L. H. Lampitt and E. B. Hughes, *Analyst,* 53, 32 (1928).
[985] M. D. Sweetman, *Maine Agr. Expt. Sta.,* Bull. No. 383 (1936).
[986] M. E. Freeman and W. R. Ritchie, *Food Research,* 5, 167 (1940).
[987] H. Coudon and L. Bussard, *Ann. de sci. agron.,* 3, 250 (1897).
[988] F. R. Davison and J. J. Willaman, *Botan. Gaz.,* 83, 329 (1930).

in hot water but soluble in ammonium citrate or oxalate solutions. But, neither of these fractions extracted from raw, dried, or baked potatoes showed any definite relationship to mealiness.

In an attempt to explain the softening which occurs in storage, the pectic changes in Simla seed potatoes have been studied by Dastur and Agnihotri.[989] The tubers were sorted according to size and the size was assumed to represent the advancing age of the potatoes. The results, shown in Table 50, indicate a progressive increase in the soluble fraction while the total pectic substances also increase, indicating the continuous formation of pectic substances during growth. During storage the soluble pectin increases and the total pectic substances decrease, but the increase in the former is less than the loss in the latter. Dastur and Agnihotri state that similar changes occurred in all other varieties tested. The transformation proceeds much faster at 40°C. (104°F.) than at 27°C. (79°F.).

TABLE 50

PECTIC SUBSTANCES IN POTATO TUBERS OF DIFFERENT DIAMETERS (ADAPTED FROM DASTUR AND AGNIHOTRI)

Average diameter, cm.	Pectic substances (fresh wt. basis), %	
	Soluble	Total
1.0–1.4	0.16	2.91
2.2–2.6	0.19	3.17
3.1–3.3	0.22	3.35
4.2–4.6	0.28	3.61
5.3 and up	0.30	3.75

A sample of rotten potatoes from the same lot used in the tests reported in Table 50 contained 0.74% soluble and only 1.71% total pectic substances.[989] Hornby[990] found more pectin in the skin than in the potato. Völksen[991] reported 15–20% total pectin in the residue left from potato starch manufacture.

39. Pumpkin and Squash

Doty, MacGillivray, and Kraybill[992] reported the pectic changes in pumpkin and squash. Some of the results obtained by these authors are summarized in Table 51.

[989] R. H. Dastur and S. D. Agnihotri, *Indian J. Agr. Sci.*, **4**, 430 (1934).
[990] A. J. W. Hornby, *J. Chem. Ind.*, **39**, 246 (1920).
[991] W. Völksen, *Z. Lebensm.-Unters. Forsch.*, **90**, 177 (1950).
[992] D. M. Doty, H. R. MacGillivray, and H. R. Kraybill, *Purdue Univ. Agr. Expt. Sta.*, Bull. No. 402 (1935).

The increases in the early part of development are more spectacular when calculated on the dry matter basis because the solids content of the fruit more than doubles during that period. The pectic changes in Connecticut Field pumpkin were similar to those in Kentucky Field pumpkin. The proportion of pectic constituents in Boston Marrow squash was about 30% lower throughout than those in Golden Delicious. It is apparent from these data that most of the pectic constituents in pumpkin and squash are water soluble. The changes in the pectic constituents did not show any definite relationship to the consistency of the raw or canned

TABLE 51

PECTIC SUBSTANCES IN GROWING, STORED, AND CANNED PUMPKIN AND SQUASH (ADAPTED FROM DOTY, MACGILLIVRAY, AND KRAYBILL)

| Fruit age, days | Pectic substances (fresh wt. basis), % | | | | | |
| | Flesh | | Connecting tissue | | Seeds | |
	Soluble	Total	Soluble	Total	Soluble	Total
Kentucky Field pumpkin						
10	0.12	0.29	0.14	0.28	—	—
20	0.21	0.35	0.24	0.52	—	—
30	0.20	0.49	0.23	0.45	0.18	1.50
40	0.37	0.51	0.23	0.37	0.32	2.15
50	0.45	0.55	0.24	0.37	0.35	2.60
a	0.40	0.55	—	—	—	—
b	0.37	0.52	—	—	—	—
Golden Delicious squash						
10	0.11	0.38	0.17	0.40	—	—
20	0.20	0.42	0.20	0.52	—	—
30	0.41	0.86	0.40	0.81	0.20	0.85
40	0.52	0.67	0.42	0.59	0.36	1.47
50	0.66	0.67	0.53	0.45	0.40	1.60
a	0.40	0.66	—	—	—	—
b	0.48	0.69	—	—	—	—

a Mature fruit stored for 18 days.
b Mature canned fruit.

fruit. The same conclusion was reached previously by a still partly unpublished study by Sayre and Green.[993] It seems that it is mostly the condition of the starches and dextrins which governs the texture of raw, and consistency of canned, pumpkin and squash.

Bennett[958] found in a sample of squash 3.3%, and Savur and Sreenivasan[962] 2.70% total pectic substances (on the dry matter basis).

[993] C. B. Sayre and E. L. Green, *Canner*, 72 (22), 10 (1931).

40. Radishes

In a sample of pithy radishes, Conrad[914] found 26.9% total pectic substances (on the dry matter basis). Of this, 15.4% was characterized as pectic acid. Buston[994] determined the pectic constituents in various parts of the radish plant and found in the whole plant 10.3–11.8%, in shoots 10.7–13.6%, and in "roots" 7.8–9.5% total pectic substances (on the dry matter basis). More recently Bennett[958] reported 7.8% total pectic substances (on the dry matter basis) in some radishes.

41. Raspberries

In four samples of raspberries Lampitt and Hughes[984] found an average of 0.71% (0.58–0.86%) total pectic substances (as pectic acid on the fresh weight basis). Eight samples of Lloyd George raspberries grown in Tasmania showed an average content of 0.55% (0.42–0.69%) on the same basis.[995] Money and Christian[996] found in 264 samples of raspberries an average of 0.40% total pectic substances, as calcium pectate, on the fresh weight basis.

Leinbach, Seegmiller, and Wilbur[997] determined the total pectic constituents in four varieties of red raspberries grown in Washington State during two years. The pectin content (as calcium pectate on fresh basis) ranged from 0.68 to 0.97% and showed no relation to the "mushiness" of the berries. The methoxyl contents (on uronic anhydride basis) ranged from 11.7 to 14.0%. Rendle[998] made some observations on the pectic changes in raspberries stored at 18 to 24°C. (65–75°F.) and found that the soluble fraction decreased in one day from 0.54 to 0.45%, and in six days to 0.17%. The total pectic substances dropped in six days from 0.92 to 0.34%. Rendle states that the ripening process in the raspberry fruit is very rapid, and the disappearance of pectic constituents is well borne out by the decrease in jellying power. The occurrence of pectic changes in stored raspberries is arrested by the use of heat. Morris[999] found that the destruction of the pectic constituents in frozen raspberries stored at −25°C. is almost complete in six months. Diemair and Mayr[1000] commented on the great variation in the pectin content of raspberries. They found in raspberry juice the range of 0.28 to 0.51% in 1935 and 0.16 to 0.40% in 1936.

[994] H. W. Buston, *Biochem. J.*, **29**, 196 (1935).
[995] H. E. Hill, *personal communication*, January, 1949.
[996] R. W. Money and W. A. Christian, *J. Sci. Food Agr.*, **1**, 8 (1950).
[997] L. R. Leinbach, C. G. Seegmiller, and J. S. Wilbur, *Food Technol.*, **5**, 51 (1951).
[998] T. Rendle, *Analyst*, **58**, 73 (1933).
[999] T. N. Morris, *Dept. Sci. Ind. Research Brit. Rept. Food Invest. Board*, **1933**, 155.
[1000] W. Diemair and F. Mayr, *Z. Untersuch. Lebensm.*, **72**, 470 (1936).

42. Rhubarb

Savur and Sreenivasan[962] found in a sample of rhubarb 1.02% total pectic substances (on the dry matter basis).

43. Strawberries

In six samples of ripe strawberries (of undefined varieties) Lampitt and Hughes[984] found an average of 0.68% (0.60–0.73%) total pectic substances (expressed as pectic acid on the fresh weight basis). Conrad[916] determined the pectic constituents in Klondike strawberries at four different stages of maturity, and the changes in four more varieties were determined in the author's laboratory.[1001] The dry matter content of the Klondike berries was 7% and of the other varieties 11–12% at the mature stage. These results are shown in Table 52.

TABLE 52

PERCENTAGE PECTIC CONSTITUENTS ON FRESH WEIGHT BASIS IN RIPENING STRAW-
BERRIES (ADAPTED FROM CONRAD, AND ROUSE, MACK, AND KERTESZ)

Condition	Klondike		Culver		Parsons Beauty		Redhearth		Howard 17	
	Sol.	Tot.	Sol.	Tot.	Sol.	Tot.	Sol.	Tot.	Sol.	Tot.
White........	0.23	0.62	1.31	1.42	0.75	0.77	0.94	0.96	0.66	0.69
50% red......	0.32	0.48	0.50	0.51	0.49	0.53	0.69	0.71	0.44	0.44
Fully ripe.....	0.32	0.40	0.54	0.54	0.21	0.21	0.55	0.55	0.38	0.38
Overripe......	—	—	0.51	0.51	0.47	0.47	0.73	0.73	0.50	0.50

In the Klondike berries there seems to be comparatively more insoluble pectin than in the varieties grown at Geneva, New York. The irregularities in the absolute values are not unexpected when the great sampling error and the difficulty in obtaining berries of similar ages is taken into consideration. It is surprising that the percentage of pectic constituents does not decrease when the berries become overripe. This observation is supported by a test made by Conrad[1002] in holding ripe Klondike berries at 30°C. (86°F.) for 47 hours. Subsequent analysis showed that the soluble fraction increased only immaterially, while the total pectic substances decreased somewhat. The berries lost 14% of their weight during storage, but the percentage of dry matter was practically unchanged.

These data seem to indicate that the pectic constituents of strawberries are more stable than those of raspberries.

[1001] A. H. Rouse, G. L. Mack, and Z. I. Kertesz, *unpublished work*, 1932–33.
[1002] C. M. Conrad, *Plant Physiol.*, **5**, 93 (1930).

Conrad[1003] also reported, for a sample of green strawberries (of unspecified variety), 8.82% total pectic substances (on the dry matter basis) and 6.16% for the corresponding ripe sample. No pectic acid was found in these berries. Webster and Gray[1004] state that the pectin content of strawberries was not significantly changed by the use of chemical fertilizers. Cochran and Webster[1005] found, in 12 samples of strawberries grown with different fertilizers, an average of 0.25% (0.22–0.29%) soluble pectin and 0.41% (0.35–0.44%) total pectic substances (on the fresh weight basis). They also observed that the firmest berries seemed to show the highest proportion of pectic constituents.

44. Sunflower

Colin and Lemoyne[1006] reported the presence in sunflowers of some pectin of possible commercial usefulness. Recently Stoikoff[1007] published an extensive investigation of this subject. Of the various parts of the sunflower, the seed head (receptacle) has the highest pectin content. Stoikoff used precipitation from an oxalic acid extract with 70% ethanol for the quantitative estimation and then corrected the values for the amount of starch in this precipitate. The seed head contained 23% pectin (corrected) and this showed approximately 50% esterification. By titration the purity of this pectin proved to be 87%. Stoikoff believes that sunflower seed receptacle, which is available in great quantities in some countries, would make a suitable raw material for pectin manufacture since in his tests the jellying power proved to be similar to that of an average quality commercial apple pectin.

45. Sweet Potatoes

The determination of pectic substances in sweet potatoes is difficult on account of the large proportions of starch, hemicellulose, and nitrogenous compounds. Heinze and Appleman,[1008] in a study of the process of curing sweet potatoes, devised a special method for the determination of the pectic constituents; this was discussed in Chapter VIII. Samples of sweet potatoes analyzed before storage contained 0.43% soluble and 0.78% total pectic substances (on the fresh weight basis). When these sweet potatoes were cured and stored for 5 months, there was first a slight increase followed by a decrease in the percentage of soluble pectin. The insoluble pectic substances (protopectin) increased during the same period

[1003] C. M. Conrad, *Am. J. Botany,* **13,** 531 (1926).
[1004] J. E. Webster and G. F. Gray, *Proc. Am. Soc. Hort. Sci.,* **35,** 204 (1937).
[1005] G. W. Cochran and J. E. Webster, *Proc. Am. Soc. Hort. Sci.,* **28,** 236 (1931).
[1006] H. Colin and S. Lemoyne, *Compt. rend.,* **211,** 44 (1940).
[1007] S. Stoikoff, *Mitt. Geb. Lebensm. Hyg.,* **39,** 292 (1948).
[1008] P. H. Heinze and C. O. Appleman, *Plant Physiol.,* **18,** 548 (1943).

in a gradual manner from the original 0.35% to 0.65%. To the author's knowledge this is the only case where an increase in the insoluble pectic constituents during storage of a plant tissue has been reported. Unfortunately, the loss in weight and dry matter during the curing and subsequent storage are not reported by Heinze and Appleman; thus it is difficult to say whether this apparent increase in protopectin might have been the result of the types of changes described in the introduction to this chapter.

46. Tea

Lamb[1009] found that Ceylon-grown tea leaves contain 4.94–7.59% total pectic substances, on the dry weight basis. The bulk of the pectic constituents were water-soluble. A sample of Lipton's (fermented or black) tea, analyzed in the writer's laboratory, contained 0.28% water-soluble pectin (as calcium pectate) and 1.65% total pectic substances. See also Table 42.

47. Tomatoes

The pectic constituents of tomatoes are of much interest as well as of great practical importance. Accordingly, they have been extensively studied. Their role in tomato products will be noted in Chapter XXVII.

(a) Changes during Growth

Appleman and Conrad[1010] and Kassab[1011] reported the percentages of pectic constituents in growing tomatoes and emphasized the increase in soluble pectin and decrease in insoluble pectic constituents (protopectin). Some of these results are shown in Table 53.

TABLE 53

Pectic Components of Growing Tomatoes (Adapted from Appleman and Conrad, and Kassab)

	Pectic substances (dry matter basis), %					
	Bonny Best		San Jose Early		Alemada Trophy	
Condition	Soluble[a]	Total[a]	Soluble[b]	Total[b]	Soluble[b]	Total[b]
Green, full size.....	1.06	3.43	2.28	3.53	0.98	2.28
Pink..............	2.47	4.65	—	—	—	—
Fully ripe.........	3.05	4.63	2.58	2.68	2.70	2.73

[a] As calcium pectate.
[b] As pectic acid.

[1009] J. Lamb, Tea Research Inst. of Ceylon, Bull. No. 30 (1948).
[1010] C. O. Appleman and C. M. Conrad, Univ. Maryland Agr. Expt. Sta., Bull. No. 291 (1927).
[1011] M. A. Kassab, Fruit Products J., 11, 442 (1931).

More recently Paech[975] reported a study of the changes which occur in the color, firmness (as measured by the pressure needed to puncture), and pectic constituents (in the outer layer) of tomatoes. These results are shown in Table 54.

TABLE 54

RELATION BETWEEN COLOR, FIRMNESS, AND PECTIC CONSTITUENTS OF OUTER LAYER OF TOMATOES (ADAPTED FROM PAECH)

Color	Firmness, g. (see text)	Pectic substances (fresh wt. basis), %	
		Soluble	Total
Green.....................	2000	0.02	0.48
Yellow.....................	1500	0.04	0.47
Orange.....................	1000	0.07	0.42
Deep orange................	—	0.05	0.32
Light red..................	400	0.06	0.25
Deep red..................	250	0.05	0.12

Unfortunately, the variety and dry matter content of Paech's tomatoes are not given; it is obvious, however, that the trend was quite different from that reported in Table 53. The percentage of soluble pectin was much higher in the tomatoes analyzed by Appleman and Conrad and by Kassab. It is difficult to reconcile these results unless the use of different varieties under different climatic conditions is taken into consideration. The trend of Paech's results may perhaps find its explanation in his use of the undefined "outer layer" of the tomatoes for the analyses, while the other authors used the whole fruit. At any rate, there is ample evidence that the trends shown in Table 53 are typical of canning tomatoes grown in the United States.

Appleman and Conrad[1010] also recommended the use of the pectin-protopectin ratio as an expression of the changes in the growing tomato fruit. As may be seen from Table 53, this ratio increases from a fraction to 2.6 in the Bonny Best tomatoes and even much higher in the other varieties. At times the proportion of insoluble pectic constituents at full maturity is only a small fraction of the total proportion of pectic constituents.

Conrad[1003] found, in a sample of green tomatoes, 5.45% total pectic substances (on the dry matter basis). The corresponding ripe sample gave 2.92%, but neither the green nor the ripe fruit contained any pectic acid.

(b) Pectic Composition of Ripe Tomatoes

Although during growth pectic changes in tomatoes follow a definite trend, the changes which occur once the fruit attains full coloration are not quite as clear. According to Table 53, a continuation of the increase in the soluble and decrease in the insoluble pectic constituents would be expected; in reality such changes in the ripe fruit are not pronounced enough to avoid being masked by changes caused by other factors, especially those of seasonal and cultural nature. Table 55 shows the changes which were found by Appleman and Conrad[1010] to occur in four varieties of tomatoes during the canning period. The total pectic constituents tended to increase in these varieties during the picking season.

Savur and Sreenivasan[962] found, in ripe tomatoes grown in India, 4.72% total pectic substances on the dry matter basis.

In a recent investigation, Kertesz and McColloch[1012] sought information on the chemical and physical properties of pectins isolated from slightly underripe, ripe, and overripe tomatoes. Large numbers of individually picked and selected John Bear tomatoes from the same plot were used in this study, and the fruit at 7 different dates was classified according to the above maturity grouping. The pectic constituents were

TABLE 55

PECTIC CHANGES IN RIPE TOMATOES (ADAPTED FROM APPLEMAN AND CONRAD)

Date of picking	Pectic substances (dry wt. basis), %							
	Bonny Best		Greater Baltimore		Stone		Marglobe	
	Soluble	Total	Soluble	Total	Soluble	Total	Soluble	Total
Aug. 16	2.33	3.35	—	—	—	—	—	—
Aug. 24	1.69	2.62	2.12	3.11	1.95	2.79	—	—
Sept. 7	2.20	3.73	1.84	3.29	2.40	3.85	2.45	4.27
Sept. 14	2.32	3.78	2.18	3.98	1.96	3.40	2.54	4.00
Sept. 21	—	—	—	—	2.87	4.29	2.64	3.71

prepared by cutting the tomatoes into a large volume of boiling ethanol, followed by extraction from the dried ethanol-insoluble residues by water, ammonium oxalate, and hydrochloric acid. The methyl ester content and viscosities of these extracted pectins were also determined. Table 56 shows some of the data obtained in this study.

The results show no definite trends in the pectic changes as the tomatoes matured. The water-extracted ("soluble") fraction had a higher methyl ester content than the other fractions. The viscosities of the water- and acid-extracted pectinic acids increased, while that of the oxalate-extracted fraction decreased, indicating possible changes in the distribution of various pectinic acids among the different fractions. The main conclusion of the whole experiment is that, with our present methods of

[1012] Z. I. Kertesz and R. J. McColloch, *New York State Agr. Expt. Sta.*, Bull. No. 745 (1950).

definition, the trends observed in the behavior of tomatoes as they reach full maturity cannot be correlated with changes in the pectic constituents.

TABLE 56

PECTIC COMPONENTS OF JOHN BEAR TOMATOES (ADAPTED FROM KERTESZ AND MC-COLLOCH)

| Condition | Pectic substances (fresh wt. basis) | | Fractions extracted by: | | | | | |
| | | | water ("soluble") | | ammonium oxalate | | acid | |
	Soluble, %	Total, %	CH_3O, %	Viscosity[a]	CH_3O, %	Viscosity[a]	CH_3O, %	Viscosity[a]
Unripe......	0.080	0.172	11.9	1.57	5.5	1.67	8.2	1.39
Ripe........	0.062	0.134	11.4	1.98	6.0	1.53	10.9	1.73
Overripe....	0.061	0.162	11.2	1.93	5.9	1.26	9.0	1.80

[a] Relative viscosity at 30°C. of 0.1% solution at pH 2.0 and containing 0.9% sodium chloride.

(c) Effects of Variety, Locality, Irrigation (Water Supply), etc.

It should be obvious from the foregoing discussions that both variety and growing conditions have a profound effect on the pectic constituents of tomatoes. Kassab[1011] compared the proportions of total pectic substances in five varieties of tomatoes grown in the same field and of comparable ripeness and found a range of 1.27–2.49% (as pectic acid on the dry matter basis). Locality of growing has an even more pronounced influence. Kassab also determined the effect of irrigation, and the results suggest that abundance of water may result in a lower proportion of pectic constituents in the tomatoes as compared with the fruit from nonirrigated plants.

Bohart[1013] found, in 141 samples of mature tomatoes grown in the western United States, an average of 0.14% soluble and 0.22% total pectic substances (as pectic acid on the fresh weight basis). Smith[1014] reported that the total pectic substances in four different varieties of Arkansas-grown tomatoes averaged 3.63, 3.00, 3.37, and 2.38% (on the dry matter basis). These averages were obtained from about 20 samples.

(d) Pectic Changes in Stored Tomatoes

Storage and delayed ripening of tomatoes are constantly gaining in commercial importance. To obtain information on the pectic changes which occur under such conditions, LeCrone and Haber[1015] kept green-ripe and fully ripe tomatoes at three different storage temperatures and

[1013] G. S. Bohart, Canner, 82, 113 (1936).
[1014] M. E. Smith, Fruit Products J., 15, 365 (1936); 16, 302 (1937).
[1015] F. LeCrone and E. S. Haber, Iowa State College J. Sci., 7, 467 (1933).

determined the ensuing changes in the pectic constituents. The results obtained are shown in Table 57.

Unfortunately, the analysis of the fruit at the beginning of the storage period and the weight losses in storage are not given. The soluble fraction increased in the green-ripe tomatoes at all three temperatures, while in the ripe fruit it showed some increase at 10°C. (50°F.) and was rather

TABLE 57

PECTIC CHANGES IN STORED TOMATOES (ADAPTED FROM LeCRONE AND HABER)

Days in storage	2°C. storage		10°C. storage		21°C. storage[a]	
	Pectic substances (fresh wt. basis), %					
	Sol.	Tot.	Sol.	Tot.	Sol.	Tot.
Green ripe when picked						
7	0.018	0.159	0.024	0.152	0.021[b]	0.137
14	0.019	0.158	0.040	0.154	0.046	0.139
21	0.019	0.167	0.048	0.158	0.063	0.133
28	0.022	0.167	0.043[b]	0.131	0.042	0.107
35	0.022	0.160	0.056	0.138	—	—
42	—	—	0.062	0.134	—	—
Ripe when picked						
7	0.052	0.147	0.042	0.125	0.042	0.147
14	0.052	0.134	0.038	0.112	0.067	0.157
21	0.042	0.147	0.047	0.127	0.056	0.131
28	0.038	0.135	0.056	0.131	0.042	0.129
35	0.040	0.134	0.059	0.128	—	—
42	—	—	0.058	0.125	—	—

[a] 35°, 50°, and 70°F., respectively.
[b] Ripe as judged by color.

irregular at the other two temperatures. The tomatoes stored at the two higher temperatures showed the expected slow decrease in total pectin. LeCrone and Haber conclude that in the fruit ripened in storage the pectic constituents were present approximately in the same proportions as in the freshly picked ripe tomatoes. They recommend 10°C. as the most suitable temperature for the delayed storage ripening of tomatoes.

Frazier[1016] found no relation between changes in the pectin constituents and cracking of tomatoes.

48. Turnips

Conrad[1003] found, in a sample of turnips, 11.93% total pectic substances (on the dry matter basis), and no pectic acid. Bennett[958] re-

[1016] W. A. Frazier, *Trans. Peninsula Hort. Soc.*, **1936**, 13.

ported 5.07% and Savur and Sreenivasan[962] 2.56% total pectic substances (calculated on the same basis) in other samples.

49. Watermelon

Ohno[1017] found in the meat of watermelon (grown in Japan, variety undefined) only 0.02% total pectic substances (on the fresh weight basis). This was the lowest proportion found among 31 different fruits investigated by Ohno. Savur and Sreenivasan[962] found in a sample of watermelon (containing 5.3% dry matter), 1.58% total pectic substances on the dry matter basis.

50. Woods

As we have stated above, pectic substances occur in all plant tissues, including woods. For some time the opinion prevailed that woods do not contain pectic materials, but refinements in methods of extraction and estimation made it clear that this contention was erroneous.

Birch bark pectin and pine bark pectin are apparently quite similar but, in spite of their high methyl ester content, will not form sugar–acid jellies.[1018]

Practically all the information available on the pectic constituents of woods originated in the laboratories of workers principally interested in hemicelluloses. Table 58 contains some of the information which may be found in the literature on this topic.

Anderson, Seigle, Krznarich, Richards, and Marteny[1019] state that the pectic substances in woods are apparently laid down early in growth and remain at their original location even as the tissue undergoes changes. The proportion diminishes due to the formation of other compounds and in mature wood may reach very low levels. It appears that the bark and the cambium-phloem layer are both much richer in pectic substances than the sapwood or heartwood.

Soluble pectic substances may be assumed to be generally present in the bark and the cambium-phloem layer, although there is little information on this point. It is known to be true, on the other hand, that the heartwoods contain no soluble pectic substances—in fact the fractions found in these tissues seem to be exceedingly insoluble. The reason, according to Anderson,[1020] is that the pectic substances in woods have been

---

[1017] S. Ohno, *J. Taihoku Soc. Agr. Forestry,* 1, 29 (1936); through *C. A.,* 30, 7710 (1936).

[1018] V. I. Sharkov and A. Girchits, *Lesokhim. Prom.,* 1939 (2), 9; through *C. A.,* 34, 6324 (1940).

[1019] E. Anderson, L. W. Seigle, P. W. Krznarich, L. Richards, and W. W. Marteny, *J. Biol. Chem.,* 121, 165 (1937).

[1020] E. Anderson, *J. Biol. Chem.,* 165, 233 (1946).

transformed into the (acid) calcium salts of pectic acid and may be further immobilized by association with other tissue components.

In a recent study of the inner bark and cambial zone of the black spruce (*Picea mariana*.) Anderson and Pigman[1021] have found that pectic materials occur in large amounts in the inner bark, where they are mixed with starch. The pectic constituents could be isolated by successive extractions with hot water, very dilute hydrochloric acid, and 3% ammonium oxalate, and then precipitated as calcium pectate.[1022] They were also isolated from the holocellulose of the inner bark. Anderson and Pigman again emphasize that the presence of pectic constituents in the greatest proportions in young tissues suggests that they are laid down during the early stages of cell wall formation in wood. Some of these extracted pectic substances were hydrolyzed by pectic enzymes and the D-galacturonic acid was isolated to prove the pectic nature of these compounds.[1023]

TABLE 58
PECTIC SUBSTANCES IN WOODS

Wood	Total pectic substances (dry wt. basis), %	Author
Ash		
Bark............................	*ca.* 7	Buston and Hopf[1024]
Sapwood......................	<1	Buston and Hopf[1024]
Black locust		
Sapwood......................	*ca.* 0.2	Anderson *et al.*[1019]
Heartwood..................	0.6–0.7	Anderson *et al.*[1019]
Citrus (various) bark[a].........	22–31	Haas[1025]
Cottonwood..................	1.5	Anderson *et al.*[1026]
Lemon........................	*ca.* 1.7	Anderson *et al.*[1026]
Maple........................	4.4	Rogers[1027]
Mulberry (paper) bark.........	9.1	Heiduschka and Chang[1028]
Mesquite.....................	0.66	Anderson *et al.*[1026]
Rose (shoots).................	4.8–5.0	Buston[994]
White Pine		
Sapwood......................	0.3	Anderson *et al.*[1026]
Cambium-phloem.............	21	Anderson *et al.*[1026]
Pine..........................	0.7	Hägglund *et al.*[1029]

[a] Including orange, grapefruit, lemon, limequat, tangelo, kumquat, etc., scions no sour orange and other stock.

[1021] E. Anderson and W. W. Pigman, *Science*, 105, 601 (1947).

[1022] E. Anderson and L. Sands, in W. W. Pigman and M. L. Wolfrom, *Advances in Carbohydrate Chemistry*. Vol. 1, Academic Press, 1945, p. 329.

[1023] W. W. Pigman, E. Anderson, and R. L. Leaf, *J. Am. Chem. Soc.*, 70, 432 (1948).

[1024] H. W. Buston and H. S. Hopf, *Biochem. J.*, 32, 44 (1938).

[1025] A. R. C. Haas, *Proc. Am. Soc. Hort. Sci.*, 34, 84 (1937).

[1021] E. Anderson and W. W. Pigman, *Science*, 105, 601 (1947).

[1027] H. J. Rogers, *Nature*, 157, 395 (1946).

[1028] A. Heiduschka and Y. Chang, *Cellulosechemie*, 17, 77 (1936).

[1029] E. Hägglund, F. W. Klingstedt, T. Rosenquist, and H. Urban, *Z. physiol. Chem.*, 177, 248 (1928).

PART THREE
THE BIOCHEMISTRY OF PECTIC SUBSTANCES

CHAPTER XIV

Pectic Enzymes

Enzymes are characterized by, and often known only as the result of their action.[1030] Thus, with a few notable exceptions, their existence is ascertained and their activity is assessed by means of the changes which they bring about or, more correctly, which they catalyze. Although enzymes are usually inactivated by heat, this characteristic can no longer be regarded as part of the definition.

Enzymes show considerable, although not universal, specificity in acting only (or acting most effectively) on one definite compound or type of compound. This compound is the substrate of the enzyme and the latter's action is measured by: (1) the disappearance of the substrate; (2) the formation of certain products or groupings from the substrate molecule; or (3) changes in the physical properties of the mixture in which the enzyme action occurs.

The complex macromolecules of pectic substances would seem to offer a number of possibilities for enzyme action. In spite of this there are still only two enzymes which are definitely known and very strong indications concerning the existence of another. These enzymes are *pectin-methyl-esterase*, illustrated by A in the schematic picture of a pectinic acid molecule on page 334; *pectin-polygalacturonase, B*; and the newly discovered *depolymerase, C*; a *protopectinase* might also exist.

The history of pectic enzymes is characterized by a confusion of nomenclature. This is not surprising when the status of the nomenclature of the pectic substances themselves is taken into consideration (see Chapter I). Furthermore, the chemical changes involved in the action of the two definitely known pectic enzymes have been known only since 1918. Progress has been rapid in this field and the debates over terminology are now governed by personal preferences for certain terms rather than by dissimilarities in opinions concerning the action of the enzymes. There

[1030] J. B. Sumner and G. F. Somers, *Chemistry and Methods of Enzymes.* 2nd ed., Academic Press, New York, 1947.

are several thorough reviews of the subject of pectic enzymes in the literature.[1031-1037]

```
                              C
                              |
                    A      CCCCCCOOH
                    |   ↓  CCCCCCO—O—CH₃     CCCCCCOOH
        CCCCCCO—O—CH₃     CCCCCCOOH      .. CCCCCCOOH    A
                                                         ↗
        CCCCCCOOH      .. CCCCCCO—O—CH₂    CCCCCCO—O—CH₃
  B →   CCCCCCO—O—CH₃    CCCCCCO—O—CH₃    CCCCCCOOH
  ..    CCCCCCO—O—CH₃    CCCCCCO—O—CH₃    CCCCCCOOH
        CCCCCCOOH        CCCCCCO—O—CH₃    CCCCCCO—O—CH₃
  B →   CCCCCCO—O—CH₃ .. CCCCCCOOH    \   CCCCCCOOH .........
        etc.              etc.        A   etc.              ↑
                                                            C
```

I. PROTOPECTINASE

1. Definition and Nomenclature

The name *protopectinase* is applied to the enzyme which hydrolyzes or dissolves protopectin (see Chapter III) with resultant separation of the plant cells from each other, a process usually spoken of as maceration.[1038] This term *protopectinase*, which has been officially accepted by the American Chemical Society,[1039] supersedes the older term *pectosinase*.[1040] Thus far this enzyme has been demonstrated only by its action on plant tissues and a chemical definition of the reaction involved is impossible until the nature of protopectin itself is clarified. Kolb[1041] in 1868 showed that the retting of flax is caused by the action of an en-

[1031] F. Ehrlich, in Abderhalden, *Handbuch der biologischen Arbeitsmethoden.* Vol. IV, 1936, p. 2405.

[1032] Z. I. Kertesz, *Ergeb. Enzymforsch.*, **5**, 233 (1936).

[1033] H. Bock, in E. Bamann and K. Myrbäck, *Die Methoden der Fermentforschung.* Thieme, Leipzig, 1941, p. 1914.

[1034] H. J. Phaff and M. A. Joslyn, *Wallerstein Labs. Communs.*, **10**, 133 (1947).

[1035] Z. I. Kertesz and R. J. McColloch, in C. S. Hudson and S. Cantor, *Advances in Carbohydrate Chemistry.* Vol. V, Academic Press, New York, 1949, p. 79.

[1036] H. Lineweaver and E. F. Jansen, in F. F. Nord, *Advances in Enzymology*, Vol. XI. Interscience, New York, 1951.

[1037] Z. I. Kertesz, in J. B. Sumner and K. Myrbäck, *The Enzymes.* Vol. I, Academic Press, New York, 1951.

[1038] F. R. Davison and J. J. Willaman, *Botan. Gaz.*, **83**, 329 (1927).

[1039] C. S. Brinton, W. H. Dore, H. J. Wichmann, J. J. Willaman, and C. P. Wilson, *J. Am. Chem. Soc.*, **49**, 38 (1927).

[1040] E. Bourquelot and H. Hérissey, *J. pharm. chim.*, **8**, 145 (1898).

[1041] M. J. Kolb, *Compt. rend.*, **66**, 1024 (1868).

zyme, assumed to be protopectinase. Some of the early workers believed that the maceration was due to the effect of oxalates but later systematic work by Brown[1042] and Davison and Willaman[1038] clearly established the existence of a macerating enzyme.

Until a few years ago it was believed that protopectinase is distinct from the enzyme which hydrolyzes the 1,4 glycosidic linkages in pectinic acids as shown by B in the diagram above. However, there is now a growing tendency toward the view that the two enzymes (protopectinase and pectin-polygalacturonase) are identical; this is in harmony with the assumption that protopectin is either a modification of pectinic acid or is composed of very large pectinic acid molecules (see Chapter III). If either of these assumptions is correct, there is no need to assume the existence of a protopectinase different from the enzyme performing the fissure noted by B in the diagram. A major argument for the identity of the two enzymes is that whenever the macerating action of protopectinase can be demonstrated, the enzyme action invariably proceeds to hydrolyze the pectinic acids formed from protopectin into nonpectic polyuronides and galacturonic acid. It is now also known that certain changes in plant tissues in the past attributed to protopectinase action can occur through different, nonenzymic mechanisms (Chapter VII, Section VI).

In comparison with other pectic enzymes, only very few investigations seem to deal with protopectinase and our knowledge of this enzyme is hardly better than it was 15–20 years ago.[1031,1032] For this reason we shall deal with protopectinase briefly.

2. Determination

The lack of knowledge about protopectin (the substrate) is well reflected in the methods of estimating protopectinase activity. Qualitatively, the action of protopectinase may be observed under the microscope. Quantitatively, protopectinase is usually measured by the progress of the maceration.

Brown[1042] and Harter and Weimer[1043] determined the time required for the loss of coherence in carrot discs (1 mm. thick) suspended in the enzyme solution. The coherence is assumed to be lost when the disc does not offer any perceptible resistance to a pulling stress. Davison and Willaman[1038] improved this method by standardizing the pulling stress and suggested the use of a strip of potato tuber 0.5 mm. thick, 5.0 mm. wide, and 20 mm. long. The strip is suspended at one end by a clamp while a weight of 10 g. is hung at the other end of the strip by means of a second clamp. The slice with the weight attached

[1042] W. Brown, Ann. Botany, 29, 319 (1915).
[1043] L. L. Harter and J. L. Weimer, J. Agr. Research, 21, 609 (1921); 22, 371 (1921); 24, 861 (1923); 25, 472 (1923).

is then submerged in the enzyme solution and the time noted when the co-hesion of the cells is reduced to the extent that the weight drops. Sloep[1044] followed the action of protopectinase by exposing a disc of the medlar fruit (*Mespilus germanica* L.) to the enzyme solution. Ehrlich[1031] made extensive observations of protopectinase action by following both the loss of water-insoluble solids and the changes in the optical rotation in reaction mixtures containing the enzyme and the protopectin preparations in the form of suspensions. This latter technic must be considered even more inadequate than those listed above because the optical rotation of the liquid will depend on two factors: (*1*) the progress of solubilization ("hydrolysis of the protopectin"); and (*2*) the subsequent hy-drolysis of the dissolved pectic constituents. The specific optical rotation of pectinic acids is usually about +250°, while that of galacturonic acid—derived from the former by hydrolysis—is only about +51°

The dangers of using substrates as ill defined as "carrot slices" or "potato tuber strips" are obvious. In Chapters IX and XIII the variations which may occur in the proportions and conditions of the pectic constitu-ents of plants were mentioned and this factor will obviously have a pro-found effect on the rate and extent of the digestion of the tissue by the protopectinase. None of the methods listed above are exact and without major weaknesses but no improvements can be expected until the nature of protopectin becomes clearer.

3. Occurrence and Preparation

In view of the unreliable methods of measurement and the possible identity of protopectinase with the enzyme responsible for the fissure of the 1,4 glycosidic linkages in pectinic and pectic acids, it seems un-desirable to give any detailed information on the occurrence of protopec-tinase. This enzyme has been prepared from a great number of fungi and microorganisms. As far as we know all sources of pectin-polygalacturonase given later in Table 61 probably contained protopectinase in addition to pectin-polygalacturonase. For specific information on this subject the reader is referred to the several reviews dealing with this topic.[1031-1035]

4. Properties

Brown[1042] has found the optimum pH for protopectinase action in a slightly acid medium. Davison and Willaman[1038] found an optimum range of 4.5–5.0 with a number of different substrates, using an extract from *Rhizopus tritici* as a source of enzyme. In a recent study of the pectolytic digestion of beet pulp by commercial mold enzyme (Pectinol, see Chap. XV). Roboz and Kertesz[1045] found an optimum pH range around 3.5–4.0.

[1044] A. C. Sloep, *Dissertation*, Delft (1928).
[1045] E. Roboz and Z. I. Kertesz, *unpublished work*, 1948.

It is now clear that many factors, such as the rate of diffusion of the enzyme into the tissue, the presence of other pectic enzymes, or the extent of esterification of the pectinic acid component, will influence such optima. Davison and Willaman found that protopectinase was completely inactivated by being heated to 48°C. for 20 minutes.

The whole subject of protopectinase is in dire need of a thorough re-examination.

II. PECTIN-POLYGALACTURONASE (PECTINASE, PECTOLASE)

1. Definition and Nomenclature

It has been known for about fifty years[1046] that an enzyme which hydrolyzes pectinic acids occurs in barley malt and in various microorganisms. This enzyme is characterized by destruction of the pectinic acid (as shown by the loss of ethanol precipitate in the reaction mixture) and by simultaneous formation of water-soluble reaction products of high reducing power. It is now clear that the enzyme hydrolyzes the 1,4 glycosidic linkages in the polygalacturonic acid skeleton of pectic or pectinic acids with the resulting formation of polygalacturonic acids of smaller molecular sizes and of (mono-) galacturonic acid. The term *pectinase,* generally used before 1935, is now regarded as a designation for an enzyme complex composed of at least one more pectic enzyme in addition to pectin-polygalacturonase. In the past pectinic acid (pectin) was commonly used as the substrate for pectinase action. Since it is now evident that the true substrate of pectin-polygalacturonase is pectic acid and not pectinic acid (see below), and since the presence of other enzymes might at times have an effect on the apparent activity of pectin-polygalacturonase,[1047] it is desirable to use the more specific term *pectin-polygalacturonase.*[1035] The older name pectinase is still retained for preparations containing several enzymes acting upon pectic substances, for example, the commercial mold enzymes sold for fruit juice clarification (see Chapter XV). Some authors use the term *polygalacturonase.*[1036,1048] The abbreviation PG is often used for both terms.

Ehrlich[1049] rediscovered pectin-polygalacturonase in molds and considered it a specific enzyme for the hydrolysis of some of his tetragalacturonic acids, especially pectolic and gelpectolic acids. He named the enzyme *pectolase.* With the accumulation of proof that the tetragalacturonic acids do not represent the basic structure of pectic substances

[1046] E. Bourquelot and H. Hérissey, *J. pharm. chim.,* **8,** 49 (1898).

[1047] E. F. Jansen, L. R. MacDonnell, and R. Jang, *Arch. Biochem.,* **8,** 113 (1945).

[1048] E. F. Jansen and L. R. MacDonnell, *Arch. Biochem.,* **8,** 97 (1945).

[1049] F. Ehrlich, *Biochem. Z.,* **250,** 525 (1932); **251,** 204 (1932).

TABLE 59

CHANGES DURING ENZYMIC DECOMPOSITION OF PECTINIC ACID BY A COMMERCIAL PECTINASE

Reaction time, hrs.	Fractional precipitation with ethanol				Specific viscosity at 30°C.	Reducing power by method		Free acidity as galacturonic acid,c %	Methyl ester,c %	Specific rotation c	Calcium pectate,e %
	Insoluble in 50% ethanol, %	Soluble in				I,a %	II,b %				
		50-70%	70-90%	90%							
0	100.0	0	0	0	5.02	4.8	3.5	31.1	9.6	+242	108.3
0.5	85.6	8.3	0	(6.1)	0.85	14.5	11.6	34.2	9.3	239	97.8
1	76.1	10.0	0	(13.9)	0.41	17.6	15.4	36.4	8.8	211	95.0
2	60.3	14.1	3.6	(22.0)	0.16	23.1	23.6	42.1	7.9	205	78.3
4	25.4	24.8	10.2	(39.6)	0.05	33.0	35.4	51.8	6.4	180	36.3
30	0	6.7	8.9	(84.4)	—	84.2	—	99.5	1.8	94	0
168	0	1.8	7.5	(90.7)	0.03	(102.3)	—	—	(0)	53	0

a By Willstätter-Schudel method (see Chapter II) expressed on basis of original pectinic acid content.

b By Bertrand method (see Chapter II) expressed on basis of original pectinic acid content.

c Expressed on basis of original pectinic acid content.

(see Chapter III), the term pectolase became obsolete and is now used only to a very limited extent.

The reasons for the retention of the term *pectin* in pectin-polygalacturonase are given in the discussion of its specificity (see below). A discussion of some other possible hydrolytic enzymes which seem to be related to pectin-polygalacturonase can be found in Section III.

2. Determination of Pectin-Polygalacturonase Activity

As stated above, the action of an enzyme may be followed by determining the loss of the substrate, by estimating some new groups formed during the course of the reaction, or by measuring the physical changes which occur. All three approaches have been used in the case of pectin-polygalacturonase. Unfortunately, the interpretation of the results obtained by all of these methods is often very difficult on account of the lack of exact knowledge concerning the macromolecular structure of pectic substances. As an example, Table 59 shows a set of determinations[1050] made on a reaction mixture containing 0.65% of a purified pectinic acid and 0.065% commercial pectinase and kept at 30°C. The enzyme used in this case had considerable pectin-methylesterase activity and therefore the objections raised (see below) against the use of pectinic acid as a substrate for pectin-galacturonase do not hold here. Similar experiments following the action of pectin-polygalacturonase obtained from various sources on pectinic and pectic acids may be found in the literature. The comparative usefulness of the various measurements will be briefly discussed below.

(a) Measurements by Loss of Substrate

The significance which may be attached to measurements of the rate of disappearance of the pectinic or pectic acid used as a substrate depends on the purpose of the investigation. If the chief point of interest is the loss of true pectic substance resulting from pectin-polygalacturonase action, then the use of such methods is suitable. Any of the procedures cited in Chapter VIII for the determination of pectinic and pectic acids may be used. Three limitations should be noted in this connection. (1) The results may be quite different depending upon whether they are obtained by precipitation with ethanol or acetone, or as pectic acid or calcium pectate. The precipitability of decomposing polygalacturonic acids depends on many factors (see Chapter VIII). (2) Such measurements follow the disappearance of the pectic material serving as a sub-

---

[1050] J. D. Loconti and Z. I. Kertesz, *unpublished work*, 1939–40.

strate. Naturally, they do not give information on the progress of poly-uronide hydrolysis beyond the stage where the polygalacturonic acid molecules cease to be of sufficient size to be precipitable by any of the methods used. (*3*) There are certain intermediate stages of decomposition where, in spite of the fact that the pectinic or pectic acid can be deter-mined by such methods, they no longer satisfy the "colloidal" part of the definition as indicated by solution viscosity or jellying power. We have noted several such instances in Chapter VII.

Another method which has been used[1051] in following the action of pectin-polygalacturonase on pectinic and pectic acids is the one de-scribed by Fellers and Rice[1052] which measures the volume of the acid-precipitated pectic acid. The limitations of this method have already been noted in Chapter VIII. In rare cases this procedure, upon proper stand-ardization, provides means to perform many determinations with com-parative ease.

The greatest drawback of such methods following the enzyme action by the determination of the proportion of unchanged substrate is the time-consuming nature of all the precipitations, filtrations, drying, etc. needed. Modifications of such procedures using volumetric measurement of the pectic acid or titration of the precipitates will only partly eliminate these objections.

Table 59 shows some changes which occur in several properties during the enzymic hydrolysis of pectinic acid.

(b) Measurement of Reducing Groups Formed

Pectin-polygalacturonase is defined as the enzyme which catalyzes the hydrolysis of the 1,4 glycosidic linkages in pectic polyuronides. Every fissure of such a bondage produces a reducing group which was previously engaged in the formation of the polymer. The formation of such reduc-ing groups has always been regarded as characteristic of pectin-poly-galacturonase action. Therefore, this measurement of the increase in re-ducing power has been used more frequently than any other property for following pectin-polygalacturonase action.[1032,1048,1049,1053]

The reducing power of pectic substances was discussed in Chapter VII. While there is difficulty in arriving at definite reducing power values for pectinic and pectic acids, these difficulties for the most part disappear with even partial hydrolysis. In Table 59 the agreement between the hypoiodite and copper reducing methods is quite satisfactory. A great

[1051] R. J. McColloch and Z. I. Kertesz, *J. Biol. Chem.*, 160, 149 (1945).
[1052] C. R. Fellers and C. C. Rice, *Ind. Eng. Chem., Anal. Ed.*, 4, 268 (1932).
[1053] F. Ehrlich, *Enzymologia*, 3, 185 (1937).

advantage of the method is that it can follow the reaction through its whole course until the polygalacturonic acid substrate is completely hydrolyzed into (mono-) galacturonic acid.

It has been observed by most investigators that the hydrolysis of a pectic acid by pectin-polygalacturonase slows down after about one half of the substrate has been hydrolyzed, as indicated by the increase in the reducing power. It is not clear now whether this is caused by the loss of enzyme activity or by the formation of lower polyuronides which are hydrolyzed at a different rate, or both. We shall return to this matter in Sect. 9. The early phases of the hydrolysis (as measured by increase in the reducing power) produce reducing power increases proportional to the reaction time. The comparative extent of hydrolysis in these very early phases is also proportional to the amount of pectin-polygalacturonase used. Based on these observations, pectin-polygalacturonase activity is usually estimated by the increase in the reducing power during this part of the reaction.[1048]   In a recent study in the author's laboratory,[1045] a similar scheme was used except that the difference in the increase in reducing power was measured during a short period, not immediately after mixing the enzyme and substrate, but 15 minutes later. Such a procedure eliminates the uncertainties caused by the irregularities of reducing power determinations on the original pectic acid substrate.

(c) Measurement of Physical Properties

Viscosity changes have been extensively used in the estimation of pectin-polygalacturonase activity. As shown in Table 59, the major viscosity changes occur very early in the reaction. After about one fourth of all glycosidic linkages have been hydrolyzed (as measured by increase in the reducing power), the viscosity scarcely changes. For this reason the measurement of viscosity changes is a very sensitive indication of even traces of pectin-polygalacturonase action. We shall return to this observation later. The meaning of viscosity changes is not at all clear at the present time. Some workers in this field have expressed views[1054] that the apparent discrepancy between the changes in viscosity and the reducing power of a pectic acid solution undergoing hydrolysis by pectin-polygalacturonase indicates the existence of structural units or other than the 1,4 glycosidic linkages in the pectin macromolecule. Although others have contested such an assumption, there is still a notable absence of any comprehensive theory which would interrelate in some other manner the various changes which can be observed when pectic acid is hydrolyzed.

[1054] Z. I. Kertesz, *J. Am. Chem. Soc.*, **61**, 2544 (1939).

In spite of this limitation, viscosity measurements have been extensively used for the standardization of commercial pectinases, as well as in some research investigations. In criticizing a paper suggesting the use of viscosity measurements for the determination of pectin-polygalacturonase action,[1055] Deuel and Weber[1056] have summarized the objections to the use of viscosity changes in research studies. The course of the reaction is not unimolecular but it shows parallelism to the amount of unchanged substrate present.[1057] Recently, Reid[1058] discussed in some detail the various anomalies observed in viscosity changes during the enzymic hydrolysis of sodium pectate. The percentage loss in viscosity plotted against the log of the amount of enzyme used gives a straight line.[1058a]

Changes in the optical rotation have also been used to follow pectin-polygalacturonase action, especially by Ehrlich.[1031,1053] Table 59 shows how the optical rotation of a solution diminishes as pectinic acid is hydrolyzed. The change is very slow during the early phase of hydrolysis. While in the mixture shown in Table 59 some 83% of the viscosity attributable to the pectinic acid was lost in the first 30 minutes, during the same time the optical rotation changed only 1.6% of its full possible course, even less than did the calcium pectate number. This small change in the optical rotation is in good agreement with other observations that the optical rotation of pectinic acids is scarcely affected during excessive degradation by heating or by ascorbic acid (see Chapter VII). There are no kinetic analyses of optical rotation changes during hydrolysis in the literature and thus, for the present at least, this property cannot be regarded as suitable for following pectin-polygalacturonase action.

(d) Suggested Methods for Detection and Determination of Pectin-Polygalacturonase Activity

A survey of the literature shows considerable disagreement on the methods to be used for the detection of slight pectin-polygalacturonase activity. One difficulty is that prolonged tests are of questionable value because the pectinic or pectic acid solutions undergo some changes even in the absence of enzymes (see Chap. VII). Second, the effectiveness of toluol and thymol—usually applied in keeping such solutions free from contamination with microorganisms—is questionable, since it has been common experience that such contamination is delayed but not prevented

[1055] G. Weitnauer, Helv. Chim. Acta, 29, 1382 (1946).
[1056] H. Deuel and F. Weber, Helv. Chim. Acta, 29, 1872 (1946).
[1057] A. Mehlitz and M. Scheuer, Biochem. Z., 268, 355 (1934).
[1058] W. W. Reid, J. Sci. Food Agr., 1, 234 (1950).
[1058a] W W. Reid, Food Technol., 5, 170 (1951).

by antiseptics. Thymol affects reducing power determinations. Contamination by microorganisms may occur quite soon after solutions of pectinic and pectic acids are made. Since microorganisms, especially when grown in the presence of pectic substances, abound in pectin-attacking enzymes, digestion tests of extended duration give questionable results.

One precaution which is usually taken in the author's laboratory is to attempt to detect slight pectin-polygalacturonase activity by the use of sterile substrate solutions and, wherever possible, filtered solutions of the enzyme.

Since tests of long duration are considered unreliable, a property which changes greatly in the early phases of hydrolysis must be used for the detection of pectin-polygalacturonase activity. Viscosity measurements are very suitable for this purpose and have been used extensively. Care should be exercised in setting up control reaction mixtures without the enzyme, with an inactivated enzyme, or preferably with both, since some other agents or compounds present in the test material may affect viscosity.

Another property which has been found quite useful in such tests is the *colloidality* of the ethanol precipitate. To those experienced with ethanol precipitates obtained from solutions of pectin or pectinic acid which are being degraded or hydrolyzed by enzymes, the physical appearance of the ethanol precipitate is a good indication of even minute pectin-polygalacturonase action. However, this involves personal judgment and therefore such an approach should be used with caution.

It may be worth noting that during the digestion of pectinic and pectic acids by pectin-polygalacturonase (mono-) galacturonic acid does not appear in the reaction mixture until the hydrolysis has proceeded about 30%, as judged by the increase in the reducing power. Table 60 shows the results of an experiment in which the hydrolysis was followed by several qualitative tests.[1045] The Ehrlich test for galacturonic acid[1059] gave a definitely positive reaction only after hydrolysis for 24 hours. This test is therefore not suitable for the detection of minute pectin-polygalacturonase activity.

For the quantitative estimation of pectin-polygalacturonase activity any of the precipitation methods discussed above may be used if the limitations of such determinations are clearly understood. The major method now applied in research studies is the estimation of the increase in the reducing power by the Willstätter-Schudel method. The limitations and experimental difficulties encountered in the use of this method were discussed previously in detail.

[1059] F. Ehrlich, *Ber.,* **65,** 352 (1932).

TABLE 60

CHANGES WHICH OCCUR UPON DECOMPOSITION OF PECTIC ACID BY A COMMERCIAL PEC-
TINASE (PECTINOL 100 D) (ADAPTED FROM ROBOZ AND KERTESZ)

Duration of hydrolysis	Ehrlich test for galacturonic acid	Alcohol precipitate	Reducing power as galacturonic acid,[b] %	Calcium pectate,[b] %
0	Negative	+++	0	100
15 min.	Negative	+++	1.4	90
30 min.	Negative	+++	7.3	79
60 min.	Lt. yellow	++	13.2	72
90 min.	Yellow	++	21.9	62
2 hrs.	Yellow	++	30.0	55
3 hrs.	Orange	+	38.0	40
5.5 hrs.	Orange	+	59.8	19.5
7.5 hrs.	Orange	(+)[a]	72.2	11.5
12 hrs.	Orange	−	85.6	2.6
20 hrs.	Pink orange	−	90.3	—
24 hrs.	Brick red	−	91.0	—
48 hrs.	Brick red	−	100	(1.5)

[a] Precipitate not hydrophilic.
[b] Expressed in percentage of the maximum possible change.

(e) Units of Measurement

At the present time there is no generally accepted unit for the expression of pectin-polygalacturonase activity. This is understandable in view of the lack of generally accepted methods for estimating this enzyme.

Waksman and Allen[1060] described a *pectolytic unit*, which was the enzyme activity capable of hydrolyzing 1 mg. of a pectic polygalacturonide at 40°C. in 1 hour. Later the author[1061] suggested a pectin-polygalacturonase unit defined as the enzyme activity which, when 1 g. of dry enzyme material is used, results in the production of 1 mg. of reducing power increase (expressed as galacturonic acid) in 30 minutes at pH 3.5 and 30°C. It is now obvious that pectic acid should be used as the substrate. More recently Jansen and MacDonnell[1048] described a set of conditions and gave a definition of a pectin-polygalacturonase unit which may be summarized as follows:

For the assay, 1 cc. of enzyme solution is added to 99 cc. of a pectic acid solution previously adjusted to pH 4.0 and containing, in the final mixture, 0.5% pectic acid. The mixture is kept at 25°C. and 5 cc. aliquots are removed at definite time intervals and added to 0.9 cc. of a 1 M sodium carbonate solution in a glass-stoppered Erlenmeyer flask. Thereupon 5 cc. of 0.1 N iodine solution is added and the mixture is allowed to stand for exactly 20 minutes. The mixture is then acidified by the addition of 2 cc. of 2 M sulfuric acid and the residual iodine is titrated with standard thiosulfate solution. The reducing power is expressed in terms of galacturonic acid and the activity of the

[1060] S. A. Waksman and M. C. Allen, *J. Am. Chem. Soc.*, **55**, 3408 (1933).
[1061] Z. I. Kertesz, *Food Research*, **3**, 481 (1938).

enzyme is expressed in milliequivalents of reducing groups liberated from the pectic acid per minute per unit of enzyme, *i.e.*, as $(PG.u)_{cc}$. or $(PG.u)_{mg}$. or $(PG.u)_{mg.PN}$. The latter expression signifies the activity on a milligram of protein nitrogen basis.

None of these activity definitions has gained general acceptance.

3. Effect of Degree of Esterification on Pectin-Polygalacturonase Activity

Waksman and Allen[1060] observed that pectic acid was hydrolyzed about twice as fast by a mold pectin-polygalacturonase as pectinic acid. Jansen and MacDonnell[1048] investigated this subject and used a whole series of pectinic acids with ester contents ranging from 0.46 to 9.47% methoxyl as substrate for a pectin-polygalacturonase preparation from which the bulk of the pectin-methylesterase had been removed by treatment with strong acid. The results of these tests (Fig. 25) show that the

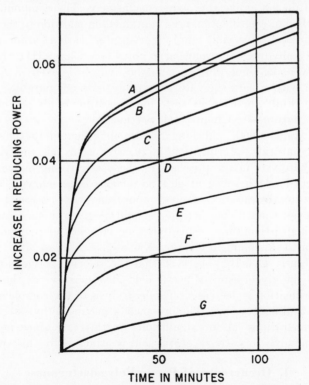

Fig. 25. Effect of the extent of esterification on the enzymic hydrolysis of pectinic acids (from Jansen and MacDonnell). Curves *A, B, C, D, E, F* and *G* were obtained on pectinic acids which contained 0.46, 1.61, 3.05, 4.70, 6.50, 8.14 and 9.47% methoxyl, respectively.

velocity of the hydrolysis increases roughly in proportion to the decrease in the extent of esterification. The effect of ester content was similar whether these low-ester pectinic acids were prepared by the use of alkali or pectin-methylesterase. Reducing power determinations were used to measure pectin-polygalacturonase activity. Weber and Deuel[1062] obtained similar results using the viscometric technic. It appears, therefore, that the true substrate of pectin-polygalacturonase is pectic acid (polygalacturonic acids).

Jansen and MacDonnell also prepared a fully esterified (methyl) polygalacturonic acid by the method described in Chap. IX, and determined the activity of pectin-polygalacturonase on this material; the hydrolysis was exceedingly slow. These authors concluded that pectin-polygalacturonase has little, if any, action on fully esterified pectic substances. While there is little doubt concerning the effect of the ester content on the velocity of the hydrolysis, the experiments on artificially methylated pectic acid do not prove the point conclusively. The compound derived by the method of esterification used contained, in addition to the esterified carboxyl groups, glycosidic methyl groups on carbon atom number 1 of the end anhydrogalacturonic acid units (see Chap. III). This might conceivably make some difference in the hydrolysis even if, upon deesterification with alkali, the rate of hydrolysis is comparable to that of pectic acid. Fully methylated (esterified) pectinic acids are not known to occur in nature (see Chapter III, Section II).

Jansen, MacDonnell, and Jang[1047] also investigated the effect of the extent of (natural) esterification in pectinic acids on the velocity of enzymic hydrolysis in the presence of the deesterifying enzyme pectin-methylesterase. With sufficient activity of this latter enzyme in the reaction mixture, the rate of hydrolysis approaches that observed for pectic acid. However, careful consideration should be given in such cases to the relatively high pH optima of deesterifying enzymes of plant origin. We shall return to this point in Chapter XV.

More recently Deuel[1063] observed that the velocity of the enzymic hydrolysis of the glycol ester of pectic acid also increases as the extent of initial esterification is decreased. The hydrolysis of the completely esterified pectic acid is very slow. The presence of pectin-methylesterase in the enzyme preparations has no significance in this case since neither this ester nor the glycerol ester of pectic acid is attacked by this enzyme.

4. Occurrence of Pectin-Polygalacturonase

For many years it was assumed that pectin-polygalacturonase is present in higher plants, especially fruits. As matters stand today, there

[1062] F. Weber and H. Deuel, *Mitt. Lebensm. Hyg.*, **36**, 368 (1945).
[1063] H. Deuel, *Helv. Chim. Acta*, **30**, 1523 (1947).

is considerable uncertainty as to whether this is the case. In apples, for example, in which well-demonstrated pectic transformations have been consistently ascribed to the presence of pectic enzymes,[1064] years of concentrated effort in the author's laboratory failed to produce conclusive evidence that pectin-polygalacturonase is a natural constituent of the apple fruit.[1065,1066] In some instances pectic transformations which might have been caused by this enzyme were observed. Almost invariably such occasions were accompanied by a simultaneous rapid increase in the number of microorganisms in the test mixture. It is only fair to state that some investigators still feel that pectin-polygalacturonase occurs in apples.[1067,1067a] Whichever point of view will be proved to be correct, it is clear that if apples do contain this enzyme, its activity is very slight.

The case of tomatoes is similarly unclear. Contrary to early reports,[1061] it is now clear that a pectolytic factor occurs in tomatoes.[1068,1069] There is considerable doubt, however, whether this enzyme is identical with pectin-polygalacturonase inasmuch as it does not seeem to be able to hydrolyze polygalacturonic acids into the monomer D-galacturonic acids but only into molecules of much larger size.[1070] This enzyme, provisionally designated as *depolymerase*,[1071] will be discussed in Section IV.

Pectin-polygalacturonase was discovered[1046,1072] in germinating barley (malt); this is perhaps the only definitely known occurrence of this enzyme in a higher plant. A further possible occurrence is in citrus fruits, but here again the information in the literature is insufficient to decide this point with certainty. The presence of a pectolytic enzyme has been reported in pollen grains,[1073] and in various commercial gums.[1074] We shall deal in Chap. XXIX with the "fermentation" of coffee and cacao beans which at times has been ascribed to enzymes occurring in the plant tissues but is now known to be the result of microbial invasion.

There are many references in the literature concerning the occurrence of pectin-polygalacturonase in microorganisms. Unfortunately, most of these investigations were conducted when the methodology of pectic en-

[1064] M. H. Branfoot (Carré), "A critical and Historical Study of the Pectic Substances of Plants," *Dept. Sci. Ind. Research Brit. Food Invest.*, Special Rept. No. 33 (1929).

[1065] Z. I. Kertesz, *Plant Physiol.*, 18, 308 (1943).

[1066] J. H. Griffin and Z. I. Kertesz, *Botan. Gaz.*, 108, 279 (1946).

[1067] C. H. Hills, *personal communication*, Sept., 28, 1948.

[1067a] M. A. Joslyn, S. Mist, and E. Lambert, *Food Technol.*, in press.

[1068] H. H. Mottern and C. H. Hills, *Ind. Eng. Chem.*, 38, 1153 (1946).

[1069] L. R. MacDonnell, E. F. Jansen, and H. Lineweaver, *Arch. Biochem.*, 6, 389 (1945).

[1070] R. J. McColloch and Z. I. Kertesz, *unpublished work*, 1948.

[1071] R. J. McColloch and Z. I. Kertesz, *Arch. Biochem.*, 17, 197 (1948).

[1072] J. J. Willaman, *Arkiv. Kemi, Mineral, Geol.*, A10, No. 3 (1928).

[1073] J. B. Paton, *Am. J. Botany*, 8, 471 (1921).

[1074] H. T. Leo, C. C. Taylor, and J. W. Lindsey, U. S. Pat. 2,380,115 (1945).

zymes was insufficiently developed. As a result, many of these reports do not stand scrutiny. For this reason, compilations of data from the literature on the presence of pectin-polygalacturonase in microorganisms are of little use and might even be misleading. A further point which weakens the significance of such tabulations is the well-known flexibility of microorganisms in forming enzymes. The composition of the medium and other conditions have a profound effect on enzyme formation. Enzyme formation can be induced, enhanced, or retarded by changing the cultural conditions.[1075] Thus, within genetic limitations, microorganisms show the capacity to be "educated." For this reason incidental cultures, as tested by most investigators, will not conclusively answer the question of the ability of the microorganism to form pectin-polygalacturonase. For example, Coles[1076] tested 500 organisms, mainly bacteria, and found that only 15 of these were capable of hydrolyzing pectinic acid. It is more than likely, however, that variations in the culture media would have increased the number of positive organisms. Bearing in mind such limitations, in Table 61 references are given to some of the reports which can be found on this subject in the literature. It may be said that the fact that an organism is listed in Table 61 is a good indication that it is capable of producing pectin-polygalacturonase; its absence from this list must not be regarded as proof to the contrary. According to Ehrlich,[1049] a *Penicillium Ehrlichii* isolated by him showed exceptionally high pectin-polygalacturonase activity, but there are no reports available in which the activity has been directly compared with the same enzyme obtained from other molds.

Cultural conditions also determine the proportion of enzyme which remains in the microorganism and that which is eluted into the nutrient solution. The variations in this respect are considerable.[1077] Phaff[1078] found that for cultures of a strain of *Penicillium chrysogenum* most of the pectin-polygalacturonase could be found in the nutrient solution.

Most yeasts are unable to hydrolyze pectic compounds. In a recent study of 143 yeast cultures representing 66 species and varieties in 15 genera, Etchells and Bell[1078a] found only 4 cultures that gave definite indication of pectin-polygalacturonase activity. These were a *Saccharomyces fragilis*, a *S. fragilis* variety, and a *S. cerevisiae*—all obtained from citrus concentrates, and unidentified yeast Y-659.

There are many observations concerning the effect of various nutrients on the formation of pectin-polygalacturonase but the relationship is far from clear. Phaff states that the use of ammonium salts is more bene-

[1075] Z. I. Kertesz, *Fermentforsch.*, **9**, 300 (1928); **10**, 36 (1928).
[1076] H. W. Coles, *Plant Physiol.*, **1**, 379 (1926).
[1077] H. R. Pithawala, *Dissertation*, Univ. of Bombay (1949).
[1078] H. J. Phaff, *Arch. Biochem.*, **13**, 67 (1947).
[1078a] J. L. Etchells and T. A. Bell, *unpublished work*, 1950.

ficial for enzyme formation than nitrates, glycocoll (glycine), or alanine. On the basis of experience with other enzymes a direct relationship between the presence of pectinic acids in the culture medium and the formation of pectin-polygalacturonase might be expected. Such an effect of the composition of the substrate has been observed by only a few authors.[1034]

See also Chapters XVI and XXIX for the pectic enzymes of microorganisms. The large-scale commercial production of pectinases containing pectin-polygalacturonase from molds is discussed in Chapter XV.

There is no evidence that human or other vertebrates produce pectin-polygalacturonase.[1079] The disappearance of ingested pectin is caused by the action of microorganisms in the large intestine (see Chapter XVII). The addition of human feces to solutions of pectinic acids causes rapid digestion of the latter, even in the presence of bactericidal agents which prevent the growth and multiplication of microorganisms.[1080]

Both the garden snail (*Helix pomatia*) and water snail (*Torbo cornutus*) were shown to contain pectin-polygalacturonase in their hepatic-pancreatic secretions.[1031,1081–1083] The pectin-polygalacturonase of snail juice is quite stable when stored with toluene at ice-chest temperatures. Apparently silkworms[1084] do not produce a pectin-polygalacturonase since ingested pectin can be recovered from the feces.

5. Preparation and Purification

Although it is likely that a great deal of experience has been accumulated about preparation and purification in connection with the commercial production of pectinases, very little of this information can be found in the literature. In the past, precipitation with ethanol was most commonly used in the separation of crude pectin-polygalacturonase preparations from the original fungal extracts.[1038] Such crude preparations usually contain many other enzymes in addition to pectin-polygalacturonase.[1085] For example, one of the commercially produced pectinases, Pectinol (see Chapter XV), was shown to contain enzymes capable of hydrolyzing maltose, sucrose, starch, inulin,[1086] modified cellulose (carboxymethylcellulose),[1087] proteins,[1088] and xylan.[1058]

[1079] J. Matus, *Ber. schweiz. bot. Ges.*, **58**, 319 (1948).

[1080] Z. I. Kertesz, *J. Nutrition*, **20**, 289 (1940).

[1081] H. Z. Hoesslin, *Kinderheilkunde*, **1**, 81 (1911).

[1082] A. C. Faberge, *Stain Technol.*, **20**, 1 (1945).

[1083] T. Mori and O. Tokaturo, *J. Agr. Chem. Soc. Japan*, **16**, 886 (1940); through *C. A.*, **35**, 4399 (1941).

[1084] T. Nakasone, *Bull. Sericulture Silk-Ind.* (Japan), **12**, 84 (1940); through *C. A.*, **35**, 3289 (1941).

[1085] Z. I. Kertesz, *J. Biol. Chem.*, **121**, 589 (1937).

[1086] V. B. Fish and R. B. Dustman, *J. Am. Chem. Soc.*, **67**, 1155 (1945).

[1087] H. Lineweaver, R. Jang, and E. F. Jansen, *Arch. Biochem.*, **20**, 137 (1949).

[1088] D. C. Carpenter and W. F. Walsh, *New York State Agr. Expt. Sta.*, Tech. Bull. No. 202 (1932).

TABLE 61
OCCURRENCE OF PECTIN-POLYGALACTURONASE IN MICROORGANISMS

Class: *Schizomycetes*

Family	Genera and species	Ref. No.
Pseudomonadaceae	*Pseudomonas* spp.: *marginalis, syringae*	1089–1091
Corynebacteriacae	*Corynebacterium sepedonicum*	1089–1091
Lactobacteriaceae	*Lactobacillus* spp.:	1092
	Micrococcus spp.:	1092
	Erwinia spp.: *phytophthorum, aroideae, solaniperda (B. krameri), caratovora (Pseudomonas destructans)*	1091,1093,1094
	Aerobacter aerogenes (A. pectinovorum)	1095
	Escherichia spp.: (varieties of the coliform group)	1096
Bacillaceae	*Bacillus* spp.: *mesentericus, subtilis, polymyxa (Bac.* or *Aerobacillus asterosporus), macerans, acetoethylicus*	1092–1094, 1097–1105,1106
	Clostridium spp.: *butyricum (Plectridium pectinovorum, Granulobacter pectinovorum, Bac. amylobacter), felsineum (Bac. felsineus), corallium,* etc.	1097,1102,1105, 1107–1114

Order	Genera and species	Ref. No.
Actinomycetales		1112,1115

Class: *Phycomycetes*

Subclass	Genera and species	Ref. No.
Oomycetes	*Pythium debaryanum*	1093,1101,1116,1117
	Phytophthora erythroseptica	1116,1117
Zygomycetes	*Mucor* spp.: *racemosus, stolonifer, piriformis, hiemalis,* etc.	1109,1118,1119
	Rhizopus spp.: *nigricans, tritici, artocarpi, chinensis, microsporus,* etc.	1038,1043,1119,1120

Class: *Ascomycetes*

Order	Genera and species	Ref. No.
Endomycetales	*Byssochlamys fulva*	1121,1122
Plectascales	*Aspergillus* spp.: *oryzae, niger,* etc.	1031,1038,1077,1101, 1119,1123–1125
	Penicillium spp.: *luteum, glaucum, citrinum, expansum, chrysogenum, notatum, Ehrlichii, (P. glaucum?),* etc.	1043,1049,1078,1101, 1123–1128
Sphaeriales	*Chaetomium globosum*	1129
	Glomerella cingulata (Gloeosporium fructigena)	1117
Pezizales	*Sclerotinia* spp.: *cinerea, minor, fructigena (Monilia fructigena), Fuckeliana (Botrytis cinerea)*	1038,1042,1043,1093, 1094,1117,1119, 1130,1131

Class: *Basidiomycetes*

Order	Genera and species	Ref. No.
Polyporales	*Lenzites sepiaria*	1132
	Stereum purpureum	1133
	Polyporus spp.	1134

Table Continued

TABLE 61 (*Continued*)
OCCURRENCE OF PECTIN-POLYGALACTURONASE IN MICROORGANISMS

Family	Genera and species	Ref. No.
	Fungi imperfecti	
	Fusarium spp.: *niveum, lycopersici, chromiophthoron, fructigenum,* etc.	1079,1116,1117,1135
	Alternaria spp.	1112,1136
	Cephalosporium spp.	1136
	Cladosporium spp.	1109
	Hormodendrum spp.	1136
	Metarrhizium spp.	1129
	Phoma spp.	1136
	Trichothecium roseum	1136

[1089] A. E. Oxford, *Nature*, **154**, 271 (1944).

[1090] M. C. Potter and M. Foster, *Centr. Bakt.*, *II*, **7**, 353 (1901).

[1091] C. Stapp, in Honamp, *Handbuch der Pflanz. Düngenlehre.* Vol. I, 1931, p. 526; quoted from ref. 1079.

[1092] S C. Werch, R. W. Jung, A. A. Day, T. E. Friedemann, and A. C. Ivy, *J. Infectious Diseases*, **70**, 231 (1942).

[1093] M. Fernando, *Ann. Botany.* **1**, 727 (1937).

[1094] D. R. Jones, *Nature*, **158**, 625 (1946).

[1095] L. A. Burkey, *Iowa State College J. Sci.*, **3**, 57 (1928).

[1096] H. W. Coles, *Plant Physiol.*, **1**, 379 (1926).

[1097] M. W. Beijerinck and A. van Delden, *Koninkl. Akad. Wetenschap. Amsterdam*, VI, **2**, 462 (1904); quoted from ref. 1079.

[1098] W. Omelianski, *Centr. Bakt.*, *II*, **12**, 33 (1904).

[1099] F. Schardinger, *Centr. Bakt.*, *II*, **14**, 772 (1905); **19**, 161 (1907).

[1100] M. W. Beijerinck, *Wis.-Natuurk. Tijd.*, **31**, 354 (1922); quoted from ref. 1079.

[1101] G. A. Pitman and W. V. Cruess, *Ind. Eng. Chem.*, **21**, 1292 (1929).

[1102] G. Ruschman, *Faserforsch.*, **1** (1923); *Forschungsdienst*, **2**, 245 (1936); quoted from ref. 1079.

[1103] F. W. Fabian and E. A. Johnson, *Michigan Agr. Expt. Sta.*, Tech. Bull. No. 157 (1938).

[1104] L. A. Allen, *Nature*, **153**, 224 (1944).

[1105] S. A. Barinova, *Microbiol. (Russ.)*, **15**, 313 (1946); quoted from ref. 1079.

[1106] T. A. Bell, J. L. Etchells, and I. D. Jones, *Food Technol.*, **4**, 157 (1950).

[1107] W. Omelianski and M. Komonowa, *Arch. sci. biol. St. Petersbourg*, **26**, 53 (1926); quoted from ref. 1079.

[1108] I. A. Makrinov and A. M. Tschischowa, *Centr. Bakt.*, *II*, **79**, 177 (1929); quoted from ref. 1079.

[1109] M. P. Korsakowa and E. A. Nikitin, *Allruss. Inst. Landw. Mikrobiol.*, **5**, 37 (1933); quoted from ref. 1079.

[1110] A. D. Orla-Jensen and A. J. Kluyver, *Centr. Bakt.*, *II*, **101**, 257 (1939); quoted from ref. 1079.

[1111] H. Rothschild, *Enzymologia*, **5**, 359 (1939).

[1112] G. Ruschman and H. Bartram, *Centr. Bakt.*, *II*, **102**, 300 (1940); **105**, 326 (1942); quoted from ref. 1079.

[1113] L. Bonnet, *Teintex*, **8**, 175 (1943); quoted from ref. 1079.

[1114] A. R. Prévot and M. Raynaud, *Compt. rend.*, **222**, 1531 (1946); quoted from ref. 1079.

[1115] A. C. Thaysen and H. J. Bunker, *Microbiology of Cellulose, Hemicellulose. Pectin and Gums.* Oxford Univ. Press, London, 1927.

[1116] B. L. Chona, *Ann. Botany*, **46**, 1035 (1932).

[1117] K. P. V. Menon, *Ann. Botany*, **48**, 187 (1934).

Bourquelot and Hérissey[1040] in their original work on pectinase (pectin-poly-galacturonase) extracted dried malt at 30–35°C. with water in the presence of chloroform for 12 hours. The filtered extract was precipitated with a 2-fold quantity of ethanol, and the precipitate was washed with ethanol and ether, and dried under vacuum. Acetone, ammonium sulfate, and ammonium phosphate were also used for the precipitation by these authors. Davison and Willaman[1088] evaporated the malt extract directly under vacuum.

Ehrlich[1049] prepared crude preparations of this enzyme in the following manner: the mold *Penicillium Ehrlichii* was grown on a mixture of yeast and malt extracts containing 2% citrus pectin. The mold was allowed to grow for 23 days at 22–25°C., whereupon the formed mycellium was ground and the whole culture autolyzed at room temperature for 24 hours in the presence of toluene. The clear filtered extract was then precipitated with 4-fold volumes of ethanol, washed with ethanol and ether, and dried in a desiccator over calcium chloride.

In a recent article describing the purification of the pectin-polygalac-turonase from a commercial fungal pectinase (Pectinol), Lineweaver, Jang, and Jansen[1087] give the following procedure:

The filtrate from a 20% extract of Pectinol 46 AP is brought to pH 0.6 with 4 N hydrochloric acid, allowed to stand for 20 minutes at 25°C., and readjusted to pH 5 with 5 N sodium hydroxide. The enzyme is then precipitated at 0.9 saturation with ammonium sulfate, filtered with the aid of diatomaceous earth (Celite), and dissolved in about one tenth of the original volume of water. The acid treatment is repeated, impurities are precipitated at 0.7 saturation with ammonium sulfate, and the residual pectin-polygalacturonase is precipitated by 0.9 saturation with ammonium sulfate. The precipitate is dissolved

[1118] L. L. Harter, *J. Agr. Research*, **30**, 961 (1925).

[1119] N. J. Proskuryakov and F. M. Ossipow, *Biochem. (Russ.)*, **4**, 50 (1939); quoted from ref. 1079.

[1120] J. L. Weimer and L. L. Harter, *Am. J. Botany*, **10**, 167 (1923).

[1121] M. Olliver and T. Rendle, *J. Soc. Chem. Ind. (London)*, **53**, 166 T (1934).

[1122] G. H. Beaven and F. Brown, *Biochem. J.*, **45**, 221 (1949).

[1123] H. Z. Gaertner, *Ver. deut. Zuckerind.*, **69**, 233 (1919); quoted from ref. 1079.

[1124] A. Mehlitz, *Konserven-Ind.*, **17**, 306 (1930).

[1125] C. R. Fellers, J. A. Clague, and R. L. France, *Massachusetts Agr. Expt. Sta.*, Bull. No. 293 (1933).

[1126] Z. I. Kertesz, *New York State Agr. Expt. Sta.*, Bull. No. 589 (1930).

[1127] J. J. Willaman and Z. I. Kertesz, *New York State Agr. Expt. Sta.*, Tech. Bull. No. 178 (1931).

[1128] L. Jirak and M. Niederle, *Vorratspflege u. Lebensmittelforsch.*, **4**, 515 (1941).

[1129] N. W. Stuart and S. L. Emsweller, *Science*, **98**, 569 (1943).

[1130] E. Gäumann and E. Böhni, *Helv. Chim. Acta*, **30**, 24, 1591 (1947).

[1131] E. M. Popova, *Microbiology (U. S. S. R.)*, **4**, 243 (1935).

[1132] S. M. Zeller, *Ann. Missouri Botan. Garden*, **3**, 439 (1916).

[1133] J. K. Mayo, *New Phytologist*, **24**, 162 (1925).

[1134] S. R. Bose, *Ergeb. Enzymforsch.*, **8**, 267 (1938).

[1135] C. P. Sideris, *Phytopathology*, **14**, 481 (1924).

[1136] W. H. Fuller and A. G. Norman, *J. Bact.*, **50**, 667 (1946).

and dialyzed in the cold for not more than 24 hours if Cellophane membranes are used. The traces of cellulase present may cause the Cellophane to weaken and break. Small aliquots of lead acetate are then added and the suspension centrifuged after each addition until it is evident that most of the color has been precipitated. The filtrate is now freed from excess lead by the addition of dipotassium phosphate. Addition of too much lead acetate will cause excessive precipitation of the pectin-polygalacturonase with the impurities. In such cases the precipitate may be suspended in water and treated with phosphate; the filtrate is then dialyzed and treated with lead as was the original.

The enzyme yield obtained by this method was only 3–5% and apparently the procedure was not directly applicable to Pectinol 45 AP. Lineweaver, Jang, and Jansen therefore suggested a second procedure which gave much better results with this latter crude enzyme. This method may be summarized as follows:

A cold (5°C.) 5% extract of the crude enzyme is adjusted to pH 3 with 4 N hydrochloric acid and stirred in the ice bath with freshly washed alginic acid for about 5 minutes. The amount of alginic acid used is 0.1 g. per unit of pectin-polygalacturonase activity (see above). Next the acid on which the enzyme is adsorbed is collected by centrifugation in the cold. Impurities and a trace of the enzyme are eluted by washing with half the original volume of cold 1 M sodium chloride. The eluate, which has a pH of 2.2–2.3, is immediately adjusted to approximately pH 5 to prevent inactivation of the pectin-polygalacturonase. The elution is repeated 2 or 3 times with convenient volumes of cold 1 M sodium chloride. To inactivate the pectin-methylesterase still present in the solution, the combined eluates are adjusted to pH 3.2, allowed to stand under toluene at room temperature (about 23°C.) for 18 hours, and then the pH is readjusted to 5. The solution is dialyzed and dried by lyophilization (see Chap. VI) unless the adsorption cycle is to be repeated. The enzyme yield obtained by this method was 42%.

Further work in applying modern technics to the purification of pectin-polygalacturonase is much needed. A hopeful approach might be paper chromatography, as noted by Reid.[1137] The commercial production of pectinases will be discussed in Chapter XV.

6. Effect of pH on Pectin-Polygalacturonase Action

The pH optimum of fungal pectin-polygalacturonase (Pectinol) has been found in many experiments to be in the neighborhood of 3.5.[1032,1086] The literature contains data which indicate optimum ranges from 3.0 to about 5.0 with a few extremes reported by Mehlitz and Scheuer[1057] of 4.5–6.3, Ehrlich, Guttman, and Haensel[1138] of 4–6, and Mehlitz[1124] of

[1137] W. W. Reid, Nature, 166, 569 (1950).
[1138] F. Ehrlich, R. Guttman, and R. Haensel, Biochem. Z., 281, 93 (1935).

4-7. The explanation for this wide variation consists mainly in three facts. First of all, many of the older measurements were made with pectinic acids and not pectic acid which we now know to be the true substrate of this enzyme. Second, throughout the years there were variations in the experimental methods used by the various authors. Third, the possible presence of deesterifying enzymes (changing pectinic acid to pectic acid) might have had a profound effect on the pH optimum found. Since many authors used pectinic acid substrate and unpurified pectinase preparations, simultaneous action of the two enzymes must have been common. Viscosity measurements were often also used in such work, in which case the deesterification not only altered the substrate but also lowered the pH of the reaction mixture, changing the viscosity characteristics of the solution (see Chapter VII) irrespective of hydrolysis.

Jansen and MacDonnell[1048] and Lineweaver, Jang, and Jansen[1087] used pH 4.0 in their studies of this enzyme and it may be assumed that this has been ascertained to be the pH optimum. Recently Pallmann, Matus, Deuel, and Weber[1139] reported a pH optimum of 3.8 for a pectinase when using pectinic acid substrate and 4.2 when using pectic acid. With a pectinic acid of 72% esterification, Matus[1079] found the pH optimum at 3.9.

On the basis of this information, it is safe to assume that the pH optimum of fungal pectin-polygalacturonase preparations is, under most conditions, in the range of 3.5-4.0. Bacterial pectin-polygalacturonases seem to have much higher pH optima.[1089,1093] The water-soluble pectin-polygalacturonase of *Pseudomonas* is very active at pH 7-8, while that of *Penicillium chrysogenum* is rapidly inactivated at such pH values.[1034] Phaff[1140] found the pH optimum of the latter enzyme at 3.7.

7. Temperature Effects

Like most enzymes, the pectin-polygalacturonase of fungal pectinases in the form of a dry powder is quite resistant to heat. Matus[1079] reports that in one experiment heating to 80°, 90°, and 100°C. for 3 hours reduced the activity of this enzyme by 7, 30, and 85%, respectively.

The instability of pectin-polygalacturonase in water solution (suspension) is well appreciated. When kept at 55°C. for 30 minutes or at pH 4.0 for 3 hours at 50°C.[1079] complete loss of activity may result. When stored overnight, pectinase solutions usually lose 20-40% of their activity,

[1139] H. Pallmann, J. Matus, H. Deuel, and F. Weber, *Rec. trav. chim.*, **69**, 633 (1946).
[1140] H. J. Phaff, "The Biochemistry of the Exocellular Pectinase of *Penicillium chrysogenum*," *Dissertation*, Univ. of California. Berkeley, 1943; quoted from ref. 1034.

even if the enzyme solution is placed in an ice chest. Apparently purified preparations are even more sensitive to heat.[1087] The resistance to heating is much enhanced by the addition of over 80 milligram per cent of sodium alginate, gelatin, glycerol, and of the glycerol and glycol esters of pectic acid.[1079] Sucrose in concentrations of more than 8% was shown to exert a similar protective action.

The temperature optimum of an enzyme is a hypothetical value greatly dependent on the experimental conditions, especially the length of heating time.[1030] When short periods of heating are used the temperature optimum appears to be much higher than when longer periods of exposure are applied. On this account, the temperature optima given in the literature for pectin-polygalacturonase range from 30° to 55°C. Using a reaction period of 3 hours, Matus[1079] found the temperature optimum at 50°C.

8. Activation, Inhibition, and Inactivation

Pallmann, Matus, Deuel, and Weber[1139] found that fungal pectin-polygalacturonase is activated by the addition of alkali chlorides. However, these investigators used a commercial pectinase preparation and pectinic acid as substrate. Because of the known activating effect of alkali chlorides on the deesterifying enzyme likely present, it is difficult to say whether the observed activation of pectin-polygalacturonase action was direct or caused by enhancement of the simultaneous deesterification, which in turn facilitated pectin-polygalacturonase action. At pH 3.1 and in 0.1 N concentrations, the following order of activation was observed:

$$Li < Na < K < Rb < Cs$$

The effect of polyvalent ions on pectinase action is further complicated by the effect of such ions on the solubility (dispersibility) of pectic and pectinic acids. Chona[1116] observed that potato juice inhibited the pectinase of certain microorganisms and explained this effect on the basis of the formation of more insoluble substrate complexes. Manville, Reithel, and Yamada,[1141] Loconti and Kertesz,[1050] and Jansen, MacDonnell, and Jang[1047] found that calcium and magesium chlorides had a similar inhibitory effect in the case of low-ester pectinic acids and pectic acid. However, it seems that the inhibition might be typical of regions of esterification only where, under the experimental conditions, the substrates form insoluble complexes with these cations. Matus[1079] found that in the case of a pectinic acid of 72% esterification a series of chlo-

[1141] I. A. Manville, F. J. Reithel, and P. M. Yamada, *J. Am. Chem. Soc.*, **61**, 2973 (1939).

rides composed of cations of increasing valences showed increasing activation:

$$Na^+ < Ca^{++} < Al^{+++} < Th^{++++}$$

The increase in activity was especially marked in substituting the bivalent Ca^{++} for the monovalent Na^+. However, this author used an unpurified commercial pectinase and therefore enzymic deesterification might have occurred simultaneously, bringing into play all the complicating factors noted above. Further work with purified enzymes and well-defined substrates is needed to clarify this matter of ionic activation.

Tannin was reported to inhibit pectin-polygalacturonase action[1142] but later work could not confirm this observation.[1143] Mehlitz and Maass[1142] used formaldehyde for the rapid and complete inactivation of this enzyme. The claimed inactivation of fungal pectin-polygalacturonase by glycine[1144] could not be confirmed.[1070] The detergent alkyl aryl sulfonate, which inactivates pectin-methylesterase[1145] easily, is much less effective as an inactivator of pectin-polygalacturonase.[1070] The addition of galacturonic acid[1079] or of partially hydrolyzed pectic acid[1047] to reaction mixtures composed of pectic acid and fungal pectin-poly-galacturonase has no effect on the velocity of the reaction.

Exposure to high acidity is as injurious to this enzyme as to most others. At pH 0.6 and 25°C. a solution of pectin-polygalacturonase lost 90% of its activity in 20 minutes; subsequent treatments under the same conditions caused only slow further loss.[1083] Pectin-polygalacturonase in 0.5 N sodium hydroxide is completely inactivated at 20°C. in 40 minutes.[1079] Therefore, making the reaction mixtures alkaline (as in the determination of the reducing power by the Willstätter-Schudel method) is a convenient way of stopping enzyme action.

9. Mode of Action and Specificity

The mode of action of pectin-polygalacturonase is far from clear. The fact that the enzyme acts faster on pectic acid than on pectinic acids does provide a certain extent of insight into its probable action mechanism. Jansen and MacDonnell[1047] suggested that this enzyme requires at least two adjacent free carboxyl groups in order to hydrolyze pectic polygalacturonides. Matus[1079] contests this statement and cites evidence that completely esterified pectic acid is hydrolyzed (although much more slowly), and that complete hydrolysis of apparently still

---

[1142] A. Mehlitz and H. Maass, Z. Untersuch. Lebensm., 70, 180 (1935).
[1143] F. Weber, J. Matus, and E. Schubert, Schweiz. landw. Monatsh., 25, 209 (1947).
[1144] R. Otto and G. Winkler, German Pat. 729,667 (1942).
[1145] R. J. McColloch and Z. I. Kertesz, Arch. Biochem., 13, 217 (1947).

partially esterified pectinic acids has also been accomplished. This latter author feels that the whole picture is confused by the possible existence of different polygalacturonases, a point which will be discussed in Section III. On the basis of results obtained in the paper partition chromatography of pectin digests, Jermyn and Tomkins[1145a] believe that the hydrolysis of pectic polyuronides by pectin-polygalacturonidase proceeds at random scission rather than by removing either (mono) galacturonic acid or small polygalacturonic acid units from the ends of the polymer chains.

Matus[1079] has also demonstrated that fungal pectin-polygalacturonase seems to possess increased affinity toward polygalacturonic acids of high average molecular weights. Some of these results are shown in Table 62. Although this experiment is somewhat reduced in significance because of the different substrate concentrations used, the drop in the velocity of hydrolysis is impressive.

Very little work has been done thus far with pectin-polygalacturonase of such purity that specificity observations are of much meaning. Recent experiments of Lineweaver, Jang, and Jansen[1087] are important in this

TABLE 62

EFFECT OF (AVERAGE) MACROMOLECULAR SIZE ON VELOCITY OF PECTIC ACID (SODIUM PECTATE) HYDROLYSIS BY PECTIN-POLYGALACTURONASE (ADAPTED FROM MATUS)[a]

Specific viscosity of substrate solution	Sodium pectate in reaction mixture, milliequiv.	Comparative hydrolysis from reducing power measurements[b]
0.596	1000	62
0.312	1070	55
0.244	1130	52
0.143	1260	45
0.042	1620	29
0.014	1920	19
0.014	2060	17

[a] Pectic acid samples prepared by enzymic hydrolysis.
[b] In 20 hours at pH 3.9 and 25°C.

respect. A purified pectin-polygalacturonase prepared by these authors failed to hydrolyze the following substrates: methyl-D-galacturonic acid; glucuronic acid compounds such as mesquite gum; oxidized cellulose, carboxymethylcellulose, and hyaluronic acid; a polymannuronic acid compound like alginic acid; glucose and glucosamine-containing compounds like starch, sucrose, maltose, ovomucoid, and heparin; fructose-containing compounds like sucrose and inulin, and pentose-containing

[1145a] M. A. Jermyn and R. G. Tomkins, *Biochem. J.*, **47**, 437 (1950).

compounds like gum ghatti, mesquite gum, gum arabic, and gum trag-acanth. Furthermore, this purified enzyme failed to hydrolyze *Pneumococcus* polysaccharide Type I which contains some 60% anhydro-D-galacturonic acid units of apparently the same configuration and ring structure as those which exist in pectic substances. Thus pectin-polygalacturonase is not a simple glycosidase but an enzyme specific for the polygalacturonide structures of pectic substances. This unusual qualitative specificity is the reason for the retention of the specific term *pectin-polygalacturonidase*. It will be shown below that further complications in the terminology may be introduced if the now suspected size or structural specificity of pectin-polygalacturonases can be definitely established.

During the enzymic decomposition of pectinic and pectic acids a small amount of water-insoluble precipitate often forms in the reaction mixture. Some investigators attach definite significance to the formation of this precipitate.[1031,1060] It is likely that it only represents some impurities from the substrate although this has not been clearly established.[1032]

III. PECTIC ACID "DEPOLYMERASE"

Repeated references have been made in earlier sections to the presence in tomatoes of a pectolytic factor different from pectin-polygalacturonase. Because of the importance of this subject in tomato technology (see Chapter XXVII) and because of the unusual behavior of this enzyme, a summary of our present knowledge will be presented.

Early tests in the author's laboratory[1061] to determine the presence of pectolytic enzymes in tomatoes gave mainly negative results. These tests were made at pH values now known to have been too low to allow the pectolytic factor of tomatoes to exert its activity. Later tests by other investigators[1069,1146,1147] proved that a pectolytic enzyme, thought by some to be identical with pectin-polygalacturonase, is present in macerated tomato tissue. Tests with tomato macerates and salt extracts from tomato macerates[1071] indicated that this enzyme has a fairly sharp pH optimum at 4.5 and that it is activated by sodium chloride. It is almost entirely without action on pectinic acids but very active on pectic acid, the difference being much more pronounced than in the case of fungal pectin-polygalacturonase. It is clear that the activity of this enzyme on tomato pectinic acids in tomato macerates depends on the simultaneous presence of a deesterifying enzyme.[1148]

[1146] H. H. Mottern and C. H. Hills, *Ind. Eng. Chem.,* 38, 1153 (1946).

[1147] R. J. McColloch, "An Electrophoretic Investigation of Some Pectic Enzymes," *Dissertation,* Kansas State College, Manhattan, Kansas, 1948.

[1148] R. J. McColloch and Z. I. Kertesz, *Food Technol.,* 3, 94 (1949).

It seems, however, that the nature of this enzyme differs from that of the fungal enzyme in more fundamental aspects than that of pH optimum. When the relationship between the disappearance of calcium pectate precipitate and the increase in reducing power during the action of this enzyme on pectic acid was studied, it became clear that the tomato enzyme caused the complete disappearance of fractions precipitable as calcium pectate at much lower reducing power values than fungal pectin-polygalacturonase.[1070] Even more important, hydrolysis by the tomato enzyme proceeded only to what appears to be partial degradation and further addition of the enzyme did not result in an increased extent of hydrolysis. Qualitative tests for galacturonic acid in the reaction mixture were negative. However, the addition of fungal pectin-polygalacturonase results in the rapid hydrolysis of the polygalacturonic acids to the monomer galacturonic acid. Thus, the tomato enzyme seems to be either specific for large polygalacturonic acid molecules or to cause some type of fissures different from that effected by the fungal enzyme. On the basis of these observations, the pectolytic factor of tomatoes has been provisionally named pectic acid *depolymerase*.[1071]

The thermal behavior of this tomato pectolytic factor is also different from that of fungal pectin-polygalacturonase.[1071] Upon being heated in 10% salt solution the enzyme is rapidly inactivated to the extent of about 85% but further inactivation proceeds very slowly. After an hour of heating in a boiling water bath the enzyme still retains 3–4% activity and traces of activity have been observed even after two hours of heating. The use of saline solutions may have something to do with the retention of this activity. It was possible to show the presence of this depolymerase in commercially packed canned tomatoes and tomato juice.[1148]

The existence of separate enzymes for the degradation of pectic polyuronides of different molecular sizes is not as surprising as it might first appear to be. Reference is made, for example, to the "limit dextrins" formed upon the hydrolysis of starch.[1149]

If the regular rhythm of anhydrogalacturonic acids connected by 1,4 glycosidic bondages[1150-1152] is interrupted by either different linkages or different nonuronide units, it would seem most reasonable to assume that a different enzyme is responsible for the fissure in the molecule

[1149] K. Myrbäck, in W. W. Pigman and M. L. Wolfrom, *Advances in Carbohydrate Chemistry*. Vol. III, Academic Press, New York, 1948, p. 251.

[1150] E. L. Hirst and J. K. N. Jones, in W. W. Pigman and M. L. Wolfrom, *Advances in Carbohydrate Chemistry*. Vol. II, Academic Press, New York, 1946, p. 235.

[1151] R. M. McCready, N. Jeung, and W. D. Maclay, paper given at the Portland, Oregon, meeting of the American Chemical Society, Sept. 13, 1948.

[1152] E. F. Jansen, L. R. MacDonnell, and W. H. Ward, *J. Biol. Chem.*, 21, 149 (1949).

at such places. As was mentioned in Chapter III, there is a distinct possibility that such structural irregularities occur in pectic substances. There are also various observations in the literature which indicate the existence of a separate depolymerase or of size-specific polygalacturonases. Jansen and MacDonnell[1048] observed that two rather distinct phases occur during the hydrolysis of pectic acid, but were able to show that the change in the rate of the reaction after the initial hydrolysis was not caused by the inhibitory action of reaction products. Matus[1079] also observed irregularities in the course of hydrolysis which seem to indicate the action of two types of enzymes during the hydrolysis. Since the appearance of the first report on depolymerase from this laboratory, Luh and Phaff[1153] reported the presence in the yeast *Saccharomyces fragilis* of an enzyme capable of hydrolyzing only 11% of the glycosidic bonds of pectic acid. This enzyme had a pH optimum in the range of 3.4–4.0. Finally, a recent paper by Beaven and Brown[1122] describes a pectolytic enzyme obtained from cultures of *Byssochlamis fulva*. This mold is remarkable for the abnormally high heat resistance of its ascospores, and because it can grow under greatly reduced oxygen tension such as exists in canned or bottled fruit products. The enzyme which was prepared was able to reduce the viscosity of a citrus pectin solution without any substantial increase in the reducing power and thus the enzyme may again be regarded as a depolymerase. Reid[1154] thought that the results of Beaven and Brown were due simply to the low pectin-polygalacturonase activity of their preparation, although in a later paper[1058] the possibility that such a hydrolytic enzyme different from pectin-polygalacturonase might exist is admitted on theoretical grounds.

Elucidation of the action mechanism of such pectolytic enzymes is of great importance, not only to clarify the methods of hydrolysis, but also because it is more than likely that by their use important insight into the structure of pectic polygalacturonides can be obtained.

IV. PECTIN-METHYLESTERASE (PECTASE)

1. Definition and Nomenclature

Pectin-methylesterase[1051] is the enzyme which catalyzes the hydrolysis of the methyl ester groups in pectinic acids and pectin. The older term *pectase*,[1155] once universally used for this enzyme, is now used only by a few workers. The reason for the abandonment of this designation lies

[1153] B. S. Luh and H. J. Phaff, paper given at the American Chemical Society meetings, April, 1948.

[1154] W. W. Reid, *Nature*, 166, 76 (1950).

[1155] E. Frémy, *J. pharm. chim.*, 26, 292 (1940).

in the definition of pectase as the enzyme held responsible for the formation of a gel from solutions of pectinic acids in the presence of polyvalent ions (calcium).[1156] It is now clear that the gel formation itself is a reaction which has nothing to do with the enzyme action, and that under some conditions gel formation might not occur at all in spite of very active deesterification.[1032] In order to divorce this physical phenomenon from the enzyme action, designations other than pectase have been sought. The term *pectin methoxylase* suggested some time ago by the author[1085] has now also been abandoned. Most workers in the field either use the term pectin-methylesterase or pectinesterase.[1157] It seems that on account of the extreme specificity of this enzyme (see below) the designation pectin-methylesterase is more desirable and will therefore be used here. Depending on the choice of terminology, the abbreviations PM (pectin-methylesterase) and PE (pectinesterase) are frequently used for this enzyme.

This enzyme was first described by Frémy[1155] in 1840 as responsible for the coagulation of soluble pectin into a gel in the presence of calcium salts. The discovery of the presence of methyl ester groups in pectinic acids[1158] clarified the chemistry of the reaction involved. Further work by Bertrand and Mallèvre[1159] showed that other alkali earth metals may be substituted for calcium, and Tutin[1160] conclusively demonstrated the similarity between the action of alkali and pectin-methylesterase in deesterifying pectinic acids.

2. Determination of Activity

The presence of pectin-methylesterase activity in a solution can be easily detected by the following simple test.[1161] 1 cc. of the solution or extract is added to 25 cc. of slightly acid pectin solution and the mixture is titrated with 0.1 N sodium or potassium hydroxide in the presence of methyl red indicator until the mixture loses its last pink tint from one drop of alkali. In the presence of active pectin-methylesterase, the mixture will turn red in less than ten minutes (at 30°C.).

There are several types of methods which have been used for the quantitative determination of pectin-methylesterase activity. One of these is the formation of a gel in a solution of pectinic acid containing a trace of added calcium chloride at about pH 6. As noted previously, this method is qualitatively inconclusive and unsuitable for quantitative

[1156] J. J. Willaman, *Minn. Studies in Biol. Sci.*, 6, 333 (1927).
[1157] H. Lineweaver and G. A. Ballou, *Arch. Biochem.*, 6, 373 (1945).
[1158] T. Fellenberg, *Biochem. Z.*, 85, 45 (1918).
[1159] G. Bertrand and A. Mallèvre, *Compt. rend.*, 119, 1013 (1894); 121, 726 (1895).
[1160] F. Tutin, *Biochem. J.*, 15, 494 (1921); 17, 83 (1923).
[1161] Z. I. Kertesz, *Food Research*, 4, 113 (1939).

estimation of the enzyme; it will therefore not be described here in further detail.

There are dependable chemical means for following the reaction, either by determining the changes in ester content, the increase in free carboxyl groups,[1085,1158] or by estimating the amount of methanol liberated.[1044,1162] Of these possibilities, the estimation of free carboxyl groups produced is used most extensively although a few workers still use the more elaborate method of estimating the methanol which is produced. A manometric method has also been described.[1163,1164]

(a) Determination by Increase in Free Carboxyl Groups

This procedure[1085] was described by the author in 1937 and was subsequently modified by Fish and Dustman,[1086] Lineweaver and Ballou,[1157] and McColloch and Kertesz.[1145] The original method consists of maintaining a solution containing pectin, the enzyme, and methyl red indicator at a pH of about 6.2 for 30 minutes. The enzyme action produces free carboxyl groups and 0.1 N sodium hydroxide is added at frequent intervals to maintain the pH as constant as possible. The now generally available electrical pH meters with glass electrodes offer much easier operation and better control. The following procedure, used in the author's laboratory, incorporates the desirable features of most subsequent modifications:

50 to 100 cc. of a solution of a good grade of commercial pectin containing at least 8% methoxyl (on polyuronide basis) is made 0.1 N with respect to sodium chloride in a 250-cc. beaker provided with a suitable stirring arrangement. The extension electrodes of a good pH meter are inserted and the mixture is titrated with 0.1 N sodium hydroxide to the pH desired for the experiment. (The matter of pH optimum is complicated and will be discussed later. Suffice it to say here that both the origin of the enzyme and the quantity and kind of salts present in the final mixture will influence the pH optimum.) The amount of base used in this adjustment is noted. The solution containing the enzyme is then added and the timer started. As the enzyme acts, the pH of the solution drops and is constantly adjusted to the original value by the dropwise addition of the base with constant stirring. At the end of the reaction period (usually 15, or at most 30, minutes) the amount of base consumed is noted and the mixture is rapidly titrated to pH 7.5, the equivalent point of pectinic acid, and the quantity of base used is again noted. A blank value is obtained by titrating an identical mixture of substrate and heat-inactivated enzyme to pH 7.5. The total base consumed during the reaction minus the base consumed by the blank gives the consumption of alkali due to pectin-methylesterase activity.

[1162] M. Holden, Biochem. J., 40, 103 (1946).
[1163] F. Kiermeier, Ann., 561, 232 (1948).
[1164] G. B. Mills, Biochem. J., 44, 302 (1949).

A further improvement of this method is the application of some detergent for the quick and complete inactivation of the enzyme at the end of the reaction period but before the reaction mixture is titrated to pH 7.5. For instance, the addition of 2 cc. of a 1% solution of Nacconol NRSF (Swerl) accomplishes this inactivation. The addition of Nacconol does not affect the titration and its use affords considerable advantage in that it prevents any enzyme action which might occur during the final titration. Otherwise the final titration must be made in haste and there is therefore danger of overshooting the very sharp end point. This is of little significance with mold pectin-methylesterase since, contrary to the behavior of the enzyme of higher plants, the activity of fungal pectin-methylesterase drops rapidly as the pH is raised above 5.0.

Since pectinic acids are rapidly deesterified in alkaline solutions (see Chapter VII), the determination of pectin-methylesterase in solutions at pH values exceeding 8.0 is of doubtful accuracy and meaning. The pH limit at which the reaction becomes unreliable cannot be set too sharply since experimental conditions such as the reaction temperature[1165] or the presence of salts will affect it.

(b) Determination by Estimation of Methanol

This method, described by Fellenberg,[1158] is more laborious and has been used only to a limited extent. The methanol split off by the enzyme is distilled and then determined, usually by means of colorimetric methods (see Chap. VIII). However, the distillation is a rather tedious operation, and in the subsequent colorimetric determination of ethanol difficulties are often experienced because of the presence in the distillate of other compounds in addition to the methanol.[1162] A further complication is that the pH of the mixture changes during the reaction. This can be counteracted in part by the use of buffers in the reaction mixture. The use of buffer mixtures is scarcely free from objections and their presence in the reaction mixture makes studies of salt activation—a very important matter with this enzyme—difficult. It would seem that the direct titration method described above offers considerable advantages both in convenience and accuracy over estimation of the methanol.

(c) Units of Measurement

Methods of expressing pectin-methylesterase action in terms of activity units suffer from uncertainties concerning the order of the reaction.[1166] The literature contains statements to the effect that the reaction is of

---

[1165] H. R. Pithawala, G. R. Savur, and A. Sreenivasan, *Arch. Biochem.*, **17**, 235 (1948).

[1166] R. Speiser, C. R. Eddy, and C. H. Hills, *J. Phys. Chem.*, **49**, 563 (1945).

zero[1157] or first order,[1085] while recent work[1167] seems to indicate that the reaction might be of zero order for the initial 40 or 50% of the hydrolysis but deviates from this afterward. All investigators emphasize that velocity measurements must be made during the initial phases of deesterification. While the exact reasons for this behavior are not known, it is possible that the influence of deesterification on the solubility (dispersibility) of the substrate might be a cause for the variations. Simultaneous hydrolysis of the polyuronide structure by pectin-polygalacturonase also affects the velocity of deesterification.[1047]

At the present time there are a number of different units of activity used for this enzyme. One of these[1085] defines the unit of pectin-methylesterase activity (PMU) as the milligrams of methoxyl split off by 1 g. or 1 cc. of the enzyme at pH 6.0 and 30°C. in 30 minutes. According to a more recent definition,[1157] one enzyme unit [PE.u] is the quantity of enzyme which, at 30°C. and at the optimum pH, will catalyze the hydrolysis of pectinic acid at an initial rate of 1 milliequivalent of ester bonds per minute in the presence of 0.15 M sodium chloride. A 0.5% solution of citrus pectin containing 8–11% methoxyl should be used. 1 PMU equals 930 [PE.u]. Thus, one advantage of PMU is that activities can be expressed most often as whole numbers. Another activity unit for this enzyme is defined as the amount of enzyme which will liberate, in 1 minute at pH 8.0 and 20°C., 32 mg. of methanol from pectinic acid dissolved in 0.1 M phosphate buffer solution.[1162] There is little choice between these units. It is clear, however, that the activity measurement should be performed at the pH of maximum activity and in the presence of ions which will effect maximum activation of the enzyme.

All the above expressions may be used to define the enzyme activity on a weight or volume basis. Also, some investigators express activities on the basis of total or protein N content of the enzyme preparations.[1157]

3. Occurrence of Pectin-Methylesterase

This enzyme occurs commonly in the roots, stems, leaves, and fruits of many higher plants and is also produced by microorganisms.[1085,1168–1169] In higher plants, or at least in macerates,[1085] pectin-methylesterase is usually strongly adsorbed on the water-insoluble cellular components,[1170] and press juices and extracts often contain only a fraction of the total amount of this enzyme present in the tissue.[1061] This fact, coupled with almost general use of the *gel test*, makes older information on the occurrence of this enzyme of little value. Until recently, it was

[1167] C. H. Hills and H. H. Mottern, *J. Biol. Chem.*, **168**, 651 (1947).
[1168] J. J. Willaman, *Botan. Gaz.*, **70**, 221 (1920).
[1169] E. J. Calesnick, C. H. Hills, and J. J. Willaman, *Arch. Biochem.*, **28**, 433 (1950).
[1170] J. J. Willaman and C. H. Hills, U. S. Pat. 2,358,429 (1944).

generally assumed that pectin-methylesterase at times occurs in higher plants together with pectin-polygalacturonase, but at the time of writing this is doubtful. This was discussed early in this Chapter. Pectolytic factors, however, do occur in some plants together with pectin-methylesterase, as in the case of the tomato fruit where a pectolytic factor now designated as depolymerase seems to accompany pectin-methylesterase. There are references to the presence of this enzyme in apples,[1067a,1171] but efforts in the author's laboratory have failed to give clear-cut evidence that pectin-methylesterase is a natural constituent of this fruit.[1070] Without any claim to completeness, some of the substantiated reports of the occurrence of pectin-methylesterase in higher plants are listed in Table 63. Sprouting legumes are also a rich source of this enzyme.[1172]

TABLE 63

OCCURRENCE OF PECTIN-METHYLESTERASE IN SOME PLANTS

Plant	Remarks	Ref. No.
Alfalfa (*Medicago sativa* L.)	High activity	1155,1157
Beaked parsley (*Chareophyllum sylvestre* L.)	—	1162
Black currants (*Rubus nigrum* L.)	—	1173
Carrot roots (*Daucus carota* L.)	—	1044
Castor beans (*Ricinus communis* L.)	In a lipase preparation	1174
Cherries (*Prunus cerasus*)	—	1142
Citrus fruit: grapefruit (*Citrus maxima* Mer.), lemon (*C. limonum* Risso), and oranges (*C. aurantium* L. and *C. sinensis* L. Osbeck)	High activity, especially in flavedo and albedo	1069,1175
Drumstick (*Moringa oleifera*) leaves	—	1077
Eggplant (*Solanum melongea* L.) fruit	—	1176
Elder (*Sambucus nigra*) leaves	—	1162
Gooseberries (*Ribes grossularia* L.)	—	1173
Lilac (*Syringa vulgaris* L.) leaves	—	1177
Nightshade (*Solanum dulcamara* L.) leaves	—	1162
Potato (*Solanum tuberosum* L.) leaves	—	1162
Red currants (*Ribes rubrum* L.)	—	1173
Tobacco (*Nicotiana tabacum* L.) leaves and stems	High activity even after curing and drying	1032,1178
Tomatoes (*Lycopersicum esculentum* L.) fruit and leaves	High activity in both	1061,1145,1162
White clover (*Trifolium repens* L.)	High activity	1179

[1171] H. S. Owens, R. M. McCready, and W. D. Maclay, *Ind. Eng. Chem.*, 36, 936 (1944).

[1172] R. Paul and R. H. Grandseigne, German Pat. 545,546 (1929); through *C. A.*, 26, 3533 (1932).

[1173] H. v. Euler and O. Svanberg, *Biochem. Z.*, 100, 271 (1919).

[1174] Z. I. Kertesz, *J. Am. Chem. Soc.*, 55, 2605 (1933).

[1175] L. R. MacDonnell, R. Jang, E. F. Jansen, and H. Lineweaver, *Arch. Biochem.*, 28, 260 (1950).

[1176] J. J. Willaman, H. H. Mottern, C. H. Hills, and G. L. Baker, U. S. Pat. 2,358,430 (1944).

[1177] N. G. Ball, *Sci. Proc. Roy. Dublin Soc.*, 1915, 14.

[1178] C. Neuberg and M. Kobel, *Biochem. Z.*, 190, 232 (1927).

[1179] A. Mehlitz, *Biochem. Z.*, 221, 217 (1930).

In a study of the influence of fertilizers on the pectin-methylesterase of tobacco leaves, Holden and Tracey[1180] found that when nitrogen is supplied to the plant the amount of enzyme present in the leaves is increased, while the opposite effect was observed with phosphorus fertilizer. The activity of this enzyme in the leaves of plants infected with tobacco-mosaic virus showed no significant change when the results were calculated on a dry matter basis, but showed a slight increase when computed on the basis of the nitrogen content of the tissue.[1181] Treatment with 2,4-D (2,4-dichlorophenoxyacetic acid) increased the pectin-methylesterase activity in the stems and leaves of red kidney bean plants.[1182]

As Phaff and Joslyn[1034] remark, it is not surprising that the pectin-methylesterase of microbial origin was not discovered until long after its occurrence in higher plants had been established. Microorganisms, as mentioned earlier, very often produce active pectin-polygalacturonase, and the presence of this latter enzyme in the material to be tested by the *pectase test* may entirely prevent the formation of a gel. Willaman[1168] reported the presence of this enzyme in the mold *Sclerotinia cinerea*, and with improved methods of estimation it became clear that pectin-methyl-esterase commonly accompanies pectin-polygalacturonase in various microorganisms. The presence of pectin-methylesterase has been established in commercial fungal pectinases,[1067a, 1086,1145,1169] however, a sample of molds mycelia used in the manufacture of citric acid (*Penicillium citrinum* and other *Penicillium* species) was devoid of this enzyme.[1045]

4. Preparation and Purification

The methods used by investigators until about a decade ago for the preparation and purification of this enzyme now have little significance. It is well established that the bulk of pectin-methylesterase is usually strongly adsorbed on water-insoluble cellular constituents[1170] and, therefore, press juices and water extracts recover only a fraction of the enzyme activity originally present in the tissue and in the macerates. In the methods described by Mehlitz[1179] and Paul and Grandseigne,[1172] for example, press juice from alfalfa or a water extract from sprouting legumes was used. Holden[1162] recently studied the distribution of this enzyme in leaf macerates and press juices made from these. From ten different plants the expressed juice contained an average of only 17%

[1180] M. Holden and M. V. Tracey, *Biochem. J.*, **43**, 147 (1948).
[1181] M. Holden and M. V. Tracey, *Biochem. J.*, **43**, 151 (1948).
[1182] W. B. Neely, C. D. Ball, C. L. Hamner, and H. M. Sell, *Plant Physiol.*, **25**, 525 (1950).

of the total enzyme content of the tissue, the range being from 8% in the case of elder leaves to 43% in the case of melilot (*Melilotus altissima* Thuill.). However, for melilot, the press juice had an exceptionally high pH (8.6) which, as will be shown below, explains the high proportion of dissolved pectin-methylesterase.

Pectin-methylesterase can be easily desorbed from the water-insoluble cellular tissues by the use of fairly strong salt solutions,[1183] by raising the pH of the tissue macerate above 5.0, or by a combination of these two conditions. Willaman and Hills[1170] describe the following procedure:

The plant tissue is macerated by any suitable means or sliced into thin slices. The enzyme can be obtained from this macerate by raising its pH to 6.0 and then filtering it. However, such a filtrate contains the various water-soluble constituents of the tissue, such as sugars and acids. It is more desirable, therefore, first to remove these water-soluble constituents by adjusting the pH of the macerate to a value of 3–4 and then to filter it. Tomato fruit macerate usually has a pH of 4.0–4.3 and therefore no adjustment is required. The macerate is filtered or pressed in a hydraulic press or by other means and the liquid, which contains only a small proportion of the pectin-methylesterase, is discarded. Now the residual pulp is suspended in a small quantity of water, the pH is adjusted to 6.0, and after a few minutes the mixture is pressed. The extract contains the bulk of the pectin-methylesterase. These authors also found it advantageous to dry the pressed pulp in a current of air or first to treat it twice with acetone and then filter it and dry the pulp by any means without excessive heating.

One point to bear in mind is that, as will be shown, this enzyme is rather sensitive to exposure to pH values under 3.0 and above 8.0. Thus, it is important to make the pH adjustments without "overshooting" the desired values. It is interesting to note that in the case of tomato pectin-methylesterase, desorption by pH adjustment alone is at a minimum in the region of pH 4.0, which is close to the natural pH of the macerate.

MacDonnell, Jansen, and Lineweaver[1069] found that drying orange flavedo overnight at 45°C. caused little, if any, loss of enzyme activity. These authors studied the extraction of pectin-methylesterase from samples and found that the salt concentration in the extraction medium is an important factor as well as pH. Using a 0.25 M solution of sodium chloride adjusted to pH 8.0 the extraction of the enzyme was complete in a short time. However, as the pH of dry albedo slurry in water is about 4.5, much higher sodium chloride concentrations are required to increase the efficiency of the extraction. The maximum activity with the use of salt alone was always below that obtained at higher pH values. In a further simplification of the extraction procedure these authors suggested the following method:

[1183] R. J. McColloch, J. C. Moyer, and Z. I. Kertesz, *Arch. Biochem.*, 10, 479 (1946).

The dried, powdered flavedo (100 g.) is suspended in 200 cc. of a special borate–phosphate buffer mixture of pH 8.2 and consisting of 42.5 g. of borax ($Na_2B_4O_7.10H_2O$), 27.5 g. of boric acid, and 40.0 g. of sodium acetate ($CH_3.CO_2Na.3H_2O$) per liter of water. The mixture is comminuted in a Waring Blendor for 5 minutes and allowed to stand for 1 hour to facilitate filtration. The buffer has sufficient power to maintain the pH in the desired range in spite of the acid formed by the progressive deesterification of the pectic substances in, and dissolved from, the albedo. After filtration, the extract can be concentrated by precipitation with ammonium sulfate at 0.6 saturation at pH 7 or above. The special borate–phosphate buffer used in the extraction is sufficient to maintain this range. Precipitation in more acid solutions causes inactivation of the enzyme.

In the absence of salt, the enzyme is readily adsorbed from a dialyzed solution on diatomaceous earth (Celite).[1069,1157] The pectin-methylesterase can then be eluted with a dilute salt solution. In the case of tobacco leaf pectin-methylesterase, Holden[1162] found that elution with 0.2 M disodium phosphate was more effective than with sodium chloride. Tomato fruit pectin-methylesterase behaves differently from the orange, tobacco, and alfalfa enzymes inasmuch as it is precipitated from its solutions during dialysis.[1183] This property is the basis of the following method of purification developed in the author's laboratory:

An extract of the enzyme is prepared in the manner described above, using 10% sodium chloride solution. The extract is then dialyzed in viscose sausage casings against distilled water in a rocking dialysis machine with a marble inserted in the tube to give constant stirring. The dialysis is continued until a test made on the water shows the absence of chloride ions. During dialysis the enzyme precipitates and can be recovered by centrifugation. The precipitate is dissolved in a small quantity of 10% salt solution and again dialyzed. This operation is repeated several times. The loss of enzyme during such purifications has been found to be about 40–60% in the first dialysis, but repetitions of the dialysis cycle result in very little further loss. The purified enzyme precipitate can be dried *in vacuo* at room temperature without significant loss of activity. The progress of purification by this process is shown in Table 64.

TABLE 64

EXTRACTION OF PECTIN-METHYLESTERASE FROM WASHED TOMATO PULP (FROM MC-COLLOCH, MOYER, AND KERTESZ)

Sample	Total extract volume, cc.	PMU per cc.	Total PMU	Recovery, %
Extract of enzyme from pulp				
First extract.............	100	64.80	6480	70
Second extract...........	100	12.60	1260	83
Third extract.............	100	4.26	426	88
Dialysis concentrates				
First concentrate........	15	206.00	3085	40
Second concentrate.......	1	3060.00	3060	99

The pectin-methylesterase obtained by this method is the most active preparation yet obtained, whether the results are calculated on the dry matter or total nitrogen basis. The most active preparation described by MacDonnell, Jansen, and Lineweaver[1069] and Jansen and MacDonnell[1048] had activities in the neighborhood of 2300 and 2800 PMU per milligram of protein nitrogen, while the dry preparation obtained by the dialysis method contained 3800 PMU per milligram of total nitrogen There is little doubt that further efforts at purification will yield even more active enzyme preparations.

MacDonnell, Jang, Jansen, and Lineweaver[1175] have recently described a method for the purification of orange flavedo pectin-methylesterase by a fractionation and adsorption technic.

Leo and Taylor[1184] described a method for the preparation of colorless pectin-methylesterase solution from alfalfa or clover leaves. Press juices and extracts from these plants are usually green because of the presence of chlorophyll and other pigments.

The freshly grown alfalfa or clover is finely ground or otherwise mechanically disintegrated, and to each pound of macerate 1 gallon of cold water is added. After standing for a short time, the mixture is pressed on a hydraulic press. Enough calcium carbonate is added to the press juice to raise the pH of the mixture to 6.5. A 25% aqueous solution of aluminum chloride is then added until the pH is reduced to between 4.0 and 4.5. The aluminum hydroxide which is produced carries down the particles containing green pigments, but not the enzyme. The precipitate is filtered or centrifuged off, leaving a clear, colorless enzyme solution.

These authors state that the calcium chloride which is produced "does not interfere with the activity" of the enzyme. This is most probable since, as will be shown below, this salt is a powerful activator for pectin-methylesterase.

5. Effect of pH on Activity of Pectin-Methylesterase

The activity–pH relationship of pectin-methylesterase of plant origin is complicated. The activity of this enzyme is profoundly affected by the pH of the reaction mixture and the salt concentration, as well as by the cation component of the salt present.[1157] In salt-free solutions, the activity of pectin-methylesterase of plant origin is nearly zero[1145] at pH 4.0 and increases rapidly as the pH is raised to 8.0. Although many authors give results obtained under more alkaline conditions,[1157] these are of little value because of the simultaneous demethylating action of the alkali. Even at pH 8.0 very careful manipulation is required to avoid deesterification by the local alkalinization caused by the addition of sodium hydroxide to maintain this pH value in the reaction mixture as enzyme action progresses.

[1184] H. T. Leo and C. C. Taylor, U. S. Pat. 2,406,840 (1946).

Recent extensive studies of the effect of salts on the pectin-methylesterase of alfalfa leaves,[1157] oranges,[1069] tobacco leaf,[1162] and the tomato fruit[1145] show considerable agreement concerning the behavior of this enzyme when obtained from various higher plants. In general, the effect of salts is to lower the pH at which maximum activity is attained and to extend the activity into lower pH regions. However, in the range of pH 7.0–8.0, salts have little or no effect on the activity. Thus, the chief usefulness of salt activation of pectin-methylesterase seems to consist in counteracting adverse pH conditions.

There is some disagreement among various authors as to whether pectin-methylesterase of plant origin possesses a true pH optimum. Curves showing definite optima have been reported,[1032,1162] but in most cases these were obtained at higher pH values by subtracting the extent of deesterification effected by alkali alone. There is some doubt whether such a calculation is justified. A further difficulty consists in exact control of the salt content of the reaction mixture since alkali is used first to adjust the reaction mixture to the desired pH value and again for neutralization of the acid formed during the reaction. However, the general statement can be made that the activity of pectin-methylesterase of plant origin increases as the pH is elevated from 4.0 to 7.0 and that the picture above pH 7.0 is still confused.

The pectin-methylesterase of molds is different in many respects from that found in higher plants.[1145] Fungal pectin-methylesterase (from a commercial pectinase, see Chapter XV) is active in a salt-free medium at pH 4.0 and has a well-defined optimum at about pH 4.5–5.0. The addition of salts increases the activity of the enzyme, especially near the pH optimum, but does not cause drift in the pH value at which the maximum activity is observed. Calesnick, Hills, and Willaman[1169] found for the same enzyme a broad pH optimum in the range of 4.0–5.5, with a maximum at 5.0. Phaff[1140] found the pH optimum of pectin-methylesterase from *Penicillium chrysogenum* at 4.3.

6. Activation, Inhibition, and Inactivation

(a) Pectin-Methylesterase of Higher Plants

As noted above, the effect of salts on the pectin-methylesterase of several higher plants has been studied extensively. Salt activation of this enzyme falls into two classes with respect to the valence of the cation component. With divalent cations and at pH 6.0, maximum activation is produced in the neighborhood of 0.03 M concentration. At higher concentrations and at the same pH the activity is suppressed. Monovalent cations usually produce maximum activation at pH 6.0 in 0.10 M concentration and do not suppress activity below molarities of 1.0. Furthermore, maximum activity is obtained at a lower pH and lower concentration of divalent cations than monovalent. The maximum activity obser᪐ the optimum concentration for a given pH is roughly the same ᪐ maximum obtained at any other pH value at the optimum salt conc᪐ tion, at least between the pH values 4.5 and 8.0. In the presence of 0.05 M calcium chloride, for example, the pH–activity curve of orange pectin-methylesterase forms an almost level plateau from pH 5.0 to 8.0.[1069]

A mechanism to explain how cations influence the activity of the pectin-methylesterase of higher plants has been suggested by Lineweaver and Ballou.[1157] In spite of the fact that salts or alkali are needed to keep this enzyme in solution (dispersion), the major effect of salts does not consist in peptization of the enzyme, but instead the salts added prevent the inhibition of the enzyme by the free carboxyl groups present in the pectinic acid substrate and formed during the reaction. The cations are assumed to form cation–carboxyl complexes thus eliminating this inhibitory effect.

The pectin-methylesterase of higher plants is unusually resistant to the effect of chemical agents.[1145] Such enzyme inhibitors as formaldehyde, iodine, iodoacetic acid, hydrogen cyanide, mercuric chloride, copper sulfate, and a long list of other compounds were found to be ineffective in reasonable concentrations in the presence of the substrate. Pyridine and quinoline showed some tendency to inactivate the enzyme. On the other hand, soap solutions inactivate this enzyme easily and completely.[1145] Synthetic detergents of the sodium lauryl sulfate and alkyl aryl sulfonate types are capable of inactivating pectin-methylesterase in concentrations as low as 11 milligram per cent. The inactivation is irreversible and practically unaffected by pH and the presence of salts.

Pectin-methylesterase which is desorbed from cellular plant constituents by the methods described is usually very sensitive toward ethanol; therefore the use of this solvent should be avoided in preparative work.

(b) Fungal Pectin-Methylesterase

Of the pectin-methylesterase of microorganisms only that of some molds used in the commercial production of pectinases has been thoroughly investigated by modern methods.[1086,1145,1169] As stated above, this enzyme seems to be different in many respects from the corresponding enzyme found in higher plants. The mold enzyme is active in a salt-free medium and the effect of added salt is primarily to increase the activity at the pH optimum (4.5–5.0), rather than to cause a drift in the position of the optimum as is the case with the pectin-methylesterase of higher plants. The extent of activation by the presence of 0.1 M sodium chloride drops rapidly as the pH of the reaction mixture is increased above the optimum, and at pH 7.0 no significant activation can be observed.

Fungal pectin-methylesterase is much more resistant to chemical inactivation than the enzyme of higher plants. Detergent concentrations which inactivate the plant enzyme do not affect, or only partially inhibit, the mold enzyme. The latter enzyme is also more resistant to exposure to ethanol and is not precipitated from a solution upon dialysis.[1145] When mold and tomato pectin-methylesterase are allowed to act simultaneously on pectinic acids their actions can be shown to be independent of each other.[1145]

7. Temperature Effects

The pectin-methylesterase of higher plants is comparatively heat resistant.[1161,1162,1165] Solutions of this enzyme obtained from tomatoes or tobacco leaves and in the pH range of 4.0–6.0 do not show any loss of activity when heated to 55°C. for 1 hour.[1145] Above 60°C. the enzyme is gradually inactivated, but for the rapid inactivation of the tomato enzyme as required in manufacturing processes (see Chapter XXVII), temperatures above 80°C. are needed.[1161] The enzyme found in orange albedo is somewhat more sensitive to heat.

The Q_{10} of tomato and tobacco pectin-methylesterase between 20 and 60°C. is about 1.45.[1145,1162] The tomato enzyme has a Q_{10} of 1.80 between 0 and 20°C. The energy of activation calculated from such data is in the range of 5500–7500 cal. per mole but of course will depend on the assumed order of reaction.[1145,1166] As stated above, opinions differ as to whether the enzymic deesterification is a zero- or first-order reaction.

The pectin-methylesterase of molds is much more sensitive to heat than that of higher plants, and the heat inactivation of the fungal enzyme is quite noticeable at 30°C.[1145] Below this temperature the mold enzyme has about the same Q_{10} as the corresponding enzyme of higher plants. Mold pectin-methylesterase can be completely inactivated by heating which does not noticeably affect the activity of the tomato enzyme.

It is now clear that temperature optima as such are meaningless, since the maximum activity exerted at different temperatures by an enzyme depends on the temperature coefficient as well as on the comparative rates of inactivation at these temperatures. Thus the optima found depend largely on the length of the experimental period used.[1030] The striking differences between the thermal behavior of the pectin-methylesterase of higher plants on one hand, and of molds on the other, make it obvious that a marked difference between the temperature optima of these two enzymes can be demonstrated, whether the experimental periods chosen are short or long.

8. Mode of Action and Specificity

It is interesting to note that in attempts to effect complete enzymic demethylation of pectinic acids by pectin-methylesterase, the reaction usually stops short of complete hydrolysis at a methoxyl content of about 0.5% (see Chapter VIII). The meaning of this phenomenon is not clear. Attempts to reverse the enzymic deesterification of pectinic acids have been unsuccessful.

Lineweaver and Ballou[1157] have suggested that cations free the enzyme from the inhibiting action of the carboxyl groups originally present and those formed during the reaction. The formation of the pectinic acid–cation complex is supported by the finding that cations also accelerate the rate of alkaline deesterification of pectinic acids several fold.

The hydrolysis of synthetic polygalacturonic acid polymethyl ester methyl glucoside (see Chapter IX) is much slower[1085,1157] than hydrolysis of the natural methyl ester in pectinic acids. Furthermore, the deesterification of α-D-galacturonic acid methyl ester and of its methyl glycoside is again much slower than that of the artificial polymethyl ester. All three compounds, however, are saponified with similar velocities by alkali at pH 9.0. The glycol and glycerol esters of pectic acid are not hydrolyzed by pectin-methylesterase.[1185] In a recent study MacDonnell, Jang, Jansen, and Lineweaver[1175] found that pectin-methylesterase hydrolyzes pectin at least 1000 times faster than some 50 nongalacturonide esters tested.

It would seem, therefore, that pectin-methylesterase is an enzyme with considerable qualitative specificity toward the methyl ester and also with quantitative specificity toward the methyl ester groups as they occur in nature in pectinic acids. It is for these reasons that, in spite of its clumsiness, the name *pectin-methylesterase* is preferred to the more general term *pectinesterase*.

However, there is at least one observation which mars this picture of remarkable specificity. Neuberg and Ostendorf[1186] found that the pectin-methylesterase (pectase) of tobacco and alfalfa leaves hydrolyzes the half-calcium salt of methyl-D-tartaric acid:

$$Ca(COO.CHOH.CHOH.COO.CH_3)_2$$

The hydrolysis is accompanied by precipitation from the reaction mix-

[1185] H. Deuel, *Helv. Chim. Acta*, **30**, 1523 (1947).
[1186] C. Neuberg and C. Ostendorf, *Biochem. Z.*, **229**, 464 (1930).

ture of the formed half-calcium salt of tartaric acid, which can be used for the detection of this enzyme. This reaction has been used by some investigators to test for pectin-methylesterase. It would seem that reinvestigation of this reaction would be most desirable in order to confirm that it is actually caused by pectin-methylesterase and not by another co-occuring enzyme.

V. SEPARATION OF PECTIC ENZYMES

There are several reports in the literature dealing with the separation of the enzymes protopectinase, pectin-polygalacturonase, and pectin-methylesterase. In view of the very major uncertainties concerning the nature and, indeed, the existence of protopectin (see Chapter III Sect. III) and of any enzyme which might act specifically on protopectin (see Sect. I, this chapter), it would serve little purpose to discuss the separation of protopectinase from the other pectic enzymes. For this reason the present discussion will be restricted to the separation of pectin-polygalacturonase from pectin-methylesterase.

In some plants, like tobacco leaves and stems,[1032] and in orange flavedo,[1069] pectin-methylesterase is known to occur free from pectin-polygalacturonase. On the other hand, most known sources of pectin-polygalacturonase, especially the *pectinase* preparations obtained from fungal cultures, usually contain some pectin-methylesterase.[1085,1086] It was mostly as a result of attempts to obtain pectin-polygalacturonase free from pectin-methylesterase that a number of workers developed methods for the separation of these enzymes. For this reason some investigators were satisfied to eliminate the pectin-methylesterase activity from the mixture rather than to strive for actual separation and recovery of both enzymes.

Rothschild,[1187] working with *Clostridium* and *Bacillus* species, separated the two enzymes on the basis of their different stabilities when heated in solutions adjusted to various pH values. He also used Chamberland filters (L2) for separation by filtration. Unfortunately, the methods of enzyme estimation used in this work were such that the results cannot be regarded as conclusive. However, this same method of heating the two enzymes in acid solutions was later used by Lineweaver, Jang, and Jansen,[1087] who studied the inactivation of the two enzymes in fungal pectinase preparations. Their results confirm the previous observation[1051] that the enzymes in various fungal preparations behave quite differently and that it would therefore be difficult to state any set of conditions which would be generally applicable. The conditions leading to complete

[1187] H. Rothschild, *Enzymologia*, **5**, 359 (1938).

destruction of pectin-methylesterase but only to partial inactivation of pectin-polygalacturonase must therefore be separately established for any given enzyme preparation. Purification usually increases the sensitivity of pectin-methylesterase to strongly acid solutions. The use of pH values in the range of 0.5–3.2 at room temperature for periods up to 24 hours gives some combinations of these conditions leading to essentially complete inactivation of pectin-methylesterase, with only partial inactivation of pectin-polygalacturonase activity.[1087]

McColloch and Kertesz[1051] have used a commercial synthetic cation exchange resin (Amberlite 1R-100) for the removal of pectin-methylesterase from commercial preparations. In the case of some preparations the removal of the pectin-methylesterase was accomplished by putting a water solution of the enzyme through a column of the resin. With other preparations the separation was not very satisfactory, although at times the use of a buffer in the enzyme solution aided in removing the pectin-methylesterase. More recently Lineweaver, Jang, and Jansen[1087] found that the batchwise use of the resin is also satisfactory although it does not provide the continuity in operation afforded by the column.

Reid[1137] recently published a preliminary note describing a chromatographic method for the separation of pectic enzymes.

CHAPTER XV

Commercial Pectic Enzymes

I. INTRODUCTION

Commercial enzyme preparations containing active pectic enzymes have been on the market for many years. Takadiastase,[1188] for example, which Neuberg so aptly described as "an arsenal of enzymes," possesses some pectolytic activity.[1189] It was not until the early thirties, however, that the commercial production of enzymes specifically developed for pectin hydrolysis commenced. Since about 1934 such enzymes of high and standardized activity have been manufactured and used all over the world for various purposes of which the clarification of fruit juices is the most important.

Interestingly enough, enzyme preparations for the clarification of fruit juices through the hydrolysis of the pectic substances which they contain were simultaneously and independently developed in the United States[1190-1193] and in Germany.[1194,1195] Development in this country led to the Pectinols which are now sold[1196] in preparations which have various enzyme activities and which contain some other constituents which will be discussed below. In addition to the large-scale production of this enzyme in the United States, some Pectinol (Pektinol) was, and perhaps is,

[1188] J. Takamine, *J. Soc. Chem. Ind.*, **17**, 118 (1898).

[1189] R. Ripa, *Die Pektinstoffe.* Serger und Hempel, Braunschweig, 1937.

[1190] J. J. Willaman and Z. I. Kertesz, U. S. Pat. 1,932,833 (1933).

[1191] Z. I. Kertesz, *New York State Agr. Expt. Sta.*, Bull. 589 (1930).

[1192] J. J. Willaman and Z. I. Kertesz, *New York State Agr. Expt. Sta.*, Tech. Bull. 178 (1931).

[1193] J. J. Willaman, *Food Inds.*, **5**, 294 (1933).

[1194] A. Mehlitz and H. Maass, *Biochem. Z.*, **276**, 66, 86 (1935).

[1195] A. Mehlitz, German Pat. 680,602 (1932).

[1196] The Pectinols are manufactured by Rohm and Haas Co. of Philadelphia, Pa., Other commercial pectinases are produced by Wallerstein Laboratories of New York, Takamine Laboratory, Inc., of Clifton, N. J., and perhaps by others.

[1197] B. Hottenroth, *Chem. Ing.-Technik*, **21**, 142 (1949). In a very confusing manner a diastatic enzyme preparation for the removal of starch from pectin extracts is also sold in Germany under the name "Pektinol."

also manufactured in Germany,[1197,1198] although to a limited extent. German development led to the commercial preparation[1199] sold under the name of Filtragol which attained widespread use on the continent, but especially in Germany. During the past ten years a whole series of other pectolytic enzymes of various sorts reached the market in different countries, in part at least as the result of transportation difficulties during the war and of exchange difficulties afterward. Some of these were marketed under names like Ido, Pectasin, and Filtrazym. A Danish pectolytic preparation for similar purposes is mentioned by Hansen[1200] and a Swiss pectinase is noted by Pallmann, Matus, Deuel, and Weber.[1201] It is also quite clear now that attempts to produce such enzymes are under way in a number of other countries such as England[1202] and Australia.

These preparations may all be classified as *pectinases* and, as far as is known, they all contain high pectin-polygalacturonase activities and some pectin-methylesterase activity. It is interesting to note that the American pectolytic enzyme was developed for the purpose of clarifying fruit juices, whereas in the case of the German preparation and process the emphasis was on the beneficial effects of the pectolysis and the resulting drop in viscosity on the rate of filtration. Of course, in reality both types of preparation effect the same changes although wide differences always existed in the purity and activity of these enzymes. It is now also known that the comparative activity of the above two pectic enzymes in the preparations varies. The discovery that the true substrate of pectin-polygalacturonase is pectic acid and not pectinic acids gave considerable importance to the occurrence of pectin-methylesterase in these pectinase preparations. In fact, as will be shown, it has been suggested that pectin-methylesterase be added to pectinase preparations deficient in pectin-methylesterase and this is perhaps done with commercial pectinases.

The various purposes for which pectinases are used will be discussed in Chapter XXIX.

Attempts are now being made by various manufacturers to put pectin-methylesterase preparations on the market. This enzyme[1169] may be used for the determination of the ester content of pectinic acids (Chapter VIII, Sect. VI-1-(c)), for the manufacture of low-ester pectins (Chapter XXIV), for the fortification of pectinase preparations, and for other purposes.

[1198] C. L. Hinton, B.I.O.S. Final Report No. 388, Item No. 22 (1946).
[1199] Manufactured by the I. G. Farbenindustrie, A.-G. at Leverkusen, Germany.
[1200] A. Hansen, *J. Chem. Education*, 24, 223 (1947).
[1201] H. Pallmann, J. Matus, H. Deuel, and F. Weber, *Rec. trav. chim.*, 65, 633 (1946).
[1202] W. W. Reid, *J. Sci. Food Agr.*, 1, 234 (1950).

II. METHODS OF MANUFACTURING PECTINASES

The general technics of mold enzyme manufacture have been discussed by Bernhauer and Knobloch,[1203] Mehlitz,[1204] and others. Only a glimpse of this topic can be gained from the patents dealing with the production and use of pectinases, although it is clear that the methods used are still based on those described by Takamine.[1188]

It is not clear, for example, what organisms are used at the present time for the production of this enzyme. The patents name a long series of organisms, among them *Aspergillus* and *Penicillin* spp., including *A. Wentii, A. niger, A. flavus, A. oryzae, A. fumigatus,* as well as aspergilli of the *parasitans* and *Tamari* types; *P. glaucum* and *Rhizopus tritici, R. nigricans.* It is also known that a mold culture designated as *A. aureus* Nakazawa and *A. Wentii* were used in the manufacture of pectinase in Germany.[1205] It is perfectly clear, however, that any manufacturer contemplating the manufacture of pectinase isolates and selects the most suitable strains of these organisms and that such cultures are not publicized. There is no information in the literature as to whether the organism designated by Ehrlich[1206] as *Penicillium Ehrlichii* and claimed to be of unusually high pectolytic activity was ever used for the manufacture of pectinases. It is only natural that any manufacturer would try to keep secret the organism or organisms used and sell only preparations which do not contain living organisms. It is also quite clear that any given culture which proves to be suitable for the manufacture of pectolytic enzymes under any given set of manufacturing conditions might not necessarily be as useful and successful under a different set of conditions.

The manufacturing process used for the production of the German pectinase Filtragol may be summarized[1205] as follows:

The starting material for the production of the enzyme is wheat bran with a starch content of about 20%. To increase the starch content, potato flakes are sometimes added. Molasses has also been used in conjunction with wheat bran. The latter or the mixture of various materials used is first sterilized and allowed to stand for 2 or 3 days. It is then mixed with water to give a thick slurry, heated to about 120°C., and held at this temperature for 2 hours. This heating may be performed in a large mixer fed with live steam. The bran or mixture is allowed to cool overnight to about 35°C. and then the inoculum (see below) is added and mixed with the bran mixture for about 2 hours. The mixture is now

[1203] K. Bernhauer and H. Knobloch, in E. Bamann and K. Myrbäck, *Die Methoden der Fermentforschung.* Thieme, Leipzig, 1941, p. 1303.
[1204] A. Mehlitz, in *Die Methoden der Fermentforschung,* p. 2865.
[1205] W. M. Swangard, FIAT Final Report No. 910, Jan. 24, 1947.
[1206] F. Ehrlich, *Enzymologia,* **3, 185** (1947).

spread out on the shelves of a (sterilized) drier in layers about 2 cm. in thickness; the apparatus is closed and ventilation is started. The temperature is kept at about 37°C. by occasionally blowing steam into the chamber. The air circulation must be quite efficient and the arrangements are usually such that the air passes in front of one tray and in back of the next one, thus providing means of passage over the entire growing surface. The mold growth virtually ceases after 36–48 hours; by this time the trays have the appearance of a great sugar cake and have a pleasant spicy odor. After full growth, the batch is dried by indirect steam at 35°C., using the same ventilation system as before. The trays are then emptied into the mixer and the cake is broken up and ground. During this operation it is desirable to provide the workers with effective masks since many people are sensitive to the air-borne spores.

In the preparation of Filtragol, the dry crude enzyme preparation is extracted with denatured ethanol and then centrifuged and dried in an air current, ground again, and sieved. The larger particles are ground further in a ball mill and sieved; finally the whole batch of dry, sieved enzyme is mixed in a mixing drum. Using a wheat bran–molasses mixture, this process gives about 67% yield on a dry weight basis. The preparation is then standardized and packaged for sale.

The inoculum used in this process is started by inoculating a 2% beerwort agar medium in petri dishes with the stock culture of *Aspergillus aureus* Nakazawa. After 7 days the mass of spores from the surface of the culture is washed into 2 liters of sterile water from which, after shaking, the bits of agar are removed by filtration through a fine-mesh sieve. This whole operation is carried out under sterile conditions. The suspension of spores is used to inoculate layers of coarsely ground dry peas or corn, previously soaked, sterilized, and placed in an incubator on aluminum trays. In the incubator, trays containing this material and sterile water alternate. The incubator is now closed and kept closed with an automatic temperature control at 30–33°C. After 4–5 days the surface of the media is covered with black spores of the *A. aureus*. Any spots visibly infected by other molds are removed and the spores are washed off from the rest of the material with sterile tap water and used for the inoculation of the final cultures.

The effect of various compounds on the formation of pectin polygalacturonase was discussed in Chapter XIV, Section II-3. Observations made on liquid cultures containing pure compounds have little significance for the large-scale production of such mold enzymes on bran or other similar materials.

It is clear from this description that the German commercial pectinase consists essentially of a ground, dried, and extracted mold culture. It has been common experience that such materials are very difficult to free completely from objectionable odors and flavors. Chloroform and ether have been also used for the extractions.[1207] It is chiefly for this reason that different methods are used in the manufacture of the Pectinols in the United States. In this process the mold cultures, presumably produced

[1207] Anon., *Food Manuf.*, 24, 436 (1949).

by a method similar to the one described above, are extracted with water or a buffer solution. At times some extent of disintegration in the wet state aids in the more complete recovery of the enzymes from the culture. The extract is first separated from the solid materials by centrifuging and then filtered, if necessary. Thereupon several times the volume of ethanol is added and the precipitate which is formed is separated from the ethanol by centrifuging, suspended once more in ethanol, centrifuged, and dried in an air current or under vacuum. Acetone and saturation with ammonium sulfate have also been used for the precipitation. The enzyme preparation obtained by this method is practically free from odor and objectionable flavors and is also, of course, much more concentrated than the pectinase obtained by grinding the dried culture. After standardization and adjustment of the activity by mixing different batches or by the use of diluents, as described below, the pectinase is ready for packaging.

The suggestion has also been made[1208] that such pectinases be manufactured from the mold mycelia left over from the manufacture of citric acid or penicillin. While such waste materials are known to have considerable pectin-polygalacturonase activity at times, at the present time there seems to be no pectic enzyme preparation on the market which is manufactured from such sources. There is a distinct possibility, however, that with the rapidly extending industrial application of molds and other microorganisms the recovery of by-product pectinases may eventually become a feasible commercial process.

III.   DETERMINATION OF PECTOLYTIC ACTIVITY AND STANDARDIZATION

Whatever the purpose for which a commercial pectinase preparation is purchased, different lots of the enzyme are expected to show consistently similar activities. The proportion of an enzyme in such mixtures cannot as yet be determined; the determinations which must be used in reality show a composite effect of the quantity and activity of the enzyme in question.

One difficulty in any attempt to evaluate the pectolytic activity of a pectinase preparation consists in the choice of substrate. These enzymes are used for a variety of purposes (see Chapter XXIX) and the suitability of a preparation for one application might not necessarily parallel its usefulness for other purposes. While it is established beyond doubt that the major action of such pectinases when used in connection with fruit products consists in their pectolytic activity, these preparations,

[1208] H. S. Isbell and H. Frush, *J. Research Natl. Bur. Standards,* **33,** 389 (1944).

as noted in Chapter XIV, always contain other enzymes as well. These other enzymes, then, may at times have a definite influence on the practical usefulness of the enzyme. Since fruit juice clarification is the chief process for which these commercial pectinases are produced, it would seem logical to standardize them on the basis of their clarifying action, e.g., on some standardized sample of apple juice. Such methods have been used to a limited extent but have caused considerable confusion. The manner in which apple juice reacts to the same quantity of the same clarifying enzyme varies, depending on the type, variety, and maturity of the apples, as well as on the method which is used in pressing the juice from these apples. The ease with which cloudy apple juice clarifies changes during storage of the juice, whether it is stored frozen or pasteurized. On the basis of such considerations many workers in the field turned to the use of pectin and pectic acid solutions for the standardization, although some still use mixtures of apple juice and pectin solutions.

There is little doubt that much information on methods of standardization has been collected by manufacturers of pectinases, but very little has appeared in the literature. Mehlitz and Scheuer[1209] studied the viscosity changes in an apple pectin extract, as well as the increase in reducing power and the drop in the "calcium pectate value," when the extract was treated with various commercial pectinases. They concluded that the calcium pectate changes are most accurate for the evaluation of such enzymes and suggest the following procedure:

1 g. of the enzyme preparation is added to 200 cc. of a pectin solution containing 2% pectin, as determined by the calcium pectate method. The pH of the mixture, if necessary, is adjusted to 3.6, and the mixture is allowed to stand at 25°C. for 18 hours. Thereupon some formaldehyde is added to stop the enzyme action, the solution is filtered, and the "calcium pectate value" is again determined and expressed for 100 cc. of the solution.

The important relationship between the extent of esterification and pectin-polygalacturonase action (Chapter XIV, Section II-3) was unknown at that time. It would seem that, in order to determine both this latter enzyme and the efficiency of the pectinase preparation in hydrolyzing a pectinic acid, the digestion should in addition also be performed with a pectic acid substrate. The results of these two determinations then give a fairly clear picture of the usefulness of the pectinase.

This method is too unwieldy because of the tedious calcium pectate determinations, an objection which is not eliminated by suggested simplifications.[1210] Mehlitz and Scheuer[1209] stated that changes in the viscosity

[1209] A. Mehlitz and M. Scheuer, *Biochem. Z.*, **268**, 345, 355 (1934).
[1210] A. Mehlitz, *Konserven-Ind.*, **13**, 149 (1926).

of a pectic solution are also a good measure of the pectolytic activity. This method is known to have been used most extensively for the commercial standardization of pectinase preparations. It will suffice here to discuss only recent developments on this phase of the subject.

At the present time the picture of the reactions involved in the enzymic hydrolysis of pectic substances is still confused (see Chapter XIV). Although Weitnauer[1211] claimed to have developed a method and a formula for kinetic measurements of such hydrolyses, he entirely overlooked some important factors,[1212] such as the effect of pH on the viscosity of pectin solutions (see Chapter VII), the influence of the extent of esterification, and the presence of deesterifying enzymes. In spite of these limitations, viscosity measurements are suitable for obtaining comparative results of practical value. Weber and Deuel[1213] recently discussed this subject and suggested the following procedure:

It is imperative to use rigorously standardized experimental conditions. 5 g. of dry powdered pectin is moistened in a beaker with about 5 cc. of 90% ethanol and then mixed with 500 cc. of apple juice concentrate, reconstituted to the original solid content of the apple juice. (The pectin is removed from this product during the course of its manufacture.) The mixture is stirred and warmed to 50°C., and, after all pectin is dissolved, made up to 1l. with reconstituted apple juice and filtered through a fritted glass filter. If 0.15% sodium benzoate is added to this solution, it will keep at ice-chest temperatures for several weeks without noticeable changes. 2 g. of the pectinase preparation in question is then dissolved in 100 cc. of the reconstituted apple juice, allowed to stand for 2 hours with occasional stirring, and then filtered. Exactly 10 cc. of this enzyme solution is measured into a 100-cc. volumetric flask and made up to the mark with the apple juice–pectin solution. The well-mixed solution is kept at 20°C. After exactly 6 hours the viscosity is determined with either the Höppler or the Ostwald viscometer. The activity of the enzyme is expressed by the formula:

$$A = (t_a - t)/(t_a - t_0) \times 100$$

in which $t_0 =$ the viscosity of the pectin-free reconstituted apple juice; $t_a =$ the viscosity of the reaction mixture without enzyme or, even better, with heat-inactivated enzyme; and $t =$ the viscosity of the mixture after 6 hours. As will be obvious from the above formula, it does not matter what units are used to express the results of viscosity measurements and therefore the time values obtained from the determination may be used directly without further calculations. The value, A, indicates the percentage drop in the specific viscosity of the pectin–apple juice solution but has no absolute meaning.

This method is open to criticism on many counts, a fact admitted by Weber and Deuel. However, if the enzyme preparations are used for the

[1211] G. Weitnauer, *Helv. Chim. Acta,* 29, 1382 (1946).
[1212] H. Deuel and F. Weber, *Helv. Chim. Acta,* 29, 1872 (1946).
[1213] F. Weber and H. Deuel, *Mitt. Lebensm. Hyg.,* 36, 368 (1945).

clarification of apple juice, the results show good correlation with the efficiency of the enzyme preparation in this process.

It is of interest to note that in a recent study Joslyn, Mist, and Lambert[1067a] found no relation between the pectin-polygalacturonase and pectin-methylesterase activities and the rate or type of clarification of apple juice by several commercial pectic enzymes.

Since it is now clear that the true substrate of pectin-polygalacturonase is pectic acid rather than pectinic acids (pectin), considerable stress is put on the presence of pectin-methylesterase in commercial pectinases.[1214] As was stated previously, in the presence of sufficient pectin-methylesterase activity, the pectolysis of pectinic acids proceeds at a velocity comparable to that of pectic acid. A study of the deesterifying enzymes of molds and of higher plants showed that they possess different properties[1215] of which the lower pH optimum of mold pectin-methylesterase is the most important. The pectin-methylesterase of higher plants may be practically inactive in the absence of salts at the pH values which often exist in fruit juices, while mold pectin-methylesterase has an optimum at a much lower pH value (see Chapter XIV). Fruit juices are known to contain salts in sufficient concentrations to result in some activity of plant pectin-methylesterase in the pH range of 3.5–4.5 shown by most fruit juices. It would be of considerable advantage to find easily available sources of pectin-methylesterase with pH optima lower than that of the enzyme of higher plants. Mold or bacterial pectin-methylesterase would seem to fulfill such requirements. The addition of the esterase to pectinase preparations was recently patented.[1214] The claim states, with the customary dubious exactness of patents, that the invention covers the addition of "about 0.085 to about 2.360 parts" of pectin-methylesterase preparation per part of commercial pectinase.

Once the pectolytic activity of a given lot of pectinase is ascertained, it is usually brought to a standard activity set by the manufacturer. Perhaps some day, when there is more unanimity in the methods used to determine pectic enzymes and to express their activities, the activities of commercial preparations will be stated in such a manner that the purchaser will know upon reading the label what pectolytic activity the preparation possesses. This is not the case at present; activity determinations are made by different methods and the standard strengths are set and followed by the manufacturer with no other compulsion except to maintain his reputation.

In any efficient scheme of pectinase manufacture, the aim is to produce the enzyme with a much higher activity than the standard strength

[1214] E. F. Jansen and H. Lineweaver, U. S. Pat. 2,457,560 (1948).
[1215] R. J. McColloch and Z. I. Kertesz, *Arch. Biochem.*, 13, 217 (1947).

of the product. Thus the enzyme must be diluted to bring it to standard activity. This is done: (*1*) by blending different lots of the enzymes, and (*2*) by mixing with diluents. Since the bulk of commercial pectinase is used by food industries, there are rigorous requirements which any diluent must meet: (*1*) it must be acceptable to the various food authorities concerned with pure food laws and public health. (*2*) It must be void of any objectionable odor or flavor and should either be entirely insoluble or easily soluble in water, since addition of either type of diluent enhances dissolution of the pectinase. (*3*) It must be void of any detrimental effect on the enzyme. (*4*) It must be inexpensive.

The kind of diluent used varies according to the purpose for which the enzyme is recommended. Sucrose and glucose (Cerelose) have been extensively used in standardizing such preparations. Various kinds of diatomaceous earths now available in a wide range of types and sizes as filtration aids (Chapter XIX) are also used. Under certain conditions, especially exigencies of war and other economic disturbances, many other materials have been used as diluents, *e.g.*, the ground, extracted coffee bean hulls which were used in Germany during World War II. Decreosoted sawdust was also used when coffee bean hulls became unavailable.[1205]

It is clear from Chapter XIV, Sections II-8 and IV-6 that the addition of certain agents such as salts can be definitely beneficial to the activity of such enzymes. However, since these preparations are used mostly in foods, such activating salts cannot be added to the preparations lest they affect the flavor of the food product adversely. On the other hand, materials are added at times which aid in the clarification of fruit juices by producing, in effect, a means for better flocculation of the materials which are held in dispersion by the pectic substances until the latter are decomposed. For this purpose gelatin in various proportions from a fraction of 1% to as high as 25% is used in commercial pectinases[1215a] recommended for fruit juice clarification. Very often in such cases clarification is *de facto* caused by two essentially independent processes: (*1*) by gelatin–tannin clarification[1216] (in which the natural tannin content of the fruit juice plays a major part), and (*2*) by enzymic clarification. The addition to commercial pectinases of charcoal together with filter aids has also been suggested. Such a mixture is supposed to hydrolyze the pectic constituents of the juice, decolorize the latter (to a certain extent, at least), and then further enhance filtration by means of the filter aid.

[1215a] From a manufacturer's letter circular, Rohm and Haas Co., Philadelphia, Pa., 1949.
[1216] D. K. Tressler, M. A. Joslyn, and G. L. Marsh, *Fruit and Vegetable Juices*. Avi, New York, 1939.

CHAPTER XVI

Utilization of Pectic Substances by Microorganisms

It seems a safe assumption that complex compounds like the pectic polyuronides must be hydrolyzed before they can be utilized by microorganisms. Therefore, the ability to use pectic substances as a source of carbon and energy will depend on the formation of enzymes capable of hydrolyzing them into their simple constituents, in this case, into D-galacturonic acid. Thus, the previous discussion on the occurrence of pectolytic enzymes, more specifically of pectin-polygalacturonase (see Chapter XIV, Sect. II-4),in microorganisms will have direct bearing on this point. Reference is made, therefore, to Table 61 (Chapter XIV) in which are listed some of the microorganisms known to produce pectolytic enzymes.

The question might be raised: Is it true that a microorganism capable of hydrolyzing pectic substances will be also able to grow on galacturonic acid? Unfortunately, the answer is not definitely known. When grown in pure cultures, with pectic substances as the only source of carbon and energy, the organism will have to utilize galacturonic acid or not grow. The situation is different when the organism is growing in its natural habitat. For example, Bacillus carotovorus (Erwinia carotovora), the soft rot organism of carrots,[1217] will produce pectolytic enzymes as it grows in a carrot root, but we have little assurance that the galacturonic acid formed is utilized in the presence of the simple sugars which are preferred by most organisms. Thus, in such a case the enzyme might be produced only as a means of reducing the resistance of the tissue to the penetration of the growing organism. It is also clear that, through the production of pectolytic enzymes and the destruction of the natural cell structure, the various nutrients present in the tissue and previously surrounded or blocked by cell walls will become more accessible to the organism. Some cases are known of microorganisms that are able to produce pectin-digesting enzymes without an ability to utilize pectin

[1217] L. R. Jones, New York State Agr. Expt. Sta., Tech. Bull. 11 (1909).

or galacturonic acid. McCoy and Peterson[1218] found that laboratory cultures of some retting organisms were unable to ferment pectin.

The number of different organisms capable of utilizing pectic substances must be legion. This is only natural since millions of tons of plant residues of annual plants and of leaves of perennial plants must be disposed of every year. The disintegration and destruction of these plant residues (see Chapter XII) generally proceeds through the action of microorganisms. It is, therefore, very disappointing that so little is known about the utilization of pectic substances by microorganisms and even less about the mechanism by which microorganisms make use of D-galacturonic acid.

The meager information one can find in the literature is especially concerned with two matters of great economic importance. One is the retting of textile plants like flax, hemp, jute, etc., the other the effect of plant disease organisms on various economic crops, mostly fruits and vegetables. We shall deal with retting and plant disease later in Chapter XXIX in some detail. Some information has also been collected by medical bacteriologists interested in the fate of pectin in the animal body. But it will be clear that the behavior of various organisms in all three instances will have little direct bearing on the utilization of the pectic substances or of the galacturonic acid produced from it. As already stated, the fact that an organism is capable of forming pectolytic enzymes may not be taken as evidence that the same organism can also utilize galacturonic acid, at least until such a relationship is definitely established. This was realized by many investigators who then proceeded to grow pure cultures of the organisms on specific media. In such tests, Jones[1217] found that the addition of carbohydrates to the medium of *Bacillus carotovorus* (*Erwinia carotovora*) resulted in more intense production of pectolytic enzymes. On the other hand, the presence of cellular tissues in the culture had no marked effect, suggesting that the pectic constituents of tissues had, at most, an insignificant nutritive value for the organism.

A complicating factor in the evaluation of earlier investigations is the impurity of the pectic preparations used in such work. These usually contained a considerable proportion of nonpectic materials. Therefore, growth in cultures in which pectic substances were assumed to be the only source of carbon might at times have been the result of the presence of such admixed nonpectic constituents.

[1218] E. McCoy and W. H. Peterson, *J. Infectious Diseases*, **43**, 475 (1928).

[1219] M. H. Branfoot (Carré), "A Critical and Historical Study of the Pectic Substances of Plants," *Dept. Sci. Ind. Research Brit. Food Invest.*, Special Rept. No. 33 (1929).

Branfoot[1219] ably reviewed this field twenty years ago. Since then, only little progress has been made. Modern textbooks and handbooks of bacteriology give insufficient systematic attention to this topic.

A further general point to be kept in mind is the adaptation of microorganisms to the utilization of certain compounds. We have already discussed this in connection with enzyme formation. Incidental tests on an organism are hardly conclusive. Coles' work illustrates this point well.[1220] He studied the fermentation of a purified pectin by many organisms of fecal origin, isolated from the sludge of creamery wastes, and from miscellaneous other sources. All together, some 80 different organisms were tested. Various strains of the same organism behaved quite differently. For example only 7 out of 13 strains of *Bacterium oxytocum* (*Aerobacter oxytocum*) and 4 out of 9 strains of *Aerobacter aerogenes* were able to ferment pectin (as indicated by acid or gas formation). Only those organisms commonly occurring in soil were found to be capable of fermenting pectin with acid and gas formation. The organisms isolated from creamery wastes were not able to ferment pectin.

Burkey[1221] in a very thorough study of the fermentation of corn stalks and of the various chemical constituents found in corn stalks, reviews the literature of pectin fermentation and concludes that the work reported in the literature has been conducted under such varied conditions that it is impossible to make direct comparisons and to draw general conclusions. This observation still holds. In some cases isolated pectins were used, while in others plant tissues were employed. In many reports there is no description at all of the kind of the pectin used. Burkey worked with organisms of the *Aerobacter, Bacillus,* and *Clostridium* genera and described the various species of these groups capable of fermenting pectin. The active organisms are commonly associated with the decay of plant tissue and are widely distributed in nature.

Thaysen[1222] and Thaysen and Bunker[1223] dealt with the bacterial decomposition of pectin, mostly from the standpoint of retting. Some of the bacteria found to be capable of fermenting pectin were *Clostridium pectinovorum, C. felsineum,* and *Bacillus comesii,* the latter apparently including several organisms.

In a study involving chemical and physical measurements of the changes caused by microorganisms, Pitman and Cruess[1224] studied the effect on pectin of some 30 organisms. The latter were used to inoculate

[1220] H. W. Coles, *Plant Physiol.,* 1, 379 (1926).
[1221] L. A. Burkey, *Iowa State College J. Sci.,* 3, 57 (1928).
[1222] A. C. Thaysen, in *A System of Bacteriology in Relation to Medicine.* Vol. III, H. M. Stationery Office, London, 1929, p. 16.
[1223] A. C. Thaysen and H. J. Bunker, *Microbiology of Cellulose, Hemicellulose, Pectin and Gums.* Oxford Univ. Press, London, 1927.
[1224] G. A. Pitman and W. V. Cruess, *Ind. Eng. Chem.,* 21, 1292 (1929).

a 1% solution of pectin dissolved in apple juice. Pectin content, viscosity, jellying power, acidity, and the pH of the media were determined after four months. All organisms tested except *Saccharomyces cerevisiae, S. ellipsoideus, F. niveum,* and three samples of *Mycoderma* attacked the pectin while *Acetobacter aceti* and *Bacillus amylovorus (Erwinia amylovora)* had little effect. Of course, one would not know from the results whether the pectin or the galacturonic acid was utilized by the organisms tested. As expected, molds were most destructive. The fact that yeasts will not ferment galacturonic acid has been known for some time, and yeasts have been used in the removal of various fermentable sugars from mixtures of these with uronic acids.[1225] Yeast also has been recommended for the purification of pectin extracts. Bailey[1226] suggests that the extract be adjusted to pH 3.5–3.8 and then inoculated with a pure culture of yeast of the genus *Saccharomyces* previously cultured in orange juice for 24 hours. However, in a recent study, Luh and Phaff[1227] found that yeasts such as *Saccharomyces fragilis, S. thermantitonum, Candida pseudotropicalis,* and *Torulopsis lactose* will form a pectin-digesting enzyme of the type tentatively designated as a "depolymerase" (see Chapter XIV Sect. III). It is not clear whether these organisms will utilize pectin or galacturonic acid as a source of energy. We have already noted that Etchells and Bell[1078a] found that, of 143 yeast cultures representing 66 species and varieties and 15 genera, only 4 cultures seemed to show the ability to digest pectin.

Waksman and Allen[1228] studied the decomposition of purified pectin and pectic acid by fungi and bacteria and observed that various microorganisms will attack pectin in different ways. Of the many organisms tested (mostly *Penicillium, Aspergillus,* and *Fusarium* spp.) the fungus *Trichoderma* proved to be very active in decomposing pectin. These authors observe that the pectin and pectic acid have to be decomposed before being utilized by the organisms.

Cohen[1229] in a recent investigation of the K-12 strain of *Escherichia coli* found that this organism could be adapted to the utilization of uronic acids. Once adapted, galacturonic and glucuronic acids were fermented with equal facility while D-xylose, L-arabinose, and D-ribose were not utilized. The interesting conclusion drawn by Cohen is that

[1225] A. W. van der Haar, *Anleitung zum Nachweis, zur Trennung und Bestimmung der Monosaccharide und Aldehydsäuren.* Borntraeger, Berlin, 1920.

[1226] H. S. Bailey, U. S. Pat. 2,387,635 (1945).

[1227] B. S. Luh and H. J. Phaff, paper given at the American Chemical Society meetings, April, 1948.

[1228] S. A. Waksman and R. A. Allen, *J. Am. Chem. Soc.,* **55,** 3408 (1933).

[1229] S. S. Cohen, *J. Biol. Chem.,* **77,** 607 (1949).

this organism does not utilize the uronic acids directly but that an intermediate, whose formation is accelerated by products of glucose metabolism, must be produced before the oxidation or acid formation from uronic acids can begin.

Schneider[1230] was one of the first investigators of the digestion of pectin by fecal bacteria. His tests with pure cultures of *Bacillus coli communis* (*Eschericha coli*) indicated that, in the digestion of pectin by intestinal bacteria, this organism was neither the chief nor an important factor. Coles' work on this subject has already been noted.[1220] Baker and Martin[1231] studied the iodophil microflora of the cecum of the rabbit with special regard to the disintegration of plant cell wall constituents and described a number of bacteria involved. Werch, Jung, Day, Friedemann, and Ivy[1232] have used a liquid medium containing purified pectin or galacturonic acid in a study of pectin fermentation by intestinal organisms. The pectin-fermenting organisms which were isolated and identified belonged to *Aerobacillus, Lactobacillus, Micrococcus,* and *Enterococcus* (probably *Streptococcus faecalis*). Both pectin and galacturonic acid fermentation resulted in the formation of formic and acetic acids. Very little galacturonic acid could be found during the fermentation of pectin; apparently the galacturonic acid is rapidly utilized as it is formed from pectin.

There are many references in the literature to the bactericidal action of pectin and of the galacturonic acid derived from pectin by hydrolysis but the situation is far from clear. The well-established beneficial effect of pectin as a surgical dressing of wounds (Chapter XXVIII, I-2) is one of the important related matters but it seems that, contrary to former claims, this wound-healing property of pectin does not depend on bactericidal action.

Haynes, Tompkins, Washburn, and Winters[1233] found that, in using a commercial pectin preparation, bactericidal effects could be observed. Subsequently it was discovered that this preparation contained some nickel[1234] and this started a vigorous investigation to demonstrate the benefits[1235] and the working mechanism of nickel pectinate as a bacteri-

[1230] E. C. Schneider, *Am. J. Physiol.,* **30,** 258 (1912).
[1231] F. Baker and R. Martin, *Zentr. Bakt., II,* **96,** 18 (1937); quoted from G. H. Joseph, *Bull. Natl. Formulary Comm.,* **9,** (1), 2 (1940).
[1232] S. C. Werch, R. W. Jung, A. A. Day, T. E. Friedemann, and A. C. Ivy, *J. Infectious Diseases,* **70,** 231 (1942).
[1233] E. Haynes, C. A. Tompkins, G. Washburn, and M. Winters, *Proc. Soc. Exptl. Biol. Med.,* **36,** 839 (1937).
[1234] E. Haynes, C. A. Tompkins, G. W. Crook, and M. Winters, *Proc. Soc. Exptl. Biol. Med.,* **39,** 478 (1938).
[1235] P. B Myers and A. H. Rouse, *Am. J. Digestive Diseases,* **7,** 39 (1940).

cidal agent. These experiments[1234] showed that nickel pectinate inhibited the growth of a number of organisms, among them *Staphylococcus aureus*, *Shigella paradysenteriae* Flexner, *Pseudomonas aeruginosa*, *Erwinia carotovora*, *Escherichia coli*, and beta-hemolytic *Streptococcus*. Arnold[1236] reported that combinations of certain metals with pectin have more bactericidal action than the metals alone. In due time nickel pectinate was patented[1237] and supplied through the drug trade[1238] for various medicinal purposes. It was also clearly established that nickel pectinate was not toxic to young rats.[1239] In fact the feeding of this compound was claimed to increase the efficiency of thiamine and vitamin A in their diet.[1240]

It is clear from scores of references in the literature that pectin has no bactericidal action. For instance, Prickett and Miller[1241] found no inhibitory effect on the growth of *E. coli* cultures even when 1% pectin was used.

At the present time there is considerable doubt whether the bactericidal action of nickel pectinate is a specific effect. Manville and Sullivan[1242] found that the addition of pectin does not enhance the inhibitory effect of metallic ions (copper, cobalt, and nickel) on bacterial growth (*Escherichia coli* and *Staphylococcus aureus*). In fact, in small concentrations, the metallic ions were more effective in the absence of dehydrated apples. Prickett and Miller[1243] also observed that the bactericidal effect of nickel pectinate is proportional to the nickel concentration in the media and is not affected by pectin. It would seem, therefore, that if nickel pectinate does have any beneficial action in certain cases, this does not depend on the specific bactericidal effectiveness of this compound. On the other hand, the possibility that the use of nickel as a pectinate might make the otherwise toxic metal harmless to the human or animal body and yet retain the effectiveness of the bactericidal action of the nickel should not be overlooked. We shall return in Chapter XXVIII, Section I, to the detoxicating effect of pectin in the case of metal poisonings.

In a recent article suggesting the use of low-ester pectins for bacteriological media, Jones[1244] observed the growth of *Bacterium phytoph-*

[1236] L. Arnold, *Am. J. Digestive Diseases*, **6**, 104 (1939).

[1237] P. B. Myers, U. S. Pat. 2,259,767 (1941).

[1238] Manufactured by Eli Lilly & Co., Indianapolis, Indiana. Nickel pectinate is also used in various mixtures, such as *Tomectin* (manufactured by Ayerst, McKenna and Harrison Ltd. of Montreal), for combating diarrhea.

[1239] L. Arnold, *Am. J. Digestive Diseases*, **6**, 103 (1939).

[1240] W. H. Eddy, *Med. Record*, **153**, 211 (1941); through *C. A.*, **36**, 562 (1942).

[1241] P. S. Prickett and N. J. Miller, *Proc. Soc. Exptl. Biol. Med.*, **40**, 27 (1939).

[1242] I. A. Manville and N. P. Sullivan, *Am. J. Digestive Diseases*, **7**, 106 (1940).

[1243] P. S. Prickett and N. J. Miller, *J. Pediat.*, **15**, 710 (1939).

[1244] D. R. Jones, *Nature*, **158**, 625 (1946).

thorum (*Erwinia*), *B. carotovorum* (*Erwinia*), *B. aroidea* (*Erwinia*), *Bacillus polymyxa*, *B. subtilis*, and some other organisms when the low-ester pectin was the only source of carbon. We shall return later to the use of various pectic substances in bacteriological media (see Chapter XXVIII).

One cannot conclude this discussion more appropriately than with a quotation from Burkey,[1221] who stated two decades ago that "our knowledge concerning the pectin fermenting bacteria is limited and fragmentary." One might extend this statement to the whole field of microbial utilization of pectic substances. Further systematic work in this field with the modern technics of bacteriology and pectin chemistry is sorely needed.

CHAPTER XVII

Behavior of Pectic Substances in the Animal Body

I. DIGESTIBILITY AND NUTRITIONAL VALUE

Schneider[1245] in 1912 fed apple pomace and pectin to human subjects and found that practically no pectin could be recovered from the feces. McCance and Lawrence[1246] reviewed this subject in 1929 and stated that the fate of ingested pectin was uncertain. Imhäuser[1247] found that starved dogs which had been fed phlorizin were not protected from fatty degeneration of the liver by pectin. He claimed, however, that pectin administered orally to these dogs had a definite effect on the formation of ketone bodies, and that a portion of the pectin molecule must be connected with carbohydrate metabolism. Voit and Friedrich[1248] found that pectin fed in doses of 100 g. per day was not toxic to human subjects but caused a 4-fold increase in the formic acid content of the urine. He thought that the formic acid was produced by the oxidation of the methanol split off from the pectinic acid.

There is now ample evidence[1249] that pectin, even when fed in large quantities to healthy humans, dogs, rabbits, etc., does not reappear in the feces except possibly in small quantities. Some investigators, such as Fürth and Engel,[1250] Manville, Bradway, and McMinis,[1251] and others, believe that pectin is a digestible carbohydrate and is hydrolyzed and utilized in the animal body in a manner similar to other polysaccharides. However, it is now quite clear that this is not the case. There is over-

[1245] E. C. Schneider, *Am. J. Physiol.*, 30, 258 (1912).
[1246] R. A. McCance and R. D. Lawrence, *The Carbohydrate Content of Foods.* Med. Research Council (London) Special Rept. Series 135 (1939).
[1247] K. Imhäuser, *Arch. exptl. Path. Pharmakol.*, 167, 702 (1932); quoted from G. H. Joseph, *Bull. Natl. Formulary Comm.*, 9 (1), 2 (1940).
[1248] K. Voit and H. Friedrich, *Klin. Wochschr.*, 14, 1792 (1935); through *C. A.*, 30, 3030 (1936).
[1249] S. C. Werch, R. W. Jung, A. A. Day, T. E. Friedmann, and A. C. Ivy, *J. Infectious Diseases*, 70, 231 (1942).
[1250] O. Fürth and P. Engel, *Biochem. Z.*, 237, 159 (1931).
[1251] I. A. Manville, E. M. Bradway, and A. S. McMinis, *Can. Med. Assoc. J.*, 36, 252 (1937).

whelming evidence that ingested pectin passes through the animal body until it reaches the large intestine (colon) where it is attacked and digested by the microbial flora.[1245,1249,1252-1254] Tests to find pectin-digesting enzymes in the human and animal body have failed.[1253]

The efficiency of bacterial digestion depends on the rate at which the food residues pass through the colon and on the composition and vigor of the bacterial cultures in the latter. Most investigators have found that pectin is easily, and in most cases completely, digested upon incubation with feces; others have found that digestion is incomplete, and McFadden, Weaver, and Scherago[1255] could find no digestion of the feces at all. While this last observation is contrary to many other reports, it would be a mistake to assume that it is therefore erroneous. There are endless variations in the composition of the intestinal flora and it is quite plausible that in this unusual case for some unknown reason the microorganisms were unable to attack pectin. The effect of diet on intestinal flora is now well appreciated, as is the fact that the flora change radically in the case of fasting or any disease such as dysentery. Indeed, the efficiency of pectin in the treatment of diarrhea (Chap. XXVIII) depends on the fact that the pectin does to a considerable extent escape digestion. Of course, other conditions, such as the pH of the content of the colon, also have a major influence and this factor alone might cause much variation in the effectiveness of digestion. The pH of human feces may also vary from 5.9 to 8.8.[1256]

The bacterial fermentation of pectin was discussed in Chapter XVI. However, it is of additional interest whether the human or animal body derives any benefit from the ingestion and subsequent bacterial digestion of pectin.

Altogether, there is some doubt concerning the extent of adsorption from the large intestine. It is quite certain that pectin as such is not absorbed. Werch and Ivy[1257] state that it is doubtful whether any of the galacturonic acid produced from pectin may be absorbed at all; but if it is, the extent is certain to be below 10% of the total amount of galacturonic acid ingested in the form of pectin. Imhäuser[1247] fed pectin to dogs and was unable to show any increase in the blood sugar, a good indication that most of the pectin was fermented rather than absorbed as galacturonic acid. From feeding experiments with rats, Ershoff and

[1252] F. Ehrlich, K. Imhäuser, and K. Voit, *Schl. Gesel. f. Vaterlande,* **103,** 104 (1930–31); quoted in reference 1249.

[1253] Z. I. Kertesz, *J. Nutrition,* **20,** 289 (1940).

[1254] S. C. Werch and A. C. Ivy, *Am. J. Digestive Diseases,* **8,** 101 (1941).

[1255] D. B. McFadden, R. W. Weaver, and M. Scherago, *J. Bact.,* **44,** 191 (1942).

[1256] E. G. Wakefield and M. H. Power, *Am. J. Digestive Diseases,* **6,** 308 (1939).

[1257] S. C. Werch and A. C. Ivy, *Proc. Soc. Exptl. Biol. Med.,* **48,** 9 (1941).

McWilliams[1258] concluded that pectin, when added to a polysaccharide-free but otherwise nutritionally adequate diet, has no beneficial effect on growth, gross appearance, appetite, or food utilization. On the contrary, a certain extent of interference with the absorption and utilization of other nutrients can be observed. These authors state that, in the case of nutritionally inadequate diets or with other species of animals, the results might be different. Suffice it to say here that thus far there is no indication that the pectin ingested by any animal is of direct nutritional benefit.

The situation may be different if indirect benefits from pectin are considered, although here again observations are spotty and often inconclusive. There is no doubt that ingested pectin exerts a definite action in reducing the coagulation time of blood. Manville, Bradway, and Mc-Minis[1259] believe that ingested pectin and especially the galacturonic acid formed upon its hydrolysis are useful to the body as detoxicants and in the synthesis of mucus. Galacturonic acid can detoxicate some compounds in a manner similar to glucuronic acid and Manville[1260] feels that, when uronic acids are abundantly supplied for detoxication purposes, the mucous membrane is spared the danger of being deprived of materials essential in the synthesis of mucin. Indeed, Kobren, Fellers, and Esselen[1261] found that feeding pectin to rats retarded xerosis of the mucous membranes.

Ingested pectin and galacturonic acid may also have some effect on the intestinal flora[1262] and on the well being of the animal through the assumed bactericidal effect of both pectin and galacturonic acid. Although this point was discussed in Chapter XVI, it can be repeated that this matter is still far from clear. Werch, Jung, Plenk, Day, and Ivy[1263] believe that, if pectin and galacturonic acid have any bactericidal action, it is caused by the acid nature of these compounds rather than by any specific effect.

Flaschenträger, Cagianut, and Meier[1264] found that when galacturonic acid is fed to human subjects, there is a 5- to 15-fold increase in 2,5-furandicarboxylic acid in the urine.

From the experiments of Millis and Reed[1265] on the effect of sodium

[1258] B. H. Ershoff and H. B. McWilliams, *Am. J. Digestive Diseases,* 12, 21 (1945).
[1259] I. A. Manville, E. M. Bradway, and A. S. McMinis, *Am. J. Digestive Diseases,* 3, 570 (1936).
[1260] I. A. Manville, *Arch. Pediat.,* 55, 76 (1938).
[1261] A. Kobren, C. R. Fellers, and W. B. Esselen, Jr., *Proc. Soc. Exptl. Biol. Med.,* 41, 117 (1939).
[1262] W. E. Woolridge and G. W. Mast, *Am. J. Surg.,* 78, 881 (1949).
[1263] S. C. Werch, R. W. Jung, H. Plenk, A. A. Day, and A. C. Ivy, *Am. J. Diseases Children,* 63, 839 (1942).
[1264] B. Flaschenträger, B. Cagianut, and F. Meier, *Helv. Chim. Acta,* 28, 1489 (1945); through *C. A.,* 40, 2199 (1946).
[1265] J. Millis and F. B. Reed, *Biochem. J.,* 41, 273 (1947).

alginate on calcium absorption, it is likely that pectin does not interfere with calcium absorption. This is a plausible assumption since in healthy animals the pectin is mostly or entirely decomposed and therefore an opportunity is provided for the absorption of any calcium which may be bound to a pectinic or pectic acid.

Rothschild[1266] reported that the specific antibodies of antiserum from rabbits are fixed only through the mono- and polygalacturonic acids in the "complement fixation" test. This, he claims, gives a new method— other than diazotization—for demonstrating the antigenic properties of galacturonic acid.

II. PECTIC SUBSTANCES IN THE BLOOD STREAM

Although blood flows continually through the many arteries and veins of the body without clotting, the delicate balance of blood constituents shifts to allow coagulation on wounds. Hemostatic substances added to blood in the living animal must not cause clotting in the circulating blood but must hasten coagulation of drawn blood.[1267]   Pectin, when ingested orally or introduced intramuscularly or intravenously, has been found to accelerate the coagulation of drawn blood; when added outside the body to previously drawn blood, it does not seem to have any particular effect. Orally administered pectin also exhibits a styptic action throughout the gastrointestinal tract.

The hemostatic effect of pectin was discovered by Violle and Saint-Rat[1268] and this subject now has a very extensive literature. It would be out of place in this volume to discuss this matter in detail and therefore only a short summary of the most important developments will be given. Reference should be made to the summaries in the literature of this topic by Joseph[1267] and Marx,[1269] and to the excellent review by Deuel.[1270]

In spite of the many articles which discuss this phenomenon, the hemostatic effect of pectin is not clearly understood. This is at least partly the result of the ever-changing conceptions concerning the mechanism of blood coagulation. The methodology of this subject is also far from standardized. The variations in the pectin preparations used in the past and the lack of definitions for these also constituted major drawbacks. Many of the older experiments will have to be repeated on this account.

[1266] H. Rothschild, *Enzymologia*, 5, 329 (1938).
[1267] G. H. Joseph, *Bull. Natl. Formulary Comm.*, 9 (1), 2 (1940).
[1268] H. Violle and L. de Saint-Rat, *Compt. rend.*, 180, 603 (1925).
[1269] R. Marx, "Beitrag zur experimentellen Untersuchung des Mechanismus der Wirkung von Pektin auf Blutgerinnung und Blutstillung und zum Studium des Verhaltens von Pektin im Stoffwechel," *Dissertation*, Munich, 1939.
[1270] H. Deuel, *Schweiz. med. Wochschr.*, 75, 1 (1945).

The hemostatic effect of pectin does not depend on gel formation. In fact, the experiments of Kopaczewski and Muttermilch[1271] have shown that if rabbits are injected with sodium pectate embolism ensues. This apparently occurs through precipitation of a calcium pectate formed with the calcium of blood serum and subsequent blocking of the blood capillaries. Violle and Saint-Rat[1268] injected a pectin solution followed by injection of a pectin-methylesterase solution. This again resulted in the death of the animals, showing that the enzyme deesterifies the pectinic acid in the blood stream. It is now clear that the pectinic acids used in injections must not be precipitable by calcium. While this is clear in the case of direct introduction into the blood stream, the situation is different with ingested pectin where toxic effects have not been observed whether the pectinic acid is precipitable by calcium or not.

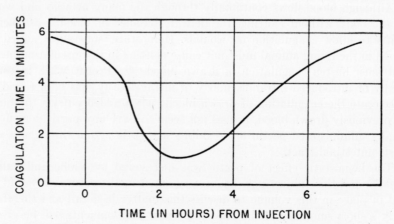

TIME (IN HOURS) FROM INJECTION

Fig. 26. Effect of intramuscular injection of a pectin solution on the coagulation of rabbit blood (adapted from Riesser and Nagel).
The 20 cc. pectin solution was injected at zero hour.

There is very good agreement among the many authors who studied this subject that this specific hemostatic action exists. The results of a typical experiment with rabbits[1272] are shown in Figure 26. However, when it comes to experimental work with drawn blood, there is a great deal of discrepancy among the various observations and the mechanism of the reaction is not at all clear. As noted above, when pectin is added to drawn blood it does not affect coagulation time. This would make one believe that the pectin does not directly cause the increased tendency to

[1271] W. Kopaczewski and S. Muttermilch, Z. Immunitätsforsch., 22, I, 539 (1914); quoted in reference 1270.
[1272] O. Riesser and A. Nagel, Arch. exptl. Path. Pharmakol., 179, 748 (1935).

coagulate, but that in the animal organism its presence effects some changes which lead to this property. Thus, Riesser and Nagel[1272] believe that the effect of pectin consists in stimulation of the production of thrombokinase. Dietrich and Oettel[1273] feel that pectin affects not one but several phases of the blood coagulation mechanism. Barth and Rumpelt[1274] recently found in laboratory and clinical tests that the hemostatic action is typical of the pectin macromolecule and not of its split products. They feel that pectin acts on the prothrombin-antithrombin complex. It is also clear now that the ingestion or injection of pectin has little effect on the coagulation time of normal blood, whereas the effect is pronounced in cases in which for some reason the coagulation time is abnormally long.

Of the many *in vitro* studies of the effect of pectin on blood constituents only a few will be mentioned here. Baumann[1275] found that the addition of pectin increased the coagulation time in proportion to the lowering of the pH effected in the test solution. Wunderly[1276] states that pectin does not react with serum nor with serum albumin, but does so with fractions of paraglobulin. Ziegelmayer[1277] found that the addition of pectin to uncoagulated human and horse blood increased the amount of serum which separated. Bergström[1277a] and Karrer, König, and Usteri[1277b] found that the sulfuric ester of pectin had a heparin-like delaying effect on blood coagulation.

Bryant, Palmer, and Joseph[1278] have demonstrated that when pectin is injected intravenously into rabbits, it disappears in 7 days and that there is no pectin accumulation in the liver and kidneys. Thus the pectin is eventually removed from the body. The fate of the pectin is not entirely clear since it is well established that only a part of the polyuronide can be recovered in the urine. Some constituents not normally present in blood and urine[1269] have been found after pectin injection.

The fact that ingested pectin is also effective as a hemostatic may indicate a certain extent of absorption in the animal body. Orally administered pectin, as a rule, is less effective and becomes effective later than injected pectin. Some clinicians prefer to administer the pectin solution

[1273] S. Dietrich and H. Oettel, *Deut. med. Wochschr.*, 65, 1690 (1937); quoted in reference 1267.

[1274] H. Barth and H. Rumpelt, *Pharmazie*, 2, 504 (1947); through *Z. Lebensm.-Untersuch. u. Frosh.*, 89, 465 (1949).

[1275] E. Baumann, *Bruns' Beitr. klin. Chir.*, 166, 298 (1937); quoted in reference 1267.

[1276] C. Wunderly, *Schweiz. Z. Path. u. Bakt.*, 6, 437 (1943).

[1277] W. Ziegelmayer, *Kolloid-Z.*, 71, 214 (1935).

[1277a] S. Bergström, *Z. physiol. Chem.*, 238, 163 (1936).

[1277b] P. Karrer, H. König, and E. Usteri, *Helv. Chim. Acta*, 26, 1296 (1944).

[1278] E. F. Bryant, G. H. Palmer, and G. H. Joseph, *Proc. Soc. Exptl. Biol. Med.*, 49, 279 (1942).

intravenously; others believe that intramuscular administration is more effective.[1267,1270]

We shall return in Chapter XXVIII to the various commercial pectin preparations which are used as hemostatics and to some of the specific instances in which the use of pectin as a hemostatic agent in the human has been suggested. The use of pectin as a plasma substitute will also be discussed in Chapter XXVIII.

PART FOUR
MANUFACTURE OF PECTIC SUBSTANCES

CHAPTER XVIII

Pectin Manufacture

I. INTRODUCTION

The goal of pectin manufacture is to obtain a product representing the highest jelly grade yield economically from the raw material in a condition which conforms with legal standards and trade requirements.

Because of the many unknown factors which must be faced in connection with pectic substances (especially concerning the nature of protopectin), pectin manufacture is still as much an art as a science; its success depends on the skillful balancing of many important factors. Laboratory methods for the preparation of various pectic substances were discussed in Chapter VI; in the following chapters pectin manufacture will be discussed, together with methods of evaluating raw products and pectin itself. In fairness to the reader, it should be stated that there are gaps in the information presented here and that there is no doubt that on some important points many manufacturers have better information on hand. This condition is essentially the result of a situation common in industrial production, namely, that the scientific, technologic, and patent literatures are far behind actual developments as practiced by more progressive manufacturers. Much of the essential information on manufacturing processes is never published and it can be said without malice that patents are often applied for only when the danger of the information becoming available to others is imminent. Even then, the amount of enlightenment which is gained makes it doubtful at times whether the purpose of the patent is disclosure or just the opposite. This is not said in criticism; such methods are an essential part of competitive free enterprise.

The development of the pectin industry in the United States was reviewed by Rooker,[1279] in whose book Daughters has also dealt with the patents issued in this field. Lathrop[1280] in 1929 reviewed pectin patents

---

[1279] W. A. Rooker, *Fruit Pectin*. Avi, New York, 1928.
[1280] C. P. Lathrop, *Glass Packer*, **2**, 463 (1929).

for the National Preservers Association. Ripa[1281] lists all the major pectin patents up to about 1936.

The patent situation with regard to pectin manufacture is exceptionally confused. Ever since the first pectin patents were issued, overlapping claims, claims of an unreasonable nature, and claims of extreme looseness abound. The many ill-defined and unclear phases of the chemistry and technology of pectic substances make this confusion inevitable. As a consequence, lawsuits and litigations have been so frequent in the pectin industry that it would take the better part of this volume to discuss this topic in detail and in fairness to all. For this reason, patents will be quoted in the text only in their appropriate connection without any attempt to cover and evaluate the pectin patent literature which now contains several hundred patents issued in a dozen countries.

The following outline of the development of pectin industries makes no claim for completeness either in historical detail or in statistics. Its only purpose is to provide some background for the discussion of manufacturing methods. May it be said, furthermore, that this is not a handbook on pectin manufacture. The variations in production processes are mostly dictated by ever-changing interplay of many factors. The present purpose is only to make these factors and variations clear, thereby to provide some foundation for judgment to those workers who must select conditions which, under the given conditions, will give the best results. The written word, however, can substitute at best for only part of the unavoidable experimentation, and experience must have the final word.

II. DEVELOPMENT OF THE PECTIN INDUSTRY

Jelly making was practiced long before pectin was discovered. An article which appeared in the *London Housewife's Family Companion* in 1750 gives instructions for the preparation of apple, currant, and quince jellies. Many old cook books give recipes for making fruit products which are now classified as jellies and jams.

Braconnot[1282] made jellies with pectin as early as 1820, but it was not until the early part of the present century that pectin manufacture on a substantial commercial scale commenced. Before this time the use of fruit juices and fruit juice concentrates for jelly making was quite common. At times these "jellying juices" were combinations of fruit juices and pectin extracted from the insoluble pulp, while in other cases they simply represented heat-preserved concentrates of fruit

[1281] R. Ripa (Sucharipa), *Die Pektinstoffe*. 2nd ed., Serger und Hempel, Braunschweig, 1937.
[1282] H. Braconnot, *Ann. chim. phys.*, **28**, 173 (1925).

juices. Very often, especially in Europe, they were made in a manner which incorporated the water-insoluble pulp of the fruit.

During the early years of the twentieth century, pectin manufacture was developed step-by-step in Europe and in this country. Apple pomace was the first major source of pectin. The commercial-scale drying of apple pomace was practiced for a long time in Germany, especially on the upper Rhine, and the product was sold to manufacturers of jams and jellies. In 1908 the Pomosin Werke, at Frankfort, started the production of concentrated liquid apple pectin. A crude pectin extract, sold under the name *Pastazzo*, was on the market in Italy in the same year.[1281] The latter was made from the residue of citric acid manufacture from lemons and contained about 10% total solids. The large-scale commercial drying of apple pomace commenced in England about 1910, in France in 1911, and in the United States about 1915.[1283]

The publications of Goldthwaite[1284,1285] in 1909–1910, which contain both theoretical information (such as the formation of jellies with polyhydroxy compounds like glycerol instead of sugars) and the results of experiments on pectin extraction, undoubtedly had a profound effect on the development of the pectin industry in this country. Goldthwaite recognized the importance of acidity control in jelly making, as well as the significance of the pectin–sugar–acid ratio, and this new knowledge greatly enhanced the commercial usefulness of pectins. The information contained in these articles, together with the news that pectin could be successfully manufactured and marketed, made the time ripe for the beginning of large-scale developments. In 1913 Douglas[1286] obtained his now classical U. S. Patent 1,082,682, which had much to do with the development of the pectin industry and for this reason will be quoted in part:

"Jelly forming substances may be obtained from fruits or vegetables and I prefer to employ apples as the source of the product on account of the cheapness, the ease with which they may be handled and the comparatively large content of pectose substances which form constituent elements of this fruit. The latter may be treated in various ways to yield the pectous or jelly forming substances, preferably by processing the fruit pulp after the fruit juices have been expressed from the raw fruit to remove the saccharine juices, or natural sugar. This removal of the saccharine juices may also be accomplished by the process of diffusion with water. The fruit pulp thus prepared is then treated with a suitable solvent such as hot or boiling water to which may be added a small proportion of any suitable acid. The addition of the said acid is not at all times necessary and

[1283] G. P. Walton and G. L. Bidwell, *U. S. Dept. Agr.*, Bull. No. 1166 (1923).
[1284] N. E. Goldthwaite, *Ind. Eng. Chem.*, **1**, 333 (1909); **2**, 457 (1910).
[1285] N. E. Goldthwaite, *Univ. Illinois*, Bull. No. 31 (1914); revised 1917.
[1286] R. Douglas, U. S. Pat. 1,082,682 (1913).

depends largely upon the degree of ripeness of the fruit or its acidity and I only deem its use desirable in comparatively small quantities for the purpose of assisting in liberating the pectous properties of the fruit from the pulp. The treatment of the fruit pulp, it will be understood, may be treated in a digester and the processing done under pressure.

"The pectous liquors obtained from the fruit pulp are nearly devoid of all natural sugar and I have discovered that the removal or separation of the sugar contents of the fruit from the pectous or jelly forming substance renders these incapable of jellifying by themselves and permits the liquor to be highly reduced or concentrated. To accomplish and to obtain the desired density I evaporate, preferably in vacuo, the excess water and form a syrupy viscous extract. In using the latter a given quantity thereof may be added to a simple syrup of sugar and water of proper proportion, depending upon the degree of concentration of the pectous product, whereupon the formation of a jelly immediately commences.

"A food product obtained in accordance with my invention may be in various degrees of concentration and when packed in proper containers may be kept indefinitely...."

The apple pectin concentrate developed by Douglas was a phenomenal success. The product, mostly sold in small bottles under the name of Certo for the making of jams and jellies in the home, became an everyday article all over the world. In 1929 18,000,000 bottles of Certo were sold and it has been estimated that 40% of homemakers making jams and jellies in this country have used it. It was reported that in test sales at Cooper's in Liverpool, England, 1800 bottles were sold in two weeks.[1287] The Douglas Corporation, through several stages of development, eventually became the Certo Division of General Foods Corporation, now located at Albion, N. Y. Meanwhile other groups also commenced pectin manufacture. The first dry apple pectin powder is claimed to have been introduced by Speas Company of Kansas City, now the largest manufacturer of apple pectin. The first citrus pectin was sold in the United States in 1924, and in 1926 the California Fruit Grower's Exchange erected a plant for its manufacture. By 1930 the major domestic manufacturers of pectin were well established and included, in addition to the above companies, National Fruit Product Co. of Winchester, Virginia, and Mutual Citrus Products Co. of Anaheim, California. A number of other manufacturers are or were since engaged in pectin production and of these the following may be noted: John C. Morgan Co., Traverse City, Michigan; Krouse Corporation, Peach Glenn, Pa.; Enzo Jell Co., Sheboygan, Wisc.; Germantown Manufacturing Co., Philadelphia, Pa.; Universal Colloid Co., McAllen, Texas (a subsidiary of Sardik Food Products Co.); Citrus Concentrates, Inc., Dunedin, Florida

[1287] J. L. Reade, *Canning Age,* 13 (6), 284 (1932).

Tasty Food Inc., Oregon; and Jam-Jel Corporation, Pacific Food Products Co., and West Coast Products Co. on the West Coast. Some of these companies, including many preservers not noted here, made pectin extracts for their own use. The great expansion of pectin production in this country during the war did not result in the development of any new major pectin producer.

In 1940 about 60% of the pectin produced consisted of citrus pectin, while in recent years the proportion of apple pectin has decreased to about 25% of the total production. This preferential development of citrus pectin production at the expense of apple pectin is at least partly caused by the great abundance of cheap citrus peel which has resulted from the tremendously increased production of canned and frozen citrus juices and concentrates. This trend toward citrus pectin is unfortunate in view of the slight but definite preference given by some manufacturers of jams and especially of jellies to apple pectin over citrus pectin. The reason for the preference appears to be an apparently never clearly demonstrated contention that products made with apple pectin show, in comparable firmness, more "resilience" and are therefore less liable to damage during transportation. A better texture has also been often claimed for products (especially jellies) made with apple pectin.

III. PECTIN PRODUCTION IN THE UNITED STATES. IMPORTS AND EXPORTS

There are no dependable statistics concerning the quantity of pectin manufactured in the United States before 1937. Production between 1937 and 1946 is shown in Table 66. The estimated 1947 production was about

TABLE 65

Dry (Solid) Pectin Production and Usage in the United States from July 1, 1941 to June 30, 1942

Source of pectin	Preserving industry	Household users	Export	Miscel- laneous[a]	Govt. purchases	Total
	In 1000 lbs. dry pectin calculated on 100 grade basis					
Apple........	684	427	52	23	60	1246
Citrus........	1161	167	79	499	775	2681
Totals........	1845	594	131	522	835	3927

[a] Includes a variety of usages such as in the baking industry, for confections, in pharmaceuticals and cosmetics, etc.

the same as in 1946. The present extent of pectin manufacture is very much affected by the dollar shortage in many countries.

The increase in production from 1940 to 1942 was spectacular. In

1942 about 66% of the pectin produced was solid powdered pectin and the rest in the form of pectin concentrates. Part of this rapid expansion was the direct result of government purchases and aid given for the extension of production facilities. To illustrate this point, Table 67 shows the amount of dry pectin purchased by the United States Government for shipment abroad, mostly to England and Australia.

In addition, great quantities of pectin raw materials, such as apple pomace and dried and sulfited citrus peel, were also shipped to England

TABLE 66

PECTIN PRODUCTION IN THE UNITED STATES (COMPILED FROM VARIOUS SOURCES)[a]

Year	Total pectin production (on basis of 100 grade solid pectin), lbs.
1937	2,000,000
1938	2,500,000
1940	2,500,000
1942	6,000,000
1943	6,300,000
1944	6,300,000
1945	6,500,000
1946	6,200,000

[a] Includes all types of products.

TABLE 67

LEND-LEASE PURCHASES OF PECTIN DURING WORLD WAR II (COMPILED FROM VARIOUS SOURCES)

Fiscal year	Pectin (on 100 grade basis), lbs.
1942–43	2,300,000
1943–44	2,300,000
1944–45	1,400,000
1945–46	1,000,000
1946–47	None

for pectin making or direct use by jam manufacturers. During the period April, 1941 to August, 1942, such shipments amounted to over 20,000,-000 lbs.

These shipments abroad of pectin and pectin raw materials left domestic users with insufficient pectin. The "deficit" was estimated in 1944 as approximately 1,000,000 lbs. of pectin. In the latter year about one half of the pectin produced was used in preserves, and one fourth each in confections and for other miscellaneous purposes (see Table 65).

International trade in pectin has been considerable ever since the pectin industries were developed in various countries. Pectin has been imported into this country at times from Canada, while at the same time much larger quantities were exported into the same country. As shown in Table 68, Germany frequently shipped pectin to the United States but the surprising figure is the comparatively large shipments which, according to government records, came from India and Hong-Kong. It

TABLE 68

UNITED STATES PECTIN IMPORTS, IN POUNDS, AS TAKEN FROM U. S. DEPARTMENT OF COMMERCE REPORTS[a]

Country of origin	1934	1935	1936	1938	1939	1942	1943	1945
Canada.........	780	25	—	—	—	40	530	169,245
Germany........	6400	8,335	8018	—	—	—	—	—
Italy...........	—	—	—	4050	5100	—	—	—
Netherlands.....	137	—	—	—	—	—	—	—
India and Dependencies....	—	22,500	—	—	—	—	—	—
Hong Kong.....	—	138	—	—	—	—	—	—

[a] These values are not standardized for 100 grade pectin equivalents.

is hard to avoid the impression that other materials, likely some gums or mucilages (of which large quantities are imported from the East), might have been misclassified as "pectin." Such a suspicion is in agreement with a recent statement by Savur and Sreenivasan[1288] that even now in India pectin is manufactured only by one small plant.

There were no imports of pectin into this country in 1937, 1940, 1941, and 1946 from any sources.

The export statistics, shown in Table 69, clearly indicate the dominant position of the United States pectin industry. It should be mentioned that the quantities of pectin given in Table 69 have not been standardized to 100 grade solid (dry) pectin. Statistics have been omitted for countries to which pectin exports did not exceed 500 lbs. during at least one year during the period shown. The effect of Lend-Lease shipments during the war is quite obvious. It can justly be said that American pectin reaches all parts of the globe.

At the present time, the status of pectin production in the United States is unsettled because of a number of factors. It remains to be seen how much of the export market can be retained by American manufacturers in view of increasing difficulties with insufficient dollar reserves in many former purchasing countries. While government purchases—often amount-

[1288] G. R. Savur and A. Sreenivasan, *J. Sci. Ind. Research* (*India*), **B5**, 41 (1946).

TABLE 69.

UNITED STATES PECTIN EXPORTS, 1938–1948, IN POUNDS, AS TAKEN FROM U. S. DEPARTMENT OF COMMERCE REPORTS[a]

Country	1938	1939	1940	1941	1942	1943	1944	1945	1946	1947	1948
Iceland	—	—	430	30	644	338	15	925	260	—	—
Canada	74,713	118,772	96,099	101,503	132,383	172,084	25,180	51,686	61,637	70,199	92,350
Newfoundland and Labrador	970	3,728	5,196	7,405	4,860	9,962	13,952	10,433	49,313	14,565	16,585
Mexico	3,915	3,757	934	4,062	4,321	3,922	3,024	4,793	3,379	3,273	8,904
Guatemala	—	—	159	—	200	—	132	950	595	1,131	587
Costa Rica	—	120	—	912	—	—	—	—	500	—	—
Panama, C. Z.	150	200	220	334	850	—	—	—	200	400	400
Bermuda	—	40	—	169	—	—	726	—	—	—	—
Cuba	600	350	830	2,463	1,055	1,448	1,714	3,785	7,607	2,331	1,055
Jamaica	—	—	—	—	—	—	517	300	1,111	400	5,200
Colombia	150	100	321	743	—	290	467	1,764	684	—	650
Venezuela	100	1,072	2,103	5,593	646	2,734	1,729	2,448	4,491	7,340	16,461
Peru	100	888	784	850	585	535	—	1,169	733	1,690	—
Bolivia	—	—	—	30	—	—	—	100	600	—	429
Chile	—	—	22	363	231	1,255	965	382	405	860	1,190
Brazil	200	3,322	800	5,410	80	415	145	4,072	17,743	26,212	10,950
Argentina	2,500	6,200	2,400	17,410	3,842	—	—	1,085	16,671	32,974	14,565
Sweden	8,870	20,652	3,200	12,700	11,000	4,050	3,100	22,100	131,594	37,650	31,450

Country	1938	1939	1940	1941	1942	1943	1944	1945	1946	1947	1948
Norway	4,100	8,500	3,000	—	—	—	—	—	2,500	344	800
Denmark	—	—	—	—	—	—	—	—	—	—	—
United Kingdom	125,290	199,175	145,387	278,571	3,732,944	1,549,753	1,178,924	488,054	404,592	—	500
Eire	3,000	16,500	2,000	—	—	—	—	—	7,500	17,850	11,000
Netherlands	29,600	21,010	8,230	—	—	—	—	—	—	10,800	60,350
Belgium and Luxembourg	9,660	5,916	—	—	—	—	—	—	—	—	200
France	5,120	3,200	500	—	—	—	—	—	66,000	4,000	—
Czechoslovakia	—	—	—	—	400	—	—	—	5,725	9,450	—
Switzerland	—	—	—	—	—	—	—	—	1,600	8,700	600
Portugal	—	—	—	—	675	1,350	400	980	1,000	800	—
Syria	—	—	—	—	—	—	—	—	—	—	—
China	—	—	—	—	—	—	—	—	2,685	500	—
Australia	—	—	—	—	11,700	29,814	34,600	25,135	29,500	149,600	23,450
Egypt	—	—	—	—	—	—	—	60,051	454	3,100	—
Union of S. Africa	—	—	—	—	—	2,200	7,736	23,540	45,476	53,995	65,680
Palestine and Transjordan	—	—	—	—	26,925	17,800	13,400	54,559	—	17,400	14,200
Italy	—	—	—	—	—	—	—	42,348	—	—	—
Total, lbs.	—	—	—	—	*3,834,707*	*1,798,500*	*1,287,726*	*804,734*	*866,212*	*682,155*	*389,147*
Total, dollar value	—	—	—	—	*3,421,918*	*1,528,059*	*1,535,698*	*1,060,387*	*962,026*	*905,490*	*514,095*

a These values are not standardized for 100 grade pectin equivalents.

ing to about one third or one half of the total production—have been discontinued, the shortage of pectin in 1945 and 1946 was only partly relieved because of the new high level in the volume of manufactured foods in these years. At the same time, the restricted supply of sugar actually kept down the production of preserves; the demand for pectin, therefore, would have been higher if not for this factor. By 1948 an approximate normal balance between unrestricted production of preserves and utilization of manufactured pectin was established; the crystallization of foreign markets, however, may take much longer.

The manufacture of pectin from sources other than apple pomace and citrus peel is still not significant in this country. Of the other raw materials, extracted beet slices and sweet potatoes may eventually achieve significance as a source of pectin for other uses than preserves. On the other hand, even this market may be maintained by apple and especially citrus pectin unless the products from other sources show some specific properties which enhance their particular usefulness or sell at a much lower price.

IV. PECTIN PRODUCTION IN OTHER COUNTRIES

Information is scanty on the production of pectin in other countries; most of what is known comes from newspapers and similar sources. No systematic statistical data are available concerning the foreign production of pectin and the movements of this commodity in international trade except as related to the United States.

Concurrently with the evolution of pectin production in this country, a sizeable industry was also developed in Germany. The German pectin field is dominated by the thirty-year-old Pomosin Werke, which produced at least two thirds of the pectin (Pomosinextrakt) made in Germany immediately before and during the recent war.[1289,1290] Some six companies supplied the other one third. The raw material was apple pomace until the manufacture of beet pectin commenced during the war. This change was due to lack of apple pomace and not to a preference for beet pectin over apple pectin. While apple pectin was also available, beet pectin was mixed with it; by 1944, however, the latter was sold without mixing. It will be of interest to see whether German manufacturers return to apple pomace as a raw material when it is made available in sufficient quantities.

The total production of pectin in Germany during 1935 was about 7223 metric tons (expressed as a "standard" concentrate), while the 1943–44

[1289] C. L. Hinton, Final Rept. No. 388, Item No. 22, H. M. Stationery Office, London (1946).
[1290] Z. I. Kertesz, Joint Intelligence Objective Agency, FIAT Final Report No. 567 (1945).

production was at the annual rate of about 20,000 tons. During the early war years Henglein[1291] estimated annual German pectin production as about 30,000 metric tons of dry pectin, but there is serious doubt concerning the validity of this figure.

Pectin production in Germany is concentrated in the Rheinland with a few other plants scattered all over the country. Although before the war Germany was not only able to supply all her own needs but also shipped pectin to other countries, during the last years of the war pectin production deteriorated rapidly in both quality and quantity until, in 1945, it was only a fraction of prewar production. Since the pectin plants were only superficially damaged during the war, production is expected to increase rapidly as conditions return to normal. It is known that some pectin is exported now (1950) by German manufacturers. Preserves played an important part in the nutrition of the German people during World War II. The mixed jams which were manufactured[1292] were used as a bread spread instead of butter and similar foods.

The commercial production of apple pectin (Elpex) was started in England in 1917 by William Evans and Co., who are still the largest manufacturers of pectin in that country. The amount of pectin produced in England was apparently never sufficient to satisfy the country's needs and, as shown in Tables 67 and 69, large quantities of pectin were regularly imported from the United States. Additional pectin was imported before the war from Germany; it is also probable that Canadian imports play an important role. The production of pectin is said to have increased considerably in England during the war and it is also known that several large manufacturers of preserves make their own pectin concentrates.

In addition to the United States, Germany, and England, pectin is produced in many other countries. Pectin production was started in the U.S.S.R. in 1930 but there is no information available on the present size and production figures of the Russian pectin industry. Large quantities of cranberry pectin have also been said to be produced in Russia. France is said to have two pectin plants, but the situation concerning the use of pectin in that country is far from satisfactory. Although Italy was one of the early producers both of solid pectin and concentrates, the present condition of its pectin industry is not known; most of the manufacture of pectin was concentrated around Messina in Sicily. In 1931 there was at least one factory in Belgium (at Materne) producing pectin. It is also claimed that Czechoslovakia has produced some pectin. Switzerland possesses at least two sizeable pectin factories, at Zürich and Bischofszell.

[1291] F. A. Henglein, unidentified reprint (1943).
[1292] Z. I. Kertesz, Joint Intelligence Objectives Agency, FIAT Final Report No. 51 (1945).

In Eire pectin production from apple pomace was started in 1941 by Pectin, Ltd., at Clownel, and by 1946 this firm was able to satisfy about one half the domestic requirements. Until World War II pectin extract was imported into Eire from Canada and Great Britain. The manufacture of liquid apple pectin was started in Denmark during the war, but the present status of the industry is unknown.

The Canadian production of pectin is apparently on the increase and was about 4,500,000 and 4,000,000 lbs. of liquid extract in 1944 and 1945, respectively. At least one plant in Nova Scotia is now producing sizeable quantities of apple pectin concentrate. It has been stated that South Africa is a current producer. In Australia pectin is produced by Pectin Australia Pty. Ltd., of Sydney, N. S. W.

Pectin is also made from the by-products of the citrus industry in Palestine.[1293] Production was started in 1942 at Sorocaba, State of Sao Paulo, Brazil,[1294] but the fate of this enterprise is not known. In India pectin is manufactured in one small plant in the Punjab.[1295]

V. RAW MATERIALS

Although pectic substances occur commonly in plants, the number of sources which may be used for the commercial manufacture of pectins is quite limited. One reason for this is that the pectic substances present in most plant tissues are not suitable for the making of the customary pectin–sugar–acid jellies. Furthermore, a manufacturing plant represents a considerable investment, and, in order to warrant this, the source material must be available for extended periods in large quantities and at a reasonable price. For these reasons there are still only two principal sources of commercial pectin, apple pomace (pumace or apple marc) obtained from cider presses and citrus peel left over after the production of citrus juices and other products. These will be discussed in detail below.

Of the secondary sources, extracted beet slices obtained during the manufacture of beet sugar are the most important. This material has for a long time been dried and used in feed mixtures and for other similar purposes. There is some question as to whether beet slices may ever become an important source for pectin production in this country, although their possible usefulness for the manufacture of types of pectic materials other than the presently accepted high jelly grade pectin should not be overlooked. Beet slices have apparently been used in Russia and with some success in Germany[1289,1290] and research on their possible usefulness is in progress in the United States.[1295]

[1293] Anonymous, Soap, Perfumery & Cosmetics, 17, 337 (1944).
[1294] C. E. Nabuco de Araujo, Chem. Eng. News, 20, 45 (1942).
[1295] H. G. Fisk, Chem. Eng. News, 26, 677 (1948).

Grape pomace has also been used for pectin manufacture. It is known that producers of grape juice and wines have, with some success, used the grape pomace left over after pressing operations. There is little reason to assume that grape pomace may become an important source material for pectin, although it contains up to 2% pectin[1296] and is available in large quantities. Mehlitz[1297] found grape pomace unsuitable for pectin making and Marsh and Pitman[1298] reached similar conclusions.

Many other sources of pectin have been suggested at various times, especially during shortages. The possible use of the seed receptacle of sunflowers was mentioned[1299] in Chapter XIII. Carrot pomace[1300] left over after expressing the juice contains about as much pectin as does apple pomace. The pectin can be extracted from sweet potatoes[1301,1302] after removal of the starch by diastatic enzymes.[1303] The crude pectin isolated by ethanol precipitation contains about 60% uronic acid and 4 to 5% methoxyl. The jellying properties of sweet potato pectin were also investigated.[1304] The commercial possibilities of this process are doubtful unless the residue obtained during the manufacture of sweet potato starch can be used for making pectin. Similar processes may also be used for the production of pectin from the residues of other root crops used for starch manufacture, such as the cassava.[1303] Bean pods and the press residue from mountain ash berries[1305] have also been investigated as a raw material for pectin. The alleged use of cranberries for pectin making in Russia was noted above. The commercial possibilities of all these raw materials for pectin are very doubtful.

Tropical plants have frequently been suggested for pectin making.[1306] The flesh of some plants of the *Agave* genus, including sisal, has been recommended as a source of pectin.[1307,1308] The pod of the pinkshower (*Cassia grandis*) has recently been described as a suitable potential

[1296] A. Mehlitz, *Konserven-Ind.*, 19, 320, 325 (1932).
[1297] A. Mehlitz, *Allgem. deut. Konserven-Ztg.*, 20, 113 (1933).
[1298] G. Marsh and G. A. Pitman, *Fruit Products J.*, 9, 187 (1930).
[1299] S. Stoikoff, *Mitt. Geb. Lebensm. Hyg.*, 39, 292 (1948).
[1300] V. L. S. Charley, D. P. Hopkins, and A. Pollard, Long Ashton Research Station, Annual Report for 1941, p. 102.
[1301] E. Yanovsky, *Food Inds.*, 11, 710 (December, 1939).
[1302] Anonymous, *Canner*, 90, 27 (March 16, 1940).
[1303] G. D. Sherman and Y. Kanehiro, *Chemurgic Digest*, 6, 65 (1947).
[1304] N. C. Boyd and M. P. Hood, personal communication, Sept. 25, 1950.
[1305] H. Hafel, Norwegian Pat. 69,651 (1945); through *C. A.*, 40, 2244 (1946).
[1306] T. M. Meyer, L. De Vos, and J. P. J. Samwel, *Ing. Nederland.-Indië*, 7, No. 9, 5 (1940); through *C. A.*, 35, 4511 (1941).
[1307] African Sisal and Produce Co. Ltd., British Pat. 556,808 (1943); through *C. A.*, 39, 1944 (1945).
[1308] C. L. Walsh, E. L. James, and T. P. Hoar, British Pat. 582,147 (1946); through *C. A.*, 41, 1778 (1947).

source of pectin.[1303] The pods contain a water-soluble gum in addition to pectin and the latter should be extracted from the residue left over from the gum manufacture. Tamarind (*Tamarindus indica*) seed received considerable publicity a short time ago as a good source of pectin,[1309] but later work makes it clear that the material obtained from this source is not a pectin at all.[1310,1311] Guava pectin was noted by Kanehiro and Sherman.[1312] Thus far, tropical plants other than citrus fruits are only potential sources of pectin, although sodium pectate is now apparently manufactured on a commercial scale from sisal.[1313,1314] In view of experience with tamarind seed "pectin" and of the statement that sisal pectin is "similar to gum tragacanth"[1308] further verification of the polygalacturonide nature of this material would be highly desirable. Banana and banana peel have also been suggested[1315,1316] for the manufacture of pectin, but, at the time at which this is being written, do not seem to offer important possibilities. It is a fitting finish for this list that the mesocarp of the bacury,[1317] Persian lime,[1318] and shoots of the Dawadawa fruit (*fernleaf nittatree* or *Parkia filicoidea*) grown on the Gold Coast[1319] have also been suggested as possible raw materials for the commercial production of pectin.

It is possible, of course, that as new types of pectin substances are developed and applied to novel uses, some of the above raw materials may attain significance. It is more than likely, for instance, that, in the rapidly developing science of low-ester pectins, eventual use can be made of some of these raw materials. It should be realized that until very recently evaluation of raw materials was made entirely on the basis of their usefulness for the customary high-ester pectin, suitable for the production of jellies which contain a high proportion of sugar. This subject will require reconsideration in view of the new fields opened up by low-ester pectins and other pectic substances for use in low-sugar jellies and other new products.

[1309] T. P. Ghose and S. Krishna, *J. Indian Chem. Soc., Ind. and News Ed.*, 5, 114 (1942).

[1310] G. R. Savur and A. Sreenivasan, *J. Biol. Chem.*, 172, 501 (1948).

[1311] H. R. Pithawala, Dissertation, U. of Bombay, 1949.

[1312] Y. Kanehiro and G. D. Sherman, *Food Inds.*, 18, 1688 (1946).

[1313] Anonymous, *Foreign Commerce Weekly*, May 6, 1944, p. 22.

[1314] Anonymous, *Food Manuf.*, 24, 245 (1949).

[1315] H. W. von Loesecke, *Fruit Products J.*, 6, 17 (1928).

[1316] H. W. von Loesecke, *J. Chem. Education*, 7, 1537 (1930).

[1317] P. R. Descartes de Garcia, *Anais assoc. quim. Brasil*, 4, 173 (1945); through *C. A*,. 40, 7309 (1946).

[1318] M. J. Mustard, *Proc. Florida Acad. Sci.*, 8, 290 (1945).

[1319] Anonymous, *Bull. Imp. Inst.*, London, 20, 461 (1922).

VI. MANUFACTURING PLANTS AND EQUIPMENT

It has been mentioned that pectin manufacturing plants should be established wherever a sufficient supply of raw materials is available. Most apple pectin plants are in apple-growing districts where the pomace is produced and is available without costly shipping. Citrus pectin factories in this country are located in California, Florida, and Texas. Beet pectin factories have thus far been restricted to countries whose climate is suitable for growing sugar beets and where this crop is the main source of sugar, such as in the U.S.S.R. and Germany.

In a pectin plant the type of construction used is not important except that the customary sanitary requirements for food plants must be met and the greatest convenience and flexibility in the manufacturing process must be provided. Pectin manufacture is a complicated process and involves considerable capital investment. Unlike many other manufacturing processes, the production of pectin needs constant vigilance and adjustment, as well as almost continuous experimentation in order to assure a maximum return, *i.e.*, the production of the highest economical yield of jelly grade units.

Pectin may be manufactured with a great variety of equipment; the control of various conditions, however, is of such dominant importance that the equipment and machinery can almost be regarded as being only of secondary significance. The variations in the equipment now used are great and scarcely two plants use similar machinery even if the steps in manufacture are essentially alike.

The purity of the water used is of major importance. In the preliminary steps, such as washing the pomace or citrus peel, the presence of excessive proportions of calcium and magnesium salts in the water causes subsequent difficulties. This is even more true of the actual extraction process, in which the use of acidulated water containing more than the smallest trace of these elements (or other metal ions) may seriously interfere with operations. This point was realized early in the industrial production of pectin and attempts are now made in all progressive pectin plants to purify the water as much as possible. Modern methods using zeolite softeners, ion exchange agents, and demineralization processes[1320] are extensively applied in pectin manufacture. Since the sensitiveness of pectins to cations increases as the ester content decreases (Chapter VII), for the manufacture of low-ester pectins of 3 to 7% methoxyl content, and of pectic acid, the purity of the water is even more important than in the case of pectins.

[1320] R. W. Porter, *Food Inds.*, 20, 691 (1948).

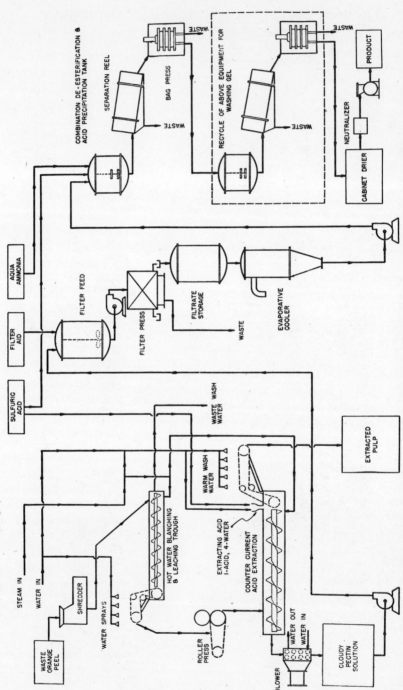

Fig. 27. Flow sheet of continuous countercurrent extraction of pectin from orange peel and of making low-ester pectin (from Owens, McCready, and Maclay).

The transportation of pomace or peel to the leaching and extraction tanks is accomplished through the customary conveyors and screws. Pectin extraction is usually a batch process and the extracted pomace or peel is either drained and extracted again or pressed after one extraction. For the latter case Rooker[1279] recommends that an individual batch be of sufficient size to be handled in one load on one of the large presses customarily used for this purpose.

Continuous extractors were sought for some time for the extraction of pectin. A continuous extraction procedure was developed during World War II at Citrus Concentrates, Inc., Dunedin, Florida, and patented

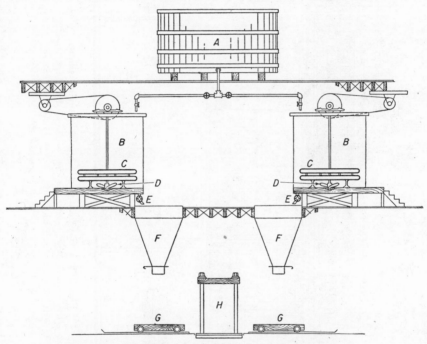

Fig. 28. Rooker's apple pectin extraction apparatus.

The acid mixing tank *A* serves two extraction units *B*. The mixture of leached pomace and dilute acid is heated by steam coils *C* and mixed by agitators *D*. After the extraction is completed, the mixture is drained through valves *E* and hoppers *F* on filter cloths held in frames on cars *G*. After the cloths are built up, the car is wheeled to hydraulic press *H* to express the pectin extract.

under the name of Nelson.[1321] Owens, McCready, and Maclay have recently described[1322] a continuous process using a countercurrent extractor for the manufacture of citrus pectin and low-ester pectin; this process is

[1321] R. C. Nelson, U. S. Pat. 2,455,382 (1948).
[1322] H. S. Owens, R. M. McCready, and W. D. Maclay, *Food Technol.*, **3**, 77 (1949).

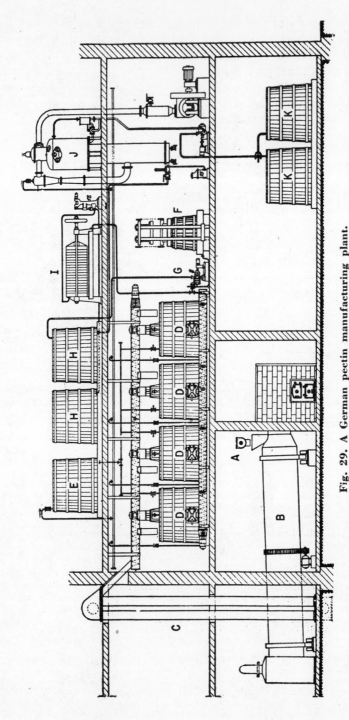

Fig. 29.   A German pectin manufacturing plant.

The wet pomace enters at A the drum dryer B and after drying is elevated C to extraction tanks D. The water is preheated in tank E. The pomace is pressed after extraction by hydraulic press F and the extract is pumped G to storage tanks H. The pectin extract is then filtered in press I and concentrated in evaporator J from where it is pumped to storage tanks K.

illustrated in Figure 27. This scheme was developed for orange peel as the starting material and it is not known just how the countercurrent extractors would work with apple pomace. Figure 28 shows the conventional type of extraction arrangement as described by Rooker,[1279] while Figure 29 illustrates a battery of extraction units used in Germany.[1323] Wooden tanks are indicated in the two latter schemes; indeed, wood was used almost universally in older plants and is still used to a considerable extent. In Europe iron tanks with an earthenware lining have also been frequently used and, of course, stainless steel equipment is being applied everywhere to an increasing extent. Since pectin extraction procedures generally use hot dilute acid, only special kinds of stainless steel equipment should be used. Inconel[1324] has been claimed to show superior resistance under conditions encountered in pectin manufacture.

The heating of the extraction mixture is usually performed through coils, although at times direct injection of live steam has also been used. The latter method is not free from objections because the overheating of some of the pomace when in contact with the steam may cause disintegration of the peel or pomace with ensuing difficulties during later steps in the process. At times the water is heated in large tanks through the direct introduction of steam and then used without any attempt at further temperature control in the extraction tank. In more modern factories steam-jacketed vessels made of stainless steel are used. Stirring in pectin extraction tanks should always be slow in order to avoid breaking up the raw material.

Of course, the acid must be introduced through acid-resistant piping and similarly, the acid extract which is produced must be transported in the same manner. Piping which is not resistant to acid not only becomes quickly corroded, but also introduces objectionable metal ions into the extract. Glass and vitreous porcelain piping is used extensively in pectin factories; the former offers many advantages in addition to acid resistance, especially in maintaining sanitary conditions. The machinery used during individual steps in pectin manufacture will be described in Chapters XIX and XX.

[1323] E. Bosche and L. Werner, *Süsswaren-Wirtschaft*, 15, Special No. 358/59, p. 22 (1943?).

[1324] Anonymous, *Chem. Eng. News*, 22, 779 (1944).

CHAPTER XIX

Apple Pectin

I. USE OF WHOLE APPLES FOR PECTIN MAKING

While apple pomace, a by-product of the manufacture of apple juice, cider, and vinegar, is the customary raw material for making apple pectin, whole apples of several varieties which become unsuitable for other purposes may also be used. Although there are some general objections to the direct use of apples for pectin making, they are potentially an important source of raw material and will therefore be discussed briefly.

Gerritz[1325] recommended the use of fresh apples to obtain pectin extracts of light color. Apple "thinnings," culls, and "June drop" apples become available at times in large quantities, and, as a rule, are not utilized in any efficient manner. Several attempts were made in recent years to encourage the use of thinnings, especially in districts where large quantities of apples are grown, but to the author's knowledge they have not been used on any significant scale in the commercial production of pectin.

Apples at this stage of development contain more and better pectin than do more mature apples.[1326] On the other hand, the fruit obtained from thinnings and "June drops" represents apples early in their development and therefore contains a considerable proportion of starch. The presence of an excessive amount of starch may cause difficulties in the production of clear pectin extracts (Section IV). The amount of starch which Browne[1327] found in a lot of maturing Baldwin apples is shown in Table 70. It is obvious from this table that Baldwin apples which are still green may contain excessive amounts of starch. Bigelow, Gore, and Howard[1328] found 2–4% starch in some unripe apples. The starch content of "culls" selected at the time of picking or later is much

[1325] H. W. Gerritz, *Ind. Eng. Chem.*, 27, 1458 (1935).
[1326] W. Eggenberger, *Ber. schweiz. botan. Ges.*, 59, 91 (1949).
[1327] C. A. Browne, Jr., *Pennsylvania Dept. Agr.*, Bull. No. 58 (1899).
[1328] W. D. Bigelow, H. C. Gore, and B. J. Howard, *U. S. Dept. Agr.*, Bull. No. 94 (1905).

lower, as is the starch content of apple pomace, because most apples
used for juice pressing are more advanced in maturity.

TABLE 70

STARCH CONTENT OF BALDWIN APPLES (ADAPTED FROM BROWNE)

Date	Condition	Starch, %
August 7	Very Green	4.14
September 13	Green	3.67
November 15	Ripe	0.17
December 15	Overripe	None

Thinnings and other undeveloped apples may also carry excessive
quantities of spray residues. The application of these economic poisons
is so calculated that, while they provide efficient control of pests and
diseases during the growing season, their concentration by the time of
picking is greatly reduced due to growth of the apple and weathering of
the residue. For this reason, it is important to wash small apples (or,
generally, apples which have been heavily sprayed) in a 1% solution of
hydrochloric acid or in some other efficient manner before further operations are started.

Baker and Goodwin[1329] recommend the following procedure for the
manufacture of pectin extracts from such apples:

After removal of the spray material, the apples are ground to about 3–6 mm.
particles and pressed with about 2500 lbs./in.² pressure. The extracted juice may
be saved for alcoholic fermentation or for the manufacture of vinegar. The
pressed pomace is leached with five times its weight of hot water at 80°C.
(176°F) for 10 minutes, with agitation. At the end of the leaching, the hot
water is drained off and cold water is added to the pomace. Grinding to a finer
particle size may be performed at this point and is beneficial for later operations.
The temperature is adjusted to about 35°C. (96°F.) and sufficient diastatic
enzyme (Section IV) is added to hydrolyze the starch within 1 hour. The completeness of hydrolysis may be checked by the customary iodine test for starch.
At this time the water is drained off and the pomace is again pressed to remove
dissolved sugars; enough water and acid are then added to obtain conditions
suitable for the extraction of the pectin. From this point on, any of the procedures which will be described in Section III for apple pomace may be used.

When the clarity of the extract is of no significance, as in the making
of some jams, treatment with the diastatic enzyme may be omitted.

Apples have also been preserved by pasteurization after grinding
(*pulping*) for subsequent use for pectin extraction. Saburov and Kalebin[1330]

[1329] G. L. Baker and M. W. Goodwin, *Fruit Products J.*, 18, 36 (1938).
[1330] N. V. Saburov and M. I. Kalebin, *Fruit Products J.*, 14, 275 (1935).

and Morris[1331] state that the addition of 0.1% sulfur dioxide is sufficient for preservation and that the preservative apparently has little harmful effect during storage. This observation is contradictory to more recent findings on the storage of wet apple pomace, as discussed in Section II.

In home preparation of pectin extracts from thinnings or June drop apples, the use of hot water is the simplest method,[1332] although an acid extract gives more pectin of better jelly grade.[1325] In home preparation from such apples the following procedure may be used:

The thinly sliced or ground apples are extracted with an equal weight of water by boiling for 20 minutes. If the fruit was pressed, an additional quantity of water equal to the amount of cider removed is used. After boiling, the extract is drained while hot through four thicknesses of cheesecloth. The bag should not be squeezed, but the mixture may be slightly pressed with a spoon. The residue removed from the bag is then boiled again with an equal amount of water for 20 minutes and the extract drained in the previously described manner. After draining, the extracts are combined and placed in a large pan so that the liquid is not more than 2 inches deep and are boiled down rapidly to about one third of the original volume or weight. This usually requires about 30 minutes. Care should be taken to avoid scorching on the bottom of the pan.

The concentrated extract is a thick, sirupy liquid. When made from sliced immature apples, the color is much lighter than when ground apples were used. Upon cooling, a sediment containing a considerable amount of pectin is usually formed. If it is desired to preserve the extract, it should be put, while boiling hot, into clean bottles or jars which have been standing in boiling water, and sealed at once. The bottles or jars should then be cooled slowly to 10°C. (50°F.) or below and stored in a cool place. About 1 pound of concentrated pectin extract can be obtained from 5 pounds of apples.[1332] Of course, the jellying ability of such concentrates varies.

II. APPLE POMACE

The use of dry apple pomace for the manufacture of pectin offers several advantages[1333] over the use of apples or wet pomace. When dry pomace is used, pectin production is not limited to the period when apples or fresh pomace are available and may be carried on at any time of the year. Drying permits storage of pomace without spoilage. Furthermore, heating of the pomace during drying causes some desirable changes in its constituents, making screening and filtering operations easier. The

[1331] T. N. Morris, *Dept. Sci. Ind. Research Brit. Rept. Food Invest. Board,* 1935, 182.
[1332] Z. I. Kertesz, *Farm Research,* 9, No. 3 (1943).
[1333] H. Ohler, *Chem.-Ztg.,* 57, 215 (1933); through *C. A.,* 27, 4598 (1933).

particles of dried pomace can be extracted to yield their pectin without disintegration; this is almost impossible with fresh apples or pomace which was not dried. The water-imbibing capacity of the pomace is reduced by drying and thus efficient extraction and subsequent drainage or pressing can be accomplished with less retention of liquid by the pomace and with a lower ratio of water to dry pomace. In addition, apple pomace is a by-product of the apple juice, cider, and vinegar mills and is thus available in large quantities at low cost. According to Petz,[1334] the drying of apple pomace is preferable to its preservation because of the lower handling and transportation costs, decreased loss of jellying value, and higher pectin yields.

The changes which occur in the pectic constituents of apples during ripening have already been discussed. At the time when apples are used in the cider mill, they contain a large proportion of their pectin in the form of protopectin, which is insoluble in water. When the cider is pressed out from the ground apples, most of the low-grade pectin dissolved in the cell sap is removed together with sugars and other soluble constituents. The residual material, called "pomace," "pumace," or "apple marc" is the chief commercial source of apple pectin.

Variety, climatic variations and other conditions of growth and maturity play an important part in the value of apples for subsequent pectin extraction. Apples grown in climates with severe winters are considered to be better sources of raw material than those grown in Southern climates. The maturity is of paramount importance because firm, hard, ripe apples give a much more suitable pomace than overripe and mealy ones in which the pectin constituents have already undergone degradation. On the other hand, the apples should contain as little starch as possible. Unripe apples contain some starch which disappears at the time when the apples reach maturity for raw eating. Apples from which the starch has completely disappeared are usually too mature to give high-grade pomace and pectin. There is, therefore, a period during the ripening of the apples when they are most suitable for giving a high-quality pomace for pectin making. Unfortunately, the pomace is a by-product and its quality is not the major consideration influencing juice-pressing operations. The present trend in this country of using for the manufacture of apple juice table apples which have proved unsaleable on the fresh market is a detrimental one from the standpoint of both the juice and the pomace. A good selection and blend of apples which gives an apple juice or cider of high quality usually also gives a high-grade pomace eminently suitable for pectin manufacture.

[1334] L. Petz, *Süsswaren-Wirtschaft*, **15,** Special No. 358/59, p. 17 (1943).

It has been estimated[1335] that during the years 1920–30 the annual output of dried apple pomace in the Eastern United States alone ranged from 2,000,000 to 5,000,000 lbs. The 1937 production was about 7,000,-000 lbs., while, with a shorter apple crop in 1940, the quantity of dried pomace amounted to about 3,000,000 lbs. The Eastern production in 1946 is estimated to have been about 6,000,000 to 7,000,000 lbs. During these periods the largest output came from Pennsylvania, West Virginia and Virginia. These three states produced nearly twice as much as New York State; in recent years their production has been even larger in proportion. Massachusetts and Michigan each produces anywhere from 500,000 to 1,000,000 lbs. of dry pomace and several hundred thousand pounds are usually produced in Wisconsin and Illinois. In addition, sizable quantities of dried pomace are produced in the Western United States, especially in the states of Washington, Oregon, and California.

Dried apple pomace has been used almost entirely for pectin manufacture. In years of abundant production some pomace is sold for stock feed[1336] but this use has never developed because of fluctuating production and higher prices paid by pectin manufacturers. It seems, however, that the use of apple pomace in insecticides is definitely on the increase.

Dried pomace made in the United States was often exported to other countries, especially England and Germany. The high comparative price commanded by American pomace on the German market[1337] in comparison with pomace of different (mostly French) origin and of lower quality[1338] is noteworthy.

1. Preparation and Preservation of Apple Pomace

In the commercial pressing of apples,[1339] the fruit is first washed. Frequently there is some spray residue on the apples, and in such cases special precautions must be taken. Soaking the apples in a 1 or 2% solution of hydrochloric acid for 5 minutes, followed by thorough rinsing in running water, removes a considerable portion of spray residue from lead arsenate. The toxic spray residues on apples formerly consisted mostly of lead and arsenic; when the juice was pressed, the pomace con-

[1335] C. C. Hall, *personal communication,* April 14, 1947.

[1336] F. W. Atkeson and G. C. Anderson, *Univ. Idaho Agr. Sta.,* Bull. No. 150 (1927).

[1337] Z. I. Kertesz, Joint Intelligence Objectives Agency, FIAT Final Report No. 51 (1945).

[1338] P. Devos, *Bull. assoc. chim.,* **61,** 361 (1944); through *C. A.,* **40,** 3221 (1946).

[1339] For further details concerning the methods of manufacture of apple products, including pomace, the reader is referred to R. M. Smock and A. M. Neubert, *Apples and Apple Products,* Interscience, New York, 1949.

tained most of the residue while the juice had only traces.[1340,1341] The pomace, therefore, sometimes contained spray residues above the permissible amounts. It is possible to remove these undesirable components from extracts made from the pomace,[1342,1343] but it is much more economical to provide for suitable washing of the fruit before the juice is pressed. The spray residue situation is now somewhat complicated because of the extensive use of DDT (dichlorophenyltrichloroethane), the residues of which are also toxic and much more difficult to remove. Hydrochloric acid wash cannot be considered effective for this purpose. Although considerable work is in progress on this important matter, there is no commonly available simple procedure known at this time which may be used effectively to remove DDT residues. Another organic spray material, parathion (O,O-diethyl O,p-nitrophenyl thiophosphate), seems to weather sufficiently not to be a serious problem.

After washing, the apples are ground in a hammer mill or preferably in a grinder or grater. It is important that this be done without excessive crushing ("mushing") of the fruit; for this reason, equipment designed to use knives is preferred.

The crushed pulp is next pressed. The old-fashioned screw press is rather inefficient and even some old types of hydraulic presses do not give sufficient freedom in manipulation to obtain good results. Up-to-date hydraulic presses are most expedient for large-scale operations and are now generally used. The pressure used depends on the design and size of the press and on other factors and is usually in the range of 5–20 kg./cm.^{2} (100–250 lbs./in.^{2}). The apples are often pressed in two steps, first using a lower pressure. Pressing is a batch operation and involves much hand work.

The "cake" or "cheese" left in the filter cloths after pressing is immediately passed through a pomace picker (disintegrator) and repressed without delay. When modern presses are used, the pomace is usually pressed once only.[1344] At times some water is used for the second pressing, usually by addition to the center of the loaded cloth. This second pressing removes more sugar and other soluble constituents from the pomace, facilitating its subsequent drying. At times the extract obtained contains enough sugar to warrant its use as vinegar stock. The pomace

[1340] H. C. McLean and A. L. Weber, *New Jersey Agr. Expt. Sta.*, J., Series (unnumbered) 1933, p. 1.

[1341] H. H. Mottern, A. M. Neubert, and P. D. Isham, *Washington Agr. Expt. Sta.*, Bull. No. 368 (1930).

[1342] V. E. Speas and N. M. Mnookin, U. S. Pat. 2,080,582 (1937).

[1343] V. E. Speas, N. M. Mnookin, and A. C. Metcalf, U. S. Pat. 2,070,870 (1937).

[1344] G. L. Baker, in E. M. Mrak and G. F. Stewart, *Advances in Food Research*, Vol. II, Academic Press, New York, 1948, p. 395.

may then be disintegrated, moistened, and repressed once more. The degree of purification attained at this time affects the success of pectin extraction. Repeated pressings also remove some of the low-grade soluble pectins which may be present in the apples (especially if they were partly mature) and, although this decreases the yield somewhat, the quality of the product is enhanced.

Recognizing the importance of thorough elimination of sugar and other soluble constituents from pomace, Douglas, in a previously noted patent,[1345] recommended their removal by pressing or by diffusion with water. This point is further amplified in one of his later patents: "In the production of the pectin solution from fruit pulps, I first extract from these the fruit juices to remove the natural sugar and flavor, as this treatment renders the pectic substances capable of concentration into stable syrupy state without jellying."[1346] Thorough washing of the apple pulp is also recommended by Barker.[1347] Several workers do not consider washing with cold water sufficiently efficient and recommend the use of hot water,[1348] acidulated water,[1349,1350] or various concentrations of ethanol.[1351–1353] Combining the benefits of acid and ethanol extractions, Leo uses a mixture of 35 to 60% ethanol with 0.5–2.0% hydrochloric acid for the purification of the pomace.[1354] Baker[1355] recommends treatment of apple pomace with diastatic enzymes after pressing and before drying. This not only eliminates the starch and the need for diastatic treatment of the extract, but also facilitates washing and drying of the pomace.

The pomace after the last pressing should contain not more than 65–75% water.

There are essentially three different ways in which the wet apple pomace may be utilized. It may be: (1) used at once in the wet form—various arguments against this were advanced earlier (in this Chapter); (2) stored in the wet condition, perhaps with the use of chemical agents to retard deterioration; or (3) dried at once.

Changes in the apple pomace occur within a few hours after pressing and the "sweetness" of the pomace is quickly lost. This is a very serious consideration when pomace dryers are not in operation in conjunction

[1345] R. Douglas, U. S. Pat. 1,082,682 (1913).
[1346] R. Douglas, U. S. Pat. 1,304,166 (1919).
[1347] B. T. P. Barker, British Pat. 125,330 (1919); U. S. Pat. 1,386,224 (1921).
[1348] G. L. Baker, U. S. Pat. 2,088,458 (1937).
[1349] Schwartauer Honigwerke, British Pat. 281,513 (1927).
[1350] Pectineire du Kervor, British Pat. 302,734 (1927).
[1351] R. H. Grandseigne, French Pat. 549,808 (1923).
[1352] J. Renotte, French Pat. 578,463 (1924).
[1353] G. L. Baker, Fruit Products J., 14, 110 (1940).
[1354] H. T. Leo, U. S. Pat. 2,038,582 (1936).
[1355] G. L. Baker, Fruit Products J., 17, 37 (1937).

with the juice presses. Bock[1356] determined the jellying value of pectin extracted from well-dried, slightly fermented, and fermented apple pomace and found that even slight fermentation reduces the commercial usefulness of the pomace. In another case, 20% loss in jellying value was found when the pectin was extracted from the pomace after standing for one day.[1357] Treatment of the pomace with 0.15% sulfur dioxide retarded the fermentation of the pomace but did not entirely prevent the loss in jellying value. The effect of keeping the wet pomace in baskets or heaps was also studied,[1357] but such practices are of little use in normal commercial production.

In Germany, where much of the cider is pressed in smaller plants dispersed over the countryside, the storage behavior of wet pomace is of more importance. At times wet pomace is transported for an entire day to drying plants[1337]; in such cases the use of sulfur dioxide may prevent some of the loss of jelly grade.[1358] Mehlitz reached similar conclusions[1359] concerning the quick loss of pectin and recommends storage of the wet pulp with sulfur dioxide at 1 to 4°C. (34 to 40°F.) or preferably at freezing temperatures. Freezing storage has been found in the author's laboratory to preserve the original value of the wet pomace for long periods; this method of preservation, however, is impracticable because of the high cost.

Impregnation of the pomace with a 5 to 10% solution of phosphoric acid and subsequent ramming into containers has also been suggested as a means of preservation.[1360]

2. Drying of Apple Pomace

The wet pomace is usually run through the picker and dried as soon after pressing as possible. Drying may be performed by a great variety of methods. It may also be aided by mixing certain materials with the pomace, for example, both the pressing and subsequent drying may be made more effective by the addition of diatomaceous earth (Filter-Cel).[1361] Myers and Cowgill[1362] recommend the addition of enough glycerol to make the dried pomace contain 3–4%. This compound makes the later extraction of pectin easier although the commercial feasibility of using glycerol in such a manner is doubtful.

[1356] H. Bock, Chem.-Ztg., 65, 461 (1941).
[1357] V. L. S. Charley, L. F. Burroughs, M. E. Kieser, and J. Steedman, Long Ashton Research Station, Annual Report for 1942, p. 89.
[1358] H. Henkel, Süsswaren-Wirtschaft, 15, Special No. 358/59, p. 19 (1943?).
[1359] A. Mehlitz, Vorratspflege u. Lebensmittelforsch., 4, 572 (1941); through C. A., 37, 4490 (1943).
[1360] Pomosin Werke, Belgian Pat. 444,952 (1942); through C. A., 39, 565 (1945).
[1361] Mutual Citrus Products Co. (U.S.A.), British Pat. 432,244 (1935).
[1362] P. B. Myers and W. W. Cowgill, U. S. Pat. 2,185,472 (1940).

Knowledge of drying food materials has developed a great deal during the past few years. For a discussion of this topic, the reader is referred to other publications.[1339,1363-1365] The brief discussion below will deal mostly with the principles involved in these methods and their specific usefulness for drying apple pomace. For the details of design, the reader is referred to the above publications and to manufacturers' pamphlets.

Until about two decades ago the usual apple kiln or loft was used predominantly for drying pomace. A kiln consists of a slat-floored drying chamber placed above a heat source so that cold air, which enters the heating unit at the bottom, rises as it is heated, passes through the upper

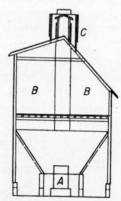

Fig. 30. Kiln for drying apple pomace.
The air is heated in furnace *A* and the pomace dried in room *B*. The flow of air (and temperature) are governed by vent *C*.

drying chamber over, around, and through the pomace, and finally escapes. The floor of the drying room is constructed to permit the hot air to pass through and is often covered with coarse burlap or a fine screen of sufficiently small mesh to hold the dry pomace. The operation of a kiln is claimed to be more expensive that that of dryers of more modern design because the heat losses are greater and the degree of moisture saturation of the escaping air is much lower. The exact control of the air temperature is also well-nigh impossible, and the occasional periods of excessive heating may seriously impair the usefulness of the pomace. By using electric fans the efficiency may be greatly improved.

[1363] W. V. Cruess, *Commercial Fruit and Vegetable Products.* 2nd ed., McGraw-Hill, New York, 1938.

[1364] H. W. von Loesecke, *Drying and Dehydration of Foods.* Reinhold, New York, 1943.

[1365] H. W. von Loesecke, *Outlines of Food Technology.* Reinhold, New York, 1942.

The labor costs involved in using a kiln are high because it requires frequent manual turning of the pomace. A cross section of a kiln is shown in Figure 30.

It takes from 7 to 24 hours or more to dry a load of pomace in a kiln. Forced circulation speeds up the drying and also produces a pomace of better quality. A serious objection to kiln dryers is their extreme vulnerability to fire hazard. Thus, while comparatively cheap to install, fires too frequently cause their destruction and interruption of production.

In the old-fashioned rotary pomace dryer the material is introduced into a revolving drum equipped with steam coils and the pomace is moved

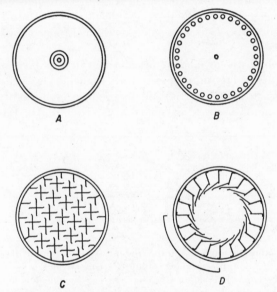

Fig. 31. Cross sections of some types of rotary drum dryers.
Drum *A* is heated by a central steam pipe, drum *B* by coils on the periphery of the drum. Drum *C* is of German design and keeps the pomace from forming a pile. Design *D* shows the Roto-Louvre dryer. The drum turns clockwise and is heated with hot gases while at the section noted by span.

on by a series of baffles. As the dryer rotates, the pomace which is in contact with the steam coils, dries. This contact with the steam coils often causes localized overheating of the pomace, with injury to its quality. In modern rotary dryers, the pomace is not in contact with the steam coils. Rotary dryers are now built according to many principles. They are essentially mounted rollers of large dimensions and may have a single or double shell. They are inclined horizontally, are charged at the upper end with the wet pomace, and deliver the dried product at the lower end; they rotate at speeds of 5 to 10 r.p.m. They may be heated by flue gases or hot air passing through the tube, either parallel to or against the direction of the moving pomace. The heating may be entirely indirect when a double shell is used, or both direct and indirect by using heated walls and passing hot air or gases through the shell. Some of the designs used are shown in Figure 31. It may be stated that design (d) is considered by many to be the best design now available and has been said to produce pomace of the highest quality.[1366]

One objection often leveled in the past against tubular dryers was that the pomace picks up more than traces of iron which cause later difficulties during pectin manufacture. The application of corrosion-resisting metals such as stainless steel eliminates this difficulty. The Roto-Louvre dryer shown in Figure 31 (d) is also made with such noncorrosive tangential inner plates.

Cabinet, compartment, and tunnel and belt dryers have also been used for drying pomace. Drying in forced draft tunnel dryers is used in several installations in Canada and is said to produce high-quality pomace. A section of a tunnel used as a pomace dryer is shown in Figure 32. This

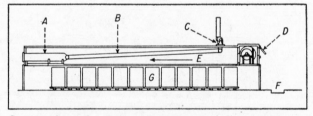

Fig. 32. Section through a countercurrent type of tunnel dryer used for apple pomace (adapted from Mrak).
The hot air from combustion chamber A is led through four flues B and by fan C into the drying chamber where it flows in the direction of arrow E. Fresh air is admitted at D. The trays from cars G are transferred to cars moved on track F.

equipment is essentially the same as that used for dehydration of vegetables and has been described elsewhere.[1364] In one plant the air circulates through a tunnel holding seven trucks which move in a countercurrent manner. Each truck carries 50 heavily galvanized trays loaded with about 20 lbs. of wet pomace. The capacity of this dryer is about one ton of wet pomace per hour. This method of drying has proved to be very reliable for various other plant materials, but its construction is fairly expensive. Current practice points toward the application of such equipment during the summer for the drying of other plant foods and

[1364] Anonymous, *Food Packer*, 26 (8), 52 (1945).

for pomace during the late fall months, thus rendering the installation economical by using it for several purposes.

In Germany a combination of different drying methods is used at times. One plant in Frankfurt, for example,[1337] first exposes the wet pomace to the furnace gases while the pomace is moving in a large brick oven on two tiers of three rotating iron baffles. It then enters a tubular dryer of customary design. This two-phase operation permits the use of high temperatures on the wet pomace, while subsequent drying in the rotating dryer is performed at lower and more carefully controlled temperatures.

The temperature of the air used for drying depends on the equipment and on the moisture content of the pomace. While the pomace is still wet, temperatures of 80–90°C. (177–195°F.) or even higher may be used without harm. During this period the actual temperature of the wet pomace is much lower than that of the surrounding air or gases because it is substantially cooled by evaporation. When the moisture content is reduced to 20 or 25%, this differential caused by evaporation disappears and the air temperature must be lowered to 65 or 70°C. (150 or 160°F.). However, some manufacturers feel that finishing temperatures up to 82°C. (180°F.) can be used without decreasing the quality of the pomace.

The pomace is usually dried to 4 to 8% moisture content. During the last period the progress of drying should be followed by moisture determinations. Although experienced operators are very skillful in following the progress of evaporation by judging how the pomace resists pressure in the hand, actual measurement, of course, is preferable. In conjunction with the development of dehydration technics, methods of rapid moisture estimation have also been evolved. A description of a variety of approaches and equipment may be found in most books dealing with dehydration. The Mojonnier, Brabender,[1367] and other grain moisture testers are applicable for this purpose. The recent model of the Moisture Teller[1368] appears to be eminently suitable for quick and accurate determination of the moisture content of apple pomace.

The dry pomace should be cooled as quickly as possible.[1369] This is usually accomplished by placing the pomace on a dry clean floor and turning it every few hours until it cools. Or it may be placed in bags which are left open for at least one day. At any rate, some provision should be made to allow the pomace to cool and equalize in moisture content ("sweating"). It is then best stored in sacks in a cool, dry storage. Some manufacturers use artificial refrigeration in order to keep the temperature below 21°C. (70°F.) because the pomace is claimed to acquire an inferior odor when

[1367] Manufactured by Mojonnier Bros. Co., Chicago, Ill., and Brabender Corp., Rochelle Park, N. J., respectively.
[1368] Made by Harry W. Dietert Co., Detroit, Mich.
[1369] E. L. Turner, *Canner*, **81** (1), 20 (1935).

stored at higher temperatures. Usually the pomace is kept in storage with windows controlling the temperature until about March or April, when it is moved into refrigerated storage, which is more readily available at this time. Of course, the dry pomace should be guarded against the access of moisture because it takes up water easily. As a rule, 10% moisture is regarded as the danger point in water content.[1370] If the moisture uptake is considerable, it may cause rapid deterioration of the value of the pomace for pectin extraction. Above 20% moisture, actual mold growth may start,[1371] which destroys the usefulness of the pomace in short order. Early in the spring the pomace should be repeatedly fumigated to prevent insect infestation. This can be done with carbon bisulfide, for example, using about 20 lbs./1000 ft.³. Proper care should be exercised because the fumes of carbon bisulfide are inflammable. Sulfur dioxide may also be used for this purpose.

3. Evaluation of Apple Pomace

In purchasing apple pomace for pectin manufacture, its quality should always be carefully appraised. The dry pomace should be light in color and uniform in appearance, feel soft and springy when handled, and the apple skin in the dried pomace should retain some of its original color. Such visual inspection, however, reveals little of the true value of apple pomace for pectin manufacture; dry matter and pectin determinations should be run in order to ascertain its worth.

The moisture content should be determined for two reasons: (1) If pomace with a high water content is bought, an undue part of the price is paid for the water. (2) High water content is undesirable from the standpoint of keeping quality even during comparatively short storage periods.

The determination of the moisture content may be easily and quickly performed with any of the dryers mentioned previously. When such equipment is not available, any of the "official" methods may be used. A 2-g. sample of the pomace may be dried in a vacuum oven at a pressure less than 100 mm. at 100°C. (212°F.) for 5 hours or dried for 2 hours at 135°C. (275°F.). In either case, the sample should be contained in a weighing dish which is permitted to cool in a desiccator for about 20 minutes after the heating period. The moisture content is calculated from the loss in weight.

Determination of the yield and quality of pectin which may be obtained from the apple pomace is more difficult. The pectin content of

[1370] S. J. Cohen, *Am. Vinegar Ind.*, 2 (5), 11 (1923).
[1371] Z. I. Kertesz and E. L. Green, *New York State Agr. Expt. Sta.*, Tech. Bull. No. 179 (1931).

ple pomace varies between 5 and 25% and the jellying power of the
ectin may differ widely. Further variations are introduced by the method
: drying and by the storage history of the pomace.

Evaluations based on the quantity of pectin obtained by exhaustive
xtraction[1372] are often misleading because a considerable proportion of
ie pectin may be entirely worthless for jelly making. Viscosity meas-
rements on pomace extracts have only a limited value in approximating
s jellying capacity because this property is subject to many influences,
ich as the presence of starch and other nonpectin colloidal materials,
ie presence of salts—especially those of calcium and magnesium—and
ie conditions of viscosity determination (Chapter VII). The value of
ie pomace is therefore usually determined by making test jellies under
mditions which simulate those in commercial jelly making. The results
re either expressed as "grade" for the pomace or as yield of "jelly-units"
xpressed on the basis of the extracted pectin.[1373] The pomace grade has
ie same meaning as when applied to commercial pectin, that is, it ex-
resses the number of (weight) units of sugar that can be made into a
elly of standard firmness (Chapter XXIII) by one unit (weight) of pom-
ce. Thus, it also indicates the per cent of 100 grade pectin potentially
xtractable from the pomace. The jelly-unit is obtained by multiplying
ie yield by the jelly grade of the extracted pectin. In either case, it is
iperative to use rigidly standardized conditions for extraction and sub-
equent jelly making and for evaluation of the jellies.

As a rule, it is best to use exactly the same procedure for testing the raw
aterial which will be applied later in the actual commercial utilization
f the pomace. The test should be performed on a small sample (5–10 g.)
f representative material. This sample is leached and extracted in a man-
er which is identical with the procedure to be used on a large scale. These
ethods will be discussed in Section III. The extract, however, is not put
irough the screening and filtration operations which will be used on the
immercial scale, but is filtered through cheese cloth or folded filter paper
 obtain a clear or fairly clear liquid. Starch is usually not removed from
iis extract which is then used without any further purification for the
raluation of the pectin it contains. The methods of evaluation of the
ectin grade in pectin extracts will be discussed in Chapter XXIII.

Of the many methods given for the evaluation of dry apple pomace
 the literature, only that described by Mottern and Karr[1374] will be
ven here in detail. These authors recommend the following procedure:

[1372] D. W. Steuart, *Analyst,* **58**, 397 (1933).
[1373] G. L. Baker and R. F. Kneeland, *Fruit Products J.,* **14**, 204 (1935).
[1374] H. H. Mottern and E. E. Karr, *Fruit Products J.,* **25**, 292 (1946).

In tared, 500-cc., wide-mouth Erlenmeyer flasks duplicate 30-g. samples o
dry pomace (ground through a 2-mm. screen in a Wiley mill) are mixed witl
1.2 g. of sodium tetraphosphate. Now 300 to 400 cc. of boiling water is adde
(depending on the quality of the pomace), followed by 4 to 7 cc. of dilute hydro
chloric acid. The pH is then adjusted to 3.2, using a glass electrode. The mix
ture is heated to 90°C. (177°F.) for 75 minutes and cooled to 70°C. (159°F.)
after which its total weight is determined. The extract is filtered through
coarse muslin or light press cloth or, preferably, pressed in a small laborator
hydraulic press at about 140 lbs. in.². The pH is now again adjusted to 3.2 b
stirring 0.5 N acid or alkali into the extract. The solids content of the extrac
is then determined by customary methods and its viscosity is also measured t
obtain an "assumed" grade to assist in approximating the pectin grade in orde
to make test jellies in the suitable firmness range. Mottern and Karr evaluate
the jellies by a modification of the Delaware jelly tester.[1375]

A good pomace gives a 25 to 35 grade by this method, a medium on
18 to 25, and a poor one less than 18—these values being without cor
rection for moisture. The use of other methods for the evaluation of th
strength of the jellies may also be applied without affecting the validit
of the method. It will be noted that Mottern and Karr do not recommenc
the preliminary leaching of the pomace because there is no standard leach
ing treatment. While this is correct in comparing pomace samples, i
would seem that leaching should be performed if any preliminary informa
tion on the jelly yield obtainable by the manufacturing method is sought

III. EXTRACTION OF PECTIN

The literature contains many methods for the extraction of pecti
from apple pomace and other raw materials.[1376–1378] Many workers hav
claimed to have attained maximum efficiency in this operation, but a
review of the details of the methods used reveals a complete lack o
agreement. This apparent contradiction disappears if the factors whicl
influence pectin extraction are taken into consideration. The quality an
condition of the raw material, the amount and purity of the water used
the acid applied and the pH attained, and the temperature and duratio
of the extraction all influence the method developed and the success o
the operation; there are, therefore, endless combinations of these condi
tions which may give good results.

Reference should be made here to previous discussions in this volum
concerning the extraction of pectin substances from plant tissues (se

[1375] G. L. Baker, *Fruit Products J.*, **17**, 329 (1938).
[1376] R. Ripa, *Die Pektinstoffe*, 2nd ed., Serger und Hempel, Braunschweig, 1937.
[1377] W. A. Rooker, *Fruit Pectin*. Avi, New York, 1928.
[1378] R. Heiss, *Lebensmitteltechnologie*. Bergmann, Munich, 1950.

Chapter VI, Sect. II). It can be said that pectin extraction from apple pomace—as indeed from any other raw material—essentially comprises two distinct steps which are intimately interdependent: (1) solubilization of the insoluble pectic constituents (protopectin, etc.) in the pomace; and (2) actual dissolution of the pectic substances which were thereby rendered soluble. The conditions most suitable for one of these steps are not necessarily favorable for the other, although progress in dissolution obviously depends on the amounts of pectic materials which are made soluble.

There is an additional important consideration in the extraction of pectin. The pectin in apple pomace is present in the form of protopectin, which is insoluble in cold water and is accompanied by cellulose, hemicelluloses, and smaller proportions of many other constituents. In order to transform the protopectin into pectin, the former is usually digested with hot acidulated water. However, as the pectin is formed from the protopectin, the reactions caused by the acid proceed beyond the solubilizing effect and in turn cause gradual degradation of the pectin, which is already soluble or in solution. This results in the loss of colloidal properties and jelly grade in a fraction of the material treated. Thus, the success of the extraction depends on an equitable balance of all factors which cause maximum solubilization and dissolution but a minimum of further degradation of the pectin.

Describing any one given procedure of extraction as best would be of little help to the reader. It has been shown by experience that a certain degree of experimentation to establish the most suitable conditions under any given set of circumstances is always necessary.

The success of pectin extraction is determined by the yield of jelly units[1373] obtained. During the process of manufacture viscosity measurements on samples under carefully selected conditions offer a very good means of following the operation. Since the viscosity depends both on the quantity and quality of the pectin, a determination of the proportion of solids in solution by means of a hydrometer, refractometer, or some other method will throw light on the quality of the pectin. The final evaluation, however, must be made by determination of pectin in solution and estimation of its jelly grade.

1. Preliminary Treatment of Pomace

It has already been emphasized that the removal of soluble constituents from the pomace is important. Part of this purification is accomplished during pressing of the apple juice, and especially by washing the press cake with water. The removal of these soluble constituents may also have been enhanced by the application of special solvents such as ethanol or acid ethanol, as noted in Section II-1 above.

Further steps are usually taken before the extraction of pectin to remove additional water-soluble components of the pomace. This leaching also hydrates (swells) the pomace and makes the extraction a more exact operation because it insures more even distribution of the acidulated extracting liquid.

The pomace is usually leached in a tank or container with a false bottom. Since no heat or acid is applied in this operation, a simple wooden tank of sufficient strength and equipped with a mechanism for tilting is suitable. The false bottom, which is a short distance (5–10 cm.) above the true bottom, is covered with a heavy-gauge wire screen to prevent the pomace from falling through. A drain valve with a hose attached is fitted to the bottom of the tank. Rooker[1377] recommends the installation of an air pipe which reaches into the space between the two bottoms and extends on the outside to the level of the top of the wall of the tank. This facilitates the flow of water through the pomace. Of course the leaching may also be performed in the extraction tanks. In Germany the use of perforated tile bottoms in large wooden tanks is common.[1323]

The use of several smaller tanks for leaching is better than fewer but larger vessels because the excessive weight of the pomace may pack it down too tightly to permit the free passage of the leaching water. Stirring is usually avoided since it may cause breaking up of the pomace and difficulties in draining the leachings as well as the pectin extract. Some factories employ very slow or intermittent stirring.

The pomace is placed in the tank and cold water is sprinkled on top.[1377] The amount of water to be added must be determined in tests because the quantity needed to "soak up" the pomace, as well as that needed for good extraction, depends on the character and purity of the dried pomace. A relationship of 10 parts of water to 1 part of pomace is an approximate average ratio. After adding enough water to have a thin layer of water above the pomace, it is allowed to soak for 30 or 40 minutes. Then the sprinkler installed on the top of the tank is turned on and the water is drained off at the bottom at about the same speed as it is added at the top. Water at 50°C. (122°F.) is often used for leaching. The extract is usually very rich in sugar at first and may be saved for vinegar stock or alcoholic fermentation. The progress of leaching can easily be followed by determining the amount of dissolved solids with an ordinary specific gravity hydrometer ("spindle"). Rooker[1377] recommends that the wash liquid be saved until the specific gravity reaches 1.005 and that leaching be continued until the extract shows a reading of 1.003. At this time the pomace will be practically free from substances which are soluble in cold water. Some 12 to 18 hours are often allowed for draining. It is more common to leach in batches by adding water and leaving the mixture alone for a short period of time, followed by draining by gravity; the procedure may be repeated if necessary. In some lants the pomace is leached in running water of 18°C. (65°F.) for 45 minutes, tarting this period when the pomace appears to be saturated by the water. In Germany the leachings are sometimes concentrated and sold as a thick rup (Apfelkraut).[1378]

The appearance of a well-leached, good pomace is light and fluffy. According to Rooker, one liter of dry pomace weighs about 360 g. (3.2 lbs./ al.). An average wet pomace when properly leached and drained, occupies bout twice the original volume of the dry pomace.

2. Acids and Acidity

Pectin can be extracted from apple pomace with the use of hot ater.[1379,1380] This method has been widely used in laboratory work and o a limited extent for the production of pectin. It is now clear, however, hat the use of hot acidulated water offers many advantages, especially in hortening the heating period.

Acid extractions were employed by some of the first pectin chemists. Iowever, little understanding of this matter could be attained until the onception and significance of hydrogen ion concentration (pH) was larified and widely accepted. Hardy[1381] was one of the first investigators o realize the importance of controlling hydrogen ion concentration in the xtraction of pectin. His experiments indicated a direct relationship beween decreasing pH of extraction and pectin yield when the operation vas performed below the boiling point. This may not have been true of he yield of jelly-units. It is now clear that the expression of acidities in ercentages and normalities based on titratable acidity (or amounts of cid added) has little meaning because of the variations introduced by lifferent quantities of other components in the mixture, and especially ecause of the varying buffer capacity of the mixture. For this reason lder information in which the pH of the extracting medium was unknown vill not be considered here.

Even now there is little agreement among various investigators conerning the most suitable pH to be used for the extraction of pectin from pple pomace. Baker and Kneeland[1373] found a pH optimum of 1.8 to .9, while Mehlitz[1382] obtained best extraction at 3.1. A pH of 2.6 to 2.8 s now commonly used in this country. Obviously, the pH of the digest

[1379] H. Gaertner, Z. Ver. deut. Zucker-Ind., 69, 233 (1919).
[1380] P. B. Myers and G. L. Baker, Univ. Delaware Agr. Expt. Sta., Bull. No. 160 (1929).
[1381] F. Hardy, Biochem. J., 18, 2 (1924).
[1382] A. Mehlitz, Pektin. 2nd ed., Applehouse, Braunschweig, 1934.

used by an operator depends on many factors in addition to effecting tl
maximum jelly grade yield, for example, on the corrosive effect of acid (
the equipment and the influence of the acidity on later steps in tl
process.

A variety of different acids have been employed for the extraction of pecti
Tartaric, malic, citric, lactic, and acetic acids have been used; phosphoric ac
has also been widely used and found satisfactory. There has been an increasi
tendency during the last decade to use the cheaper mineral acids, such as si
furic and hydrochloric acids, especially in cases in which the pectin is to be pr
cipitated from the extract. As will be shown in Sections IV and V, the use
sulfurous acid also offers specific benefits under certain conditions and h.
therefore been used in the production of pectin.[1383] When this acid is used f
the extraction, the bulk of it can be removed by aeration of the separated e
tract, i.e., by allowing it to trickle or drip down while it is exposed to air
thin flowing layers or drops. This eliminates or at least simplifies subseque
partial neutralization which must usually be accomplished whether the extra
is going to be concentrated or precipitated. At times a small proportion
sulfurous acid is used in conjunction with other acids. The principal reason f
this is to obtain the bleaching effect of sulfurous acid, thus giving a lighter color
extract.

A different approach is the use of high acid concentrations to accomplish tl
solubilization of pectin. This method, described by Olsen and Stuewer,[1383a]
usually designated as the "pickling method" because the pomace or other pecti
bearing material is treated at a pH of 0.5–0.7, usually obtained with hydr
chloric acid. The treatment is continued for periods of 24 to 48 hours at ten
peratures in the neighborhood of 40°C. (105°F.). Thereupon the pH is rais
to about 3.0 to stop the action of the acid and to facilitate the dissolution of tl
pectin. During pickling, and especially when the optimum length of treatme
to obtain the maximum yield of jelly units is exceeded, progressive deesterificatio
produces low-ester pectins.

The amount of acidulated water which is used is governed by sever
considerations. One of these is the water-holding capacity of the pomac
The amount of liquid used should be sufficient to insure an opportunity
dissolve most of the solubilized pectin and to give the digest sufficie
fluidity to be handled with ease. The yield of pectin usually increases
more extractant is used. On the other hand, the aim of the pectin man
facturer is to keep the volume at a minimum and to obtain as concentrate
a solution as possible in order to reduce the cost of subsequent operation

Rooker[1377] recommends about 3 parts of water to 1 part of wet, leache
pomace; this is about 12:1 on a dry pomace basis. A more recent descri
tion of pectin extraction from apple pomace[1384] recommends a ratio

[1383] C. P. Wilson, Ind. Eng. Chem., 17, 1065 (1925).
[1383a] A. G. Olsen and R. Stuewer, U. S. Pat. 2,132,577 (1938).
[1384] Anonymous, "The Preparation of Liquid Apple Pectin Concentrate," Weste
Regional Research Laboratory, Albany, California, Mimeograph, "AIC-28," revis
Jan., 1946.

0 parts of water to 1 part of dry pomace. The literature contains state-
ents in the range from 7:1 to 20:1.

3. Time and Temperature

Attempts to produce pectins with useful properties at temperatures
bove the boiling point (under pressure) have been unsuccessful. It has
lso been shown that the use of temperatures of 40°C. (104°F.) and
ower requires prolonged treatment, resulting at times in excessive de-
sterification. Almost any temperature within these limits (40–100°C.,
04–212°F.) has at times been recommended for the extraction of pectin
rom apple pomace.

Time and temperature work in opposite directions in the extraction of
ectin: the higher the temperature, the shorter the duration of heating
which results in the maximum jelly unit yield. Rooker[1377] recommends
5–100°C. (185–212°F.) for 60 to 80 minutes at the lower end of the tem-
erature range, and 30 to 40 minutes near the top. This general relation-
hip is still observed by most operators, although the preferred tempera-
ure range now seems to be between 80 and 90°C. (177–195°F.).
Naturally, the pH of the acid solution plays a part in determining the
emperature of extraction: high acidities (low pH) combined with high
emperatures should be avoided.

In Germany temperatures between 90 and 100°C. (195–112°F.) are
sed when open steam is applied, but with steam-jacketed vessels the
ange is usually 80–90°C. (177–195°F.). A shorter heating time at higher
emperatures—up to 90°C. (195°F.)—is apt to give the best results. An
deal procedure is the rapid extraction of pectin in two or more extractions
ecause the extracted pectin is thereby not exposed to excessive heating.[1385]
t times when such a procedure is used, the second (or third) extract is
sed for the extraction of a fresh batch of pomace. While this method
s not entirely free from objections, it gives a more concentrated extract
which may result in significant economies in later steps of the manufac-
ure. A similar effect may be accomplished by the use of countercurrent
xtraction.[1386]

4. Use of Polyphosphates in Pectin Extraction

An important development in the extraction of pectin from various raw
aterials is the use of polyphosphates. These compounds have been known
or many years, but their large-scale manufacture (mostly for use in
leaning compounds) is a recent development. Some of the polyphosphates
sed in connection with pectin extraction are sodium hexametaphosphate

[1385] P. Hussmann, German Pat. 743,067 (1941); through C. A., 40, 653 (1946).
[1386] H. S. Owens, R. M. McCready, and W. D. Maclay, Food Technol., 3, 77
(1949).

(NaPO$_3$)$_4$, sodium tetrametaphosphate (NaPO$_3$)$_4$, sodium tetraphosphate
(Na$_6$P$_4$O$_{13}$), and tetrasodium pyrophosphate (Na$_4$P$_2$O$_7$). The most im
portant property of these salts from the standpoint of pectin extraction
is that they form complexes with calcium and magnesium. The latter
(partly at least) are responsible for the insolubility of protopectin and
thus their use in pectin extraction facilitates both the solubilization of
protopectin and the actual dissolution of pectin.

The realization of the possible role of calcium and magnesium in the
insolubility of certain groups of pectin substances is not new and was
noted by many workers. Norris and Schryver[1387] were the first to elaborate
on this topic and Nanji and Paton,[1388] later obtained a patent on the use
of salts which form insoluble compounds with calcium and magnesium
thus facilitating the extraction of pectin. This procedure is now widely
used for the laboratory extraction of pectic constituents from plant tissue
(see Chapter VIII), but it is not clear to what extent it is used in the
commercial production of pectin. A more recent variation on the same
theme is the method of Myers and Rouse,[1389] who use ion exchange resin
for the removal of calcium and magnesium or any heavy metals which
may be attached to the pectin molecule and cause it to be insoluble in
water. This latter process will be described in Chapter XX.

Baker and Woodmansee[1390] used polyphosphates for the extraction of
pectin from apple pomace. Although they only measured the viscosity
of the extract, it is obvious that the use of 0.5% polyphosphate enhanced
the progress of pectin extraction over a wide pH range, especially between
pH 3 and 4. These authors also determined the usefulness of sodium
hexametaphosphate in large-scale laboratory extractions. Two batches
of the same apple pomace were extracted at pH 3.4. The control mixture
was boiled for 40 minutes, while the one containing 2.5% polyphosphate
(based on the weight of the pomace) was boiled for 30 minutes. The jelly
unit yield determined on the extracts was 19 for the control and 24 for
the polyphosphate extraction. Baker and Woodmansee conclude that the
use of polyphosphates for pectin extraction results in shorter extraction
periods above pH 3, but that even below pH 3 polyphosphates exert a
beneficial effect.

A public service patent issued later to Maclay and Nielsen[1391] cover
the use of polyphosphates for pectin extraction. These workers followed
the extraction of pectin from a variety of raw materials by determina

[1387] F. W. Norris and S. B. Schryver, *Biochem. J.,* **19,** 676 (1925).
[1388] D. R. Nanji and F. J. Paton, U. S. Pat. 1,634,879 (1927).
[1389] P. B. Myers and A. H. Rouse, U. S. Pat. 2,323,483 (1943).
[1390] G. L. Baker and C. W. Woodmansee, *Fruit Products J.,* **23,** 164 (1944).
[1391] W. D. Maclay and J. P. Nielsen, U. S. Pat. 2,375,376 (1945).

ion of the jelly unit yields and found that the use of polyphosphates was beneficial in every case tested. They also emphasize the possible reduction of the extraction time which results from the use of the polyphosphates. Although results on apple pomace are not given by Maclay and Nielsen, it is implied in the patent that similar results were or could have been obtained with this raw material. At the present time polyphosphates are used in some U. S. pectin plants in the extraction process.

It should be borne in mind that the use of polyphosphates is specifically beneficial in cases in which the insolubility of the pectin substances is caused predominantly by the presence of calcium, magnesium, and certain other metallic ions. Thus, when a source material is comparatively free from these ions, the use of polyphosphates is of questionable merit. The common occurrence of these polyvalent ions in water and the formation of their (acid) pectinic acid salts during washing and soaking the pomace and other raw materials used for pectin manufacture may be one of the causes of the effectiveness of polyphosphates. They are likely to be of less use for the laboratory extraction of pectin or pectinic acids from purified raw materials and, indeed, cases in which they offered no noticeable benefit with such preparations have been observed in the author's laboratory.

Phosphoric acid has also been recommended as a "catalyst" for the extraction of pectin.[1392] The relationship between this "catalytic" action and the working mechanism of polyphosphates is not obvious.

At the present time the legal status of the use of polyphosphates in food products is not entirely clear. For this reason caution should be exercised in using them in the commercial production of pectin extracts. It is assumed that, if the pectin is precipitated and separated from the liquid phase of the extract by any of the methods described in Section IV, the polyphosphate is removed from the pectin and thus does not appear in the product.

IV. SEPARATION, CLARIFICATION, AND FILTRATION OF EXTRACT

1. Draining or Pressing

The cooked pomace is usually pressed hot in a rack and cloth hydraulic press, especially if only one extraction is made. The hot mixture of acid pectin extract in which the pomace residue is suspended is filled into heavy cloths placed on the frames on the filter press, folded, and pressed with pressures in the neighborhood of 70 kg. cm.^{2} (1000 lbs./in.^{2}). At times two cloths, one ordinary press cloth (of 17.5-oz. twill or similar material)

[1392] R. Otto and G. Winkler, German Pat. 730,898 (1942). Also Pomosin Werke, Belgian Pat. 444,727 (1942); through *C. A.*, **39**, 566 (1945).

and the other made of coarse muslin, are used, the latter being on the inside in direct contact with the cooked pomace. The addition of abou 0.5% paper pulp and filter aid at this stage has also been recommended to facilitate the separation of the extract.[1393]

If the ratio of water to pomace is sufficiently large, the pomace may be drained off through the previously mentioned false bottoms or porous tile floor plates by gravity. This method is of little use when the extract is too thick to allow easy flow and in such cases pressure must be used to obtain the extract. The method of gravity draining (at times aided by air pressure) is applicable without much loss when more than one extraction is made. A practice known to be used in at least one factory is to use a counterflow system of extraction to six extraction vessels in series. This method avoids the necessity of several extractions.

Centrifuges have also been used for the separation of the crude extract from the spent pomace. At times the whole charge of pomace and liquid is passed into a centrifugal drum, which separates the liquid rapidly and from which the pomace residue can be mechanically discharged. Sharples centrifuges of various types have also been used in cases in which the pectin extract is already freed from the bulk of the spent pomace. The so-called self-cleaning centrifuges are particularly successful for the separation of pectin extract. Hafley[1394] designed a centrifugal press which was claimed to be exceptionally suitable for this purpose. This machine does not seem to have attained any degree of popularity.

Often a combination of pressing and subsequent centrifuging are applied in separating the pectin extract. Obviously, a continuous method for extraction followed by continuous separation of the pectin extract is the aim of all manufacturers, especially when labor costs are high. While some advance has been made toward the development of such methods, they are still used only sporadically and further improvements are needed before such methods become general practice in the pectin industry.

Like fresh and dried pomace,[1336] the extracted pomace is also used as an animal feed.[1395] The pomace left from pectin manufacture contains 55.0% total digestible nutrients (on the dry matter basis) as compared with 60.5% in the original pomace.[1396] On the other hand, the protein content of the dried extracted pomace is about one third higher because of the removal of more soluble constituents.[1397]

[1393] General Foods Corp. (U.S.A.), French Pat. 708,215 (1931).

[1394] A. H. Hafley, *Canner*, 53, No. 1, 39 (1921).

[1395] F. A. Henglein, R. Otto, and S. H. Sauerbrey, German Pat. 727,902 (1942); through *C. A.*, 37, 6760 (1943).

[1336] F. B. Morrison, *Feeds and Feeding*. 20th ed., Morrison, Ithaca, 1936.

[1397] H. Pallmann, F. Weber, and H. Deuel, *Schweiz. landw. Monatsh.*, 1944, Nos. 11–12, p. 1.

2. Settling and Clarification

The fresh, hot pectin extract is cooled rapidly to about 40–50°C. (105–123°F.). In olden days this was accomplished by letting the liquid stand in the vessel. The detrimental effect of almost any extent of heating is now clearly realized and therefore, artificial cooling such as by means of tubular coolers is used. Air-evaporative coolers may also be used for this purpose.

At this stage the pectin extract is a turbid liquid. Although suspended particles may not be visible immediately after draining, they appear after standing for a short time. For this reason the extract is often allowed to stand in tanks for 4 to 6 hours, or at times even overnight. The clearer part of the liquid is then siphoned off and handled separately from the fraction containing the sediment. After sedimentation the pectin extract is still cloudy. For this reason it is usually clarified by the use of enzyme preparations[1398,1399] specifically developed for this purpose (see Chapter VI, Section III-1). These enzymes are usually marketed in the form of dry powders and are derived from malt, molds, or bacteria. They have strong amylolytic activity together with some proteolytic action; the former causes the hydrolysis of the starches and dextrins, the latter of the various still ill-defined apple proteins. Although it is comparatively easy to obtain enzymes which accomplish these tasks, many of these enzyme preparations also contain enzymes which attack pectin. Baker[1400] made an extensive investigation of this subject. There are now numerous enzyme preparations which are sold for pectin extract clarification and most manufacturers of industrial enzymes have a product recommended for this purpose. Inasmuch as these preparations change from time to time, there is little purpose in any attempt to describe them in detail. It should be noted, however, that recent efforts lead to the production of diastatic enzymes which are suitable for pectin extract clarification but entirely void of pectolytic enzymes.

These clarifying enzymes are usually applied at pH 4.5 and at 40–50°C. (105–123°F.) in concentrations from 0.1 to 0.2% by weight of the extract. Sodium carbonate is customarily used to adjust the pH of the extract. The dry enzyme is dissolved in water and added to the extract and the treatment is continued until a small sample of the mixture no longer gives a blue color reaction for starch when filtered until clear and tested with a few drops of 0.1% iodine solution. The pH of the extract is then usually adjusted to about 3.0 by the addition of citric acid. Unless the diastase-treated extract is filtered and either precipitated or evaporated at once, rapid heating to inactivate the added enzymes is necessary afterward es-

[1398] R. Douglas, U. S. Pat. 1,235,666 (1917).
[1399] S. L. Crawford, U. S. Pat. 1,507,338 (1924).
[1400] G. L. Baker, *Univ. Delaware Agr. Expt. Sta.*, Bull. No. 204 (**1936**).

pecially if the enzyme preparation was not entirely without pectolytic activity. At times heating is performed even if the later steps in manufacture follow at once because some of the enzymes may also be precipitated by the organic solvents which are used. The pectinase present in the original preparation may thus retain its activity in the dry pectin powder, causing the hydrolysis of the pectin whenever the mixture is dissolved in water. For inactivation of the enzymes the mixture is rapidly heated to 80°C. (177°F.) and then either cooled rapidly or filtered immediately. Rooker[1377] recommends holding the extract at 75°C. (175°F.) for 10 or 15 minutes. The inactivation temperature varies somewhat with the type of enzyme used and manufacturers usually furnish information on this point. This rapid heating followed by cooling may be most efficiently performed in the tubular type of equipment now commonly used in food industries.

In Germany some pectin manufacturers have produced their own clarifying enzyme.[1337] During the war, when conditions became difficult, the clarification of pectin extracts was omitted in most German plants. The use of tannin has also been suggested for the clarification of pectin extracts.[1401] The fact that, in contrast to pectin, starch and dextrins are precipitated from solution upon freezing is the basis of a clarification method developed by Ripa.[1402] The extract is cooled to −6 to −10°C. (20–13°F.) and then filtered. There is no indication that either of these methods has been used commercially.

The amount of salts contained by the pectin extract can be reduced by the use of ion exchange agents.[1403,1404] This is especially advantageous if the extract is to be used without precipitation (see Chapter VI, Sect. III-2).

3. Filtration

At this stage the pectin extract is still cloudy and, when used to make jellies, gives a product without the brilliance and transparency required for high quality. For this reason the extract, freed from starch and dextrin, is usually treated with decolorizing agents, mixed with filter aids, and then filtered. This is one of the most difficult steps in the manufacture of pectin.

Treatment with sulfur dioxide at this time gives a light-colored extract. The sulfur dioxide may be directly introduced in a stream until an excess can be detected by odor or it may be added in the form of a concentrated solution. Chemicals which give rise to sulfur dioxide (such as sodium bisulfite) are also often used. During subsequent concentration and es-

[1401] Schwartauer Werke, German Pat. 608,036 (1935).

[1402] R. Sucharipa (Ripa), Canadian Pat. 287,308 (1928).

[1403] Pomosin Werke, Belgian Pat. 444,825 and 444,872 (1942); through *C. A.*, **39**, 556, 1480 (1945).

[1404] K. T. Williams and C. M. Johnson, *Ind. Eng. Chem., Anal. Ed.*, **16**, 23 (1944).

ɔecially precipitation, the uncombined sulfur dioxide is automatically removed. It was noted before[1383] that sulfurous acid itself may also be used in the extraction process.

Charcoal[1405] is also used both for decolorization and deodorization of the pectin extract. Rooker[1377] recommends the use of charcoal and suggests that the length of treatment be tested on a small sample of the extract.

Although the filtration of the extract becomes easier due to hydrolysis of the starch and dextrin in the solution, it is still impossible to filter the solution economically without the use of paper pulp, diatomaceous earth (kieselguhr, infusorial earth, etc.), or other filter aids.

A wide variety of diatomaceous earth filter aids have been developed to suit various requirements. They usually consist of powders with various particle sizes and shapes obtained by milling the siliceous skeletons of diatoms which are found at certain places in great quantities. When a solution like a pectin extract is filtered, some of the nonrigid colloidal particles pass through the filter, while those of borderline size find their way into the pores and, due to the pressure (or suction), soon plug up most of the holes. Eventually a continuous film

A   B

Fig. 33. Idealized illustration of the working mechanism of filter aids (adapted from Heertjes and van der Haas).
In *A* a colloidal particle blocks a pore in the filter cloth. In *B* the protecting "cupola" formed by filter aid particles over the pore is shown.

forms over the filter surface and increased pressure only drives the plugging particles more firmly into the pores, causing filtration to stop. The particles of diatomaceous earth have irregular surfaces with many cavities into which the colloidal particles of the extract enter and are thus removed from solution. When a sufficient ratio of diatomaceous earth to colloidal particles is used, most of the latter are "bound" in such a manner and form a permeable layer on the filtering surface rather than enter into the pores. Such a situation is schematically illustrated[1406] in Figure 33. Manufacturers of such filter aids in this country as well as abroad now have special products recommended for filtration of pectin extracts.

The use of filter aids has an additional benefit. Baker[1400] reported that,

[1405] W. A. Bender, R. Douglas, and L. H. Cuthbert, U. S. Pat. 1,787,467 (1931).
[1406] P. M. Heertjes and H. v. d. Haas, *Rec. Trav. chim.*, **68**, 361 (1949).

since some of the diastase is adsorbed on the diatomaceous earth, filtration after removal of starch in itself decreases the possible damage which the pectic enzymes added with the diastase may cause. In no case did Baker find complete inactivation (removal) of the enzymes. Although filtration with filter aids enhances retention of the usefulness of the pectin, it does not entirely eliminate, as heating does, the occurrence of detrimental changes.

The amount and kind of diatomaceous filter aid which may be used to best advantage under certain conditions depends on many factors, especially on the character and amount of colloidal materials in the extract. The amount of filter aid, as well as the kind which is most effective, must be determined by experimentation for any given case. Rooker[137] states that the amount of Filter-Cel[1407] which is required for efficient filtration is usually between 0.8 and 2.0% of the weight of the pectin extract. The lower quantities in this range are now considered to be sufficient in the average case.[1384]

The discussion of filtering equipment in any detail is outside the scope of this volume and the reader is referred to the extensive literature on this subject.[1408,1409]

The customary large plate and frame filter presses[1410] are most commonly used for pectin extract. Of course, they must be made either of wood or of some acid resistant metal. The canvas filter cloths are first coated ("caked") with filter aid. At times a layer of fast filtering paper[1411] is used between the "cake" and the filter cloth. This facilitates cleaning of the latter and thus prolongs its life. (Several layers of paper alone may also be used for filtration.) Then the extract, which is already mixed with some more filter aid, is pumped into the press. All such filters are pump fed and the clarified extract leaves through spigots and is collected in a trough. The addition of filter aid prevents clogging of the cloth for sufficient lengths of time to make the filtration economical. Continuous filters like the Oliver filter[1412] have also been employed in the pectin industry with some success. This type of filter, the principle of which is shown in Figure 34, consists of a drum or cylinder rotating on a horizontal axis, the lower part of which is submerged in the liquid to be filtered. The surface of the drum is divided into compartments which are covered by a screen supporting a filter cloth on which a layer of filter aid (cake) has been deposited. The drum rotates while suction is exerted only through the compartments of the drum submerged in

[1407] Filter-Cel, Celite, and a variety of other similar products are manufactured by the Johns-Manville Co., New York, and others.
[1408] C. L. Bryden and G. D. Dickey, A Text Book of Filtration. Chemical Pub Co., Brooklyn, 1923
[1409] S. A. Miller, Chem. Inds., 66, 38 (1950).
[1410] Such are manufactured by D. R. Sperry and Co., Batavia, Ill., and others.
[1411] Manufactured by Schleicher and Schuell Co., New York.
[1412] Manufactured by Oliver United Filters, Inc., New York.

he liquid. A part of the filter cake is sheared off by a stationary steel scraper. The whole process is continuous and automatic and there is no break in the various stages of the cycle. One great advantage of this type of filter over the usual large filter presses is that much less labor is needed for the preparation of the machine for operation and afterward when the filter must be cleaned. As Cooker[1377] notes, an insufficiently cleaned filter press may cause a great deal of trouble.

There are many other types of filters[1408,1409] which have been used at times with pectin extract and there is no reason why a great variety of equipment would not be found entirely suitable for this purpose. In Germany Seitz-type filters using paper pulp–asbestos pads were also

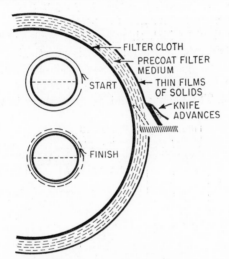

Fig. 34. Principle of a continuous Oliver rotary filter.

applied during the war, probably because of the shortage of filter cloth. At times de Laval centrifuges have also been used instead of the final filtration[1337] but they give less efficient clarification and are, as a rule, best used in conjunction with filter presses.

V. CONCENTRATION AND PRESERVATION OF PECTIN EXTRACT

The clarified pectin extract should be a brilliant clear solution which is slightly yellow or brownish in color and should contain 0.5–1.5% pectin. It also contains an approximately equal amount of other materials, such as sugars, hemicelluloses, and many other minor constituents of ill-defined nature.

The extract may be used directly for making preserves. In the production of commercial pectins and pectin solutions, however, further operations are needed to convert the extract into forms customarily used by the preserving trade.

The concentration of pectin extracts in open containers is now avoided. Continued exposure to the boiling temperature causes extensive loss of jellying power and provides a slow method of concentration. Vacuum concentrators of batch or continous types are now universally employed[1413] for removing water from pectin extracts. The customary vacuum pan may be, and has been, used for pectin extract but is not very satisfactory for large-scale operations because of the high viscosity of the solution and the fact that pectin sticks to the evaporating surface.

The correct type of evaporator for pectin extract is one with rapid circulation of the liquid which thereby has a tendency to become "self-scouring." The variety of such equipment is practically endless. Double-effect evaporators are generally employed, emphasis usually being on comparatively short exposure to heat. Such an evaporator is schematically shown in Figure 35. The vacuum employed is usually in the neighborhood

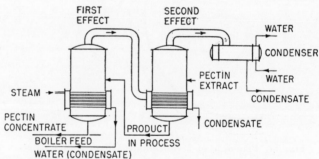

Fig. 35. One type of double-effect evaporator.

of 660 mm. (26 inches), giving boiling temperatures of about 45 to 50°C. (112 to 123°F.) in the final phase. In Germany some quadruple-effect evaporators have also been applied,[1337] which are claimed to have a full evaporating cycle of only about 10 minutes. In addition to savings in the time of exposure and avoidance of cooked flavor, multiple-phase evaporators are also more economical to operate than single-phase evaporators.

The extent of concentration is usually in the range of 4:1 or 5:1 and the extract is usually slightly overconcentrated to allow standardization by dilution. The jelly grade of a 4:1 concentrate should be about 5. If the pectin is to be precipitated from the concentrate, this is done as soon

[1413] E. Monti, U. S. Pat. 1,520,069 (1924).

as the concentrate attains room temperature. On the other hand, if the concentrate is to be sold as such, it is usually standardized with regard to its jelly grade and then diluted to a standard value. At times the concentrate is also adjusted to a uniform pH value and in other respects. Concentration by precipitation has also been used for the production of pectin concentrates. For this purpose the pectin is precipitated, usually without concentration by any of the methods described below; and then the washed, wet precipitate is redissolved in a much smaller volume of water containing a small amount of sodium citrate.

Fig. 36. One type of hand refractometer (courtesy Bausch and Lomb Co.).

For control of the progress of evaporation some rapid method should be used for determination of changes in the total solids of the extract. Hydrometers or refractometers may be used for this purpose. The hydrometer is an inexpensive instrument which gives accurate results, but care must be taken to adjust the temperature of the concentrate before the reading is taken. The Abbe refractometer is often used for this purpose and is an exact although expensive instrument. The readings are directly in refractive indices and the solids contents can be read from tables which can be found in all chemical handbooks. Here again the temperature should be carefully observed. It should be also borne in mind that the specific gravity–refractive index–sugar concentration tables are not exactly applicable to pectin solutions. The hand refractometers are eminently suitable for following the progress of the concentration although they are less accurate than the Abbe refractometer. A hand refractometer is shown in Figure 36; determination with the hand refractometer is simple and quick.

In the early days of the pectin industry the addition of sugar after concentration was recommended for the preservation of the extract. Since this introduced the danger of jellification ("setting"), this method is no longer used. There are two principal means of preserving such concentrates. In this country, as well as in some others, it is customary to sterilize the extract by flash-heating to a temperature in the neighborhood of 85°C. (185°F.), followed by packaging in suitable containers. Sterilization in smaller bottles at 70°C. (160°F.) for 30 minutes has also been used. In Germany,[1414] preservation by the addition of sulfur dioxide is customary and amounts ranging from 0.05 to 0.2% have been claimed to be used commercially. Heiss recommends 0.125% sulfur dioxide.[1378] The alternate method of preservation with 0.18% sodium benzoate, 1% formic acid, or other preservatives has also been used in some German factories.

Pectin concentrates, even if preserved, are essentially perishable since the jelly grade of the pectin gradually decreases during storage. Since the loss in jelly grade is accelerated by elevated temperatures, the concentrate is best kept at temperatures as near the freezing point as practicable. Manufacturers who supply the retail trade with small packages of concentrates for household use make it a practice at the end of the fruit canning season to pick up all pectin extract in the hands of wholesale houses and retail stores in order to replace it with fresh extract. This in spite of a considerable margin of safety allowed in the recipes supplied. Some manufacturers store the concentrate under refrigeration.[1415]

Freezing concentration has been tried also with pectin extracts.[1416,1417] This method involves exposure of the solution to temperatures below its freezing point, at which, under suitable conditions, crystals of water form and may be removed by a variety of means. Apparently such methods are not used now in the large-scale production of pectin concentrates, although concentration by such means would be very desirable because of the detrimental effect of heat on pectin. Freezing concentration is still a very expensive operation. Pectin extracts at low temperatures become very viscous, which causes various difficulties and reduces the over-all efficiency.

VI. PREPARATION OF SOLID (DRY) PECTINS

Powdered solid pectins offer many advantages over pectin solutions. Since the latter contain only 3 to 5% pectin, the bulk and weight to be shipped is very large. Solid pectins do not spoil once the container is opened which is a great advantage in practical usage. In addition, pectins

[1414] B. Hottenroth, *Chem. Ing.-Technik*, 21, 142 (1949).
[1415] Anonymous, *Food Field Reptr.*, 15 (10), 41 (1947).
[1416] J. S. Caldwell, *Washington Agr. Expt. Sta.*, Bull. No. 147 (1917).
[1417] Z. I. Kertesz, *Food Inds.*, 18, 496 (1946).

are usually purified to a considerable extent during precipitation, giving refined products; this reduces the possibility of introducing foreign flavors into various products. These factors explain the great popularity of solid pectins. On the other hand, they also show some disadvantages, such as the difficulties occasionally encountered in dissolution resulting in "lumping."

Solid pectins may be prepared from a pectin extract by various methods. Some involve evaporation of the water, others precipitation of the pectin contained in solution. The methods which have been used in the commercial production of pectin are as follows:

A. Methods involving evaporation of water.
   (a) Drying on heated surfaces (drum drying).
   (b) Drying by exposure to heated air (spray drying).
B. Methods involving precipitation.
   (c) By the use of organic solvents (ethanol, acetone, isopropyl alcohol, etc.).
   (d) By salting-out or as insoluble metal salts.
   (e) By "ionic" precipitation.

These methods were discussed in Chapter VI, dealing with the laboratory preparation of pectic substances. They will be dealt with in the following sections from the standpoint of commercial-scale production.

1. Drum Drying of Pectin Extracts

The customary method of drying by means of two heated drums with the pectin concentrate placed in the well has been used for pectin production. Prolonged exposure of the extract in the well results in excessive loss of jelly grade. For this reason investigators soon turned to the use of single drums to which the pectin extract was applied by a variety of means. In all such methods the pectin extract is first concentrated by: (1) vacuum evaporation; or (2) precipitation and redissolution of the precipitate in a smaller quantity of water. Sucharipa suggested[1418] drying pectin extract on the outside surface of a single drum with the application of a powdered substance on the surface just prior to putting on the solution. This prevents strong adherence of the produced film to the metal surface. A powdered substance of any kind is assumed to be useful for this purpose, but use of the same material as is being dried, in this case pectin, is recommended. The dried pectin is removed by a stripping plate (knife) held against the surface of the drum. Sucharipa's method apparently never attained commercial significance.

[1418] R. Sucharipa (Ripa), U. S. Pat. 1,519,561 (1924).

The Sardik patents[1419] revived interest in the drying of pectin extracts and involved a number of improvements. Stainless steel drums were used by this time and the pectin concentrate was sprayed on the surface of the drum. Addition of glycerol to the concentrate was also recommended to facilitate removal of the film. The glycerol can be removed subsequently in an ethanol bath. Various modifications of the Sardik method give pectin films which are easily dispersible even in cold water, a considerable advantage over the difficulties encountered with powdered pectins. The film is produced in a continuous layer and marketed in the form of small flakes. The main drawback of this process of drying is that the pectin film must be very thin in order to permit rapid and complete drying. This fact, together with the large investment in equipment, makes the operation expensive. The Sardik method has not been adapted by the major producers of pectin in this country in preference to the precipitation methods discussed in Sections 3 and 5 below.

2. Spray Drying

Spray drying was used successfully for pectin more than twenty years ago. As the art of spray drying developed,[1364,1420] further attempts were made by a number of manufacturers to use this method for the production of powdered pectin. The concentrated pectin extract is heated and sprayed through a nozzle under considerable pressure into the drying chamber, in which hot air is circulated to effect drying and prevent the deposition of the droplets on the walls of the chamber. The dried powder is then collected in an attached smaller chamber to which it is carried by an air current. The hot air which passes through the drying chamber, and which contains many fine particles, is passed through a spray of the pectin extract to catch these particles, or they are trapped by other means.

Spray drying has been used for the production of sizable quantities of pectin. The pectin dries in spherical particles.[1420] There is still some doubt concerning the economic feasibility of this method because of the high cost of the drying operation as compared with precipitation methods. Pectin produced in this manner, as well as that dried on drums, also includes all other materials present in the concentrate, whereas in precipitation methods the pectin is purified to a certain degree by the more-or-less specific precipitation of the pectin. The mixture of pectin and inert material obtained by spray drying pectin concentrates may be used as

[1419] W. W. Cowgill, U. S. Pats. 1,973,613 (1934); 1,973,614 (1934); 2,032,687 (1936); 2,140,788 (1939); British Pat. 565,700 (1944); etc.

[1420] E. Seltzer and J. T. Settelmeyer, in E. Mrak and G. F. Stewart, *Advances in Food Research*, Vol. II. Academic Press, New York, 1949, p. 399.

such; in order to produce pectins of customary purity, however, subsequent purification is needed to remove the bulk of these nonpectin solids.

Both the drum-dried and spray-dried pectins made directly from pectin concentrates can be purified by dissolving the nonpectin solids in 50 to 70% ethanol.[1421] At times, acidulated ethanol followed by neutral (pure) ethanol is used. Other solvents, such as acetone, isopropyl alcohol, etc., are equally suitable for this "dry extraction" in which the bulk of nonpectin solids may be removed. Such extraction results, at times, in a 50 to 100% increase in the jelly grade of the preparation. The solvents are only slightly diluted with water and their recovery therefore, is simple and efficient. The sugar recovered from the ethanol used in the extraction can be fermented, thus making up for the loss in the process. After extraction the pectin is dried by the same methods as those used for ethanol-precipitated pectin.

Spray drying has also been used in conjunction with precipitation methods. The pectin is precipitated from the extract and is redissolved to a much smaller volume, giving a more concentrated solution which is then spray-dried. This combination method takes advantage of the good points of both procedures but is costly.

3. Precipitation of Pectin by Organic Solvents

Ethanol precipitation of pectin and pectinic acids was discussed earlier in some detail in Chapter VII. In the commercial production of pectin by this method, the cost of the solvent is a major consideration; in this cost the main factors are the efficiency of pressing the precipitate and recovery of the solvent. For precipitation, ethanol is added to the concentrate under mechanical stirring, until a concentration over 50% but usually not exceeding 70% is reached. The mixture of solvent and precipitate is stirred for a short period and then the ethanol is either drained or pumped through a close-mesh screen, or pumped directly to a hydraulic press. Thereupon it is pressed out and, at times is once more suspended in more concentrated ethanol (85%) to harden the precipitate. Now the precipitate is pressed out by a hydraulic press, a vertical screw-type press, or by the type of press shown in Fig. 37 (Ch. XX) under high pressure and the liquid is collected and recovered. The hard pectin cake is broken up and dried in cabinet dryers at temperatures not exceeding 82°C. (180°F.) or preferably in vacuum dryers at lower temperatures. It is then cooled, ground, sieved, and standardized.

The precipitation of very concentrated viscous pectin solutions is none too satisfactory and therefore, when this method is used, the pectin

---

[1421] H. T. Leo, C. C. Taylor, and J. W. Lindsey, U. S. Pat. 2,367,132 (1945).

extract is concentrated only to a ratio of 2:1 or 3:1. The use of denatured ethanol for the precipitation of pectin is permitted in this country and two special formulas for denaturation[1422] are provided specifically for pectin manufacturers. Even so, it is desirable to perform at least the final rinsing with pure ethanol.

Isopropyl alcohol is another solvent which has been used extensively by manufacturers for the production of solid pectins. Other solvents such as acetone have also been used under specific conditions, but none have attained the widespread usage of ethanol and isopropyl alcohol.

4. Precipitation by "Salting Out"

Pectin may be precipitated from solution by the addition of salts.[1423,1424] Ammonium sulfate is most commonly used for this purpose. The precipitation of the pectin can be fairly complete although little is known concerning the degree of fractionating which may occur under such conditions. Salt precipitation of pectin will probably not be used for commercial production unless some novel ideas are introduced. As the matter now stands, the precipitate which is formed contains much ammonium sulfate, the removal of which is tedious and expensive.

5. Precipitation of Pectin by Polyvalent Ions

This subject was discussed previously in Chapter VI, Section IV-4. The most important of these procedures employs ammonium hydroxide or soda ash and aluminum chloride or sulfate; it was described by Jameson, Taylor, and Wilson.[1425] The conditions used for the precipitation, which is made without concentrating the extract, have already been described. Afterward the "curd" or "green salt" which is formed can be separated by decantation or centrifuging.

A method often used for the separation is to blow compressed air into the precipitating tank. The precipitated particles of pectin (more correctly, acid aluminum pectinate) pick up sufficient air to carry them to the top of the liquid. Vigorous stirring has also been used for this purpose. After standing for a short time the clear "mother liquor" can be drained off from under the precipitate. This procedure may also be repeated by suspending the precipitate in acid water or water. Recently there seems to be a preference toward using a reel for separation of the precipitated pectin. This reel is constructed of fine-mesh

[1422] Denatured alcohols No. 2B and 35A.
[1423] C. A. Magoon and J. S. Caldwell, *Science,* **47,** 592 (1918).
[1424] C. H. Hunt, *Science,* **48,** 201 (1918).
[1425] E. Jameson, F. N. Taylor, and C. P. Wilson, U. S. Pat. 1,497,884 (1924).

wire, and is cylindrical in shape and inclined. As the "curd" passes through the reel it is washed with cold water to remove the excess of the mother liquor. The precipitate is then drawn off through a screen and the excess solution removed with a basket centrifuge or a hydraulic press. The precipitate may now be washed with acidulated ethanol to remove the aluminum.[1426] It may also be dried without purification in a cabinet dryer and ground after cooling. The pectin at this point contains some 10–15% ash which is mostly aluminum and which must be removed. Aluminum hydroxide is insoluble in ethanol, while aluminum chloride is quite soluble. Treatment with ethanol containing about 10% hydrochloric acid converts the aluminum hydroxide into the chloride, which in turn is dissolved in the ethanol. Naturally, complete removal of the acid is essential and, for this reason, the pectin is washed further with neutral ethanol containing some sodium carbonate and later with pure neutral ethanol. The last traces of the ethanol are evaporated with hot air, after which the pectin is ready for grinding, standardization, and packaging.

A method[1427] has also been described in which the aluminum is only partially removed from the precipitated pectin to give a product containing more than 1.5% aluminum oxide; the degree of removal is controlled by the hydrochloric acid content of the wash ethanol. The pectin is then mixed with sodium citrate or similar salts to make it dispersible in water. Such pectin is used for various purposes, especially as a substitute for various gums, and is claimed to be superior for such uses to customary pectin. The important point is that removal of the aluminum from the wet curd is controlled by the acidity of the ethanol and that, for efficient removal of the aluminum, 45% ethanol having a pH of 1.00 is most efficient. It should be noted that the residual aluminum content of pectin prepared by this method may be objectionable.

Another precipitation method[1428] which may be used for the production of pectin is as follows:

The pectin extract is stirred vigorously and a small proportion of aluminum potassium sulfate (alum) is added. Ammonium hydroxide is added until the mixture is slightly on the alkaline side. As stirring continues, a precipitate gradually forms; when precipitation is complete, the stirrer is stopped. The precipitate is separated and, after the tank is washed down, the filtrate is returned and heated to boiling. Then small quantities of magnesium sulfate are added until no further precipitation occurs. The precipitated pectin is filtered off, washed with cold water, pressed, and dried. Such pectin contains traces of magnesium sulfate, but this is, according to Williams, of no great consequence.

As was noted in Chapter VI, copper salts have also been used for precipitation of pectin from extracts, often in combination with other methods. The copper may be removed by either of the methods described above. Complete removal is often difficult and, since the presence of

[1426] G. M. Cole and H. H. Holton, U. S. Pat. 2,300,651 (1942).
[1427] H. T. Leo and C. C. Taylor, U. S. Pat. 2,392,854 (1946).
[1428] A. E. Williams, *Food Trade Rev.*, 18, 5 (Sept., 1948).

even traces of copper is objectionable in most food products, great care should be taken to have the final preparation free from this metal. As was mentioned in Chapter VI, precipitation of pectinic acids can be accomplished with calcium and acids, but these methods are applicable only in the case of pectinic acids with reduced ester contents (low-ester pectins).

CHAPTER XX

Citrus Pectin

I. RAW MATERIALS

The white spongy albedo of citrus fruits is an eminently suitable raw product for pectin manufacture. As stated previously, most of the pectin produced in this country is now made from citrus peel; there is also a tendency toward expansion of the production of citrus pectin which is not the case with apple pectin. The production of canned and frozen citrus juices in this country has now reached exceedingly high levels, and the amount of citrus peel available as a by-product is enormous. In addition, considerable amounts of peel become available from the canning of grapefruit segments.[1429] This amount of citrus peel is much greater than can possibly be used for pectin maufacture, even allowing for important developments in the more extensive utilization of pectin and other pectic substances and derivatives.

Citrus peel of various origins contains 20 to 50% pectin, on the dry matter basis. The Hung lemon seems to be the richest[1430] source and, in general, the lemon is regarded as one of the best sources of pectin. Grapefruit peel is also a very good raw material, as is the peel of the pomelo[1431] with its thick albedo. Among the common citrus fruit, orange peel is a comparatively less suitable raw material. Naturally, the condition of the fruit and other factors have a profound effect both on the quantity and quality of the pectin obtained. It is also known that even partial freezing of the peel will cause difficulties with the pectin, presumably as the result of the demethylating action of the pectin-methylesterase (see Chapter XIV) which occurs in the peel.

At times when surplus lemons were on hand, lemon peel has been used for pectin manufacture without utilizing any other part of the fruit— an undesirable procedure in any adjusted economy. Since the lemon peel

[1429] G. N. Pulley, E. L. Moore, and C. D. Atkins, *Food Inds.*, **16**, 285 (1944).
[1430] V. Rongo and S. L. Quiatson, *Philippine Agr.*, **29**, 1 (1940).
[1431] G. D. Sherman and Y. Kanehiro, *Chemurgic Digest*, **6**, 65 (1947).

used for the manufacture of pectin is usually a by-product of the production of lemon juice and concentrates, the maturity of the fruit is therefore somewhat more advanced than is desirable for obtaining the maximum jelly unit yield. The production of citric acid also used to supply sizable quantities of lemon peel. The bulk of citrus pectin is now produced from grapefruit peel and, to a lesser degree, from lemon and orange peel. No distinction is made in the trade among pectins produced from any of these sources; they are all covered by the name *citrus pectin*. The variation in the quality of pectin which may be obtained from citrus peel is great, and for the three sources the maximum grade (Chapter XXIII) which may be obtained, under optimum conditions may be roughly set as 300–350 grade for lemon peel, 250–300 for grapefruit peel, and 150–250 grade for orange peel.

Generally speaking, in any of these citrus fruits the varieties which possess a thick, firm albedo are usually most suitable for the manufacture of pectin. This is true not only because the amounts of albedo and thus raw pectin are larger, but also because the various impurities derived from the flavedo and the "rags" remaining after the juice is expressed are present in much smaller amounts.

Until recent years, only fresh citrus peel was used for the manufacture of pectin, although large quantities of citrus peel were also limed, dewatered in presses, and dried for feed in the types of rotary tubular dryers used for apple pomace (Chapter XIX). Such peel is of course unsuitable for the manufacture of pectin without extensive treatment for the removal of the calcium and for other reasons. However, during the recent war citrus peel, more specifically grapefruit peel, was dried extensively without liming for shipment abroad as a substitute for the insufficient supply of pectin. This product will be discussed later in detail (Chapter XXV). Such peel is used to extend the season during which pectin can be manufactured from fresh peel or dried apple pomace. This is indicated by the shipment of dried citrus peel to manufacturers of apple pectin.

The manufacture of citrus pectin from the peels of lemons, grapefruit, and oranges shows great similarity and will therefore be discussed together. The basic published information concerning the manufacturing methods used is contained in an article by Wilson[1432] the important patent of Jameson, Taylor, and Wilson,[1433] and in some subsequent patents. Many of these were mentioned on previous pages.

[1432] C. P. Wilson, *Ind. Eng. Chem.*, **17**, 1065 (1925).
[1433] E. Jameson, F. N. Taylor, and C. P. Wilson, U. S. Pat. 1,497,884 (1924).

II. REMOVAL OF OIL, HEATING, AND PURIFICATION OF PEEL

The flavedo of citrus fruits contains a considerable proportion of oil, which is usually removed by some method before the original shape of the citrus fruit is destroyed or after the juice has been expressed. The oil is a valuable by-product of juice manufacture. The variety of machinery used for this purpose is great.[1434] Briefly, most methods cause oil cells to burst in a gentle manner to prevent absorption of the oil by the albedo. The oil is washed off, usually with an excess of water, and the oil is recovered by centrifuging or other means. For details of oil extraction processes and for information on other aspects of citrus product manufacture, the reader is referred to the recent monograph of Braverman.[1434]

For the manufacture of pectin, after removal of the oil and juice, the citrus peel is washed in rotating cages to remove the seeds and as much of the "rags" as possible. The peel is then either heated directly or first ground or shredded and then heated to inactivate the enzymes which are present in the peel,[1432,1435] and which may cause undesirable changes in the pectic constituents. Heating to 95–98°C. (104–108°F.) for about 10 minutes is recommended for this purpose.[1432] This preliminary step may be eliminated if the peel is to be heated promptly for extraction since that operation also inactivates the enzymes. The small pieces of peel are then thoroughly washed with large quantities of water and, at times, are heated to temperatures of 50–60°C. (123–141°F.) to facilitate removal of sugars and other soluble constituents, but especially to eliminate fine particles which form fine suspended solids. Washing extracts a small quantity of pectin but the removal of undesirable impurities, as well as of pectinic acids of low jellying power, offsets any loss of pectin. One of the purposes of washing the peel is to remove the bitter-flavored glucosides which occur in some peel. The use of a small quantity of sodium carbonate in the wash water has also been suggested, but in most cases the bitterness can be removed from the shredded peel with water alone. It is imperative that the water used for washing the peel be free from calcium and magnesium, not to speak of metal ions, since their presence may destroy the effectiveness of the extraction procedure. The washing process should not be unduly prolonged because of the loss of pectin.

This purification of the peel is especially important if the pectin extract is to be used in the form of a concentrate or dried without preliminary precipitation of the pectin. Soluble solids which are not removed find their way into the final product. The shredded pieces of inside rag

[1434] J. B. S. Braverman, *Citrus Products*. Interscience, New York, 1949.
[1435] F. W. Norris, *Biochem. J.*, 20, 993 (1926).

should also be removed as completely as possible since these contain pectins of lower quality than does the albedo. The method of washing determines the preferred method of grinding or shredding, but the latter is generally more desirable as it assures good extraction, is less wasteful, and provides easier handling.

Pressing of the washed peel removes the soluble solids in a quicker and more efficient manner than draining. The machine shown in Figure 37 has

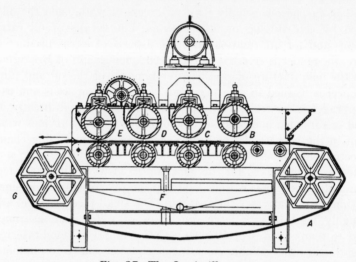

Fig. 37. The Louisville press.

The material to be pressed is carried on moving belt *A*, composed of perforated plates, and passes between a series of pairs of rolls of decreasing clearances, *B*, *C*, *D*, and *E*. The expressed liquid is collected in trough *F*. The pressed material drops off the plates as they turn downward at *G*.

been found suitable for this purpose.[1436]   In certain processes pressing is performed twice. The use of this method greatly hastens the purification of the peel. Figure 27 shows a scheme for peel preparation and extraction in which the preliminary heating (blanching) and washing are done in a continuous process.[1437]   Here the peel is pressed out between two rollers.

III. EXTRACTION OF PECTIN AND SEPARATION OF EXTRACT

Here again the principal problem is the proper selection of the pH, time, and temperature of the extraction; the role of these factors was dis-

[1436] Manufactured by Louisville Dryer Corp., Louisville Ky.
[1437] H. S. Owens, R. M. McCready, and W. D. Maclay, *Food Technol.*, **3**, 77 (1949).

cussed in Chapter XIX. Usually only enough acidulated solution is added to suspend the shredded and washed peel and the mixture is then brought to about 90°C. (195°F.). Wilson[1432] describes the use of 1% sulfurous acid solution as the extractant and states that heating to the above temperature is continued for 2 hours. Myers and Baker[1438] recommend the use of pH 2.15 and 30 minutes at the boiling point, followed by further dilution and heating at lower temperatures to enhance dissolution of the pectin. Owens, McCready, and Maclay[1437] give the following conditions: a water–peel ratio of 3:1, pH of 1.3–1.4, temperature of 90–100°C. (194–212°F.), and 1 hour of heating. As citrus fruits ripen not only do the quantity and quality of the extractable pectin change, but also the ease and the preferred method by which it may be obtained from the peel. There is little doubt that, here again, just as with apple pomace, experimentation to determine the most suitable method for the peel used, under any given set of conditions, is imperative.

The extent of softening which the pieces of peel show when cooking is completed is a major consideration. At times the cooked mixture is pressed slowly in a hydraulic press. Wilson recommends drawing off the extract through a false bottom with the pulp itself acting as a filter mat. The addition of paper pulp or filter aids facilitates separation of the extract, whatever method of pressing is used. Owens, McCready, and Maclay use continuous countercurrent extraction and drain the solution from the extraction trough (see Fig. 27). Centrifuges of the type mentioned in the previous chapter may also be used at times to advantage. The mechanical handling of the cooked peel is, according to Wilson, the greatest single problem in the production of citrus pectin, a point on which all workers in this field will heartily agree. This is also the crux of the usefulness of continuous extraction processes such as shown in Figure 27.

IV. FILTRATION, PRECIPITATION, AND SPRAY DRYING

The filtration of apple pectin extracts has been discussed in detail, and similar considerations also apply to the filtration of citrus peel extracts. The extent of the difficulties which may be encountered depends mostly on the success of washing in removing small particles and of extraction in obtaining the pectin solution without excessive softening of the peel.

The two major methods used in the preparation of citrus pectin for market are: (1) precipitation with organic solvents (ethanol or isopropanol); and (2) the so-called "ionic precipitation" method. Practically no citrus pectin extract or concentrate is marketed in this country.

[1438] P. B Myers and G. L. Baker, *Univ. Delaware Agr. Expt. Sta.*, Bull. No. 160 (1929).

During the war some citrus pectin extract was spray-dried. This process, which was recently also described in two patents,[1439,1440] is based on the previously noted principle that the pectin in such extracts is usually over 100 grade and that it contains an approximately equal proportion of nonpectin materials. These nonpectin materials are mostly soluble in dilute ethanol and can be extracted from the dried pectin (Chapter XIX). By removal of the ethanol-soluble constituents, the jelly grade of the citrus pectin is elevated (by removal of admixed "diluent" materials) and the purity (especially odor) of the pectin is greatly improved. The extraction of the pectin from citrus peel is usually conducted in a manner which results in a product with suitable jelly-forming ability and which possesses the correct setting time, a subject which will be discussed in Chapter XXII.

The pectin extraction process of Myers and Rouse[1441] in which the use of ion-exchange agents for pectin extraction is described was mentioned previously. In this interesting process grapefruit peel is ground and washed to remove electrolytes. It is then mixed with Zeo-Karb H (a sulfonated coal)[1442] and heated to 92°C. (196°F.) for 1 hour. The exchange agent takes up the calcium and magnesium in the peel, lowers the pH, and liberates the pectin. The peel and exchange agent are then separated in a centrifuge; the pectin solution goes directly to the evaporators and the exchange agent is recovered. There is some question as to whether the extraction of the pectin is predominantly accomplished by the ion-exchange effect or by the low pH which results from ion exchange. Both factors are probably involved. Mindler recently published a diagram[1443] showing this process.

[1439] H. T. Leo, C. C. Taylor, and J. W. Lindsey, U. S. Pat. 2,367,132 (1945).
[1440] R. C. Nelson, U. S. Pat. 2,455,382 (1948).
[1441] P. B. Myers and A. H. Rouse, U. S. Pat. 2,323,483 (1943).
[1442] Manufactured by Permutit Corporation, Inc., New York.
[1443] A. B. Mindler, *Food Technol.*, 3, 43 (1949).

CHAPTER XXI

Beet Pectin

I. INTRODUCTION

The enormous quantities of extracted beet slices which are available in beet sugar producing countries led a long time ago to investigations of this by-product as a source of commercial pectin. Ripa[1444] stated in his book: "the extraction of pectin from beets is thus far hopeless. The pectin of beets seems to be greatly degraded ... and shows no jelly forming ability." It has been general experience[1445-1447] that, when methods ordinarily used for apple pomace and citrus peel are applied to beet slices, these result in poor yields of low-grade pectins. The suspicion has been expressed by some workers that the low ester content of beet pectin is in part at least responsible for the low jelly-forming ability of beet pectin; the results obtained by others, however, make such a contention untenable. Säverborn[1448] prepared beet pectin by boiling for a short time at pH 2.15, followed by ethanol precipitation, and found 71.3% polyuronide and 10.2% methoxyl in the product. In spite of this high degree (81%) of esterification, and an apparent molecular weight not essentially different from apple and citrus pectin, no jellies could be obtained by Säverborn. Cohen[1446] increased the methyl ester content of beet pectin (by the diazomethane method) but again without any beneficial effect on jelly formation. This is not surprising in view of the known degradation of polymer molecules during such operations.

The occurrence of acetyl groups in beet pectin and the contention of some workers that it is the presence of these groups which prevents jelly formation was mentioned earlier in Chapter IV. This situation is far from clear and, although some investigators like Pippen, McCready, and

[1444] R. Ripa, *Die Pektinstoffe.* Serger und Hempel, Braunschweig, 1937.
[1445] A. J. Codling and H. E. Woodman, *J. Agr. Sci.,* 19, 701 (1929).
[1446] H. Cohen, *Trans. Central Sci. Research Inst. Sugar Ind.* (U. S. S. R.), 15, 14 (1933); through *C. A.,* 28, 7376 (1934).
[1447] E. Afferni, *Ind. saccar. ital.,* 30, 281 (1937); through *C. A.,* 31, 6498 (1937).
[1448] S. Säverborn, *Dissertation,* Uppsala (1945).

Owens[1449] feel that the presence of acetyl groups prevent jelly formation, the fact remains that many others (including the author) prepared beet pectin of considerable acetyl content yet capable of forming jellies.

The possibility of using extracted beet slices for making pectin attracted considerable attention during the past ten years, especially in the U. S. S. R. and in Germany.[1450-1452] In the latter country large quantities of beet pectin were manufactured during the war when it became first difficult and then impossible to obtain apple pomace from France. The intense research conducted on beet pectin resulted in a product capable of forming jellies[1453] but with principally undesirable other characteristics. The maximum jelly grade (Chapter XXIII) obtainable under commercial conditions was said to be about 50 or 60 on a dry purified pectin basis. Higher grade beet pectin has since been prepared by the author as well as by others.

The principal advance in the technic of making beet pectin is the realization of its extreme heat sensitivity. This is illustrated in Table 71, taken from Bock's dissertation.[1454]

TABLE 71

EFFECT OF EXTRACTION TEMPERATURE ON QUALITY OF BEET PECTIN[a]

(ADAPTED FROM BOCK)

Extraction temp., °C.	Jellying power	Yield
30	Good	Poor
40	Good	Good
50	Good	Maximum
60	None	—

[a] Extraction for 40 hours with 1% hydrochloric acid.

By digesting for 20 hours and raising the hydrochloric acid concentration to 5%, Bock obtained pectins capable of forming jellies in good yields. Under all conditions the methyl ester content of beet pectins was much lower (5 to 7%) than that of the customary apple and citrus pectins. This would seem to open up the possibilities of beet pectin in the field of low-ester pectins. While work on this problem is in progress in several laboratories and in a number of countries, there is at this time no substantial evidence on hand that beet pectin will be exceptionally suitable for the

[1449] E. L. Pippen, R. M. McCready, and H. S. Owens, paper given at the San Francisco meeting of the American Chemical Society, March, 1949.
[1450] Z. I. Kertesz, Joint Intelligence Objectives Subcommittee, FIAT Final Report No. 567 (1945).
[1451] B. Hottenroth, *Chem. Ing.-Technik*, 21, 142 (1949).
[1452] R. Heiss, *Lebensmitteltechnologie*. Bergmann, Munich, 1950.
[1453] Pomosin Werke, Belgian Pat. 444,871 (1942); through *C. A.*, 39, 566 (1945).
[1454] H. Bock, *Dissertation*, Karlsruhe (1943).

manufacture of low-ester pectins of the type developed in recent years (Chapter VI). A patent[1455] on the manufacture of such products from beets is available which proposes deesterifying beet pectin to cause it to set to a jelly with "sugar and the acids and salts of fruits." The latter term is apparently a subtle name for polyvalent cations such as calcium.

In recent years Henglein[1456] and Bock[1454] gave serious consideration to the reasons for the different behavior of the insoluble pectic constituents of beets. It is their opinion that, due to the observed larger proportions of free carboxyl groups in beet protopectin, the significance of inter-molecular linkages—mostly through calcium ions—greatly exceeds the role of such linkages in apple and citrus pectins. These various schemes for protopectin were discussed earlier (Chapter III). It is the differences in the extent of intramolecular and intermolecular cleavage which, ac-cording to Bock, govern the type of product obtained. This matter was also dealt with in connection with the heterogeneity of pectic substances (Chapter IV).

In Germany experimental work aiming at the commercial manufacture of beet pectin was in progress by 1933. The results were not very encour-aging and large-scale production and utilization did not commence until the war years. The beet pectin concentrate was sold for some time in a mixture containing 60% apple pectin and 40% beet pectin extracts; later (1944–45), however, some beet pectin was sold without being mixed. By that time there was some improvement in the quality and the product had a low, but usable, jellying power. Research and development work is now also under way in this country to produce beet pectin with commercial utility.[1457,1458]

II. METHODS OF MANUFACTURE

The dried beet slices obtained from the manufacture of beet sugar are mixed in the ratio of 1:10 with water preheated to 55°C. (132°F.) and a mixture of hydrochloric and sulfurous acids is added until a pH of about 1.0 is reached. The digestion is continued for 16 hours. Only 9 to 10 hours of digestion is required at 78°C. (172°F.).[1451] Then the extract is drained through perforated tiles which form the bottom of the extraction vessel. According to Mehlitz[1450] beet pectin is best extracted with sulfurous acid of about 5% concentration and at temperatures in the range of 30 to 40°C. (87 to 105°F.) for 1 or 2 days. The drained extract may be sub-

[1455] R. H. McDowell and H. P. Bulmer and Co. Ltd., British Pat. 555,842 (1943).
[1456] F. A. Henglein, *J. makromol. Chem.*, **1**, 121 (1943).
[1457] E. Roboz and A. van Hook, *Proc. Am. Soc. Sugar Beet Technol.*, **4**, 574 (1946).
[1458] P. T. Miller and J. W. Savage, *Chemurgic Digest*, **7**, No. 4, 21 (1948).

jected to the various steps of clarification and filtration. During the war in Germany the extract was precipitated with aluminum sulfate and the rinsed precipitate ("curd") was dissolved in citric or lactic acid to give an approximately 8–10% solution.[1449] This was standardized for jellying power by mixing various batches, treated with sulfur dioxide to contain about 0.05%, placed in barrels, and shipped. Apparently no dry pectin was produced in Germany from beets. Hottenroth[1458a] recently described a German beet pectin preparation process in which the dry, extracted beet slices are mixed with 12.5-fold weight of 2% hydrochloric acid and kept at 40°C. (104°F.) for 18 hours. The extract is then filtered off and precipitated in the usual manner.

Recently some samples of beet pectin were prepared in the author's laboratory for the purpose of comparative analyses.[1459] The ground, dry, extracted beet slices (500 g.) were mixed with 16 l. of water, the pH was adjusted to 0.7 with hydrochloric acid, and the mixture was kept at 40°C. (104°F.) for 22 hours. The extract was then filtered, clarified, precipitated with a 2-fold volume of 95% ethanol, washed with ethanol, and dried in a vacuum oven. The 90.4 g. of dry pectin obtained showed a jelly grade of 75 by the method of Cox and Higby.[1460]

The author recently examined a sample of dry beet pectin produced in a pilot plant in this country and a sample of a beet pectin concentrate manufactured in Denmark. Neither showed any ability to form jellies under a variety of conditions. Their jelly grade, if any, must have been below 10, on the dry matter basis.

[1458a] B. Hottenroth, *Die Pektine und ihre Verwendung*. R. Oldenbourg, Munich, 1951.
[1459] B. Crowley and Z. I. Kertesz, *unpublished work*, 1948.
[1460] R. E. Cox and R. H. Higby, *Food Inds.*, **16**, 441 (1944).

CHAPTER XXII

Control of Setting Time

Setting time is the interval of time which elapses between the instant at which all the constituents of a jelly batch (sugar, pectin, and acid) are placed in the final container after cooking and that instant at which jellification or gelation of the whole into a coherent mass may be observed.[1461]

It was assumed for some time that one type of pectin would be entirely satisfactory for the manufacture of jams, preserves, marmalades, and jellies. Experience has shown that the manufacture of some products, such as jams and marmalades, requires a pectin which "sets" rapidly into a solidified mass, whereas the jelly maker prefers a pectin which causes the product to solidify slowly. The rapidly set pectin holds the fruit and pulp particles uniformly mixed throughout the batch, thus preventing the fruit from floating. On the other hand, the use of pectin which sets too quickly may cause entrapping of air because the finished product thickens or actually solidifies too rapidly after filling, thereby preventing the air bubbles from rising to the surface. For these reasons some manufacturers put pectin preparations on the market which are designated as "rapid set" or "slow set"; these are chosen according to the product manufactured and the machinery used.

Although the variations in the setting times of different pectins may be considerable, the reason for such behavior is still not entirely clear. There are a number of patents on this topic but they only clarify the issue partially. Williams and Waugh[1462] used disodium phosphate (Na_2HPO_4), which was added to the powdered pectin together with sugar and an organic acid to retard setting. Joseph[1463] later recommended treatment of the dry pectin with an organic solvent containing acid, which, when left in contact with the pectin for several hours at room temperature, gradually increased the setting time. Afterward the acid was removed,

[1461] G. M. Cole and R. E. Cox, U. S. Pat. 2,109,792 (1938).
[1462] P. Williams and J. D. Waugh, U. S. Pat. 2,010,340 (1935).
[1463] G. H. Joseph, U. S. Pat. 2,061,158 (1937).

and the pectin was washed with pure solvent and dried. The method of treatment has been elaborated further in the patent of Cole and Cox,[1461] who treat the pectin with "gaseous, aqueous or anhydrous" acid or "acid-forming substance." In one instance the latter authors dispersed some pectin in hydrochloric acid to give a 1.25% pectin solution with an approximate pH of 0.1 and kept this mixture at room temperature. The setting time of the pectin was 9 seconds after 1 hour, 95 seconds after 21 hours, and 28 minutes after two days. Meanwhile the jelly grade rose from 180 to above 200. Cox also described a method[1464] for altering the setting time of pectins by treatment with basic reagents. In all the foregoing patents no attention was given to the temperature of setting, which, in reality, is perhaps entirely responsible for differences in setting time. The point was brought out in the interesting patent of Leo, Taylor, and Lindsey.[1465] These workers state, first of all, the well-known fact that the time of set depends on the pH of the jelly mixture. They make clear, in addition, that the time required for a jelly to set depends on the rate of cooling and on the temperature of set, which is an "inherent ability" of the pectin preparation in question. Thus, setting may be controlled to a considerable extent by the temperature at which the batch is poured and by the cooling rate of the poured product. Leo, Taylor, and Lindsey also recommend the use of acid treatments to reduce the setting time of pectins.

It is now clear that the methyl ester content of the pectin is one of the main factors determining the time (or temperature) of setting. A reduction of the methyl ester content will result in an increased setting time and this is exactly what has been accomplished in the above instances. However, acid and alkali treatment almost invariably also reduces the average macromolecular size of pectinic acids, and therefore such chemical treatments must be used with discretion. It is now known that orange peel extract containing pectin-methylesterase (see Chapter XIV) is used in one factory abroad for the reduction of the ester content in order to increase the setting time. A commercial pectin-esterase manufactured in this country and entirely void of pectin-polygalacturonase activity is used for the same purpose by at least one pectin manufacturer in this country. The details of the treatments used are not available.

The method of preparing the jelly, the pH of the mixture, and the sugar concentration, as well as the presence of salts, also influence the setting time. In most cases lower pH values cause quicker jellification. Among the salts, the effect of bivalent ions is especially noteworthy.

Olsen, Stuewer, Fehlberg, and Beach[1466] suggest a method for determination of

[1464] R. E. Cox, U. S. Pat. 2,133,273 (1938).

[1465] H. T. Leo, C. C. Taylor, and J. W. Lindsey, U. S. Pat. 2,173,260 (1939).

[1466] A. G. Olsen, R. F. Stuewer, E. R. Fehlberg, and N. M. Beach, Ind. Eng. Chem., 31, 1015 (1939).

the setting time, the essence of the procedure being holding the cooked jelly mixture in an aluminum vessel in a water bath at 15°C. (60°F.); samples of the mixture are obtained periodically through an outlet at the bottom of the container. These samples are poured into one-ounce jelly glasses which are kept for 16 to 24 hours at 20°C. (69°F.). The jelly strength is then determined by any of the conventional methods given in Chapter XXIII, Section V. The setting time is defined as the time represented by the sample which registers the first definite drop in jelly strength due to the partially "curdled" condition of the mixture at the time of pouring.

Recently Joseph and Baier described another method[1467] for determination of the setting time. The jelly glass containing the freshly poured jelly is placed immediately in a water bath filled with water and held at 30°C. (86°F.). The glass is surrounded with water almost to the top, and is held in place by a clip provided for that purpose. The water bath has glass windows on two opposite sides; by means of a light source placed behind the rear window, the jelly can be observed through the front window. The contents of the jelly glass are given a slow, easy twist at intervals and are observed through the window. As the jelly starts to set, it can be seen that the jelly particles rotate first in the direction of the twist and then move back in the opposite direction. The setting time is the period between pouring and the point in jellification when the jelly at the top of the glass can be seen to move back after a twist.

Baker and Goodwin[1468] reported observations on setting time in connection with their studies on low-ester pectins. They confirm the view that the principal effect of the acid treatments is demethylation of the pectin, although it is not correct to state that all high-ester pectins are quick-set pectins. Extraction of the pectins at various acidities does not show a definite and constant relation to the setting time.[1466] Lower sugar concentrations than 65% sometimes lengthen, sometimes shorten, the time of set. High jelly grade pectins, according to Baker and Goodwin, tend to show longer setting times.

As noted above, the addition of certain salts to the jellying mixture is known to retard setting.[1462] Sodium citrate, potassium tartrate, or disodium phosphate are frequently used for this purpose. These "buffer salts" in the proper mixture are also often added to commercial pectin preparations to increase their setting time. Retardation of setting has been considered of sufficient importance to warrant the inclusion of a special provision in various standards for food products to permit the use of such salt mixtures in conjunction with pectin. This step was taken at the behest of the preserving industries. In the United States standards[1469] for jams, for instance, the "amount of sodium citrate, sodium potassium tar-

[1467] G. H. Joseph and W. E. Baier, *Food Technol.*, 3, 18 (1949).
[1468] G. L. Baker and M. W. Goodwin, *Univ. Delaware Agr. Expt. Sta.*, Bull. No. 234 (1941); No. 246 (1944).
[1469] Federal Security Agency, Food and Drug Administration, *Definitions and Standards of Identity for Preserves, Jams,* 1947.

trate or any combination of these" permitted to be present must not exceed 3 ounces per 100 lbs. (or about 0.19%) of the "saccharine ingredient."

Hinton[1469a] recently noted that setting temperature measurements are subject to undercooling effects. Harvey[1469b] dealt with the theoretical aspects of setting temperature and attempted to explain the observed variation on the basis of a modification of Hinton's [1469c] hypothesis of pectin-sugar-acid jelly formation.

The rapid-set pectins now on the market usually start to form a jelly at about 88°C. (190°F.), while the slow-set type of product starts to jell at about 54°C. (130°F.).

In summary, it may be stated that, while the setting time of pectins can now be controlled or more correctly lengthened, the whole matter of setting time needs further clarification before a relationship between this property and chemical composition can be clearly defined. The methyl ester groups obviously play an important part in the setting time, but there seem to be other factors involved which are still unknown. Although such information may be in the hands of some manufacturers, the literature shows a woeful lack of data on this important question.

[1469a] C. L. Hinton, *J. Sci. Food Agr.*, 1, 300 (1950).
[1469b] H. G. Harvey, *J. Sci. Food Agr.*, 1, 307 (1950).
[1469c] C. L. Hinton, *Biochem. J.*, 34, 1211 (1940).

CHAPTER XXIII

Pectins of Commerce

I. TYPES

There are three principal types of pectin products sold: (a) standardized, dry, powdered pectin for the use of preserve manufacture; (b) "liquid pectin" or, more correctly, pectin concentrates sold for the same purpose; and (c) powdered pectin sold in a form which makes it most useful for uses other than preserve manufacture, chiefly in pharmaceuticals and for medicinal purposes. These will be discussed in this chapter. Other products, such as low-ester pectin, pectin pulp (protopectin), pectic acid, and pectinates and pectates will be discussed in the following chapters.

1. Powdered Pectin

The bulk of commercially produced pectin is sold in the solid form. About two thirds of the pectin produced in this country is powdered citrus pectin, although powdered apple pectin has also been manufactured in sizeable quantities (see Tables 65 and 66 in Chapter XVIII for production figures). The advantages of solid pectins over pectin concentrates were discussed earlier. Dry pectin is obtained by any of the methods described previously, ground to between 60- and 80-mesh sieve size, and then standardized for its jelly grade. This is necessary because of unavoidable variations in the raw material, as well as fluctuations in the success of the manufacturing operations. The standardization consists of equalization and dilution by mixing different batches to give a desired jelly grade and by addition of essentially inert materials, such as Cerelose or other easily soluble carbohydrate products. The admixing of these materials has an additional desirable effect on the product. The dissolution of powdered pectins requires considerable care to avoid "lumping" or "clumping." A pectin preparation which once becomes "lumped" is essentially lost or requires extensive and difficult manipulations to cause the pectin to dissolve (disperse) in water. As was noted in Chap. VII, ad-

mixing of sugar reduces the danger of lumping and, in fact, is the standard method[1470,1471] for avoiding this difficulty. Further steps are taken
at times to enhance the dissolution of the pectin in water. This has been
the subject of many patents, which cover the use of an "intimate" mixture with sugars,[1472] the use of effervescent mixtures,[1473] the treatment
of powdered pectin particles with a solution of an aliphatic fatty acid,[1474]
and the addition of an oil[1475] to the dry powder, as well as many other
methods. It appears that particle size has much to do with the tendency
to clump; apparently very small particles are more likely to stick together. For this reason very fine grinding is usually avoided.

It was noted in Chapter XXII that buffer salts are also often added
to alter the setting time of dry pectins sold for the manufacture of preserves. This is now part of the standardization procedure which has
evolved in this country, mainly due to the efforts of a few larger manufacturers.

The usefulness of any pectin employed by the preserving and related
industries is based on its jellying power. This may range from very high
to negligible in a sample of pectin and, for this reason, the commercial
value of such pectins depends on their jelly grade, which will be dealt
with in detail in Section IV. Suffice it to say here that dry pectin preparations are now standardized by the addition of sugars, acids, and other
substances to give mixtures of definite jelly grades. The grade of commercial pectins used to vary from 50 to 180 grade with a tendency to
regard 100 grade pectin as a standard. At the present time 150 grade
pectin seems to be more common than 100 grade. The commercial value
of a pectin is essentially proportional to its jelly grade, with the notable
exception of pectin mixtures packaged for retail trade for household use
and other specific purposes. Most retail brands of packages for household
use contain $2^1/_2$ ounces of standardized pectin.[1476]

2. Pectin Concentrates

The pectin concentrates ("liquid pectins") sold in this country consist
of two chief types. The product sold to preservers is usually standardized
only for jelly grade; as a rule, no attempt is now made to add acids in
order to obtain favorable conditions in the product because the pH
of the mixtures is usually adjusted during the manufacture of preserves.

[1470] H. T. Leo, U. S. Pat. 1,646,157 (1927).
[1471] A. Leo, U. S. Pat. 1,844,666 (1932).
[1472] C. P. Wilson, U. S. Pat. 2,159,194 (1939).
[1473] E. Jameson, U. S. Pat. Reissue 19,197 (1934).
[1474] R. C. Nelson, U. S. Pat. 2,412,282 (1946).
[1475] A. K. Epstein, U. S. Pat. 1,995,281 (1935).
[1476] Anonymous, *Food Inds.*, 20, 1036 (1948).

Some pectin concentrates contain buffers to adjust the setting time but such regulators are now also commonly used by makers of preserves. Pectin extracts sold in the U. S. are usually preserved by pasteurization. Both sulfur dioxide and other preservatives are extensively used in other countries. In some countries such as England, for instance, pectin extract and concentrates are often delivered by "tankers" (tank trucks) to the preserve manufacturer.

Pectin concentrates marketed for household use are usually adjusted with acid and buffer salts to give the best results with a wide range of products. The pH of the concentrates ranges from 2.7 to 3.6 and they contain 1.5 to 3.5% pectin and 7 to 12% total solids. They usually contain 1.5 to 2.7% free acid, calculated as malic acid. Edible lactic acid is most commonly used for the adjustment. The grade of such household pectins is usually in the neighborhood of 5, on the liquid basis. These household pectin extracts are marketed all over the world in small brown bottles which, as was once noted, aid in covering up the at times none too attractive appearance of such products.

One difficulty with this type of pectin extract is the gradual loss of jellying power. As noted before, this has given rise to the custom of collecting or replacing—once the fruit canning season is over,—the pectin extract which has been left on the grocery store shelf and in "trade channels."

3. Pectin for Pharmaceutical and Medicinal Purposes

In some countries, such as Germany, special pectin preparations have been sold for over twenty-five years for such purposes. In the United States the development of specific pectins for pharmaceuticals was slower. One of the principal reasons for this may have been the fact that dry pectin preparations of high purity were easily available in this country. About 1940 the pectin industry, in cooperation with the American Pharmaceutical Association, developed specifications for pectins to be used for pharmaceutical and medicinal purposes; this description of the pectins and their uses was incorporated in the seventh and a later edition of the *National Formulary*.[1477]   As will be shown in this chapter, the requirements of purity and freedom from metals are quite rigorous.

Such solid powdered pectins may be prepared from standard products by purification or may be specifically manufactured by methods which yield a pectin having the desired characteristics and purity. Actually, a combination of specific methods and subsequent purification is used.

[1477] *National Formulary VIII*. The National Formulary Committee, Washington, 1946.

TABLE 72.   CHEMICAL COMPOSITION AND PROPERTIES OF SOME COMMERCIAL PECTIN PREPARATIONS

Designation	Origin	Approx. year of analysis	Ref. No.	Moisture, %	Ash, %	Methoxyl, %	Combining wt.	Polyuronide (CO₂ × 4), %	Calcium pectate, %	Settling time, min.	Jelly grade			Acidity as malic, %
											Delaware method	Lüers method	Finger test	
Apple, rapid set	U.S.A....	1938	1481	—	—	9.3	1200	—	—	5	163	—	105	—
" slow "	"	1938	1481	—	—	9.1	577	—	—	100	476	—	264	—
" Certo No. 1[a]	U.S.A....	1940	1482	—	—	11.2	920	—	—	—	—	—	270	—
" "	Germany..	1934	1483	—	0.5	6.4	—	43.6	47.9	—	—	—	("moderate")	—
" "	"	1925	1485	11.9	4.2	—	—	—	32.4	—	—	—	—	—
" rapid set	U.S.A....	1934	1481	—	—	7.8	420	—	—	—	[b]	—	376	—
Citrus rapid "	"	1938	1481	—	—	10.7	761	—	—	15	131	—	85	—
" slow "	"	1938	1481	—	—	10.1	560	—	—	120	162	—	82	—
" "	"	1935	1485	12.1	7.9	7.9	—	65.7	—	—	200	216	—	—
" "	"	1935	1485	14.9	0.6	8.5	—	82.2	—	—	130	207	—	—
" "	"	1935	1485	14.1	0.4	7.9	—	79.5	—	—	280	443	—	—
" pure[c]	"	1939	1486	9.0	1.5	9.6[e]	—	80.5	—	—	—	—	—	—
" pure[d]	"	1939	1486	7.2	0.5	9.4[e]	—	86.0	—	—	—	—	—	—
California citrus grade 160	"	1934	1483	—	11.7	10.8	—	61.4	77.7	—	—	—	("very good")	—
California citrus grade 80	"	1934	1483	—	5.0	9.6	—	76.0	92.4	—	—	—	("very good")	—
Citrus	"	1934	1483	—	7.5	3.1	—	49.0	60.7	—	—	—	("very poor")	—
"	"	1929	1484	8.7	8.3	7.3	—	62.9	—	—	185	216	—	—
"	"	1931	1484	12.1	7.9	7.9	—	65.7	67.4	—	205	207	—	—
Lemon	"	1934	1484	14.9	0.6	8.5	—	82.8	88.2	—	130	443	—	—
"	"	1934	1484	14.1	0.4	7.9	—	79.5	87.4	—	280	443	—	—
Grapefruit, slow set	"	1938	1481	—	—	9.8	518	—	—	120	434	—	265	—
Citrus (?)	"	1939	1486	9.9	2.0	9.6[e]	—	80.5	—	—	—	—	—	—
"	"	1939	1486	8.9	0.9	9.4[e]	—	86.0	—	—	—	—	—	—
Slow set	"	1934	1483	—	1.8	9.3	—	70.2	87.0	—	—	—	("good")	—
Apple	"	1924	1485	89.5	—	—	—	—	2.1	—	—	—	—	2.0
"	"	1925	1485	89.4	—	—	—	—	1.5	—	—	—	—	2.4
Pomosin extract M	Germany..	?	1485	—	2.0	—	—	—	4.0	—	—	—	—	—
" " "	"	?	1485	—	—	—	—	—	2.1	—	—	—	—	—
" " " P	"	?	1485	92.4	—	—	—	—	1.0	—	—	—	—	2.7
" " " P	"	?	1485	90.3	—	—	—	—	3.0	—	—	—	—	1.8
" " " P	"	?	1485	87.9	—	—	—	—	3.5	—	—	—	—	1.5
" " " P	"	?	1485	—	—	—	—	—	4.1	—	—	—	—	—
Opekta	"	1934	1484	90.1	0.3	0.5	—	—	3.8	—	—	162[f]	—	—

[a] General Foods Corporation.   [b] "Curdled."   [c] Ethanol precipitated.   [d] Colloidally precipitated.   [e] On ash- and moisture-free basis.   [f] (On dry matter basis?)

The purification consists in many cases of washing with acid ethanol followed by ethanol, and drying.

II. CHEMICAL COMPOSITION OF SOME COMMERCIAL PECTINS

Although the chemical composition of commercial pectins varies considerably, the range of different constituents should be fairly clear to the reader by now since this topic has been touched on many times in earlier pages.

In solid, dry pectins the proportion of nonpectic materials varies in different preparations; the variation is wide and unavoidable. The pectin which is manufactured shows great differences in jelly grade. Thus, at times only a small proportion, while in other cases several times as much, diluent must be used to attain the standard jelly grade sought. Table 72 shows some analyses reported in the literature. It will be noted that the polyuronide (polygalacturonic acid) content of solid pectins varies from 43.6 to 86.0%, the latter value approaching the theoretical polyuronide value.

In pectin concentrates the pectin usually represents about one third to one half of the total solids in solution.

The ash content of solid pectins varies even more than is indicated by Table 72. One producer is known to sell a solid pectin with more than 11% ash, which would not be permitted in some countries. Such high ash content usually results in an improved dispersibility of the dry pectin. There is no reason, however, to assume that ash constituents as such are necessarily harmful. Table 73 shows the ranges of various elements occurring in some solid pectins as reported by Joseph.[1478] The great differences caused by the manufacturing method are well demonstrated in this table.

Jeppresen, Eastmond, and Logan[1479] found 0.23 milligram per cent of lead in a sample of commercial citrus pectin. In a sample of pectin sold for pharmaceutical purposes (Pectinum N.F. VII) Fish and Dustman[1480]

[1478] G. H. Joseph, *Bull. Natl. Formulary Comm.*, **9,** 20 (1940).
[1479] C. R. Jeppresen, E. J. Eastmond, and H. G. Logan, *J. Optical Soc. Am.*, **34,** 313 (1944).
[1480] V. B. Fish and R. B. Dustman, *J. Am. Chem. Soc.*, **67,** 1155 (1945).
[1481] A. G. Olsen, R. F. Stuewer, E. R. Fehlberg, and N. M. Beach, *Ind. Eng. Chem.*, **31,** 1015 (1939).
[1484] F. Ehrlich, in E. Abderhalden, *Handbuch der biologischen Arbeitsmethoden*, schule Breslau. 1935, p. 129.
[1483] C. J. van der Bie, *Chem. Weekblad*, **32, 557** (1935).
[1484] F. Ehrlich, in E. Abderhalden, *Handbuch der biologischen Arbeitsmethoden*, IV (2), 2405 (1936).
[1485] R. Ripa, *Die Pektinsoffe*. 2nd ed., Serger und Hempel, Braunschweig, 1937.
[1488] J. L. Powers and E. C. Beeler, *Bull. Natl. Formulary Comm.*, **9** (1), 24 (1940).

found 9.75% moisture, 82.3% uronic acid, 8.65% methoxyl, and 0.53% ash.

TABLE 73

OCCURRENCE OF VARIOUS ELEMENTS (MILLIGRAM PER CENT) IN CERTAIN AMERICAN COMMERCIAL PECTINS AS DETERMINED BY SPECTROGRAPHIC ANALYSIS (ADAPTED FROM JOSEPH)

	"Exchange" citrus pectin		Range in four other commercial pectins (1937–40)
Element	Ethanol pptd.	Colloidally pptd.	
Iron...................	40.0	6.0	60–2800
Lead...................	0.1	0.2	0.3–1.0
Tin....................	0.3	0.5	(0.3)
Aluminum..............	40.0	200.0	30–180
Chromium.............	1.5	1.0	0.3–1.5
Copper................	1.5	6.0	4–100
Nickel................	0.5	1.0	0.3–9.0
Manganese.............	0.5	0.2	1–5
Sodium...............	30.0	10.0	100–3000
Potassium.............	600.0	T[a]	1–3900
Calcium...............	1000.0	8.0	30–2800
Magnesium............	300.0	1.0	60–1800
Barium...............	4.0	0.2	3–100
Silicon...............	10.0	200.0	3–100
Boron................	0.3	0.02	3–1
Phosphorus...........	10.0	T[a]	T–30

[a] T indicates element present in less than 0.0001% in the pectin.

III. EVALUATION OF COMMERCIAL PECTINS

The information which characterizes a pectin or pectinic acid for the chemist was discussed in Chapter VIII. Pectin, however, is manufactured principally for the food technologist who uses it for the production of jams, jellies, marmalades, and similar products. Characterization of a pectin for this purpose is therefore different from the methods discussed previously.

A commercial pectin to be used in food products should be characterized by the following properties:

(1) Suitable color and flavor.
(2) Solubility (for solid pectins only).
(3) Jelly grade.
(4) Setting time.
(5) Absence of harmful ingredients.

Additional chemical characterization is also helpful. Determination of equivalent weight (combining weight) and polyuronide and methoxyl contents, for example, give important information on the calcium tolerance of the pectin, as well as concerning its expected behavior under various conditions in the making of preserves.

The absence of harmful ingredients derived from spray residues (see Chap. XVIII and XIX) or other sources is, of course, a primary consideration for pectin as for all foods. Most pectins sold in this country at present are quite neutral in flavor and color. Some pectin concentrates have a residual apple flavor and are, at times, colored. In most cases such properties are not objectionable because of the comparatively small proportion of pectin used in most food products. Preparations entirely or practically void of brownish color and any pronounced flavor, however, are preferable.

The jellying properties determine to a great extent the commercial value of both solid and liquid pectin preparations. The methods which may be used for determination of the jelly grade of pectins will be dealt with in detail in the next section of this chapter. The meaning and measurement of setting time were discussed in Chapter XXII.

As will be shown later, there are no generally accepted specifications for pectins. During World War II the United States Department of Agriculture found it desirable to define this product. The portion of this statement (1942) dealing with the description of commercial pectins is quoted below:

"Introduction: Pectin is used for a variety of purposes in the food and pharmaceutical industries. The standards for a pectin must necessarily vary depending upon the use to which it is to be put, for obviously, the requirement of a pectin to be used medicinally or in scientific investigations must necessarily be different from that used in the making of jams and jellies. The present specifications are proposed only for commercial pectin to be used in the production of fruit jellies, jams, preserves, and marmalades and this product is accordingly designated here as 'Commercial Pectin Preparation (Food) (CPPF).'

"Commercial Pectin Preparation (Food) is a product generally obtained from the dilute acid extract of the peel of citrus fruits or from apple pomace, and contains as the active jelly-forming principle partially methoxylated polygalacturonic acids, the free acid groups of which may be partially neutralized with one or more bases. It may be sold either as a solid or in the form of an aqueous solution, the latter product being frequently referred to in the trade as 'liquid pectin.' CPPF may contain as a diluent, water, dextrose (refined corn sugar), sucrose, edible fruit acids and sodium citrate or other buffer salts and the final mixture must meet the requirements of the Federal Food, Drug, and Cosmetic Act and Regulations promulgated thereunder.

"Solubility: CPPF, when added to sufficient cold water to make a 0.5% solution should dissolve completely giving an opalescent colloidal solution. If desired, solid CPPF may be mixed with either dextrose, sucrose, an effervescent mixture, or wetted either with ethanol or glycerol to hasten its solution in water.

"Color, Flavor and Taste: CPPF should be of such a quality as not to impart an undesirable, flavor or color to the final product."

This specification has been used as a general guide for government purchases, and is apparently the only definition used for such purposes.

A much more detailed definition of pectin to be used for pharmaceutical purposes was developed around 1940 by a group[1487] for incorporation in the *National Formulary*.[1477] Because of the importance of this statement, it is quoted below:

"PECTIN (*PECTINUM*)"

"Pectin is a purified carbohydrate product obtained from the dilute acid extract of the inner portion of the rind of citrus fruits or from apple pomace. It consists chiefly of partially methoxylated polygalacturonic acids.

"Pectin yields not less than 7 per cent of methoxyl groups and not less than 78 per cent of galacturonic acid when calculated on a moisture and ash free basis.

"*Note*: Commercial pectin for the production of jellied food products is standardized to the convenient '150 jelly grade' by addition of dextrose or other sugars and sometimes contains sodium citrate or other buffer salts. This monograph refers to the pure pectin to which no such additions have been made.

"Description. Pectin occurs as a coarse or fine powder, yellowish white in color, almost odorless, and with a mucilaginous taste.

"Solubility. Pectin is almost completely soluble in twenty parts of water at 25°, forming a viscous, opalescent, colloidal solution which flows readily and is acid to litmus paper. It is insoluble in alcohol or in diluted alcohol, and in other organic solvents. Pectin dissolves in water more readily if first moistened with alcohol, glycerin, or simple syrup, or if first mixed with 3 or more parts of sucrose.

"Identification. A: Heat 1 Gm. of Pectin with 9 cc. of water on a water bath until a solution is formed, replacing water lost by evaporation: it yields a stiff gel upon cooling.

B: An aqueous solution of Pectin (1 in 100) yields a translucent, gelatinous precipitate when treated with an equal volume of alcohol (difference from most gums).

C: To 10 cc. of an aqueous solution of Pectin (1 in 100) add 1 cc. of thorium nitrate T.S., stir, and allow to stand for 2 minutes: a stable precipitate or gel forms (difference from gums).

D: To 5 cc. of an aqueous solution of Pectin (1 in 100) add 1 cc. of a solution of potassium hydroxide (1 in 50) and allow to stand at room temperature for 15 minutes: a transparent gel or semi-gel forms (difference from tragacanth).

E: Acidify the gel from the preceding test with diluted hydrochloric acid and shake well: a voluminous, colorless, gelatinous precipitate forms, which upon boiling becomes white and flocculent (pectic acid).

[1487] See papers by: J. L. Powers, G. H. Joseph, A. G. Olsen, and K. B. Rosen; given in "A Symposium on Pectin and Pectin Pastes," *Bull. Natl. Formulary Comm.*, **9** (1), 1–35 (1940).

F: Heat 50 cc. of an aqueous solution of Pectin (1 in 50) to 70°, add 5 cc. of solution of sodium hydroxide (1 in 5), allow to stand 10 minutes in a stoppered flask, acidify slightly with sulfuric acid, and distill until 5 cc. of distillate is collected. The entire distillate when tested as directed under Whisky responds to the test for Methanol, page 555.

"Loss on drying. When dried at 105° for 2 hours, Pectin loses not more than 10 per cent of its weight.

"Ash. Place a crucible containing the Pectin used for the test for Loss on drying in a muffle furnace and gradually raise the temperature to 500°–600° for 3 hours. Cool and weigh the residue. The ash from Pectin does not exceed 4 per cent.

"Acid-insoluble ash. Pectin yields not more than 0.4 per cent of acid-insoluble ash, page 761.

"Arsenic. Add 2 Gm. of Pectin to 10 cc. of nitric acid and 3 cc. of sulfuric acid in a Kjeldahl flask. Heat until dense white fumes are evolved. If the mixture turns brown, add more nitric acid and heat until colorless or light yellow; cool, add 10 cc. of distilled water and 0.5 Gm. of ammonium oxalate. Heat until dense white fumes are evolved. Cool and dilute to 25 cc. When tested for Arsenic, page 689, 5 cc. of this solution produces no more stain than that of a blank with 1.4 cc. of the standard arsenic solution, using the same quantities of the same reagents, diluted and otherwise treated as directed above.

"Lead. Add 2 Gm. of Pectin to 20 cc. of nitric acid in a 250-cc. Erlenmeyer flask, mix well, and heat the contents carefully until the Pectin is dissolved. Continue the heating until the volume is reduced to about 7 cc. Cool rapidly to room temperature, transfer to a 100-cc. volumetric flask and dilute to 100 cc. with distilled water. A 50-cc. portion of this solution contains not more than 5 micrograms of lead (corresponding to not more than 5 parts per million) when tested according to the Lead limit test, page 729, using 15 cc. of ammonium citrate solution, 3 cc. of potassium cyanide solution, and 0.5 cc. of hydroxylamine hydrochloride solution. After the first dithizone extractions, wash the combined chloroform layers with 5 cc. of distilled water, discarding the water layer and continuing in the usual manner by extracting with 20 cc. of 1 per cent nitric acid.

"Starch. Boil a 1 per cent aqueous solution of Pectin, cool, and add a few drops of iodine T.S.: not even a transient blue color is produced.

"Sugars and organic acids. Place 1 Gm. of Pectin into a 500-cc. flask, moisten it with 3 to 5 cc. of alcohol, pour in rapidly 100 cc. of distilled water, shake well, and allow to stand until solution is complete. To this solution add 100 cc. of alcohol containing 0.3 cc. of hydrochloric acid, mix thoroughly, and filter rapidly. Measure 25 cc. of the filtrate into a tared dish, evaporate the liquid on a water bath and dry the residue in a vacuum oven at 50° for 2 hours: the weight of the residue does not exceed 20 mg.

"Assay for methoxyl groups. Transfer exactly 5 Gm. of Pectin to a suitable beaker and stir for 10 minutes with a mixture of 5 cc. of hydrochloric acid and 100 cc. of 60 per cent alcohol. Transfer to a fritted glass filter tube (30 to 60 cc., Gooch or Buchner type, coarse) and wash with six 15-cc. portions of the hydrochloric acid–60 per cent alcohol mixture, followed by 60 per cent alcohol until the filtrate is free of chlorides. Finally wash with 20 cc. of alcohol and dry for 1 hour in an oven at 100°, cool and weigh. Transfer exactly one-tenth of the total net weight of the dried sample (representing 0.5 Gm. of the original unwashed sample) to a 250-cc. Erlenmeyer flask and moisten the sample with 2 cc. of alcohol. Add 100 cc. of recently boiled and cooled distilled water, stopper and swirl occasionally until the Pectin is completely dissolved. Add 5 drops of phenolphthalein T. S., titrate with 0.5 N sodium hydroxide and record the results as the initial titre. Add exactly 20 cc. of 0.5 N sodium hydroxide, stopper, shake vigorously and let stand for 15 minutes. Add exactly 20 cc. of 0.5 N hydrochloric acid and shake until the pink color disappears. After adding 3 drops of phenolphthalein T.S., titrate with 0.5 N sodium hydroxide to a faint pink color which persists after vigorous shaking: record this value as the saponification titre. Each cc. of 0.5 N sodium hydroxide used in the saponification titre is equivalent to 0.0155 Gm. of OCH_3 on an undried basis.

"Assay for galacturonic acid. Each cc. of 0.5 N sodium hydroxide used in the total titration (the initial titre added to the saponification titre) is equivalent to 0.09707 Gm. of $C_5H_9O_5COOH$ on an undried basis.

"Storage. Preserve Pectin in tight containers."

IV.   JELLY GRADE AND ITS DETERMINATION

The ability to form jellies and gels is the most important property of pectins isolated from plant sources. Well over half of the pectin produced all over the world is used in making fruit jellies and other similar products like jams, preserves, and marmalades, for which complete or partial jellification is desired.

On previous pages the jelly-forming ability of pectins was often mentioned, as well as the fact that, after satisfying some fundamental requirements of all human food, it is the jelly grade which determines the commercial value of the product. In spite of the outstanding importance of jelly grade, there is still little agreement on methods by which this characteristic should be determined. As a result, a number of different procedures are used by manufacturers and there is at times an undesirable discrepancy between the grade stated on the container of pectin and that determined by a method arbitrarily selected for evaluation. A committee representing producers, users, and research workers[1488] is now laboring to attain some agreement on methods of grade evaluation.

In the present discussion the grade evaluation of high-ester pectins, whose use may be typified by a jelly containing 65% soluble solids, will

[1488] Committee on Pectin Standardization, Institute of Food Technologists, appointed in the autumn of 1948. Dr. J. J. Willaman of the Eastern Regional Research Laboratory, USDA, Philadelphia, Pa., is Chairman of the Committee.

be dealt with first. The subject of grade evaluation of the more recently developed low-ester (low-methoxyl) pectins will be discussed in Chapter XXIV.

Ever since the beginning of large-scale commercial manufacture of pectin, attempts were made to market a standardized product. In Europe it became a custom to establish a "factory standard" for the jelly grade (see below), without giving a sharp definition of this property and without passing on this information to the purchaser, except that the product was of "standard" strength. On the other hand, manufacturers in this country not only sought to turn out a standardized product, but also passed on this information on jelly grade to the consumer, thereby committing themselves to a minimum quality of the pectin in this respect. During the past decade there has been some tendency among European manufacturers to adopt the practice of American producers of selling by grade.

In the early days of the pectin industry the pectin to be used in a given product was defined by percentage and by no other means. Mehlitz[1489] and others at one time believed that calcium pectate determinations were suitable for defining the commercial usefulness of pectin preparations and extracts. It is hoped that it is clear to the reader who has studied the previous few hundred pages of this book that such measurements, as well as polyuronide determinations, etc., while important, give little direct information on the usefulness of a pectin preparation for jelly making. This fact was generally recognized as pectins of different degrees of purity, "colloidality," and jelly-forming ability appeared on the market. It is now clear that the methoxyl content of such pectins is also not a criterion of jelly-forming ability, with the exception that a minimum methoxyl content of about 7% is required for the formation of the customary pectin–acid–sugar jellies of about 65% soluble solids content.

Although considerable attention was given earlier to this point by pectin manufacturers who sought to standardize their products, jelly grade was first defined in its present meaning by Wilson[1490] in 1926. He states: "Dry powdered pectin is graded according to sugar carrying power; that is, if one pound of pectin will carry 100 pounds of sugar making a standard jelly, it is a 100 grade pectin." Or, as it is customary to state today, jelly grade is the proportion of sugar which one part of solid pectin or pectin extract is capable of turning, under prescribed conditions, into a jelly with suitable characteristics. The terms "jelly grade units" or "jelly grade yield" mean the grade of a given sample of pectin multiplied by its weight (usually in grams).[1491]

[1489] A. Mehlitz, *Z. tech. Biol.*, 11, 134 (1925).
[1490] C. P. Wilson, *Am. Food J.*, 21, 279, 313 (1926).
[1491] P. B. Myers and G. L. Baker, *Delaware Agr., Expt. Sta.*, Bull. 168 (1931).

Methods of evaluation may be divided into those which determine the jelly grade by some property other than jelly-forming ability and those in which the jelly grade is determined in test jellies.

1. Methods Determining Jelly Grade without Test Jellies

These methods are now mostly of historical interest although some are used for approximate and preliminary evaluation. Ogg[1492] used a falling

Fig. 38. Baker's "Jelmeter" viscosity pipette.

The time of outflow from A to . B is measured.

ball viscometer in a study of the relationship between pectin viscosity and jelly grade. Myers and Baker made a detailed study[1493] of the previously known relationship between the viscosity of pectin solutions and jellying power[1494] of pectins and found the viscosity method quite useful in the case of series of preparations of similar history. By the use of calibration curves, a good approximation can be obtained with the jelly grade. However, the method is of less use when pectins of unknown history or those derived from different sources are to be evaluated. Baker and Woodmansee recommend[1495] that this method be used in preliminary grading in order to ascertain the amount of pectin to be used in test jellies.

[1492] W. G. Ogg, *Dissertation*, University of Cambridge, 1925.
[1493] P. B. Myers and G. L. Baker, *Delaware Agr. Expt. Sta.*, Bull. 149 (1927).
[1494] G. Wendelmuth, *Kolloid-Beihefte*, **19**, 115 (1924).
[1495] G. L. Baker and C. W. Woodmansee, *Delaware Agr. Expt. Sta.*, Bull. 272 (1948).

A simple capillary pipette called the Jelmeter[1496] has been developed by Baker[1497] for such viscosity determinations. Using this device (shown in Fig. 38) viscosity measurements are made at pH 2.5 and 26°C. on 0.5 and 1.0% solutions; the relative viscosities are calculated by dividing these times by the time of flow of water at the same temperature. The approximate grade of the pectin can then be read from the types of curves

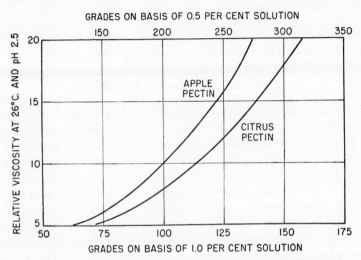

Fig. 39. **Approximate grades of pectins as determined by (capillary) viscosity measurements (from Baker and Woodmansee).**

shown in Figure 39. If the relative viscosity is more than 20, it should be reduced for the measurement by dilution with water.

Measurements with other types of viscometers are just as useful for this purpose although it is difficult to surpass the simplicity of the Jelmeter. It is doubtful whether this method is of much use to purchasers of pectin, who can read the approximate (and, in most cases, the exact) grade on the label. It was stated in Chapter XIX that viscosity measurements are very useful in certain phases of pectin manufacture.

The properties of an ethanol precipitate formed from a pectin solution may also be used as an indication of jellying properties. Geret[1498] developed a method along such lines:

In a series of test tubes varying amounts of the unknown pectin solution are introduced and all are made up to 10 cc. Now 3.33 cc. of 95% ethanol containing 2% citric acid is added to each tube and, after stoppering, they are

[1496] Distributed by Jelmeter Division, Delaware Motor Sales Co., Wilmington, Delaware.
[1497] G. L. Baker, *Food Inds.*, 6, 305 (1934).
[1498] L. Geret, *Mitt. Geb. Lebensm. Hyg.*, 21, 116 (1930).

all inverted 3 times. After the tubes have been kept in an ice-water bath for exactly 1 hour, they are inverted and the one in which the precipitate does not flow for at least 5 seconds and which has the least amount of pectin is selected as the borderline concentration. The reciprocal of the pectin concentration times 100 is the "Geret number." Although this method is arbitrary to a great degree and many factors, such as the speed of inversion at the end of the holding time, have definite effect on the readings, it has been used to some extent, especially in Europe.

A modification of the Geret test in which methanol containing sucrose and tartaric acid is used has been described by Jakovliv.[1499]

2. Pectin Grading by Test Jellies

A jelly with "suitable characteristics" may be described as one possessing a continuous smooth texture, showing no stickiness, and having sufficient firmness to withstand shipping yet not too firm to be spread easily on bread. It should be also free of excessive syneresis (weeping) upon storage.

Whether a jelly possesses the required characteristics may be ascertained by visual observation of its behavior, or by making various measurements on it. Ripa[1500] described a method for grade determination in which jellies are prepared with increasing proportions of the pectin of unknown jelly grade. After standing for some time, the jelly glasses are turned on their sides and the jelly is selected which breaks away from the glass but still retains its shape sufficiently and shows a sharp contour. The jelly grade of the pectin is then calculated from the pectin concentration in this jelly. This is the "least pectin" method. Such observations are easy to make but are, of necessity, inaccurate because there is no exact definition of "desirable characteristics." As a result, the last three decades have seen many attempts to define such jelly properties by objective and reproducible means. Pectin is a comparatively expensive commodity and those who use it in large quantities desire to know exactly the proportion which must be applied in order to produce goods of predetermined quality at the lowest cost.

It should also be noted that a test jelly made for pectin grade determination is not necessarily like a saleable product of the type desired by jelly manufacturers. The chief requirement of the test jelly is to give information on the general utility of the pectin preparation, whereas a commercial fruit jelly must have certain other properties typical of the specific product in question.

[1499] G. Jakovliv, *Bull. assoc. chim.*, **62**, 228 (1945).
[1500] R. Ripa, *Die Pektinstoffe*. 2nd ed., Serger und Hempel. Braunschweig, 1937.

The major problems of pectin grading through test jellies may be grouped into three categories:

A. Variations in the method used in making the jelly.

B. Variations in the property measured and the method (device) applied for the measurement.

C. Definitions of desirable properties, *i.e.*, adaptation of numerical standards for any given specific method.

Variations in the jelly-making procedure have a major effect on the properties of the jelly which is produced. One of the debated points here is the quantity of acid to be used and the time at which the acid should be added to the test jelly. In commercial practice, a few manufacturers add the acid to products during cooking, while most of them introduce the acid after cooking. In jellies there is a minimum and an optimum pH. Excess acid causes "pregelation" or curdling.

There is no unanimity at the present time among workers in this field on any of these three points. Thus, it is impossible to give in this discussion a single procedure which might be suitable under all conditions and be free from criticism. For this reason some of the most important methods will be given and discussed. It is appropriate to start with a specification which was developed during the recent war and which has been used by the U. S. Department of Agriculture in pectin purchases. A part of this statement, dealing with the definition of commercial pectins ("Commercial Pectin Preparation, Food, CPPF") was given above in Section III.

"STANDARD 100-GRADE 'PECTIN' AND 'STANDARD JELLY' "

"Definitions of: The term 'standard 100-grade pectin' used in these specifications means a pectin preparation which has been carefully tested under the conditions hereinafter described (see 'Method for Determining the Grade and Setting Time of CPPF') and found to be of 100-grade quality. The 'standard 100-grade pectin' preparation will be kept by the S.M.A. in a sealed container in a refrigerator. Samples of this 'standard 100-grade pectin' preparation may be submitted to pectin manufacturers in order that they may establish their own secondary standards.

"The term 'standard jelly' used in these specifications means a jelly prepared with the 'standard 100-grade pectin' under conditions and in a manner hereinafter described (see 'Method for Determining the Grade and Setting Time of CPPF'). The standard jelly is to be used as an aid in judging the quality of a jelly prepared from CPPF.

"Method for Determining the Grade and Setting Time: Sugar, water, pectin, acid and buffer jellies are made with the sample in question and compared with a jelly made under the same conditions with a standard 100-grade pectin sample.

"General Conditions for Making Comparison:

1. 65% sugar jelly.

2. Jelly pH 3.00 ±0.05 pH units.

3. Time elapsed after making jelly to be at least 18 hours and to be same length of time for both unknown and standard.

"Materials Used:

1. Cane or beet sugar (sucrose).

2. Distilled water.

3. Citric acid solution; 50 grams of citric acid (Mw. 210) made up to 100 ml. of solution.

4. Sodium citrate solution; 25 grams of sodium citrate (U.S.P.) dissolved in distilled water and made up to 100 ml. of solution.

5. Three-quart granite, aluminum, stainless steel or glass cooking vessel.

6. Stainless steel, aluminum, glass, or wooden ladle or spoon.

7. Laboratory balance with 2000-gram capacity and 1-gram sensitivity.

8. Supply of tall 8-fluid-ounce jelly glasses with covers.

9. Laboratory balance, sensitivity; 1 mg.

"Determining the Grade and Setting Time: Weigh empty cooking vessel and jelly ladle or spoon to obtain tare weight. Measure into the vessel 320 ml. of cold distilled water. Weigh 500 grams of sugar and the requisite quantity of CPPF as shown in the table below. Mix the CPPF with a portion of the sugar (about 5 times the weight of the CPPF) so that the CPPF is completely dispersed with the sugar.

"To the water in the kettle add 0.5 ml. of the citric acid solution and 1 ml. of the sodium citrate solution. Prepare three 8-fluid-ounce jelly glasses and add to each 2 ml. of citric acid solution and 0.5 ml. of the sodium citrate solution. Dump the CPPF–sugar mixture into the water and stir to disperse. Place the mixture over a hot fire, heat rapidly to boiling while stirring constantly to prevent lumping or sticking to the sides of the kettle. Boil for 30 seconds, remove from flame and stir until particles of pectin are no longer visible, and then add the balance of the sugar. Heat the solution again to boiling, stir continually and boil down to a net weight of 770 grams. Remove from the fire occasionally to check the weight or too much water will be evaporated. When the correct weight has been reached, remove the cooking vessel and contents from the fire and allow the jelly to cool for 30 seconds. This will allow the foam to rise so that it can be skimmed off.

"Pour the hot jelly into the previously prepared jelly glasses and stir for 2 or 3 seconds with a glass rod so that the acid, sodium citrate and hot jelly are thoroughly mixed. Note the time when the hot jelly was first poured into the glasses. Allow the jellies to stand at 26°C. for 18 hours and note the time when the product has first set into a coherent mass. At the end of the 18-hour period, the jellies are turned out of the glasses on a flat surface and compared as to their overall firmness and degree of resilience with a standard jelly made at the same time and under exactly the same conditions.

"Slice off a piece of jelly and squeeze between the thumb and forefinger until the jelly breaks. Compare with the standard jelly.

"Differences of 5 per cent can be detected in this way after the operator is experienced. If the jelly does not have the same strength as the standard, the comparison should be repeated increasing the amount of CPPF used in preparing the jelly."

Table 74 gives the weights of pectin to be used in testing for different grades.

TABLE 74

Amounts of Pectin Used in Jelly Tests to Determine Pectin Grade by CPPF Method (U. S. Department of Agriculture, 1942)

Grade	Weight, g.	Grade	Weight, g.
10	50.00	120	4.17
20	25.00	130	3.85
30	16.66	140	3.57
40	15.50	150	3.33
50	10.00	160	3.12
60	8.33	170	2.94
70	7.14	180	2.78
80	6.25	190	2.63
90	5.55	200	2.50
100	5.00	210	2.38
110	4.55	220	2.27

"Rate of Setting: CPPF, when tested under conditions hereinafter described (see 'Method for Determining the Grade and Setting Time of CPPF') shall be deemed 'rapid setting' if the jelly made therewith will set in 10 minutes or less; 'medium setting' if the jelly sets in 10 to 25 minutes; and 'slow setting' if the time required for the setting of the jelly is over 25 minutes.

"'Grade' Definition of: The term 'grade' used in these specifications means the weight of sugar with which one part by weight of CPPF will, under suitable conditions, form a satisfactory jelly. By the term 'satisfactory jelly' is meant one which when subjected to the usual finger testing is found to have the proper texture, resilience and consistency. The 'grade' of CPPF shall be determined by the method hereinafter described."

This procedure is admittedly arbitrary on several counts. The "desirable consistency" is characterized by comparison with a jelly made from a "standard" sample, a clear evasion of the difficulties of definition. However, this specification was set up when the United States Government was purchasing millions of pounds of pectin and more millions were needed; there was no time to argue over subtleties. This method also brings us to the "finger test," the oldest and perhaps still the most popular method of jelly evaluation. Judging jelly firmness by squeezing a slice between the fingers gives good results when performed by the expert; even so, the recording of differences is difficult. It has at times been recommended that the fourth finger of the left hand be used because this finger was assumed to be most sensitive. But there is so much pectin and there are so few experts that the need for objective measurements of jelly firmness was generally realized[1501] and led to the invention of many devices.

While these developments in the instrumentation of jelly firmness measurements took place, pectin chemistry progressed considerably. As a result, the methods of test jelly making recommended by many inventors of jelly testing devices are now out of date and will not be described here. It would seem, on the other hand, that before describing these instruments it is desirable to give some examples of the methods used by some authors.

There is very little harmony among authors on the principles used in making test jellies. This matter was discussed recently at a symposium at which no agreements were reached; as a result of these discussions, however, a series of articles appeared describing up-to-date modifications of several methods suggested some time ago. The major point of disagreement in test jelly making is still on whether the test jelly should be cooked with the acid or the acid should be added after cooking has been finished. Opinions also differ as to whether: (a) the grade should be determined at various pH values, and thus the final grade would represent the maximum jelly strength in the range used in different products; or (b) it should be based on the jelly strength at a given pH value (usually 3.0–3.4).

Baker and Woodmansee state[1502] that the jelly strength should be measured at the optimum pH of gelation and that, therefore, a series of jellies with different pH values should be prepared for measurement of the jelly grade. The presence of acid during cooking is recommended over procedures in which the acid is added upon pouring. For making up the test jellies, these authors use the salt mixture described by Olsen, Stuewer, Fehlberg, and Beach.[1503] composed of the following ingredients:

Potassium phosphate, K_3PO_4	1.54 g.
Potassium citrate, $K_3C_6H_5O_7.H_2O$	6.33
Sodium citrate, $(Na_3C_6H_5O_7)_2.11H_2O$	0.99
Calcium citrate, $Ca_3(C_6H_5O_7)_2.4H_2O$	1.19
Magnesium acetate, $Mg(C_2H_3O_2)_2.4H_2O$	2.02
Citric acid, anhydrous	25.00
Sucrose	40.00
Water to make 1 liter	

This mixture, often designated as a "synthetic strawberry juice" has been used extensively in making test jellies because the presence of salts reduces the sensitivity of jelly to changes in the hydrogen ion concentration.

[1501] H. S. Paine, *Am. Food J.*, **17** (3), 11 (1922).
[1502] G. L. Baker and C. W. Woodmansee, *Food Technol.*, **3**, 23 (1949).
[1503] A. G. Olsen, R. F. Stuewer, E. R. Fehlberg, and N. M. Beach, *Ind. Eng. Chem.*, **31**, 1015 (1939).

For making the test jellies, Baker and Woodmansee recommend the following procedure:

A. The "assumed grade" is first determined by viscosity measurement (see above). The purchaser of pectin might just as well assume that the grade given by the manufacturer is the "assumed grade."

B. Now 100 is divided by the assumed grade in order to determine the pectin concentration necessary to prepare a solution with an equivalent jellying capacity to 100 cc. of a 1% solution of 100 grade pectin.

C. This amount of pectin is mixed with five times its weight of sucrose and completely dispersed in the "synthetic strawberry juice" described above to make a final volume of 100 cc. If a liquid pectin concentrate is used, it is diluted with this synthetic mixture so that the concentration of the pectin again satisfies the conditions given under B. Care should be taken to see that all the pectin is completely dispersed.

D. Now a series of jellies is prepared with the final pH values of 3.55, 3.50, 3.45, 3.35, 3.25, 3.15, 3.05, 2.95, 2.85, and 2.65, respectively. The 100 cc. of the above pectin solution is mixed in an 0.5 quart sauce pan with sufficient sucrose to give a final soluble solids content of 97.5 g. Allowance is made here for all solids, such as the pectin, sucrose, and salts added in the "synthetic strawberry juice," as well as the acid added in the pH adjustment. The mixture is then rapidly (in 4–5 minutes) boiled down to 150 g. and poured into standard jelly glasses, covered, and held for 20–24 hours at 30°C. before being used for jelly strength measurements. The setting time should be observed on the mixtures by the methods given in Chapter XXII.

A procedure along somewhat similar lines was recently described by Meschter and Lataillade:[1504]

A. First the approximate grade is determined.

B. A pectin solution containing 3250 jelly units in 1 kg. is prepared in the following manner: For a dry (powdered) pectin, the amount to be used is determined by dividing 3250 by the assumed grade. (For example, with a 100 grade pectin, 32.50 g. is used.) Care should be taken that all the pectin is dissolved. For a "5 grade liquid pectin (concentrate), 650 g. of the concentrate is diluted to 1 kg. with distilled water.

C. Next, approximately 800 g. of distilled water at 50–60°C. is placed in a tared Waring Blendor cup. The water is stirred at a low speed and the 3250 jelly units of pectin or pectin solution are added. During the next two minutes the mixing is continued while the speed of the Blendor is gradually raised as the viscosity of the solution increases.

D. After running for 3 minutes or until pectin particles are no longer visible, the Blendor cup is returned to the scales and the contents are made up with distilled water to 1 kg. This is mixed again, with care to avoid loss of solution over the side.

[1504] E. E. Meschter and L. J. Lataillade, *Food Technol.*, 3, 28 (1949).

E. Now 4 sets of jellies are prepared at pH 3.4, 3.2, 3.0, and 2.8, respectively. In each batch 200 g. of the pectin solution from D is added to a tared stainless steel sauce pan followed by 134 g. of the following salt solution:

Sodium salicylate...	0.32 g.
Salicylic acid...	0.21
Potassium phosphate, K_3PO_4..........................	3.83
Potassium citrate, $K_3(C_6H_5O_7).H_2O$....................	15.70
Sodium citrate, $Na(C_6H_5O_7).2H_2O$.....................	2.03
Citric acid, anhydrous...............................	47.30
Magnesium acetate, $Mg(C_2H_3O_2).XH_2O$...............	5.07
Calcium citrate, $Ca_3(C_6H_5O_7)_2.4H_2O$...................	3.80
Distilled water to make 1 liter	

The salt solution is omitted in the case of liquid pectin concentrate. Now sufficient 50% citric acid solution is added to adjust the pH of the final mixture to the desired values. No acid is needed for the pH 3.4 mixture, while for the the other three batches 4, 10, and 20 cc., respectively, are required. Sufficient water is added to bring the total weight to 1100 g. and the pan is placed over a burner adjusted to boil off water from a 1-kg. batch at the rate of 100 g. every 2–3 minutes. The mixture is stirred occasionally and, when boiling commences, 650 g. of sucrose is added. However, from this weight the total weight of all other solids in the batch has been subtracted. The mixture is boiled down to 1 kg., poured into jelly glasses, skimmed after 3 minutes, and the surface immediately covered with 2 cc. of paraffin oil. The jellies are aged for 18–20 hours at 30°C. before testing.

Stuewer, Beach, and Olsen described an "excess acid" procedure[1505] which can be summarized as follows:

Into a 400-cc. beaker 300 g. of sucrose is weighed and into another similar beaker, 33 g. of sucrose. The sugar in the second beaker is moistened with a few drops of water and then the desired amount of pectin is mixed with the moist sugar and 236 cc. of water is added. The mixture is stirred to facilitate disolution of the pectin. The solution is now brought to a boil and then the larger quantity of sugar is added and the mixture is boiled down to 547 g. This mixture contains 60% sucrose. After skimming, the temperature of the mixture is determined and the jelly is poured as close to 96°C. as possible. Four standard jelly glasses are used, into all of which 2 cc. of a 12.5% citric acid solution has been pipetted beforehand. Because of the rapid setting the jellies must be skimmed at once.

When a pectin concentrate is used, the same procedure is followed except that the entire quantity of sugar is weighed into one beaker and the proper adjustment is made for the water in the pectin solution. If the concentrate contains acid, this must be partially neutralized at the beginning of the procedure by the addition of calcium carbonate. For example, the amount used with Certo,

[1505] R. F. Stuewer, N. M. Beach, and A. G. Olsen, *Ind. Eng. Chem., Anal. Ed.,* **6,** 143 (1934).

an adjusted concentrate sold for household use, was 0.14 g. for 50 g. of concentrate.

The main advantage of the excess acid method is that, when poured at 96°C., jellies of maximum strength are obtained over a wide range of pH values. This is not the case if the acid is added to the mixture before cooking.

Cox and Higby[1506] and Joseph and Baier[1507] recommend the following procedure:

A. The jelly is made according to the formula:

Pectin, 150 grade.....................................	5.2 g
Sucrose..	775.0
Distilled water.......................................	450.0

B. When the assumed grade is other than 150, an amount of pectin equal to 780 g. divided by the assumed grade is used. The weight of sugar in such cases is altered to make the total weight of sugar and pectin equal to 780 g. The final jelly contains 65% solids.

C. The pectin is mixed with about 50 g. of the previously weighed sucrose and the mixture is thoroughly dispersed, with vigorous stirring in water in a tared stainless steel or aluminum saucepan of 3.5-quart size. After 30 seconds the pan is placed on the fire and brought to boil, the sugar is added, and it is then brought to boil again with constant stirring. Now the net weight is checked and water is added, or boiling is continued if the weight is less than 1200 g. The total cooking time should not exceed 6 minutes. When the final weight of 1200 g. is reached, a thermometer is put into the mixture and, after standing for a short time, it is scraped free from scum. When the temperature reaches 95°C., the jelly is poured into Hazel-Atlas No. 85 tumbler jelly glasses containing 2.6 cc. of a 48.8% tartaric acid solution. A glass rod in the tumblers permits stirring, but as Olsen[1508] has pointed out, this is not necessary if pouring is done very rapidly. As will be shown later, for the measurement of the jelly strength by the method of Cox and Higby, the jelly glasses must be provided with "sideboards" to allow later cutting in level with the top of the tumbler.

3. Mechanical Means of Jelly Strength Measurements

As was noted previously, the major difficulties with mechanical means of jelly strength measurements are in selecting a property of the test jelly to be measured, in selecting the device for measurement, and in the standards set by the specific method selected. There is no agreement among scientists and technologists on any of these three matters. Many

[1506] R. E. Cox and R. H. Higby, *Food Inds.*, **16**, 441 (1944).
[1507] G. H. Joseph and W. E. Baier, *Food. Technol.*, **3**, 18 (1949).
[1508] A. G. Olsen, *J. Phys. Chem.*, **38**, 919 (1934).

of the early instruments which measured elongation or measured resistance to cutting by blades[1509] or conical sinkers[1510] will be mentioned in passing, but these now have only historical interest. During the past twenty years more than a score of methods which use mechanical means and give both objective and reproducible results have been described. These can be classified into two groups:

(1) Those methods in which the ridigity or elasticity of the jelly is measured without exceeding the limits of elasticity and in which a permanent change in the jelly is therefore not caused.

(2) Those in which the elastic limit is exceeded, causing rupture or permanent deformation of the jelly.[1511]

The most important methods which have been suggested and those which have attained any extent of usage will be discussed below.

(a) Fellers-Clague Penetrometer Method

The method described by Fellers and Clague[1512] is perhaps the simplest mechanical means of determining jelly strength. The instrument used is a penetrometer or firmness tester of the type shown in Figure 19 but having a much weaker spring.[1513] The glass containing the jelly is turned on its side and the penetrometer is applied in a horizontal position. Using a penetrometer of this type (plunger surface not given), the following readings (in grams of pressure to break the surface) were obtained on a series of jellies:

Weak jellies...	40–60 g.
Jellies of medium firmness...........................	70–90
Firm jellies..	130–170
Very firm jellies......................................	180–230
"Rubbery" jellies.....................................	240–270

The "skin effect" of the jellies causes considerable variation in the results as does the rate of applying the pressure. The method is very simple but scarcely suitable for exact measurements.

[1509] G. Spencer, *J. Phys. Chem.*, **34**, 654 (1930).

[1510] M. M. Boggs and G. Johnson, *Food Inds.*, **19**, 1067 (1947).

[1511] Rigidity (elasticity of shape) of an elastic body is measured by the ratio of stress to strain, *i.e.*, the ratio of the force producing the change of shape to the change of shape produced. The elastic limit is the limit of deformation which may be caused in an elastic body and still have it regain its original shape upon removing the deforming force.

[1512] C. R. Fellers and J. A. Clague, *Ind. Eng. Chem., Anal. Ed.*, **4**, 106 (1932).

[1513] Manufactured by John Chatillion and Sons, New York.

(b) Sucharipa (Ripa) Jelly Disc Method

This is the first method of measuring[1514] jelly strength which was specifically developed for pectin research. The device, shown in Figure 40, has withstood the test of time.

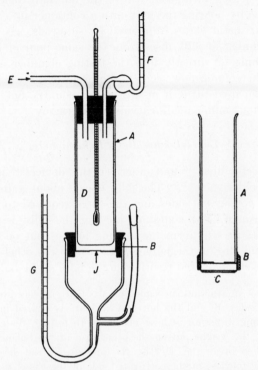

Fig. 40. Sucharipa's device to measure the strength of jellies.

To the glass tube, A, a metallic disc, B, having a round hole 1 cm. in diameter, is cemented. The glass tube is then fitted with a rubber lid, C, to close the hole and a measured amount (3 cc.) of cooked, ready jelly mixture is pipetted into it. The rubber lid used to cover the opening should be covered with a thin layer of vasoline to prevent adhesion of the jelly. After the jelly is set, it is inserted in the apparatus and brought to the desired temperature. Then gradually increased air pressure is produced through E in the chamber, D, and the pressure at which jelly, J, breaks is observed on the attached manometer, F. Since the test jellies may differ not only in the pressure required to break them but also in their elasticity, this property can be evaluated by taking a simultaneous reading on manometer, G, just before the jelly breaks. The pressure in the lower chamber thus indicates the extent of compression caused by "pouching" of the jelly.

[151] R. Sucharipa, *J. Assoc. Offic. Agr. Chemists,* **7,** 57 (1923).

This method is especially suitable for testing jellies which would be classified as very firm in this country, but is less reliable when the jelly is softer. A further difficulty with this method consists in the preparation of identical jellies (in such small containers) and damage may easily be inflicted on the jellies during removal of the lid. This difficulty has been partly overcome by pouring the jelly into a container into which a set of parallel circular metal plates, supported by side rods, has been inserted. This gives a number of jelly discs from the same pour of jelly. Pressure caused by running oil directly into the testing chamber and measuring the height of the column now seems to be preferred to air pressure. This method has been used little, if at all, in this country but is still widely used (with various minor modifications) in Germany.

(c) Lüers-Lochmüller "Pektinometer"

Lüers and Lochmüller[1515] first described this device[1516] in 1927, but it has since been redesigned.[1517] The jelly is cast about a disc in a special container with corrugated sides and the force required to pull this disc upward is measured. The container holding the jelly is illustrated in Figure 41. In its present form the moving load is put on one arm of a balance while the disc in the jelly is attached to the other arm with the jelly container held in a fixed position on the base of the balance.

Disc, D, held by an arm and suspended on a balance is placed on the container with corrugated sides, V, and the hot jelly mixture is poured in. Thereupon it is cooled in running water for at least one hour. In testing, the amount of force (as expressed by the weight put on the other arm of the balance) is measured which is needed to break the jelly by the pressure of the disc which is submerged in it. The purpose of the corrugated side of the vessel is to prevent any slipping of the jelly in the container. A scale, S, indicates the extent of compression of the jelly caused by weight, W. This "Pektinometer" has been widely used in Germany. In order to overcome the difficulties which occur due to variations in pouring the jelly into the test container, Mehlitz developed a modification[1518] in which the jelly is cooked in the same vessel in which the test is later performed. Since the merits of Mehlitz's modification are still not clear, the method will not be discussed further. For a "standard jelly strength" Henglein[1519] suggested a breaking value of 200 g., while Gudjons[1520] recommends 300 ± 15 g.

[1515] H. Lüers and K. Lochmüller, *Kolloid-Z.*, **42**, 154 (1927).

[1516] Manufactured by F. M. Lautenschläger in Munich and by Hellige Gesellschaft, Freiburg, Germany.

[1517] H. Lüers, *Obst.- u. Gemüse-Verwertungs-Ind.*, **27**, 399 (1940).

[1518] A. Mehlitz, *Konserven-Ind.*, **17**, 624 (1930).

[1519] F. A. Henglein, *Z. Lebensm.-Untersuch. u. Forsch.*, **90**, 417 (1950).

[1520] H. Gudjons, *Z. Lebensm.-Untersuch. u. Forsch.*, **90**, 426 (1950).

This method of measuring jelly strength has been used extensively in Germany and elsewhere in Europe. Recently Hamer[1521] described a modification of the method in which simultaneous observations can be made on the resistance of the jelly to deformation:

A brass disc, 0.5 to 0.75 inch in diameter, is suspended in a beaker containing the jelly by means of a wire attached to one beam of an analytical balance. Mercury is added from a burette with a removable calibrated capillary tip at a constant rate of 16 g. per minute to a container on the other pan. As the mercury is added, the height of the platform on which the jelly rests is changed

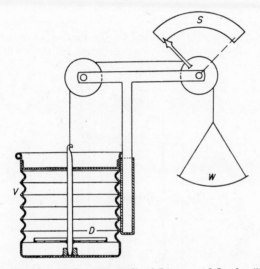

Fig. 41. The "Pektinometer" of Lüers and Lochmüller.

The jelly mixture is poured into the corrugated vessel V where disc D becomes embedded in the jelly. The weight is applied in pan W and the compression of the jelly is read on scale S.

manually, so that the pointer of the balance is always kept at zero. A vertical scale, indicating the height of the adjustable platform, is read at frequent intervals until the jelly is broken. The weight of mercury divided by the area of the disc gives the gel strength in grams per square centimeter. The rate of change in the height of the platform gives an indication of the resistance which the gel offers to deformation.

A serious criticism of this method is that no provision is made to assure that the jelly does not slip in the beaker. Manual operation of the level adjustment also introduces an element of arbitrariness.

[1521] W. J. Hamer, *J. Research Natl. Bur. Standards*, **39**, 29 (1947).

(d) "Delaware Jelly Strength Tester" and Modifications

This instrument was developed by Tarr[1522] and Baker[1523] and has perhaps been used to a greater extent for the grading of jellies than any other device. In this method the breaking strength of the jelly is measured through the use of a plunger actuated by air pressure. Measurements by this method are influenced by the formation of a "skin" on top of the test jelly. One of the precautions to avoid this is to use mineral oil to cover the jelly surface.[1504] Figure 42 shows the device[1524] in its recently described form.[1525]

The jelly, J, is placed under the plunger, A, which is actually an inverted Luer syringe. The pressure is developed by the flow of mercury from reservoir, B, regulated by stopcock, C. The plunger should operate with a minimum of

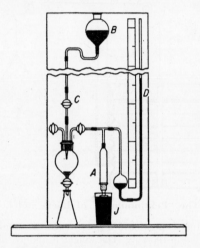

Fig. 42. The Delaware jelly strength tester.

friction and a few drops of glycerol may be used for lubrication. The pressure is regulated in such a manner that the water manometer, D, rises at the rate of 31 cm. per minute. A flat copper cap 21 mm. in diameter is fitted over the head of the plunger. The shape of this cap has considerable influence[1526] on the readings and must be standardized. The plunger is placed as near the center of the jelly as possible. With increased pressure the plunger sinks deeper and deeper into the jelly until the elastic limit is reached and the jelly breaks. The water

[1522] L. W. Tarr, *Delaware Agr. Expt. Sta.*, Bull. 142 (1926).
[1523] G. L. Baker, *Ind. Eng. Chem.*, **18**, 89 (1926).
[1524] Manufactured by Arthur H. Thomas Co., Philadelphia, Pa.
[1525] G. L. Baker, *Fruit Products J.*, **17**, 329 (1938).
[1526] H. H. Mottern and E. E. Karr, *Fruit Products J.*, **25**, 292 (1946).

manometer is read at this time and the pressure and firmness of the jelly are expressed as cm. of height of the water column in manometer, D.

Baker considers a jelly which has an elastic limit at 50 cm. of water pressure (or 33.5 g./cm.^{2} of plunger area) a "standard" jelly. One of the difficulties with this method is the unevenness of applying the pressure, a factor of considerable importance in obtaining reproducible values. Meschter and Lataillade[1504] sought to overcome this difficulty by developing a motor-driven gear system for gradual increase of the pressure:

In this "Stolmotor" modification of the Delaware tester the plunger is driven into the test jelly at a rate of 11 mm. per minute. These authors used slices of a jelly, cut to exactly 7 mm. thickness, and measured the force needed to break the jelly slice by placing the latter on the pan of a tare beam balance. A jelly designated as "standard" by these authors has a shear modulus of 3 g./cm.^{3} and a slice breaking strength of 60.7 g./cm.^{2} of plunger area.

A further modification of this method, apparently used for many years, was recently described by Bender.[1527]

The actuating pressure is developed in a large container and is regulated by a needle valve. This author uses jelly slices 6–7 mm. thick and applies the pressure at the rate of 100 cm. of water pressure in 46 seconds. The "standard" with this instrument is again defined at 60.7 g./cm.^{2} of cap surface. Bender states that this value has been used by the General Foods Corporation since 1938 in the production of pectin for household use and for preservers.

In these methods of measurement the elastic limits of the jellies are exceeded and the jellies are thus torn or ruptured. There is another line of instruments for jelly strength testing in which the deformation is measured without exceeding the elastic limits. Bloom in 1925 patented a device[1528] for the measurement of the strength of gelatin gels. The "Bloom number" (the grams of weight required to cause a 4-mm. depression with a plunger 0.5 inch in diameter in a 6.66% gelatin gel which was previously kept at 10°C. for 16–18 hours) has been used all over the world in gelatin and glue research and technology. Fellers and Griffith[1529] recommended the Bloom gelometer for jelly grading, but it was apparently not generally available because of limitations on its sale and was not used to any extent in pectin work. Recently Mottern[1530] again emphasized its potential usefulness in jelly grading.

The following are the other major devices of this type.

[1527] W. A. Bender, *Anal Chem.*, **21**, 408 (1949).
[1528] O. T. Bloom, U. S. Pat. 1,540,979 (1925).
[1529] C. R. Fellers and F. P. Griffith, *Ind. Eng. Chem.*, **20**, 857 (1928).
[1530] H. H. Mottern, *Food Technol.*, **3**, 34 (1949).

(e) Cox-Higby "Sag" Method

This apparatus, described by Cox and Higby[1506] and recently discussed by Joseph and Baier[1507] is based on the "Ridgelimeter" principle developed by Lockwood and Hayes.[1531] It permits the measurement of the distance which a jelly sags in a given time at a certain temperature from its original form. The device[1532] is shown in Figure 43. In the author's opinion this is the most useful of all the instruments described here for pectin jelly grade measurements.

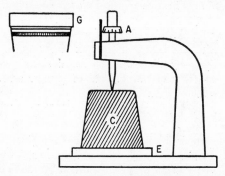

**Fig. 43. The Cox-Higby "sag" measuring device
for jelly grade determination.**

The test jelly is prepared by the method described on page 491, and poured into jelly tumblers which are ground on the rim until the inside height is exactly 79.4 mm. (3.125 inches). The side walls, G, are extended about 12 mm. (0.5 inch) higher with removable gummed paper. The skimmed jelly is poured nearly to the top of the "sideboard." The covered jelly is stored for 18 to 24 hours at 25°C. $\pm$ 5°. The "sideboard" is then removed and the exposed jelly trimmed away at the level of the ground rim of the glass with a wire cheese cutter. After being turned out on the clean, dry glass plate which is part of the apparatus, jelly, C, is allowed to stand for exactly 2 minutes before the micrometer screw is set just to touch the surface of the centered jelly; the micrometer, A, is then read. Since there are 32 threads per inch, one turn (equal to one scale division) is equivalent to 1% sag. From the slightly S-shaped curve shown in Figure 44, which represents the relationship between the sag and "assumed grade" of pectin samples of known jelly grade, the factor is obtained for correcting the "assumed grade." By multiplying the latter by the factor the grade of the pectin tested is obtained. A sag of 23.5% is considered "standard" firmness. When a calibration curve is not on hand, the factor by which the assumed grade should be multiplied may be found by dividing the scale reading

[1531] H. C. Lockwood and R. S. Hayes, *J. Soc. Chem. Ind.*, **50**, 145T (131).
[1532] Manufactured by Products Department, California Fruit Growers Exchange, Ontario, California.

or per cent of sag by 23.5 and subtracting from 2. This latter method of calculation assumes a straight-line relationship and is only approximately true.

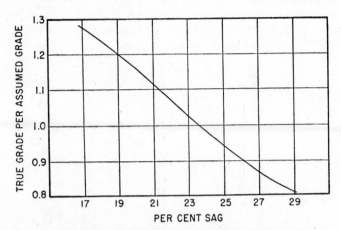

Fig. 44. The curve given by Cox and Higby to read the relationship between sag and jelly grade.

The reproducibility of measurements on test jellies by this method is very good, and the calculation of jelly grade is simple. In routine testing, only two glasses of jelly are prepared, while for more exact measurements, four glasses are used. This method of evaluation has been used with considerable success in the author's laboratory, where very satisfactory results were obtained, even with inexperienced operators.

(f) B.A.R. Jelly Tester and Modifications

The jelly and gel tester developed by the British Association of Research for Cocoa, Chocolate, Sugar, Confectionery and Jam Trades (B.A.R., now British Food Manufacturing Industries Research Association) and described by Campbell[1533] is, perhaps, based on the soundest theoretical considerations. This device measures the elastic modulus by the torque produced by a weight on a blade immersed in the jelly. The principle of this instrument is shown in Figure 45:

A 2-cm.^{2} vane, V, is held by a spindle supported by two hard steel rods, P. Scale S is independent of the steel rod and the rotation of the vane is indicated on it by a pointer fixed to the spindle. To the spindle and below the scale is attached a pully, M, which has a screw-thread groove around which a thread passes over two other pulleys and supporting vessel, A, and a counterpoise, B. Over the vessel is a tube which delivers water at a constant rate. The container with the jelly is placed on platform, D, which is then raised until the vane, V, is

[1533] L. E. Campbell, *J. Soc. Chem. Ind.*, **57**, 413 (1938).

in the center of the jelly. After adjusting the scale so that the pointer is at zero, water is run into vessel *A*, thus rotating the vane in the jelly. The water is added at the rate of 100 cc. per minute. The end point is not the point at which the vane breaks the jelly and commences to rotate freely, but at the weight of water which is necessary to turn the vane to a given degree within the elastic limit. When the vane is released again, it returns almost to its original position.

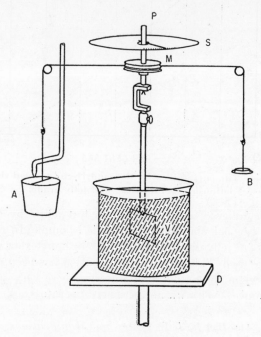

Fig. 45. The B.A.R. jelly tester.

A 30° turn is recommended as the end point for the measurement; when this is reached, the water is quickly turned off and its volume in the vessel is determined in a measuring cylinder. A correction for the force needed to turn the vane 30° in air is also determined and subtracted from the weight of water. At least three such readings are made to determine the blank value. Duplicate jellies should not differ by more than 1.2 cc. of water in testing.

The preparation of the test jellies will not be described here but it should be noted that these are boiled down with acid, then poured and covered at once with a thin layer of melted paraffin, and kept at 5°C. for 20 hours before testing. The test jellies recommended had 70 ± 0.5% soluble solids content as determined by a refractometer. The pH value specified was 2.9–3.0. The rigidity is expressed by the weight of water needed to produce the 30° torque of the vane or can be recalculated into c.g.s. units as grams of weight per square centimeter of surface. Hinton[1534] notes. that, using this expression, commercial fruit jellies of desirable firmness (in England) have rigidities of about 3–5 units.

This method has never been extensively used in the United States, perhaps because the original information on it was circulated confidentially. One of these instruments was presented in 1942 to the U. S. Department of Agriculture but it apparently did not attain any extent of popularity as compared to instruments available in this country. However, it may well be regarded as the progenitor of a number of devices which have been described during recent years.

Owens, Porter, and Maclay described a modification[1535] of the B.A.R. device:

The blade is attached to the lower end of a vertical torsion wire (a piano wire 20 cm. long and 0.047 cm. in diameter). The top end of the wire is turned by an electric motor geared to 0.05 r.p.m. The blade (vane) is imbedded in the jelly and the motor is then started. The rotation of the blade in the jelly is measured by a mirror attached to the wire immediately above the top of the jelly and is read with a telescope and scale. To calculate the results, wires of known torsional moments, such as those supplied with the MacMichael viscometer, are used. The authors call this modification the "Rigidometer," which should not be confused with the term "Ridgelimeter" used for the Exchange device measuring sag.

Cheftel and Mocquard described a modification[1536] of the B.A.R. tester which automatically and continuously records the rheological properties of the jelly during the test.

(g) Säverborn's Cylindrical Torsion Method

The last instrument to be described here is the device of Säverborn[1537] for measuring jelly strength. The method of preparing jellies used by this author has little significance for this discussion and will therefore be omitted.

Säverborn's device consists of a torsion wire which can be turned on top at angles read on a scale. To the lower end of the wire a corrugated cylinder is attached. A jelly is poured between the outside of this cylinder and another fixed, larger, corrugated cylinder to give a jelly shaped as illustrated in Figure 46. The bottom of the container is covered with mercury to eliminate bottom

[1534] C. L. Hinton, "Fruit Pectins, Their Chemical Behaviour and Jellying Properties," *Dept. Sci. Ind. Research Brit. Food Invest.*, Special Rept. No. 48 (1939).
[1535] H. S. Owens, O. Porter, and W. D. Maclay, *Food Inds.*, 19, 606 (1947).
[1536] H. Cheftel and J. Mocquard, *J. Soc. Chem. Ind.*, 66, 297 (1947).
[1537] S. Säverborn, *Dissertation*, Uppsala, 1945.

effects. In the measurement, the top of the wire is twisted and then the extent of torsion caused in the jelly is measured by a small mirror attached to the wire immediately above the jelly. The torsion is read with a telescope and mirror device. The corrugation prevents slipping between the jelly and the metal surfaces.

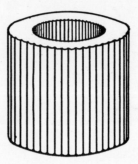

Fig. 46. The shape of the test jelly used in Säverborn's torsion method.

This is undoubtedly one of the finest instruments devised for jelly strength measurements. Unfortunately, as yet no data on well-defined commercial pectins or systematic comparisons of data obtained by this and other more established methods have been reported in the literature.

4. Present Status of Pectin Jelly Grade Evaluation

The diversity in methods of test jelly making, the property measured, the method of measurement, and the requirements of a "standard jelly" leave the matter of the exact jelly grade of any pectin preparation uncertain. One would almost agree with Sloep[1538] that none of the chemical and physical methods suggested are without objection. The present situation has been reviewed recently by a number of authors[1502,1504,1507,1527,1530] without accomplishing more than to define more precisely the differences of opinion which exist. However, these authors agree on the need for accepting some types of standards of definitions and procedures and, as noted previously, a committee is at this time (1950) working on the matter. Thus far, there are advocates of the various methods of making test jellies, of measuring the jelly grade at one pH value or in a series of determinations to establish the optimum, of cooking the jelly with the acid (and salts) or adding an excess of acid in the jelly glass.

Comparative measurements of jelly strength by several different methods have been reported by Owens, Porter, and Maclay,[1535] Baker and

[1538] A. C. Sloep, *Compt. rend. intern. tech. chim. ind. agr.,* **1,** 141 (1937).

Woodmansee,[1495] and Meschter and Lataillade.[1504] These investigators found that their respective method or modification was the soundest from the theoretical standpoint and most suitable for practical use.

A short time ago, a survey of a substantial part of the preserving industry in this country indicated that 71% of the preservers interviewed were interested in the breaking strength (limit of elasticity), 24% were interested in the sag (or elastic properties), and the rest in both. This would give more weight to the methods which were discussed under *e, f,* and *g* above. Concerning rigidity measurements, the following sobering statement of Cheftel and Mocquard[1536] should be borne in mind: "If we do not give a more detailed description of our recording jelly tester, it is because we do not now think it is the right instrument to use and, in fact, we have arrived at the conclusion that all measurements of this kind, be they automatically recorded or not, are fundamentally unsound when made on high sugar–high methoxyl pectin gels of this type usually encountered in fruit jams and jellies. As we see it, the only merit of our instrument is that it has allowed us to reach this conclusion, a better jelly tester still remaining to be devised . . . The shape of the curves indicates that while gelatin and similar gels possess true elasticity . . . pectin gels of the high sugar–high methoxyl type do not." This is not due to the sugar content since gelatin gels made with 65% sugar still act normally.

While we have not yet arrived at any one universally accepted method of jelly making and elasticity measurement, there is quite satisfactory agreement among most workers concerning the "desirable consistency" in pectin–sugar–acid jellies, at least as far as elastic properties are concerned. The definitions of "standard strength" as stated by the inventors of various devices have been incorporated in the descriptions of the instruments. It is clear that the pectin industry progressed a long way in arriving at standard products and terminology. Indeed, the present discussions aim to give a clarity to jelly grade definition and control which is far beyond the exactness attained in most other branches of the food industries.

V. GOVERNMENT REGULATIONS CONCERNING PECTINS AND THEIR USES

1. Regulations in the United States

Regulations concerning pectin and its uses may be assumed to exist in three different categories:

A. In the general regulations applicable to all food products.

B. In the lines of "definitions and standards of identities" and "quality standards" (grades for pectin).

C. In regulations dealing with the uses and applications of pectin.

A. Naturally, all the general primary requirements set forth under food laws, especially under the Federal Food, Drug, and Cosmetics Act (1938), hold for the manufacture of pectin and its use for food purposes. Of the special provisions of this law two groups of regulations are of specific interest: (1) the limit set for the presence of essentially toxic constituents; and (2) the use of preservatives.

The fact that poisonous insecticides and fungicides must be applied in the large-scale production of all fruits including apples and citrus fruits has caused considerable difficulties in the pectin industries and has at times resulted in confiscation of pectin. The problem, from the standpoint of protecting the public health, is a complicated one. The tolerances stating the permissible maximum amounts of spray residues must be set in such a manner as to safeguard the health of the consumer, but the amounts must be such as to permit commercial production. As a consequence, the tolerances have been changed several times and producers of apples and other foods often claim that these are unreasonable and difficult to meet.

As mentioned in Ch. XIX, washing apples with dilute hydrochloric acid solutions before pressing is about the only efficient method of removing such residues, which are retained mostly by the pomace; specific methods had to be developed to remove excessive amounts of lead and arsenic from pectin extracts. The United States tolerances for apples and pears are 7.2 p.p.m. (0.72 milligram per cent) of lead and 3.6 p.p.m. (0.36 milligram per cent) of arsenic (expressed as arsenic trioxide, As_2O_3). For pectin, as for food in general, the lead and arsenic tolerances are only 3.6 and 1.4 p.p.m. (0.36 and 0.14 milligram per cent), respectively. However, it is clear that pectin would be used in any food product in a very small proportion only, and therefore the same tolerances for food directly eaten and used in a small proportion seems indeed unreasonable.[1539] A tentative tolerance of 7.0 p.p.m. (0.7 milligram per cent) was in use for fluorine but the present situation is not clear.

The problem of toxic residues keeps entomologists and plant pathologists busy in a constant search for efficient insecticides which do not leave toxic residues. It was hoped that the extended usage of DDT (dichlorodiphenyltrichloroethane) and other newer organic chemicals on apples would solve the problem. It now appears that most of these materials also leave residues that are poisonous.

Solid, dry pectin preparations do not need preservatives. On the other

[1539] W. E. Baier and C. W. Wilson, *Food Technol.*, **5**, 38 (1951).

hand, pectin concentrates have often been marketed with added chemical preservatives, although now this is a rare practice in this country where the bulk of pectin concentrates is sold in a sterilized condition. The use of certain preservatives[1540] is permitted for some food materials in their "definitions and standards of identities," but no such thing exists for pectin. If and when preservatives are used with pectin concentrates, they must be declared on the label. Of the preservatives, benzoates and various derivatives of benzoic acid and sulfur dioxide may be used. As noted before, preservatives are commonly used in pectin concentrates produced in some other countries.

B. There are no official "definitions and standards of identity" or "quality standard" (grade) regulations for pectin in this country. It appears that, with the high quality of pectins now being made and the widely accepted definition of pectin grade (both voluntarily developed by the manufacturers), there may be no need at the present time for such regulations. The closest approach is the set of specifications, discussed early in this chapter, which was used for government purchases.

C. In the United States the use of pectin in preserves, jams, jellies, and marmalades is now, and has been in the past, permitted. The Federal Food, Drug, and Cosmetics Act of 1938 states that a food is adulterated "if any substance . . . has been added . . . to make it appear better or of greater value than it is." As will be shown below, pectin is regarded as a natural constituent of fruits and is used for the purpose of equalizing its presence in food products. This law also states that the food is adulterated "if it is a confectionery and it bears or contains any alcohol or non-nutritive article or substance except . . . natural gum and pectin . . ."

The "Definitions and Standard of Identity for Preserves, Jams" now in force[1541] permits the use of pectin as an optional ingredient. "Pectin, in a quantity which reasonably compensates for deficiency, if any, of the natural pectin content of the fruit ingredient." This admission of pectin is based on findings No. 33, 34, 36, 37, and 38 of the Presiding Officer concluded from evidence presented at a public hearing held before the standards were established. These state:

"Pectin and acid, substances naturally present in all preserving fruits and vegetables, are the substances which give a preserve its jellying properties." "Some such fruits and vegetables contain larger quantities of pectin and acid than others and frequently the quantity of pectin and acid varies in the same kind of fruit or vegetable, such variances being due to several factors, including the degree of ripeness, the variety, the locality where grown and other

[1540] M. B. Jacobs, ed., *The Chemistry and Technology of Food and Food Products*. Interscience, New York, 1944.
[1541] Federal Register, **5**, 3554 (1940).

factors." "A manufacturer of preserves cannot, by normal, good commercial
practice, maintain a sufficiently high content of acid and pectin for preserve
manufacture by selecting fruits and vegetables on the basis of their variety or
degree of ripeness, or on any other basis which is practicable." "When the fruit
or vegetable ingredient in preserves contains substantially less pectin or acid,
or both, than the average quantities of pectin and acid in preserving fruits
generally, a proper consistency of the finished product cannot be obtained"
and, finally: "When the fruit or vegetable ingredient of a preserve is deficient
in pectin, or acid, or both, the desirable consistency of the finished preserve is
obtained by adding a sufficient quantity of pectin or acid, or both, to compensate
for such deficiency."

Essentially the same arguments were used in the "Definitions and
Standards of Identity for Jellies" in which the use of pectin is admitted
as an optional ingredient, using substantially the same wording. The
use of pectin does not have to be declared on the label. On the other hand,
when pectin is used in other food products for which no definitions and
standards of identity have been established, pectin must be listed among
the ingredients.

There are now in force "United States Standards for Grades of Fruit
Preserves (or Jams)."[1542] The standard for preserves (or jams) deals
with the classification of fruits which may be used, alone or in mixtures,
for such products and then defines the three existing grades (U. S. Grade
A or U. S. Fancy; U. S. Grade B or U. S. Choice; and U. S. Grade D or
Substandard). The grade is determined on the basis of scores assigned to
consistency, color, absence of defects, and flavor in the case of preserves,
and consistency, color, and flavor in the case of jelly. In preserves (jams)
the consistency carries 20 of a total of 100 points and is stated in the
standard to "refer to the viscosity of the product and to the extent of dispersion of the fruit or fruit particles." The consistency may fall into three
classes:

"(A)   Fruit preserves (or jams) that possess a good consistency may be
given a score of 17 to 20 points. 'Good consistency' means that the fruit or
fruit particles are practically uniformly dispersed throughout the product;
and that the product is a tender gel or may possess no more than a very slight
tendency to flow, except that a sirupy consistency is permitted when the fruit
is chiefly in the form of whole units or large pieces.

"(B)   If the fruit preserves (or jams) possess a reasonably good consistency,
a score of 14 to 16 points may be given. 'Reasonably good consistency' means that
the fruit or fruit particles are reasonably uniformly dispersed throughout the
product; and that the product may be firm but not rubbery or may be thin
but not watery.

[1542] Federal Register, 14, 620 (1949).

"(C) Fruit preserves (or jams) that fail to meet the requirements of the foregoing paragraph (B) for any reason may be given a score of 0 to 13 points and are not graded above U. S. Grade D or Substandard, regardless of the total score for the product."

The desirability of obtaining an objective method of measurement for the consistency of preserves is now generally admitted. We shall return to this point in Chapter XXVII, Section I-3.

In the case of the "Standards for Fruit Jelly,"[1543] consistency is given a much bigger role, and carries 40 out of a total of 100 points. The standard states that the consistency "refers to the gel strength of the product," and the score value is determined as follows:

"(A) Fruit jelly that possesses a good consistency may be given a score of 34 to 40 points. 'Good consistency' means that the fruit jelly possesses a tender to slightly firm texture and retains a compact shape without excessive syneresis ('weeping').

"(B) If the fruit jelly possesses a reasonably good consistency, a score of 28 to 33 points may be given. Fruit jelly that falls into this classification is not graded above U. S. Grade B or U. S. Choice, regardless of the total score for the product (this is a limiting rule). 'Reasonably good consistency' means that the fruit jelly may lack firmness but it is not sirupy; and that it may be more than slightly firm but is not tough or rubbery.

"(D) Fruit jelly that fails to meet the requirements of the foregoing paragraph (B) may be given a score of 0 to 27 points and is not graded above U. S. Grade D or Substandard, regardless of the total score for the product (this is a limiting rule)."

The ambiguity of these definitions is quite obvious and the need for objective methods for the measurement of consistency is generally admitted. These grades are now principally used in governing the consistency of such commercial products in government purchases. The importance of consistency is brought to the fore by the assignment of 40 points for this property in jellies, essentially controlled by the proper application of pectin.

The use of benzoic acid or sodium benzoate or both is permitted in preserves and jellies but must be declared on the label.

2. Regulations in Some Foreign Countries

There are other countries in which pectin enjoys as general acceptance as in the United States. In both Great Britain and Germany the use of pectin has been a general practice for many years. It is noteworthy that in Great Britain the use of pectin in high-grade products is permitted

[1543] Federal Register, 13, 6398 (1948).

without declaration, while the use of pectin must be stated in the case of lower quality products. The "First Quality" jams must conform to certain standards[1544] as to kind and proportion (30 to 45%) of fruit used and proportion of total soluble solids. Pectin is an optional ingredient of such jams. The "Second Quality" products contain only 20% fruit and in these the use of pectin must be stated on the label. The object is, presumably, to avoid covering up low quality and fruit content by the use of pectin.

In a recent standard the designation "National Mark" is given to products which conform to certain specifications which, however, do not assure that the jam is "First Quality." Such jams may contain artificial coloring and sulfur dioxide not to exceed 4 milligram per cent, but the addition of pectin or pectin-containing fruit juices is not permitted.

In Germany[1545] the food laws make distinctions between a great variety of fruit products; these have been described in detail in the regulations of 1933. Section 7 of paragraph 7 designates the amount of pectin permitted in terms of calcium pectate, a definition which is now generally regarded as inadequate (Section IV). This law defines fruit pectin as a product which contains not less than 25% pectin as calcium pectate in solid preparations and 2.5% in concentrates (liquid pectins), and states that the concentrate or the 10% suspension of the solid pectin must be transparent in a 3-cm. layer and must contain only tartaric or lactic acid. The German food laws made distinction between pectin concentrates, as defined above, and "jellying fruit juices" ("Obstgeliersäfte"); the latter must contain not less than 2% pectin (as calcium pectate) in the solution and not less than 15% pectin on the dry matter basis. These regulations are much more rigid in some respects than those in most other countries although they are noticeably lacking in the definition of jellying power.

Similar rigid standards were promulgated in the same laws for the great variety of fruit products made in Germany. The types and definitions used are different from those used in this country and the standards underwent many modifications during and since World War II.[1546] By 1944 the amount of pectin which could be used in the 4-fruit jam (according to our definition, a mixed-fruit butter, which was the only such product permitted) was reduced to 6.5% "standard concentrate." A noteworthy feature of the German fruit products industry is the common use of chemical preservatives (benzoates, etc.) in raw and intermediate

[1544] Anonymous, *Analyst*, **55**, 695 (1930).

[1545] H. Serger and H. Krause, *Konserventechnisches Taschenbuch*. 8th ed., Serger und Hempel, Braunschweig, 1938.

[1546] Z. I. Kertesz, Joint Intelligence Objectives Agency, JIOA Report No. 51 (1945).

products, whereas in finished preserves their use is limited to protection of the surface. Sulfur dioxide, on the other hand, was almost universally used for the preservation of pectin concentrates; a concentration of 0.05% was usually applied.

Artificial coloring of fruit products is a common practice and is permitted in Germany.

In Switzerland, just as in Germany, solid pectins and pectin concentrates as well as the "jellying fruit juices" are permitted. In pectin products the jellying power must be stated and in small packages (household pectin) it must be implied through the instructions for use. The pectin concentrates are further defined as void of dark brown color and turbidity, and any strong flavor which would be noticeable after mixing with 3 to 4 parts of a 60% sugar sirup. The ash content should not exceed 12% of the pectin content and the protein content should be lower than 2% of the dry matter.[1547] It is interesting to note that this law also limits the methanol content of ethanol-precipitated pectins to 7% (on a starch-free pectin basis). The methanol limitation must be regarded as a direct outgrowth of the investigations, almost four decades ago in Switzerland, of the occurrence of methanol in fruit products, which led to the discovery of methoxyl groups in pectic substances by Fellenberg.[1548] The copper content of pectin preparations is also limited to 40 milligram per cent. On the whole, the Swiss standards and definitions are perhaps the most progressive and adequate of all such regulations in various countries.

In contrast to the general admittance of the use of pectin in some of the aforementioned countries, the situation is less favorable in others. In France, for example, the pectin situation is confused and existing regulations seem to be frankly hostile to the use of pectin. While according to French regulations the use of pectin itself is not prohibited, its use is also not explicitly permitted. If and when the use of pectin can be shown to be aimed at concealing the inferiority of a product, its use is prohibited.[1549] The regulation of 1942 represents some progress in this matter since it differentiates pectin concentrates from apple juice, although in a none too satisfactory manner. The regulation still ignores solid pectins. This attitude toward pectin is rather unrealistic and is likely to be of little help to the French pectin and preserving industries.

In many countries there is still much antagonism among manufacturers and the general public toward the use of pectin. In Australia, despite the

[1547] E. Eichenberger, *Mitt. Geb. Lebensm. Hyg.*, **34**, 33 (1943).

[1548] T. Fellenberg, *Mitt. Geb. Lebensm. Hyg.*, **4**, 122 (1913).

[1549] H. Cheftel, "Utilisation industrielle des fruits," *Etablts, J. J. Carnaud et Forges de Basse-Indre Lab. Res. (Paris)*, No. 7 (1943).

great importance of fruit products in that nation's economy, many manufacturers are still oblivious of the benefits which they might derive in economies in manufacturing, standardization, and better quality products, through the use of pectin. The lack of adequate federal food regulations (or harmonized state laws) in Australia, as in many other countries, also tends to confuse the situation. Such discrepancies between desirable practices and regulations are apt to occur when production methods developed in other countries are introduced suddenly. Difficulties of this sort were at a minimum in many countries like the United States, Germany, and Switzerland, in which pectin manufacture and utilization developed together with the food laws.

With normally extensive international trade in pectin and pectin-containing products, it is probable that changes in many existing food laws and new regulations will tend to liberalize the use of pectin, even if control of quality is apt to become more rigid. Because of the high quality of pectin products made in this country, this would be a favorable change for United States pectin manufacturers. The regulations which are still in force in some countries prohibiting the use of pectin in commercial production of preserves are surely unreasonable and, to borrow a term from our own food laws, "will not increase honesty and fair dealing" with the customer. These regulations also deprive the manufacturer of important economies in the manufacture, and the consumer of better quality and nutritional properties in many fruit products.

CHAPTER XXIV

Low-Ester (Low-Methoxyl) Pectins

By decreasing the methoxyl content below 7%, the ability of pectins to form jellies and gels is changed.[1550,1551] Above 7% methoxyl content a soluble solids content of over 50% in the product is essential for proper jelly formation. When the methoxyl content is reduced below 7%, the pectin preparation is able to form firm acid pectinate gels with traces of polyvalent cations at a much lower solids content. In fact, at times the soluble solids content required for good gel formation may be 1% or less. Some authorities on the manufacture and utilization of pectins predict that eventually the importance of the low-ester pectins will overshadow that of the now standard pectin containing more than 7% methoxyl.

The methoxyl content of low-ester pectins with "desirable properties" is now usually in the range 2.5–4.5%. Such low-ester preparations are being marketed for some specific purposes for which they are more suitable than high-ester pectins. There is still much to be learned since the manufacture and use of low-ester pectins presents some peculiar problems which are not encountered with conventional pectins. The term "pectinate" is now also used for low-ester pectins.

Frequent references were made on previous pages to the behavior of low-ester pectins. In Chapter VIII the various types of methods which may be used for their preparation were discussed. The meager information available in the literature concerning their large-scale manufacture will be dealt with briefly here; in addition, some points concerning their use and standardization will be discussed.

There are three principal methods which have been suggested for the commercial production of low-ester pectins: deesterification with acid, enzymes, or alkali. A fourth method, using ammoniacal ethanol or concentrated ammonium hydroxide in water will only be noted here.[1552,1553]

[1550] G. L. Baker, in E. Mrak and G. F. Stewart, *Advances in Food Research.* Vol. I, Academic Press, New York, 1948, p. 395.
[1551] A. G. Olsen, R. F. Stuewer, E. R. Fehlberg, and N. M. Beach, *Ind. Eng. Chem.,* **31,** 1015 (1939).
[1552] G. H. Joseph, E. F. Bryant, and A. H. Kieser, *Fruit Products J.,* **27,** 318 (1948).
[1553] G. H. Joseph, A. H. Kieser, and E. F. Bryant, *Food Technol.,* **3,** 85 (1949).

As stated in previous chapters, this method of deesterification results in the introduction of new groups and thus the resulting compound must be regarded as a derivative rather than a low-ester pectin.

The low-ester pectins produced by the first three processes differ both in their general and in their specific properties and requirements. The acid-demethylated pectinic acids usually give very viscous solutions and are not very sensitive to metallic ions. In practical usage this means that the former require large proportions of calcium for setting, while the latter are so sensitive that the calcium content of hard water may impair complete solution of the material. Alkali-demethylated low-ester pectins are between these two extremes both in solution viscosity and calcium sensitivity. The crux of this matter is that these differences are of sufficient magnitude to prevent the three types of low-ester pectins from being used interchangeably with any given recipe or formula.[1554]

It is also clear that the commercial value of low-ester pectins must be defined in a different manner than the old-fashioned high-ester pectins, since the former do not depend on the presence of sugar for gel formation. In fact, they are used chiefly in products of relatively low sugar contents. Probably, some expression which embodies concentration of low-ester pectin and gel firmness under optimal conditions will eventually be used for this purpose. It is also very doubtful, because of the statements made in the previous paragraph, whether a grading procedure for low-ester pectins which is generally or even broadly applicable can be expected. More probably—at least according to present views—every type of low-ester pectin may have to be tested and used under a specific set of conditions typical for that one sample or type of low-ester pectin.

Allusion was made frequently on previous pages to the heterogeneity of pectic substances; heterogeneity is the major complication with low-ester pectins. From the scanty information on hand, it seems that the heterogeneity of pectin preparations which are deesterified by any of the three principal methods increases, but this entire subject is still little understood. Certainly, consideration of the heterogeneity factors discussed in Chapter V makes an increase in heterogeneity during demethylation quite obvious. The chief problems are: (1) to give to the heterogeneity of any given sample an exact definition; and (2) to apply methods which produce samples composed of more uniform units. Heterogeneity is very important here because the individual types of compounds of which any given sample is composed have widely varying properties and requirements; this results, under any given set of conditions, in only partial satisfaction of the requirements of some component pectinic acids in the mixture.

[1554] California Fruit Growers Exchange, Ontario, California, "Exchange pectin L.M.," trade pamphlet, 1947.

Owens, McCready, and Maclay[1555] recently described.a pilot plant for the production of low-ester pectin from citrus peel. A diagram of this process was shown in Figure 27. The various features of this scheme were noted during the discussion of pectin manufacture.

The pectin extract, produced on a continuous line, is cooled to 13°C. (55°F.) and ammonia is then added (batchwise) to raise the pH to 10.5. The solution is kept at this pH for 2.5 hours after which the pH is reduced to 1.2 with sulfuric acid, thus stopping deesterification and precipitating the low-ester pectinic acid.[1556] The resulting weak gel is dewatered, pressed, washed, and again dewatered to about 35% solids content. Now sodium bicarbonate is milled in to about half-neutralization and the material is air-dried.

It is likely that deesterification with both dilute ammonia and strong acid is now used in the production of low-ester pectins. Of the patents issued on low-ester pectins, only a few will be noted here.[1557-1561] The peculiar low-ester pectin produced by a high concentration of ammonia contains not only the ammonium salt of pectinic acid but also some acid amide groups, and presents some interesting problems in analysis since the presence of both the ammonium salt and the acid amide groups makes many of the standard procedures inapplicable. Joseph, Kieser, and Bryant[1553] discuss in detail the behavior of this product in comparison with that of more conventional types of low-ester pectins, as well as the practical importance of the former. Since this compound cannot be regarded either as a true low-ester pectin or a pectic substance, the legal standing of the use of this product in foods is also somewhat unsettled at the time of this writing (1950).

As the science of low-ester pectins stands today,[1562-1569] the amount of

[1555] H. S. Owens, R. M. McCready, and W. D. Maclay, *Food Technol.*, 3, 77 (1949).
[1556] R. M. McCready, H. S. Owens, and W. D. Maclay, *Food Inds.*, 16, 794, 906 (1944).
[1557] G. L. Baker and M. W. Goodwin, U. S. Pat. 2,233,574 (1941).
[1558] R. H. McDowell, British Pat. 541,528 (1941).
[1559] General Foods Corp., British Pat. 639,555 (1947).
[1560] H. S. Owens, R. M. McCready, and W. D. Maclay, U. S. Pats. 2,495,756 (1950), and 2,496,306 (1950).
[1561] H. S. Owens and H. Lotzkar, U. S. Pat. 2,522,534 (1950).
[1562] G. L. Baker and C. W. Woodmansee, *Food Technol.*, 1, 11 (1947).
[1563] C. W. Kaufman, E. R. Fehlberg, and A. G. Olsen, *Food Inds.*, 14, 57 (1942).
[1564] T. H. Schultz, H. Lotzkar, H. S. Owens, and W. D. Maclay, *J. Phys. Chem.*, 49, 554 (1945).
[1565] G. L. Baker and M. W. Goodwin, *Delaware Agr. Expt. Sta.*, Bull. No. 234, (1941); also 246 (1944).
[1566] R. M. McCready, H. S. Owens, A. D. Shepherd, and W. D. Maclay, *Ind. Eng. Chem.*, 38, 1254 (1946).
[1567] C. W. Woodmansee and G. L. Baker, *Food Technol.*, 3, 82 (1949).
[1568] C. H. Hills, H. H. Mottern, G. C. Nutting, and R. Speiser, *Food Technol.*, 3, 90 (1949).
[1569] H. H. Mottern, *Food Technol.*, 3, 34 (1949).

calcium which gives the best results in forming gels must be determined for each sample. In practical usage it must also be determined in conjunction with the materials which are used together with the low-ester pectin, because of the possible presence of polyvalent ions. When used with milk, there is usually no need to add more calcium salts. In the case of fruit juices and other fruit products, the specific calcium requirement must be determined under the actual conditions of usage. Baker[1550] describes the following procedure:

The low-ester pectin is dispersed into about one half of the juice to be used in the gel test. It is then heated to boiling and the other half of the juice, containing various amounts of calcium and the necessary amount of sugar for the desired soluble solids content, also at about the boiling point, is added. The solution is now adjusted with water to the same weight for each of the gels of varying calcium contents; they are then allowed to set for a uniform length of time before determining the strength, melting temperature, and other properties. The calcium requirement varies even in the same sample of low-ester pectin when other conditions such as pH and solids content are altered. It ranges from as low as 1 mg. of calcium ions to 60 mg. or more per gram of low-ester pectin used.

In establishing the amount of low-ester pectin to be used for best gelation at any soluble solids content, Baker recommends that the grade and the methoxyl content be determined. Baker's viscosity method (Chapter XXIII) at pH 4.5 is used for grade determination. The amount of the preparation to be used can then be read from some curves given by Baker. It is clear, however, that the conditions under which the low-ester pectin shows maximum performance depend on so many factors that such determinations as those suggested by Baker are not applicable for all or even the majority of low-ester preparations. The amount of low-ester pectin which must be used in various products to obtain proper gelation varies from a fraction of 1% to several per cent.

Low-ester pectin gels (acid calcium pectinates) have some interesting properties. Conventional pectin–acid–sugar jellies show little change in rigidity until the temperature is raised above 50°C. (122°F.). Low-ester gels decrease proportionally in rigidity with increase in temperature. In fact, in the range of 0–57°C. the shear modulus of a given sample was noted[1555] to have decreased from about 8 to almost zero. The melting temperatures of the two types of products are also different but the relationship between pH, solids content, amount of calcium used, etc., is such that it is difficult to generalize.

Baker and Woodmansee[1562] investigated the storage life of some products made with low-ester pectins and found that grape gels with 30%

soluble solids increased in gel strength and melting temperature during storage. At least some of this was due to loss of ester from the pectinic acid during storage.

In a pamphlet[1554] published in 1947, a method used for grading low-ester pectins was described as follows:

Into a previously tared 3-quart saucepan 425 cc. of water, 10 cc. of a 6.0% solution of sodium citrate ($Na_3C_6H_5O_7.2H_2O$), and 5.0 cc. of a solution containing 60 g. of citric acid monohydrate per 100 cc. are measured. About $1/6$ of 180 g. of previously weighed sucrose is first mixed with 6.0 g. of standardized "Exchange Pectin L.M." and, after thorough mixing, is poured into the saucepan containing the above mixture. The mixture is now heated to boiling with constant stirring, the rest of the sugar is added, and it is again brought to boiling. At this time 25 cc. of a solution containing 22.05 g. of calcium chloride dihydrate ($CaCl_2.2H_2O$) per liter is added and the mixture is boiled to a final weight of 600 g. It is then poured into jelly glasses previously prepared for making jellies for sag measurements (Chapter XXIII) and stored at 24–26°C. (75–79°F.) for 18–24 hours before testing. If the pH of the finished gel is not 3.0 ± 0.05, the amount of citric acid used should be changed to give this value. The per cent of sag for normal firmness of this type gel is 20–21% (as contrasted with 23.5% for high-ester 65% sugar jellies). The use of milk in a 35% solids gel has also been suggested for the evaluation of low-ester pectins.[1556]

There are now several standardized low-ester preparations on the market whose pH, calcium, and solids requirements and relationships are given by the respective manufacturers. There are, as yet, no reports in the literature dealing with the variations which may be found in such low-ester pectins. Perhaps some variation is even desirable. As Mottern[1569] notes, low-ester pectins are new products and have scarcely been developed to the point at which stabilization and standardization can be regarded as desirable. Chapter XXVII will deal with some of the uses of low-ester pectins.

CHAPTER XXV

Commercial Protopectins

Crude preparations made from plant tissues for the purpose of subsequent extraction of the pectin have been prepared by many investigators of pectin chemistry. For two reasons, at least, such preparations have never attained any great commercial significance. Most investigators used organic solvents for the preparation of such materials[1570-1572] which is an expensive process. Second, it is inconvenient for the manufacturer of preserves to extract the pectin which is so easily available in a purified and standardized form. There are a number of patents on the preparation of such materials. In Chapters XIX, XX, and XXI the purification of the starting material used for pectin manufacture was discussed. If the purified pomace, albedo, or extracted beet slices is carefully dried, a crude protopectin preparation suitable for pectin manufacture is obtained (for detailed further information on the preparation of such crude protopectins, see Chapter VI).

During World War II such materials attained some importance. The demand for pectin exceeded production facilities and provisions were therefore made for the manufacture of dried "protopectin" which could be shipped more easily than wet pulp for use in the extraction of pectin. The methods used in the manufacture of such crude protopectins, usually from grapefruit peel, may best be illustrated by an outline which is based on the instructions issued by the U. S. Department of Agriculture in 1942:

After removal of seeds (by washing in rotating wire cages under a strong water spray), the pomace is ground in a suitable mill so that the pieces are approximately 0.5 inch in length. The ground pomace is added immediately to boiling water (approximately 30 gallons of water to 100 pounds of pomace) and the temperature is maintained at about 194°F. (90°C.) while the mixture is agitated for 5 to 7 minutes. At the end of this treatment period, sufficient cold water (approximately 50 gallons per 100 pounds of pomace) is added to lower the temperature of the mixture to 135°F. (57°C.) or below and, after

[1570] F. G. Beylik and N. W. Schwartzlose, U. S. Pat. 1,393,660 (1921).
[1571] H. T. Leo, U. S. Pat. 2,038,582 (1936).
[1572] R. C. Mithoff, U. S. Pat. 1,976,761 (1934).

agitating for 5 minutes, the water is drained off and discarded. The wet pomace is added to cold (ordinary temperature) water in the ratio of approximately 35 gallons to 100 pounds of pomace, agitated for 10 minutes, and the water is then drained off and discarded. The extraction with cold (ordinary temperature) water described in the last sentence is repeated once more. The leached pomace is pressed in a suitable press (like the one shown in Fig. 37) and then dried in any drier of the types discussed in Chapter XIX.

In order to reduce the loss of pectin by enzyme action, processing of the pomace should be commenced promptly, as soon as it is available from the juice extraction plant. Not over 45 minutes should elapse between juice extraction and heating of the pomace in boiling water, and not over 10 minutes should elapse between grinding the pomace and subjecting it to treatments with boiling water. Otherwise, considerable loss of pectin may result and the physical condition of the pomace may also be changed in such a way as seriously to retard the processing operation.

In order to reduce the loss of extractable pectin, it is advisable that soft water be used in the processing of the grapefruit pomace, particularly for the final extraction. Water having a hardness of 12 p.p.m. or below is satisfactory.

For the purchases of this material for the government (for Lend-Lease purposes) the Department of Agriculture issued the following specification:

"Sanitation and Quality of Water Use: The water used in processing shall be of potable quality and the pomace shall be handled throughout in a cleanly and sanitary manner.

"Moisture Content: The moisture content of the pomace shall not exceed 8 per cent, nor be less than 4 per cent.

"Fineness: The pomace shall be of such a degree of fineness that all will pass through a U. S. Sieve No. 20 (Tyler screen scale equivalent of 60).

"Color, Flavor and Taste: The pomace shall be practically free of charred or dark colored particles caused by overheating. It shall be free from seeds, seed particles, and foreign material. The jelly made from the extract of the pomace in the manner hereinafter described shall be light in color, substantially neutral in flavor, and free from objectionable odor.

"Grade: The Grapefruit Pomace, when tested by the method hereinafter described shall be found to contain pectin equivalent to 50 jelly-grade or better."

METHOD FOR DETERMINING THE GRADE OF GRAPEFRUIT POMACE

"A. Preparation of a Stock Solution of 100 Grade Citrus Pectin: Thirty grams of the pectin are suspended in 90 grams of a 66% sirup of refined sucrose, and hot water is added while stirring until the total weight is 1500 grams. If required to be kept for more than a few days, thymol may be added as a preservative, but freshly prepared solution is preferable. Special care should be taken to see that the solid pectin is effectively dissolved—in some cases a tendency to remain in finely divided suspension has been noted. As a precaution it is advisable to allow the pectin solution to stand at least one hour prior to preparing the jelly.

"B. Preparation of a Standard Extract of the Pomace: Fifty grams of the pomace are gently boiled with 2 litres of a 1% solution of citric acid (uncrystallized) for half an hour, in a flask or other suitable vessel, excessive evaporation being avoided throughout. After cooling, the mixture is made up to the original weight—i. e., 2050 grams—strained and squeezed through a dry linen or calico cloth."

Obviously, some of the previously described methods of evaluating the firmness of jellies may be used at this time to obtain more precise evaluation of the "pectin jelly grade" of the pomace. It is also clear that variations in the method of pectin extraction give different, and at times better, results.

Leo, Taylor, and Beck[1573] described a method of drying purified fruit pomace and using filter aids to standardize such crude protopectin preparations for jelly grade. Rooker[1574] described a process in which ethanol extraction is used first for the purification of pectin-containing fruit fibers, after which the product is standardized for jelly grade by the addition of depectinized fruit fibers, assumedly the residue left after pectin extraction.

There is some indication that such crude citrus pulp protopectin preparations are now used by manufacturers of apple pectin in years when the amount of apple pomace is insufficient to satisfy their needs, and by manufacturers of citrus pectin to lengthen the season of production.

A great deal of citrus peel is limed, pressed, and dried for later use in stock feed. By using various types of alkalies the dry products obtained will show different degrees of dispersibilities in weak bases.[1575] Some such "pectate pulps" and "pectic acid pulps" are manufactured on a small scale. Their uses will be noted in Chapter XXVIII.

[1573] H. T. Leo, C. C. Taylor, and F. A. Beck, U. S. Pat. 2,022,470 (1935).
[1574] W. A. Rooker, U. S. Pat. 2,095,617 (1937).
[1575] G. H. Joseph, *Econ. Botany*, 1, 415 (1947).

CHAPTER XXVI

Commercial Pectinates, Pectic Acids, and Pectates

The laboratory preparation of pectic acids, pectinates, and pectates was discussed in Chapter VI. Since some of these materials are also manufactured on a limited scale and used for a variety of purposes, they will be discussed here from the standpoint of large-scale preparation. The important developments along these lines came almost exclusively from the laboratories of the California Fruit Growers Exchange[1575] and are covered by a series of patents.[1576-1579]

Baier and Wilson[1580] reviewed this topic in some detail and described the methods of preparation. Upon treatment with cold, dilute sodium hydroxide, pectin is saponified and degraded to yield moderately viscous, water-soluble pectates. The corresponding alkaline earth salts are insoluble. The soluble pectates form alcohol precipitates which are granular gels. In the process of production the pectin solution is treated with hydrated lime and caustic soda and the precipitate is dewatered. It is then washed with dilute hydrochloric acid, followed by water which contains only a trace of this acid. Finally, it is washed with water, pressed, and dried. The pectic acid obtained is nearly white in color and should have less than 2% ash.

An interesting product designated as "fibrous pectate" has been described by Wilson[1578] and Baier and Wilson.[1580] This is essentially a sodium pectate which is formed by direct treatment of the protopectin by alkali. The crude citrus pulp is "pectated" with soda ash and then washed, pressed, dried, and ground. The sodium pectate content of the final product is around 30 to 35%. It may be solubilized by boiling with an alkaline salt of a phosphate (such as tetrasodium pyrophosphate) and sodium carbonate. The mixture is boiled for 3 or 4 minutes to solubilize the pectate between the cells and is then thoroughly disintegrated. This dispersion

[1576] F. W. Huber, U. S. Pat. 1,410,920 (1922).
[1577] C. W. Wilson, U. S. Pat. 1,975,998 (1934).
[1578] C. W. Wilson, U. S. Pat. 2,132,065 (1938); Reissue No. 21,077 (1939).
[1579] E. F. Bryant, U. S. Pats. 2,418,865 and 2,418,866 (1947).
[1580] W. E. Baier and C. W. Wilson, *Ind. Eng. Chem.*, 33, 287 (1941).

remains, after cooling, as a viscous liquid containing the suspended cellulosic material. If it is dried, the product is not dispersible in cold water and hot water is again required for its dispersion.

Upon filtration and the addition of ethanol to the solution, this pectate may be recovered in the form of a precipitate composed of tangled fibers. After drying this is redispersible in water and forms a very viscous solution.

Sodium pectate is now apparently produced on a commercial scale from sisal and other plants of the agave species.[1581] According to the patents,[1582,1583] the procedures used are similar to that described above, except that the sisal flesh is first treated to remove waxes and other similar components which are present and is only then purified to remove sugars and other water-soluble constituents.

The saponification of pectin may also be performed without hydration of metal pectinates by using alkaline ethanol solutions. The preparation of sodium calcium pectinate by applying alkaline solutions of isopropyl alcohol has been described by Bryant.[1584] The preparation of calcium pectinates has been described by Beach,[1585] while Myers[1586] dealt with the preparation and properties of nickel pectinates.

The preparation and properties of these pectates and pectinates are also discussed in Chapter IX which deals with various derivatives and salts of pectic and pectinic acids, and Chapters VI and XXIV which deal with low-ester pectins and the acid metal pectinates formed from these.

[1581] Anonymous, *Foreign Commerce Weekly*, May 6, 1944, p. 22.
[1582] African Sisal and Produce Co. Ltd. and R. J. Browne, British Pat. 556,808 (1943); through *C. A.*, 39, 1944 (1945).
[1583] African Sisal and Produce Co. Ltd., C. L. Walsh, E. L. James, and T. P. Hoar, British Pat. 582,147 (1946); through *C. A.*, 41, 1776 (1947).
[1584] E. F. Bryant, U. S. Pats. 2,349,138 (1944); 2,418,865 (1947); and 2,418,866 (1947).
[1585] N. M. Beach, U. S. Pat. 2,115,479 (1938).
[1586] P. B. Myers, U. S. Pat. 2,259,767 (1941).

PART FIVE
SOME FUNCTIONS AND APPLICATIONS OF
PECTIC SUBSTANCES AND PECTIC ENZYMES

CHAPTER XXVII

Pectic Substances in Foods

I. PECTIN IN FRUIT SPREADS: PRESERVES, JAMS, JELLIES, AND MARMALADES

1. Introduction

Although the earliest published records of jelly making appeared in the latter part of the eighteenth century, jams and fruit butters were made for a long time before that. Today, the manufacture of such products, which are usually covered by the blanket term "fruit spreads," is one of the most important branches of fruit processing industries, utilizing vast quantities of fruits, sugar, and pectin.

In the United States by 1800 many home kitchens and some small factories produced jams and similar products for sale.[1587] These pioneers were the forerunners of giant modern preserving plants engaged in the year-around manufacture of such commodities. In 1929 the total production amounted to about 137 million pounds, while by 1939 this volume reached 228 million pounds. In 1944 production approached one billion pounds, while in 1947 some 735 million pounds of such products were manufactured. Of this total, preserves and jams represented about 50%, jellies 29%, fruit butters 13%, and citrus marmalade 8%.[1588] Rapid transportation, modern machinery and methods, and especially the large-scale freezing of perishable fruits have been instrumental in the evolution of a great industry.

In spite of their importance, the manufacture of these products is still more an art than a science, although great strides have been made in recent years toward better understanding of the principles involved. These industries depend on the formation of pectin–sugar–acid jellies, often mentioned on previous pages. In some cases these products can be manufactured without added pectin because the fruit which is used contains sufficient pectin. However, the bulk of fruit spreads are produced, at least

[1587] A. J. Mullen, *Domestic Commerce,* 35 (5), 59 (1947).
[1588] Anonymous, *Food Field Reptr.,* 15 (11), 6 (1947).

in countries in which the technology of fruit products is highly developed, with added pectin of some sort. In all these products (with the possible exception of fruit butters) the consistency depends on the complete or partial jellification of the mixture of fruit and sugar; success in attaining this depends on an equitable balance in the batch of pectin, sugars, and acid. In fruit butters the pectin which is naturally present acts as a thickener without any extent of "setting"; thus, this product does not possess a structure as do jams, marmalades, and especially jellies.

The utilization of pectins as jellying aids in all sorts of fruit spreads provides the most important outlet for manufactured pectins and the pectin industry. To do justice to preserve making would occupy a volume in itself, especially since the variations in methods and products are endless. This subject is discussed in many publications and books but, to the author's knowledge, the only volume in the English language dealing exclusively with preserve making is Rauch's recent *Jam Manufacture*.[1588a] This book deals with most important technical aspects of jam and marmalade production, predominantly from the standpoint of the British manufacturer.

In the present volume we shall deal with the manufacture of these products only from the standpoint of pectin. Since every raw material and plant presents new problems, the discussion will be rather general in nature although efforts will be made to supply the reader with principles and sources of more specific information. Reference should be made here to the many allusions to this subject on previous pages, especially to the discussion of jellies in Chapter VII (Sect. XV-1) to the methods of making test jellies (Chapter XXIII, Sect. IV-2), and to the discussion of some government regulations concerning preserves in Chapter XXIII (Sect. IV and V), respectively.

A variety of different types of pectins are available for making fruit spreads (see Chapter XXIII). Some manufacturers prefer liquid pectin (pectin concentrates), while others use nothing but powdered (dry) pectins. Some prefer apple pectin, while others use citrus pectin. From the standpoint of making products suitable for the United States market, all high-grade pectins are useful, assuming that they are free from flavor, true to grade, and show a setting time suitable for the product in question.

As a rule, rapid-set pectins are used in the manufacture of jams, preserves, and marmalades, in which the fruit particles may float to the top unless setting starts soon after filling the jar. With the use of quick-set pectin the batch can be filled at customary temperatures above 190°F. (87.8°C.). On the other hand, the use of slow-set pectins enables the jelly manufacturer to add the acid to the batch without danger of inducing

[1588a] G. H. Rauch, *Jam Manufacture*. Leonard Hill, London, 1950.

partial setting, which interferes with the filling operation. Such jellies usually do not set within the time required for filling, closing, washing, and labeling the container; thus proper jelly formation is possible. Once a jelly begins to form and the slight initial set is broken, a soft jelly of poor texture results. The regulation of setting time during pectin manufacture is discussed in Chapter XXII.

The use of pectin in such products is what our food laws call "self-limiting." Too little pectin does not give the consistency required for the product, while too much pectin (if efficiently used) results in products which are thicker or firmer than required. Pectin grade was discussed in considerable detail in Chapter XXIII and it is obvious to the reader that there is a close relationship between the amount of sugar in such products and the proportion (and grade) of pectin which must be applied.

For many years the acid used in jams, preserves, and jellies was defined on the basis of its proportion (percentage). It is now clear that it is not the amount of acid but the effective hydrogen ion concentration which counts. This is universally expressed in terms of pH. Exact pH control is most essential for the successful manufacture of these products because texture, firmness, consistency, and the degree of syneresis ("bleeding" or "weeping") are markedly affected by even small deviations from the required pH values.[1589] The optimum pH value for most standard preserves and jellies is in the range of 2.6–3.4. Too much acid causes excessive syneresis, while too little acid (resulting in pH values which are too high) impairs proper jellification or prevents setting altogether. Glass-electrode electrometric pH meters are now universally used in plant control.

Citric, tartaric, phosphoric, lactic, and malic acids are used in the making of preserves, but citric and lactic acids are considered most satisfactory from the standpoint of flavor. Many other acids such as formic acid and even hydrochloric acid have also been suggested[1590] for preserve making, especially in days of scarcities.

Allusion was made previously to the great variations which may be found in the fruit spread industry relative to the time of addition of acid to various products. It may be stated categorically that in preserves and jams the acid is added at the end of the cooking period, while in jellies the acid is either added immediately before the jelly is poured or the acid is added to the containers into which the jelly is poured. However, many exceptions exist.

Some fruits and fruit juices contain natural buffer salts in such amounts that they prevent the desired pH values from being obtained when the

[1589] C. L. Hinton, *J. Soc. Chem. Ind.*, **66**, 381 (1947).
[1590] H. Eckart, *Deut. Lebensm. Rundschau*, **43**, 103 (1947); through *Z. Lebensm. Untersuch. u. Forsch.*, **89**, 395 (1949).

usual amounts of standard acid solutions are used. Conversely, some fruits and fruit juices are high in natural acids, which may cause the product to "set" even though no acid is added. To prevent this latter reaction, buffer salts are now commonly used with such fruits. Federal regulations in this country allow the use of 3 ounces of sodium citrate or sodium potassium tartrate for each 100 pounds of sugar ingredients used in preserves or jellies. The use of buffer salts to delay the setting of jellies was noted in Chapter XXII.

In addition to sucrose, other sugars, such as various corn starch hydrolyzates and pure glucose, are used regularly in this country in most preserves. However, regulations permit replacement of only 25% of the sucrose by other sugars. The situation concerning government regulations on this point is fairly fluid and further changes can be expected in the near future.

A further matter related to the use of sucrose is inversion. Some extent of inversion (hydrolysis of the sucrose into glucose and fructose) is necessary to prevent crystallization, especially at the surface of preserves which have been opened. An invert sugar content of 20–50% is now regarded as desirable for both preserves and jellies; a higher content may cause the dextrose to crystallize. Hydrolysis increases the sugar content by forming 105 lbs. of invert sugar from 100 lbs. of sucrose.

Pectin manufacturers in this country have highly developed technical services to aid their customers. In addition to giving advice, the major producers of pectin publish splendid handbooks in which explicit instructions and recipes are given for the use of their products, together with much related information. These handbooks also contain discussions of the fundamental facts involved in preserve making and there is little doubt that, as the preserving industry expanded, these handbooks played an important part in the technical education of preservers. Some of the information discussed in this volume has been taken from such handbooks.[1591–1593] The National Preservers Association in the United States, the British Food Manufacturing Industries Research Association in England, and similar organizations in some other countries are making important contributions along lines of technical aid and legal assistance to the preserving industries. Anyone contemplating the manufacture of any preserves should familiarize himself with the various regulations in force. Some of these have been noted in this volume as they concerned the dis-

[1591] "Preservers Handbook." California Fruit Growers Exchange, Products Department. Ontario, California, 1941.
[1592] "A Handbook on the Uses of Nutr-Jel Powdered Apple Pectin," Speas Co., Kansas City, Missouri (about 1946).
[1593] "White House Preservers Manual," National Fruit Products Co., Winchester, Virginia, 1949.

cussion of pectin manufacture and utilization. The above-mentioned handbooks and organizations also give advice on such matters.

2. Definitions of Various Types of Fruit Spreads

The terminology of various fruit spreads in different countries is far from uniform. In order to make clear the terms as applied in this volume, the definitions as used in the United States are given below:

A. *Jams and preserves.* Technically, jams and preserves are identical, except that products containing the whole fruit are generally designated as preserves, whereas those which contain crushed or macerated fruit are called jams. According to the official definition, preserve, fruit preserve, jam, and fruit jam are understood to mean the product made by cooking or concentrating to a suitable consistency properly prepared, clean, sound, entire edible portions of fresh fruit, cold-pack fruit, canned fruit, or a mixture of two or all of these, with sugar or with sugar and water, with or without spice or vinegar, or with such harmless organic acids as may be necessary to compensate for natural acid deficiency of the particular fruit used, but excluding acids or acid salts generally recognized as chemical preservatives, and in the preparation of which fruit product there is used not less than 45 pounds of actual fruit to each 55 pounds of sugar. In the case of fruit deficient in pectin, or whose composition or texture prevents the preparation of preserve or jam (as defined here) or the desired consistency, small quantities of pectin may be used; provided, however, that if pectin or pectinous material is added, the ratio of not less than 45 pounds of fruit to each 55 pounds of sugar is maintained, and the finished product containing such added pectin contains not less than 68% water-soluble solids derived from the fruit and sugar used in its manufacture, as determined by a refractometer at 20°C. without correction for the insoluble solids present. However, only 65% soluble solids content is required in a few products like apricot, peach, and plum jam (preserve) and in some similar products made from more than one fruit.

B. The definition of *jellies* is much more obvious. These are clean, sound, gelatinous fruit products possessing the definite characteristic flavor of the fruit or fruits named on the label, made by concentrating to a suitable consistency the strained juice, or water extract, from fresh fruit, cold-packed fruit, canned fruit, or from mixtures of these, with sugar. Here again pectin and acid may be added, provided that such jellies to which pectin or pectinous materials or acidulants are added shall contain not less than 65% soluble solids as determined under A and that their composition shall correspond to a ratio of not less than 45 pounds of standard fruit juice, exclusive of added water, to each 55 pounds of sugar in the original batch.

C. *Apple butter and other fruit butters* are products made from the edible portions of apples or screened other fruits with either sugar or fruit juice and which have a homogeneous semisolid consistency. The consistency depends mostly

on the presence of pectin but apples and most other fruits used for fruit butters
contain enough pectin to make the addition of manufactured pectin unnecessary.
Fruit butters contain not less than 43% soluble solids as determined by the refractometer at 20°C.

D. *Corn sirup preserve, corn sirup jam, corn sirup jelly, and corn sirup apple
butter* are similar to those products described above except that in their manufacture corn sirup has been entirely substituted for sugar.

E. *Honey preserve, honey jam, honey jelly, and honey apple butter* are again
like the products described above except that here honey has been entirely substituted for the sugar.

F. *Marmalade* is a jelly-like product made from properly prepared fruit peel
and juice, with sugar (or sucrose and dextrose), with or without pulp, by cooking with water. In the United States the term is confined to preparations made
from oranges and grapefruit. It contains small pieces of the peel embedded in
the jellied mass. The former are usually in the form of long shreds although more
fanciful forms like fish or stars are also used at times.

Of all these products, jellies and jams or preserves are of major interest
in this volume, because manufactured pectin is used in these products; it
must be emphasized again, however, that the texture of all the above
products depends on the presence and behavior of pectin.

3. Preserve (Jam) Making

This section should, perhaps, begin with some of the general arguments
for the use of pectins in jam making. Preservers in some countries such as
the United States are fully aware of the benefits derived from the use of
pectin; this, however, is certainly not the case in many other countries.

A statement was made above that various fruits used in the manufacture of jellied products are deficient in pectins. There are several ways
of making jam from such fruit. If no pectin is used, more fruit than is
required by law must be applied, or the product must be cooked down
excessively, or it will not have the proper consistency. The disadvantages
of all three cases are obvious, especially in countries in which competition
is keen and quality requirements high. However, by the use of pectin the
required proportion of fruit can be maintained and there is no need for
excessive cooking, which in most cases adversely affects the flavor and
color of the product. In other words, as noted on previous pages, by the
use of pectin the manufacturer is enabled to produce a standardized product of desirable consistency in a more economical manner.

Cherries, apricots, pears, blueberries, nectarines, peaches, raspberries,
strawberries, and pineapples are low in (useful) pectin and therefore, in
making preserves from these fruits alone, it is advantageous to use added
pectin. This is also often the case with blackberries, grapes, loganberries,
plums (except Damson), and many other fruits. A few fruits like apples,

cranberries, currants, Damson plums, guavas, gooseberries, quinces, and a few others are rich enough in pectin to enable the manufacturer to use only a small proportion of pectin which assures uniformity, or they may even be made into preserves without added pectin.

Aside from the comparatively small proportion of locally grown fruit, the bulk of fruit used by preservers is either canned or frozen (cold pack). Standards now exist for these raw products to assure high-quality raw material for the preserving industry. Fruits that are often used from cans include pears, figs, apricots, and plums. Other fruits like strawberries, cherries, currants, blackberries, cranberries, and others are preserved almost exclusively by freezing, in this country at least, and to an increasing extent in other countries. Most fruits are frozen with added sugar or sugar sirup, a matter which must be taken into consideration in compounding the preserve. One of the difficulties with frozen fruit in 30-pound tins or barrels is the difficulty encountered in defrosting, which involves exact timing and anticipation of production volume.

There is no standard procedure for preserve making.[1594-1602] Almost every factory has its own process and develops a peculiar type and quality of jams and preserves. In addition to different government regulations, the requirements of the trade also vary from country to country. The use of coloring matter is one major difference: in some countries food dyes are almost universally used, while in a few "purist" countries, such as the United States, dyes in such fruit products are used only to a negligible extent.

As an example of preserve making, a procedure given by a manufacturer of citrus pectin[1591] for making blackberry, strawberry, pineapple, or raspberry preserve (jam) follows:

Water (about 2.5 gal.) or	20 lbs.
Fruit	100 lbs.
Sugar	100 lbs.
100 grade Exchange Citrus Pectin, rapid set	6–8 oz.
Standard fruit acid solution (containing 1 lb. citric acid dissolved in 1 pint water)	12 fl. oz.

[1594] T. N. Morris, *Principles of Fruit Preservation.* Van Nostrand, New York, 1933.

[1595] H. W. von Loesecke, *Outlines of Food Technology.* Reinhold, New York, 1942.

[1596] A. M. Neubert and J. L. St. John, in M. B. Jacobs, *The Chemistry and Technology of Food and Food Products.* Interscience, New York, 1944.

[1597] W. V. Cruess, *Commercial Fruit and Vegetable Products.* 2nd ed., McGraw-Hill, New York, 1938.

[1598] C. H. Campbell, *Campbell's Book.* Revised ed., Vance, New York, 1937.

[1599] S. C. Prescott and B. E. Proctor, *Food Technology.* McGraw-Hill, New York, 1937.

[1600] G. Rauch, *Food Manuf.,* 19, 253 (1944).

[1601] E. E. Meschter, *Food Inds.,* 21, 747 (1949).

[1602] W. A. Rooker, *Fruit Pectin.* Avi, New York, 1928.

The water is heated in a steam-jacketed kettle. The pectin, mixed in a dry pan with about eight times its weight of sugar (taken from the 100 lbs.) is stirred into the hot water (160–180°F., 71–82°C.) in the kettle and, with occasional stirring, the solution is allowed to come to a brisk boil to dissolve the pectin. After about 0.5 minute of boiling, the fruit and sugar are added and the batch is boiled vigorously until desired finishing temperature, 223°F. (106.1°C.) at sea level or 11°F. (6.1°C.) above the boiling point of water at the given place and time, is reached. Now the batch is allowed to stand for a few moments and the acid solution is then added; the contents of the kettle are quickly mixed and immediately drawn off and filled into containers. If the containers are capped at above 190°F. (87.8°C.) there is no necessity of sterilizing them. If the preserve is not filled while sufficiently hot, it is necessary to sterilize the capped container.

The matter of finishing temperature requires some further discussion. The old fashioned jam maker used the "sheeting test," a crude but worthy index of the concentrations of pectin, sugar, and acid in the mixture. The mixing paddle was removed from the batch and the jam mixture was allowed to drip from the paddle. If it ran off in a sheet instead of a stream, it was an indication that jelly formation would take place upon cooling. This test is still used to a small extent, but is now considered to be antiquated and inadequate.

In a modern factory the finishing temperature is determined either by the boiling point of the mixture or by the percentage of soluble solids estimated by measuring the index of refraction. Density or specific gravity measurements with hydrometers have also been used for this purpose, but major inaccuracies are easily introduced in this method because any thickening or fruit particles interfere with the reading.

Accurate thermometers give fairly correct end points, especially when the composition of the batch is known. The boiling point varies, for the same mixture, with elevation and atmospheric pressure and it is therefore desirable to express and determine the finishing temperature in degrees above the boiling point of water. Preservers' handbooks usually contain extensive tabular material to show the relationship between soluble solids contents and boiling point of the mixture. Long-stemmed thermometers are usually used because the steam from the evaporation does not interfere in reading and the eye can be level with the elevation of the mercury. The introduction of automatic temperature control units offers further improvements, since they minimize human error and shut off the steam supply when a predetermined temperature is reached.

The refractive index is the most accurate means of measurement of the concentration of dissolved solids and of the end point in cooking preserves. The Abbe refractometer is chiefly used although hand refractometers of the type shown in Figure 36 have also been applied for this, purpose.[1603] Temperature control is important in order to obtain accurate results and, although temperature correction tables are available, it is best to take the reading at 68°F. (20°C.) or as close as possible. Some refractometers read directly in soluble solids (sucrose), while others show the refractive index and the corresponding sucrose concentration must be read from tables.[1604,1605]

To show the economic importance of exact finishing point control, Meschter[1601] gives the following example: In cooking a batch of grape jelly with 65% soluble solids content and 300 lbs. finished weight, the operator uses a hand thermometer to finish the cooking at 220°F. (104.4°C.). If he allows the temperature to rise to 220.4°F. (104.6°C.), the soluble solids content will be 66% and the yield only 295.4 lbs., a loss of 1.54%. This 0.4°F. (0.22°C.) "override" would cost the manufacturer (1949) about 46 cents per batch—a sizeable sum in large-scale production. This aim for exactness is a far cry from the "safety margin" of 1.5% soluble solids recommended by Rauch.[1600]

Vacuum cooking of jams and preserves reduces the harmful effect of high temperatures on flavor and color. However, with vacuum cooking, little inversion of sucrose occurs because of the lower cooking temperature. In such cases either invert sugar is added to the batch, or it is precooked in open kettles (inverters) prior to finishing in vacuum pans. Jellies are seldom cooked under vacuum.

When a batch of preserve or jelly foams excessively, it is either drained through a valve at the bottom of the kettle or a small quantity of corn or cottonseed oil or cocoa butter is added. The proportion of oil used is about one teaspoonful per 100 lbs. of sugar in the batch.

In this country, vacuum caps of all sorts are now predominantly used for jar closure. In many factories the product enters a long, slowly moving conveyor where the jars are sprayed with a fine mist of cold water from nozzles under the ceiling of the unit. Such equipment may also be used for pasteurizing the preserve by using steam jets or hot water above 190°F. (87.8°C.) along the first part of the conveyor to heat the caps and the head space in the jar. Cooling is then performed in subsequent sections of the conveyor. It is desirable to cool the preserves to below 100°F. (37.8°C.) to retard the loss of flavor and color.[1601] This is especially true of strawberry preserves.[1606]

[1603] J. A. Pearce and S. Jegard, *Can. J. Research,* **F27,** 99 (1949).

[1604] C. A. Browne and F. W. Zerban, *Handbook of Sugar Analysis.* 3rd ed., Wiley, New York, 1941.

[1605] *Official and Tentative Methods of Analysis.* 6th ed., Association of Official Agricultural Chemists, Washington, D. C., 1945.

[1606] Z. I. Kertesz and E. Sondheimer, *Food Inds.,* **20,** 1300 (1948).

Needless to say, great variation exists in the systems of production as well as in the equipment used in preserve factories. Continuous processes have also been suggested for preserve and jelly manufacture.[1607,1608]

There is a very voluminous literature on preserve making. Gallagher[1609] recently studied the causes and control of syneresis. Hinton presented a discussion of the role of pH in jams[1589] and a simplified method for pH control.[1610] Only reference can be made here to some additional discussions dealing with this topic.[1611-1615]

Evaluation of Consistency of Preserves and Jams

A preserve or jam is a partially jellied product and, as such, should flow to a limited extent when turned out on a flat surface. In Chapter XXIII the measurement of jelly firmness was extensively discussed, as well as the many methods which have been suggested for the objective evaluation of this important property. Methods of evaluating the consistency of jams and preserves will be dealt with briefly in this section.

The need for objective measurement of jam and preserve consistency is now generally recognized. The Bostwick[1616] and the Adams[1617,1618] Consistometers have been both applied for this purpose with some success.

The Bostwick Consistometer is extensively used with tomato products. It consists of a metal trough, one end of which is blocked off by a gate. A given weight of sample is put into this end of the trough and then the gate is lifted with a sudden motion. The jam now flows in the trough and the extent of flow in a given time can be read on a scale etched on the bottom of the trough. The Adams Consistometer was originally developed for the measurement of the consistency of canned cream-style corn. Here the sample is placed in an inverted stainless steel cone which is held at the center of a series of concentric circles engraved on a metal disc. Upon sudden mechanical lifting of the tightly fitting cone, the product flows on the plate and its spreading is read in 30 seconds from the distances from the center marked on the circles and is averaged.

[1607] G. T. Reich, Food Inds., 11, 190 (1939); U. S. Pat. 2,185,064 (1941); Food Technol., 3, 383 (1949).
[1608] G. L. Baker and W. D. Pheteplace, Food Inds., 12, 54 (1940).
[1609] C. Gallagher, Confectioners' J., 75, 38 (March, 1949); through Food Technol., 3, June, appendix p. 15 (1949).
[1610] C. L. Hinton, Biochem. J., 34, 1211 (1940).
[1611] C. L. Hinton, Fruit Pectins, Their Chemical Behavior and Jellying Properties. Chem. Publishing Co., New York, 1941.
[1612] R. S. Potter, Food Manuf., 10, 232 (1935).
[1613] G. L. Baker, Food Manuf., 9, 427, 633 (1936).
[1614] G. L. Baker, Food Inds., 7, 170 (1935).
[1615] T. N. Morris, Canner, 71 (15), 23 (1930).
[1616] Manufactured by Redman Division, Central Scientific Co., San Francisco, California.
[1617] E. L. Birdsall, Food, 15, 286 (1946).
[1618] Manufactured by National Manufacturing Co., Lincoln, Nebraska.

At the present time efforts are being made by the Technical Committee of the National Preservers Association[1619] to collect information on the possible inclusion in grade standards of some objective method of consistency measurement.

This Committee recommends the use[1620] of the Spreadmeter, which merely consists of a series of concentric circles engraved on a Plexiglas plate. This may be placed over a light source to facilitate reading.

The sample of preserve to be tested is carefully emptied from a one-pound jar into the center of the circles and allowed to flow on the plate. At times emptying of the jar can be facilitated by inserting a bent glass tube to the bottom of the jar and blowing the jam out. After 5 minutes the readings are taken in the manner described above and averaged. The circles are drawn 2 cm. apart and the consistency is expressed in terms of flow by this scale. The desirable consistency, as defined by Spreadmeter readings, differs from product to product. For example, pineapple and peach preserves have an optimum consistency at readings between 16 and 18, whereas raspberry preserve is more satisfactory at a reading of 20.

The consistency should be measured at a standardized temperature, 77°F. (25°C.), and not until several days after packing. In some preserves continuous consistency changes are in progress for many weeks and months. There also seem to be products with which this method does not give satisfactory results.

Some of these methods are already used in factory control, but much more information will have to be collected before any method is likely to be made a part of government standards. The obvious advantage of the method described by the above-mentioned Committee is that no expensive specialized equipment is needed and that standard one-pound jars, either from regular commercial production or jars filled at the time of packing, are used. This avoids the need of transfering the sample to a special container which then operates on a sample whose structure has already been disturbed.

4. Jelly Making

Although a jelly appears to be a simpler system than preserves and jams, the technical requirements in jelly making are perhaps even more exacting.[1594-1602,1621-1623] While in jams and preserves the manufacturer has a certain leeway in consistency, a jelly must be firm but not hard, and

[1619] Technical Committee of National Preservers Association (1948). Mr. E. E. Meschter, National Preserves Co., Philadelphia, Pa.. is chairman of this committee.
[1620] Anonymous, *Food Packer,* 30 (12), 30 (1949); *Glass Packer,* 28, 432 (1949).
[1621] A. E. Williams, *Food Trade Rev.,* 18 (8), 4 (1948).
[1622] P. A. Zook. *Canner.* 72 (21), 32 (1931).
[1623] L. Wallerstein, J. Pfanmuller, and A. R. Noe, U. S. Pats. 1,997,615 and 1,997,616 (1935).

must withstand shipping and handling but be neither leathery nor sirupy. Jellies were discussed in Chapter VII and more extensively in Chapter XXIII, in which various requirements, methods of preparation, and systems of firmness evaluation were mentioned. The definition of jellies according to the United States Standards was given earlier in this chapter.

The jellies manufactured in this country fall into two groups: pure fruit and imitation jellies.

The fruit juice used in pure fruit jellies is extracted from fresh, frozen, or canned fruit, with or without water. In most cases the trade requires that the fruit juice and the jelly made from it should be brilliantly clear. Various methods of clarification have been used for such juices, including pectinases.[1624]   In the latter case, of course, the pectin in the fruit juice is hydrolyzed and thus more pectin must be applied in making the jelly.

The amount of pectin needed varies according to the useful pectin content of the juice. It ranges from zero in the case of cranberries and not too ripe crabapples, currants, grapes, quinces, etc., to 5–15 ounces of 100 grade pectin per batch of 100 lbs. of sugar and 82 lbs. of juice for most berry juices; it is somewhat higher for a few juices like pineapple juice. Of course, in imitation jellies the pectin requirement can be stated exactly in terms of the sugar present since the grade of pectin is defined by the proportion of sugar it can turn into a jelly.

An example of a formula given by a manufacturer of apple pectin[1592] for making a pure fruit jelly may now be cited. We will assume that, since the fruit juice was not heavily sugared, it can be used to dissolve the pectin. No water is used in such cases.

Fruit juice	82 lbs.
Sugar	100 lbs.
100 grade apple pectin (Nutr-Jel)	up to 16 oz.
Citric acid solution (4 lbs. citric acid dissolved in 1 gal.)	8–16 fl. oz. (to taste)

The pectin is mixed in a dry container with about five times its weight of sugar (from the 100 lbs.). The juice is placed in the steam-jacketed kettle and the mixture of pectin and sugar is stirred into the juice while the latter is being brought to a boil. The solution is boiled for about 0.5 minute, after which the sugar is added and the mixture is boiled to a minimum soluble solids content of 65% solids or to a finishing temperature of approximately 9°F. (5.0°C.) above the boiling point of water. The acid solution is added just before the jelly is poured (not when cooking is completed) or directly to the containers prior to pouring.

As will be seen from this formula as well as from the previous discussion, the pectin is used here to supplement the jellying power of the natural pectin; for this reason it is of some importance to know the jelly

[1624] J. J. Willaman, Food Inds., 5, 294 (1933).

grade of the pectin in the juice. This may be determined by the viscosity method (Chapter XXIII) or, much more exactly, by means of test jellies. The test batches need not be large. The proportions of pectin recommended by pectin manufacturers are often somewhat more than are required since the manufacturer must be sure that the batch will set under all reasonable circumstances. Here again good judgment must be exercised by the jelly maker since the use of too much pectin may be almost (but not quite) as detrimental as not having enough. Otherwise, much of what has been said in connection with jam and preserve manufacture also applies here.

In order to increase the amount of dissolved pectin polyphosphates may be used in the extraction of juices from various fruits for jelly making. Insufficient information is on hand at this time to be able to judge the practical usefulness and legal permissibility of this method.[1625-1627]

Imitation jellies are made by procedures identical or similar to those described in Chapter XXIII, Section IV-2, except that the required flavoring and coloring materials are added at the end of the cooking period.

The texture measurements of commercial jellies will not be discussed here again since this subject was amply covered in the evaluation of pectin grading methods by means of test jellies (Chapter XXIII). As should be obvious from that discussion, many of the methods are not suitable for use in an incidental jar or thimble used by the manufacturer for packing the jelly, but some, such as the B. A. R. method, can and have been used for this purpose. Some manufacturers pour a sample of the batch into containers suitable for the selected method of jelly strength measurement at the time the product is made.

In jellies, even more than in jams, the firmness required depends to a great extent on the size of the container. This is especially true of so-called *baker's jelly*, which is usually made from corn sirup, pectin, acid, and coloring and flavoring materials, and which is used mostly in jelly doughnuts, jelly rolls, and as filling for cakes. This product is usually packed in 30-lb. pails or even in 50-gallon half-barrels, the latter holding about 600 lbs. of jelly. Such jellies must be unusually firm to withstand transportation. This may be accomplished either by raising the soluble solids content or the pectin content, or both. A higher solids content in such products is desirable since this also reduces the tendency of the jelly to soak into the cake to which it is applied.

It is interesting to note that the steam condensate from the blanching of apple slices for freezing extracts sufficient pectin from the apples to make such collected condensates of use in jelly making.[1628] However,

[1625] G. L. Baker and C. W. Woodmansee, *Fruit Products J.*, **23**, 164 (1944).
[1626] G. L. Baker and G. M. Gilligan, *J. Home Econ.*, **38**, 348 (1946).
[1627] W. D. Maclay and J. P. Nielsen, U. S. Pat. 2,375,376 (1945).
[1628] L. L. Davis, *Proc. Am. Soc. Hort. Sci.*, **53**, 193 (1950).

according to present regulations, such products could not be labeled as "jellies."

5. Marmalade Making

Variations in the making of marmalades[1588a,1595,1629] are even greater than in jams and jellies. After washing and removal of the stem "buttons," the citrus fruit is cut into halves and the juice is extracted and strained, or at times filtered, to give a brilliant juice. The peel is now sliced or shredded to give long, thin pieces; it is then cooked in water to soften and to remove bitterness; the cooking water is discarded. The softened pieces are mixed with the juice and then pectin and sugar are added in the usual manner. The batch is cooked to a finishing temperature of 8–9°F. (4.5–5.0°C.) above the boiling point of water. The acid is added just before pouring.

There are endless modifications of this process. Morris[1594] recommends using sodium carbonate or ammonium hydroxide or an autoclave for cooking the peel. Scott and Heid[1630] described a method for making grapefruit marmalade. Pectin is often extracted from the peel for later use in setting the marmalade. For details of marmalade manufacture, reference is made again to the various preservers' handbooks and manuals supplied by pectin manufacturers, and to the literature.[1588a,1591–1599,1631]

6. On the Use of Low-Ester Pectins in Gellied Fruit Products

The reasoning behind the development of low-ester pectins (Chap. XXIV) was that they would make possible the production of fruit jams, jellies, and similar products with less than 50% sugar content.[1632,1633] Although this has now been accomplished, it seems that their use for such purposes may be of less importance than in salads and desserts of low solids contents. The fact that they can be used with fruit juices at relatively high hydrogen ion concentrations also gives them a distinct advantage over many other gelling agents in this particular field.[1634] The fruit juice in ordinary canned or frozen fruits for salads can be gelled with the proper amount of low-ester pectin to form very attractive salads or desserts. More than 20 million units of such products were packed in cans[1635] for the use of the United States Armed Forces for individual servings and

[1629] T. W. Black, *Canner*, 72 (21), 32 (1931).
[1630] W. C. Scott and J. L. Heid, *Texas Citriculture*, 10, 18 (1934).
[1631] E. M. Chace and H. W. von Loesecke, *U. S. Dept. Agr.*, Circ. 577 (1940).
[1632] N. M. Mnookin, U. S. Pat. 2,207,299 (1940).
[1633] A. G. Olsen and E. R. Fehlberg, U. S. Pat. 2,334,281 (1941).
[1634] G. L. Baker, in *Advances in Food Research*. Vol. I, Academic Press, New York, 1948, p. 395.
[1635] *Nutritional Observatory* (H. J. Heinz Co., Pittsburgh, Pa.), 7 (2), 31 (1946).

were well received in many parts of the world where fruits and salads were rare sights.

There are now many formulas in the literature for the preparation of various fruit products of this type with low-ester pectins. Baker and Goodwin,[1636] for example, describe a gellied peach juice product. However, as noted in Chapter XXIV, any such recipes are applicable only with the specific sample or type of low-ester pectin for which it was developed. For this reason only one example taken from a trade pamphlet[1637] will be given here. This describes the preparation of a tomato or vegetable juice gel as follows:

To 2.25 cups of the juice 2 tablespoons of lemon juice is added and then a 1-oz. Pectin L.M. package (which contains 7 g. of Exchange Pectin L.M. No. 466, 21.5 g. of sucrose, and 0.5 g. of monocalcium phosphate) is mixed in with continuous stirring. The mixture is brought to a boil, removed from the fire, poured into serving dishes, and chilled. About one hour in the refrigerator is desirable for satisfactory gelatin. In preparing a 100-lb. commercial batch of the same product, 24.25 lbs. of Exchange Pectin L.M. No. 466, 74 lbs. of sucrose, and 1.75 lbs. of monocalcium phosphate are used. However, in making large batches, laboratory trials starting with the proportions given in the small batch should always precede calculations for the large batches, because changes in the amounts of low-ester pectin and calcium salt may be desirable in order to give characteristics suitable for the particular product.

7. Various Other Products and Processes

(a) Solid Jams

Solid jams are concentrated products[1638] which are sufficiently solid to be cut into blocks. They have been used in Europe for generations as a confection. Many other names such as paste, fruit pulp cream, and fruit center, etc., are used for similar products. The concentration of pectin in these products is much higher than in ordinary jams and marmalades and the total solids content is also at least 10% higher (70–80%). Such products can often be prepared without a pectin base, but the presence of pectin improves the texture and storage life greatly.

To prepare a solid jam from plums,[1639] 150 parts of plum pulp and 40 parts of a 5 grade liquid pectin extract or an equivalent quantity of another grade pectin are mixed with 100 parts of sugar. This mixture is boiled down rapidly to a solids content of 70 or 75%, as determined by a refractometer. After cooling, this jam is sufficiently solid to withstand much handling and has little, if any,

[1636] G. L. Baker and M. W. Goodwin, *Delaware Agr. Expt. Sta.*, Bull. 246 (1944).

[1637] Anonymous, "Pectin L.M.," California Fruit Growers Exchange, Products Department, Ontario, California, 1947.

[1638] Anonymous, *Food Trade Rev.*, 13 (8), 8 (1943); *Food Manuf.*, 18, 388 (1943).

[1639] F. E. Huelin, *Food Trade Rev.*, 15 (4), 11 (1945).

tendency to "weeping" upon standing. Although solid jams spread with difficulty they can as a rule be remade into jams of normal consistency by boiling with 1 part of water and 2 parts of sugar. To prepare solid raspberry jams of comparable strength, 200 parts of raspberry pulp and 50 parts of 5 grade liquid pectin extract are boiled with 100 parts of sugar. In the case of citrus pulp or other materials containing a high proportion of pectin, the addition of pectin may not be necessary. In the range of 70–75% total solids the best results are obtained at pH values between 3.2–3.4. Solid jams keep well under ordinary conditions and apparently retain their ascorbic acid content better than do ordinary jams and marmalades. However, when stored at temperatures above 86°F. (30°C.) they deteriorate rapidly.

(b) Miscellaneous Products

An obvious application of dry, powdered pectins is in the preparation of mixtures of pectin, sugar, and an organic acid, which when mixed with water, fruit, or a fruit juice forms a jam or a jelly. Endless kinds of such preparations are possible and many have been described. Leo[1640] in 1927 noted a dry powdered jelly base containing these three ingredients in widely varying proportions, while similar preparations containing low-ester pectins have been described by Baker and Goodwin,[1641] Olsen and Fehlberg,[1633] Pollari, Murray, and Baker,[1642] and others.

During World War II there was considerable interest in such products containing dehydrated fruit juices in addition to the pectin, sugar, and acid. This type of product was the subject of the Nelken patent[1643] issued in Germany during the war. Such products have never attained any wide popularity in this country. Woodmansee, Baker, Pollari, and Murray[1644] have studied the dispersibility of high- and low-ester pectins in such mixtures and have also described some basic formulas for such preparations.

Cox[1645] suggested the freezing of mixtures of fruit, pectin, and acid for eventual jam making. Sugar only was to be added to such mixtures. Flach[1646] described a jellying product made from fruit pulp or juice with added pectin, but without boiling. A cold-process fruit spread was also described by Johnson and Boggs.[1647] Brekke and Talburt[1648] studied the formation of sucrose hydrate in such products containing about 0.5% added pectin. A "nonrigid" spreadable jelly made with sodium

[1640] H. T. Leo, U. S. Pat. 1,646,157 (1927).
[1641] G. L. Baker and M. W. Goodwin, U. S. Pat. 2,233,574 (1941).
[1642] V. E. Pollari, W. G. Murray, and G. L. Baker, Fruit Products J., 25, 6 (1945).
[1643] H. R. Nelken, German Pat. 749,862 (1944).
[1644] C. W. Woodmansee, G. L. Baker, V. E. Pollari, and W. G. Murray, Food Inds., 18, 356 (1946).
[1645] R. E. Cox, Fruit Products J., 24, 169 (1945).
[1646] J. Flach, German Pat. 712,364 (1941); through C. A., 37, 4494 (1943).
[1647] G. Johnson and M. M. Boggs, Food Inds., 19, 1491 (1947); U. S. Pat. 2,459,431 (1949).
[1648] J. E. Brekke and W. F. Talburt, Food Technol., 4, 383 (1950).

phosphate and phosphoric acid was invented by Thompson.[1649] A product like tomato aspic but apparently made with a low-ester pectin has also been developed and sold in cans.[1650]

II. PECTIC SUBSTANCES IN FRUIT JUICES

Fruit juices are the unfermented liquid which separates from sound, ripe fruit on pressing. The fruit juice industry in Europe has a long history,[1651] but in the United States Welsh is credited with starting (in 1869) the large-scale manufacture of grape juice.[1596] The grape juice produced by Welsh and others was the only important unfermented juice manufactured until about 1925. From then on, the fruit and vegetable juice industry showed spectacular growth until the present annual commercial pack in this country is more than 100,000,000 cases. The bulk of this consists of citrus juices and tomato juice, while apple juice and berry juices have been developed to a much lesser degree.

Fruit juice technology has a very extensive literature and, therefore, only reference is made here to the excellent handbook of Tressler, Joslyn, and Marsh[1652] on fruit and vegetable juices and to several recent reviews on this topic.[1596,1653-1655]

The pectic substances play an important part in fruit juice technology. All fruit juices contain pectic substances at the time of pressing and their presence may be either beneficial or detrimental. There are many reports in the literature concerning the amount of pectin in various fruit juices, but the variation even in juice derived from the same fruit is so great that little purpose would be served by giving numerical values. Furthermore, here again not only the absolute quantity of the pectic substance, but also the quantity and colloidal properties ("extent of colloidality") govern the advantages or disadvantages derived from its presence. The pectic substances play a dominant part in the stabilization of the colloidal systems in fruit juices.[1656] Some juices are expected to be cloudy, and in such cases efforts are made to retain this stabilizing action of pectin. In other cases, the cloudiness and the high viscosity which are often found in fruit juices because of the pectic constituents are undesirable and efforts are therefore made to eliminate the pectins from the juice.

[1649] D. R. Thompson, U. S. Pat. 2,421,093 (1947).
[1650] Anonymous, *The New York Times,* July 22, 1948.
[1651] A. Mehlitz, *Süssmost.* 2nd ed., Serger und Hempel, Braunschweig, 1936.
[1652] D. K. Tressler, M. A. Joslyn, and G. L. Marsh, *Fruit and Vegetable Juices.* Avi, New York, 1939.
[1653] R. E. Marshall, *Michigan Agr. Expt. Sta.,* Circ. Bull. 206 (1947).
[1654] F. E. Atkinson and C. C. Strachan, *Can. Dept. Agr.,* Tech. Bull. 68 (1949).
[1655] V. L. S. Charley, Editor, *Recent Advances in Fruit Juice Production.* Commonwealth Bureau of Hort. and Plantation Crops, London, 1950.
[1656] J. J. Willaman and Z. I. Kertesz, *New York State Agr. Expt. Sta.,* Tech. Bull. 178 (1931).

Of the category in which cloudiness is desirable, tomato juice (see Sect. V) and citrus juices may be mentioned as examples. In both cases the juices are expected to contain suspended solid and semisolid particles in addition to colloidal constituents.[1657] At times difficulties have been observed due to the cloudiness of citrus juices because the solid particles settle out, when the juices are kept with chemical preservatives or when they are pasteurized at too low temperatures, giving an unsightly appearance to the juice or mixed drinks like "squashes" made from the juice. The "breaking of the cloud" in most cases is believed to be the result of enzyme action, particularly that of pectin methylesterase (see Chapter XIV), which has considerable activity in citrus fruit. The enzyme deesterifies the pectinic acids in the juice, thus enhancing their precipitability by naturally present polyvalent ions. This "breaking of the cloud" has led to extensive investigations in the fruit juice industry[1658] and to several patents on overcoming this difficulty. For instance, Stevens[1659] suggested a method of testing any sample of citrus juice for the presence of active enzymes which may lead to the "breaking of the cloud", and described[1660] the extent of heating which such juices require at different pH values.

Loeffler,[1661] in a study of the "cloud index" of various citrus juices, found that heating by flash pasteurization not only stabilizes but actually increases the turbidity of the juice. Bravermann[1657] believes that this increased turbidity is the result of the solubilization of additional pectin from the insoluble form in which some of it exists in the suspended particles. For a further discussion of this topic the reader must be referred to the previously mentioned literature.

In apple juice, as well as in many other fruit juices, the pectic substances play a somewhat different role; the pectic constituents again stabilize the colloidal systems which are responsible for cloudiness. In this country processors are about equally divided in their preference for a cloudy or a clear apple juice, although a few manufacturers even aim to turn out a product which contains, in addition to the juice, a great deal of course cellular debris in suspension. These are usually designated as "pulpy" juices or, to borrow a phrase from the advertisements, as "liquid apple." In this latter case stabilization of the colloidal system is very important and is accomplished, as a rule, by rapid pasteurization of the juice.

[1657] J. B. S. Braverman, *Citrus Products*. Interscience, New York, 1949.
[1658] J. W. Stevens, D. E. Pritchett, and W. E. Baier, *Food Technol.*, **4**, 469 (1950).
[1659] J. W. Stevens, U. S. Pat. 2,267,051 (1941).
[1660] J. W. Stevens, U. S. Pat. 2,217,261 (1941).
[1661] H. J. Loeffler, *Proc. Inst. Food Technol.*, 1941, 29.

When clear apple juice is desired, a number of different methods may be employed.[1653] In most of the nonenzymic processes it is difficult to clarify the juice to the extent of its becoming brilliantly clear because of the efficient stabilizing action of pectin. Even when clarified, the juice retains much of its original high viscosity, thus reducing the efficiency of filtration, which is always necessary. This led to the development of fruit juice clarification by the use of pectic enzymes. These enzymes were discussed in Chapter XV; their use will be described in Chapter XXIX. Suffice it to say here that the hydrolysis of the pectinic acids in the juice "breaks" the colloidal system and the juice clears. The hydrolysis of the pectinic acids also eliminates the high viscosity due to these compounds and juice now filters easily.

The extent of clarification desired may differ and, as will be shown later, in most cases the enzyme action is not allowed to proceed until all pectic constituents are completely hydrolyzed. As a result of the disturbance of the colloidal system by the enzyme action, as well as by subsequent heating, some precipitate often forms during later storage of such juices. Mottern, Neubert, and Eddy[1662] and Marshall[1663] found that the addition of 0.04% pectin (5 oz./100 gal.) to the finished juice prevents such sedimentation.

In several foreign countries, such as England, Germany, and Switzerland, germ-proofing filtration[1664] is extensively used on a commercial scale. In this process the pectic substances must be removed from the fruit juices because their presence stabilizes the colloidal system and thus makes clarification and filtration difficult. Juices which contain pectin "poison the filter."[1665] The filtration of viscous juices in the cold is also very slow and this factor may make the process commercially unprofitable. As a result, systems of production and storage, such as those developed by Böhi,[1666-1668] invariably employ clarifying enzymes.[1669]

When fruit juices rich in pectin are concentrated, they become viscous and difficult to handle. For this reason, the pectic constituents are often removed from fruit juice concentrates of all sorts, mostly by the use of pectinases. The high viscosity is naturally most bothersome in the

[1662] H. H. Mottern, A. M. Neubert, and C. W. Eddy, *Fruit Products J.*, **20**, 36 (1940).

[1663] R. E. Marshall, *Food Packer*, **27** (8), 4 (1946).

[1664] For a description of the Seitz germproofing process, see A. Mehlitz, *Süssmost*, 2nd ed., Serger und Hempel, Braunschweig, 1936.

[1665] G. Weitnauer, *Schweiz. Brau. Rundschau*, **58** (3), 41 (1947).

[1666] V. L. S. Charley and H. J. Harrison, "Fruit Juices and Related Products," Imperial Bureau of Horticulture and Plantation Crops, East Malling, Kent, England, 1939.

[1667] J. K. Kefford, *Refrigeration J.* (*Australia*), **2**, 2 (1948).

[1668] R. Heiss, *Lebensmitteltechnologie*. J. F. Bergmann, Munich, 1950.

[1669] Z. I. Kertesz, *Food Inds.*, **18**, 496 (1946).

case of freeze-concentration and such processes usually depend on previous removal of the pectin from the juice.[1669]

The presence of pectin in lemon juice hinders the crystallization of citric acid[1670] and the deposition of tartrates from wines.[1671] Pectic enzymes have been used in both cases to overcome these difficulties.

Ripa[1672] notes a peculiar effect of pectins in carbonated fruit juices. When such juices are kept in an open container, only very small bubbles form in the presence of pectin.

The pectic substances in fruit juices play an important part in aiding their drying[1673] (see Section VI) and in the manufacture of fruit juice powders.

As will be shown in Chapter XXIX, pectin is often removed from grapes during pressing for wine making and from wines by the use of pectinase preparations.

III. PECTIC SUBSTANCES IN BREWING AND IN BEER

The fate and role of pectic substances in brewing are rather confused. Barley, like most other cereals (Chapter XIII), contains a small proportion of pectic substances, predominantly in a water-insoluble form. In malting the proportion is reduced by about 75%.[1674] Furthermore, as Bourquelot and Hérissey[1675] and others have shown, malt contains pectolytic enzymes of considerable activity and thus any pectin which may be dissolved from malt is likely to be hydrolyzed by the malt pectin-polygalacturonic (Chapter XIV) present in the solution.

Hops contain a small quantity of pectic materials which are dissolved during boiling of the wort; meanwhile the pectolytic enzymes derived from the malt are inactivated. Thus, the boiled wort contains the hop pectin which is then partly precipitated and partly carried over to the fermentation tanks. It was noted previously that most yeasts do not attack pectic polyuronides easily and thus the latter may pass on into the finished beer.

There are many reports in the literature on pectic materials in brewing. Enders, Saji, and Schneebauer[1676] studied the furfuraldehyde-yielding substances in barley and thought that the quantity of such materials

[1670] G. Ajon, *Riv. ital. essence profumi,* **9,** 254 (1927); quoted in Ripa, *Die Pektinstoffe,* 1937.

[1671] A. Baouman, *Génie civil,* **123,** 173 (1946); through *C. A.,* **40,** 7509 (1946).

[1672] R. Ripa, *Die Pektinstoffe.* 2nd ed., Serger und Hempel, Braunschweig, 1937.

[1673] C. P. Wilson, U. S. Pat. 1,975,998 (1930).

[1674] D. R. Nanji and A. G. Norman, *Biochem. J.,* **22,** 599 (1928).

[1675] E. Bourquelot and H. Hérissey, *Compt. rend.,* **127,** 191 (1898).

[1676] C. Enders, T. Saji, and F. Schneebauer, *Wochschr. Brau.,* **55,** 121 (1938); through *C. A.,* **32,** 8067 (1938).

is a varietal characteristic. Preece[1677] states that malting produces a large increase in "furfurogenic" substances but that only 12–20% of these appear in the wort. These furfurogenic substances should include pectic polyuronides. However, there are also some reports that malt does not contain pectic substances.[1678–1680] This confusion may be explained by two facts: (1) that the determination of pectic substances in cereals is very difficult; and (2) that, unless specific precautions are taken, the pectolytic enzymes of the malt itself may destroy the pectic substances which are dissolved.

Whatever the situation with regard to the pectic substances derived from malt, it is probable that their quantity in the mash is either negligible or nonexistent.

The information which may be found in the literature on hop pectins is rather contradictory. Sterckx[1681] states that hop pectins are soluble in water and Fink and Just[1682] found that 50–60% of the hop pectin passes into the wort. With a lower hop rate, more is dissolved. The latter authors also isolated a sample of hop pectin which showed a very low proportion of methyl ester groups indicating only 15% esterification or a methoxyl content (on a uronide basis) of 2.5%. Thus, hop pectin is either a low-ester pectin or a mixture of pectinic and pectic acids. This point may be of importance in accounting for the behavior of the pectic substance dissolved in wort.

There are two major reactions which have been ascribed to the pectin in wort. It seems that it combines with some proteins and is precipitated during boiling.[1683] Salchinkin and Movshovich[1684] found that pectin coagulated albumin after 5 minutes of heating at 158°F. (60°C.). The acidic properties of the low-ester pectin or pectic acid may be of importance in this respect. The second reaction is the precipitation of heavy metals[1685] by the formation of metal derivatives, or more exactly of acid metal pectinates or pectates. This removal of heavy metals is claimed to be of much importance in preventing their poisoning effect on yeast during fermentation. However, there are no studies which would make clear just what the precipitates are and it is therefore difficult to reach any conclu-

[1677] I. A. Preece, J. Inst. Brewing, 46, 38 (1940).

[1678] H. Fink, Wochschr. Brau., 54, 281 (1937).

[1679] H. Fink and J. Hartmann, Wochschr. Brau., 52, 221 (1935).

[1680] H. Fink and E. Just, Wochschr. Brau., 53, 225 (1936).

[1681] R. Sterckx, Bières et Boissons, 1944, p. 5; through J. Inst. Brewing, 52, 92 (1946).

[1682] H. Fink and E. Just, Wochschr. Brau., 53, 33 (1936).

[1683] T. Chrzaszcz and J. Janicki, Chem. Ind., 1936, 884.

[1684] A. P. Salchinkin and F. L. Movshovich, Colloid J. (U. S. S. R.), 6, 15 (1940); through C. A., 35, 2911 (1941).

[1685] E. Schild, C. Enders, and A. Spigl, Wochschr. Brau., 53, 273 (1936); through C. A., 31, 5099 (1937).

sion as to whether the low-ester pectins remove the metals (as they well might) or they are adsorbed on some precipitated proteins. The fact remains that most of the pectin is precipitated with the "copper sediment," although some can be found in the cast wort.[1682]

Most investigators have found that pectin in small quantities is present in the finished beer. Fink and Just[1686] give an approximate average for German beers of 7.5 milligram per cent. Some random analyses made in the author's laboratory indicate the absence of any pectic substances in some American beer and ale. Methods of handling, chill-proofing, clarification, filtration, etc., may well be responsible for this variation.

In order to determine the effect of pectic substances on beer quality, Fink and Just[1687] brewed beer with hop extracts in which the pectic constituents were or were not digested. With the pectin present, flavor and head retention were superior although chill-proof qualities were inferior. No differences in stability during pasteurization and storage could be found. These authors also made some beers with added apple, beet, and hop pectin[1686] and found that the main effect of such additions was the development of haze during storage. In an attempt to clarify the effects of the presence of pectin and other constituents in beer, Kharin and Maltsev[1688] made a study of beer colloids but failed to reach any definite conclusions. De Clerck[1689] used added beet extract in brewing beer and found that it was desirable to digest the pectic constituents in the extracts with a pectinase in order to eliminate some undesirable effects, especially enzyme adsorption and clarification difficulties.

Thus, it may be concluded with some certainty that the pectic substances, mostly derived from hops, may be beneficial during beer making but there is serious doubt (1) whether pectic substances are present in all beers and ales and (2) whether, if present, they have any significant desirable effect on quality. A systematic reexamination of this matter, using recently developed analytical methods, would be desirable.

IV. PECTIC SUBSTANCES IN STORAGE, PICKLING, AND COOKING OF PLANT FOODS

In Chapters X–XIII the pectic substances in economically important plant foods were dealt with extensively and the changes which occur in pectic constituents during storage were illustrated. In an oversimplified manner it may be stated that pectic transformations often seem to be

[1686] H. Fink and E. Just, *Wochschr. Brau.*, **54**, 281 (1937).

[1687] H. Fink and E. Just, *Wochschr. Brau.*, **55**, 17 (1938).

[1688] S. E. Kharin and P. M. Maltsev, *Colloid J.* (*U. S. S. R.*), **3**, 75 (1937); through *C. A.*, **32**, 2409 (1938).

[1689] J. de Clerck, *Bières et Boissons*, **1941**, 497; through *C. A.*, **37**, 1829 (1943).

responsible to a large extent for the softening of fruits and other plant materials, during ripening and storage, although other, still little understood, reactions are also important. The major change in stored fruit is the loss of water-insoluble protopectin and pectates leading to an increase in soluble pectic constituents and to decreased cohesion between cells and layers of cells in the tissue.

The chemical changes which occur during pickling are manifold and are very little understood.[1595,1597] It seems that one of the important phases of pickling various plant tissues, especially cucumbers, is a crispness and firmness which is possible only through the retention of essentially intact cellular structure. This is the case if the cementing pectic substances remain well preserved, and difficulties are often encountered in this respect.

As an example, the cellular deterioration which causes the "mushy" texture of dill pickles appears to be the result of the partial degradation of insoluble pectic constituents caused by the presence of bacteria which produce pectic enzymes. The softening is caused by the dissolution of the pectic materials in the middle lamella between the cells in the tissue. Fabian and Johnson[1690] studied the chemical and bacteriological changes associated with the spoilage of pickles. The changes which occur in the pectic constituents during spoilage can be demonstrated both by microscopic observations and chemical analyses. Treatment of pickles with an enzyme extract from *Bacillus mesentericus fuscus* produced typical softening, but the proportion of the total pectic substances in the tissue did not change (13.0 and 12.9%, respectively, on a dry matter basis). On the other hand, the proportion of soluble pectic constituents increased from 0.53 to 1.06% (on the same basis). Fabian and Johnson state that the interaction of the many factors which lead to softening of pickles is not clear at this time, but that the transformation of insoluble pectic constituents (protopectin) into soluble ones is beyond doubt the ultimate cause of the softening. Treatment with acid after cooking may bring about similar changes. Fabian and Wenzel[1691] believe that the commercial garlic used in pickling harbors molds and bacteria which produce enzymes capable of breaking down the pectic constituents of pickles.

In the cooking of plant foods many changes occur. Considering mainly the texture or firmness of plant foods, heat treatment introduces at least two distinct types of changes.[1692] The wilting of the tissue, apparent immediately after even such restricted treatment as blanching, is the result

[1690] F. W. Fabian and E. A. Johnson, *Michigan State Agr. Expt. Sta.*, Tech. Bull. 157 (1938).
[1691] F. W. Fabian and F. W. Wenzel, *Canner*, 100 (19), 15 (1945).
[1692] T. Weier and R. Stocking, in *Advances in Food Research*. Vol. II, Academic Press, New York, 1949, p. 298.

of loss of rigidity because of reduced "turgor pressure." Heating also disturbs equilibrium within the tissue, changes the water relationship between the cells and their surroundings, and causes a generally disorganizing effect on the structure. The result is a degree of limpness typical of such tissues. Chemical changes which occur during such treatment must be regarded more as the result of disorganization than as occurring because of the effect of heat as such on the various constituents of the tissue. In this process heat may also destroy the spatial separation[1693] of enzymes and substrates within the tissue, without inactivating the enzymes concerned. Such "thermal maceration" at times results in rapid enzyme action.[1694,1695] Fortunately, as far as is now known, pectolytic enzymes are not common in the higher plants which supply most of our food (see Chapter XIV) and therefore such partial destruction or disturbance does not, as a rule, result in the loss of pectic constituents or in extensive transformations of the structurally important water-insoluble pectic constituents into soluble ones. However, it seems that such disorganization may also be caused by freezing of the tissue. When citrus fruits are frozen, for example, the deesterifying enzyme present in the skin gains access to the pectic constituents in the same tissue, resulting in what appears at times as extensive and certainly practically important deesterification.

To return to cooking, the second type of change introduced by heat is through its direct effect on various plant constituents. Proteins may be coagulated and practically all tissue components which are polymers, such as proteins, hemicelluloses, starch, pectic substances, etc., are slowly degraded during continued application of heat. The effect of heat on soluble pectic substances was dealt with in Chapter VII and it was noted in Chapter VI that heat alone changes water-insoluble pectic constituents of plants(protopectin, etc.) into soluble ones. However, it is only fair to state that, when this occurs in any plant tissue, a great many other reactions also occur which influence the progress of texture change. As an example, the dextrinization of starch and the resulting changes in swelling properties may be noted.

In the case of many plant tissues, of which carrots may be cited as an example, the "blanching" type of brief heating does not sufficiently alter the firmness. Such tissues must be cooked in order to make them edible. The main effect of the cooking process is once again reduction of the adhesion among cells and cell layers, which is accomplished by destruction of the intercellular, cementing pectic constituents. This change in the pectic components of the middle lamella is a comparatively slow process and

[1693] Z. I. Kertesz, *Plant Physiol.*, **12**, 845 (1937).
[1694] N. B. Guerrant and R. A. Dutcher, *Arch. Biochem.*, **18**, 353 (1948).
[1695] W. B. Robinson, J. C. Moyer, and Z. I. Kertesz, *Plant Physiol.*, **24**, 317 (1949).

must be accomplished by cooking for periods much longer than are required for blanching. In carrots, Simpson and Halliday[1696] found a gradual increase during cooking in the soluble pectic constituents; similar changes are known to occur in many other cases.

One reason why the role of pectic constituents in such processes as pickling and cooking is not sufficiently clear at the present time is the lack of simple and dependable means of evaluating degradation processes by means other than or in addition to quantitative determinations. It has been stated many times on previous pages that pectic substances may give the same values in a determination by the calcium pectate method, for example, but show a wide range of colloidal properties. In the case of soluble pectinic acids this degradation can be easily demonstrated by viscosity changes and changes in the jelly- or gel-forming ability. The situation is vastly more complicated in the case of the ill-defined water-insoluble pectic constituents of plants for which exact information concerning their structure, or indeed, even concerning their composition is still lacking. Thus, it seems that little further progress in the exact evaluation of the role and behavior during cooking of the cementing water-insoluble constituents of plant tissues can be expected until better methods are available for evaluation of the changes which may occur in the insoluble pectic fraction, whether these are rendered soluble in the same process or not.

The interesting matter of "hard-seededness" in leguminous vegetables and the ensuing difficulties in cooking were discussed previously in Chapter XIII.

V. PECTIC SUBSTANCES IN TOMATO PRODUCTS

The pectic constituents of maturing and stored tomatoes were discussed in Chapter XIII. The role of pectic constituents in some tomato products will be dealt with briefly here.

Apparently there is no generally applicable relationship between the proportion of total pectic constituents in canned whole tomatoes and their firmness or "wholeness." These latter properties are usually determined by placing the canned product on a 0.5-inch mesh screen of specified construction for 2 minutes and then determining the proportion of tomato tissue ("drained weight") which remains on the screen. Appleman and Conrad[1697] studied the proportion of insoluble and soluble pectic constituents in fresh and canned tomatoes and observed a pronounced degree of solubilization during canning. The change was further accentuated if the cans were not cooled immediately after processing. While such a rela-

[1696] J. I. Simpson and E. G. Halliday, *Food Research*, **6**, 189 (1941).
[1697] C. O. Appleman and C. M. Conrad, *Maryland Agr. Expt. Sta.*, Bull. 291 (1927).

tionship between the two pectic fractions before and after canning was consistently observed in various lots of tomatoes, the initial relationship of the two fractions and the extent of change during processing varied to such an extent as to make the setting of general numerical limits for this reaction useless.

The calcium firming of canned tomatoes and the role of the pectic constituents in this reaction are considered in Section VII, below.

In contrast to canned tomatoes in which it is important to retain as much of the natural structure and firmness as possible, in many other tomato products, such as tomato juice, puree, catsup, and paste, the tissue is thoroughly macerated during manufacture, resulting in consistency problems of an entirely different nature. Rooker,[1698] Wildman,[1699] and Smith[1700] have called attention to the generally recognized importance of pectic substances in these products.

In the case of tomato juice there are a number of separate considerations. This product consists of particles of colloidal tissue suspended in a dilute solution, the "serum," the latter containing some 3–8% total solids, mostly sugars. Ostwald capillary-type viscometers are generally used for determining the viscosity of the serum, while the Stormer viscometer has been used more than any other instrument for determining the viscosity of the whole juice.

The enzymes which, according to our present ideas, influence the consistency of all such types of products during manufacture were discussed previously in Chapter XIV. Briefly, it seems that the changes leading to the loss of pectic substances in processed tomato products occur as the result of the cooperative action of the tomato enzymes pectin-methylesterase and depolymerase.[1701] Apparently, the action of the former alone does not lead to appreciable loss of pectinic acids. However, upon deesterification by pectin-methylesterase, the depolymerase attacks the low-ester pectinic acids or pectic acid, resulting in rapid depolymerization and loss of useful viscous properties. Heating to 180°F. (82.2°C.) for a few seconds prevents these detrimental changes.[1702] A tomato juice produced above this temperature is usually designated as a "hot-break" juice, in contrast with the insufficiently heated "cold-break" juice which has a watery serum.[1703]

The consistency of tomato juice depends on two major factors: (1) the quantity, average size, and size distribution of the suspended particles;

[1698] W. A. Rooker, *Canner,* 71 (11), 11 (1930); 71 (12), 13 (1930).

[1699] J. D. Wildman, *Canner,* 72 (1), 11 (1930).

[1700] H. R. Smith, *Canning Trade,* 54 (1), 14 (1931).

[1701] R. J. McColloch and Z. I. Kertesz, *Food Technol.,* 3, 94 (1949).

[1702] Z. I. Kertesz, *Food Research,* 4, 113 (1939).

[1703] Z. I. Kertesz and J. D. Loconti, *New York State Agr. Expt. Sta.,* Tech. Bull. 272 (1944).

and (2) the viscosity of the serum. Pectic constituents make their contribution to the colloidality of the suspended particles, but it is believed that in tomato juice their role is a minor one. The cellulosic tissue constituents seem to be of much more importance. The average size and size distribution of the suspended particles determine in part whether, upon standing, the juice shows any separation of serum on top. Particles of the suspended tissue increase in their "water-holding capacity" as their size is reduced from a size of 20 mesh to about 100 mesh (in the hydrated condition); it seems, however, that under this size they again lose some of their water-binding ability when the comparisons are made on the basis of equal dry weights of solids of different sizes. The proportion of suspended particles in tomato juice is such that the extent of "water-holding capacity" which can be attained through this means is under optimum conditions at about the borderline of "filling up" the corresponding volume of serum.

It is therefore important that these particles be suspended in a viscous liquid which enables them to take up a larger volume than they would in water or in the serum of a "cold-break" tomato juice. This is the major function of pectic substances into tomato juice since the high viscosity of "hot-break" serum is entirely or mainly caused by the pectinic acids dissolved therein. At times viscous serum also makes a contribution to the flavor of the juice[1703] through a factor designated by Crocker[1704] as "mouth-feel" but this is of less importance than the prevention of serum separation.

In turning to more concentrated tomato products, the situation relative to the role of pectic substances is again different. In tomato puree, which according to government definition must contain at least 8.37% but not more than 25.00% salt-free tomato solids, the proportion of suspended particles is such that separation of clear serum at the top is uncommon when the puree is kept in a container. However, the colloidal properties of the suspended particles are of importance in preventing separation of the serum when the product is poured on, say, macaroni. As far as the consistency of the product is concerned however, the serum viscosity plays a role in consistency which is quite different from that in the case of tomato juice. Here the proportion of suspended particles is such that any increase in the viscosity of the liquid solution in which they are suspended makes a great difference in the final consistency or "body" of the product. The Stormer viscometer has been extensively used for measuring the consistency of tomato puree. To quote an example, a low-viscosity puree gave a Stormer reading of 38 seconds with 100 g. of driving weight, at 86°F. (30°C.). Upon digestion of the serum with a commercial pectinase, this value dropped to 29 seconds. On the other hand, a puree made

[1704] E. C. Crocker, *Flavor*. McGraw-Hill, New York, 1945.

from a hot-break juice gave a reading of more than 100 seconds under the same conditions and this dropped to 25 seconds upon digestion of the serum. In other words, the commercially significant difference in consistency was caused by the pectic constituents dissolved in the serum of the more viscous product. Both purees contained 11.6% tomato solids and no other ingredients.

As the tomato product becomes more concentrated, the contribution of the pectic substances dissolved in the serum becomes increasingly important.[1705] This is now generally recognized with catsup and tomato paste, in which precautions are usually taken to obtain a maximum extent of retention of the pectic constituents originally present in the serum at the moment of maceration. At times this is accomplished by heating the tomatoes before they are chopped.

There are no uniform methods for consistency measurements in such products. The Bostwick Consistometer described in Section I, and the Stormer viscometer are both used to a certain extent. Underwood and Keller[1706] recently described a penetrometer based on the rate of sinking into the product of a plastic cone loaded with a given weight.

Naturally, the pectin content of such products increases in proportion to the extent to which the tomato juice is concentrated, for example, in making tomato paste, which must contain not less than 25% (salt-free) tomato solids. It is very important that the detrimental effect of prolonged heating on the pectic substances be avoided. This is usually accomplished by using either vacuum pans or more frequently, continuous multiple-phase evaporators for the concentration. The use of the latter also facilitates better retention of tomato color, an important consideration in determining the commercial value of such products.

Because of the benefits which can be derived from the presence of pectin in such macerated tomato products, Rooker[1698] suggested that pectin be added when necessary during the course of manufacture. The benefits derived from added pectin were also observed by Neusbaum.[1707] Cooper[1708] suggested the addition of beet pulp to such tomato products in order to obtain a thick consistency. He describes a "tomato catsup" composed of 40% tomato pulp, 40% sugar beet pulp, and 20% red beet pulp. Under existing regulations neither of these products made with added pectin or beet pulp could be designated as a tomato puree, catsup, or pulp.

[1705] R. J. McColloch, B. W. Nielsen, and E. A. Beavens, *Food Technol.*, **4**, 339 (1950).

[1706] J. C. Underwood and G. J. Keller, *Fruit Products J.*, **28**, 103 (1948).

[1707] C. W. Neusbaum, *Glass Packer*, **21**, 28 (1942).

[1708] C. R. Cooper, U. S. Pat. 2,331,308 (1939).

VI. PECTIC SUBSTANCES IN FREEZING, DEHYDRATION, AND REHYDRATION OF FOOD PRODUCTS

Because the pectic substances in plant foods play an important role in influencing texture, firmness, and consistency, they have been studied in connection with the freezing and dehydration of fruits and vegetables.

Pectin has been added to various frozen products with some success. The use of a mixture of sugar and a small amount of pectin reduces the "run off" or "bleeding" of the juice from frozen cherries. In the case of strawberries, in which this "run off" upon thawing is very important, the addition of pectin to the whole, and especially to the sliced, fruit seems to improve the product. Baker, Grab, Wegener, and Baer[1709] found low-ester pectins quite effective, although, according to Buck, Baker, and Mottern,[1710] the extent of esterification is of little importance. The pectin is usually added mixed into the sugar. The probable upper limit of pectin concentration is around 0.3%.[1711] Baker[1712] found the effect on peaches somewhat inconsistent but, when the conditions were changed to provide a better opportunity for gelation, the beneficial effect of added low-ester pectins was quite definite.

The good drying properties of sufficiently pure pectin are well known to all workers in the food field.[1713] This characteristic was the foundation of the Sardik patents[1714] which were discussed in Chapter XIX, Section VI. In addition to the drying of pectin, various pectic materials have also been used as drying aids. Reavell,[1715] for example, added pectin to soft fruits such as raspberries, before drying. Charley[1716] performed an interesting experiment to show the importance of pectic constituents in spray-drying plum puree. This material contains about 7% pectic substances and dries very well. However, when the pectic constituents were digested with a commercial pectinase, it was impossible to dry the puree. Cowgill[1717] suggested the addition of pectin to various food products, mostly fruit and vegetable purees, to improve their film-forming and drying properties. Jameson and Wilson[1718] described the addition of pectin

[1709] G. L. Baker, E. G. Grab, J. B. Wegener, and B. H. Baer, *Food Packer*, 24, 39 (1948).

[1710] R. E. Buck, G. L. Baker, and H. H. Mottern, *Food Inds.*, 16, 113 (1944).

[1711] Anonymous, *Western Canner and Packer*. 40 (8), 63 (1948).

[1712] G. L. Baker, *Food Inds.*, 13 (1), 55 (1941); 13 (3), 56 (1941).

[1713] E. Seltzer and J. T. Settelmeyer, in *Advances in Food Research*. Vol. II, Academic Press, New York, 1949, p. 399.

[1714] W. W. Cowgill, U. S. Pats. 1,973,613 (1934); 1,973,614 (1934); 2,032,687 (1936).

[1715] J. A. Reavell, British Pat. 364,163 (1930); through *C. A.*, 27, 2225 (1933).

[1716] V. L. S. Charley, *Chem. Ind.*, 1940, 823.

[1717] W. W. Cowgill, U. S. Pat. 2,140,788 (1938).

[1718] E. Jameson and C. P. Wilson, U. S. Pat. 1,977,945 (1934).

to fruit juices in order to aid in drying and to give a nonhygroscopic product. The use of 2–3% pectin is suggested. For similar purposes Wilson[1719] also recommended the addition of pectic acid and a soluble calcium salt. The good drying properties of calcium pectate are known to everybody who has made pectin determinations by precipitation and drying of this compound (see Chapter VIII).

Reeve[1720] studied the tissue composition of some vegetables and the changes which occur upon blanching and dehydration; he states that the good keeping quality of blanched dehydrated beets is due to their high pectin content. This led to an investigation of the use of pectin dipping in the dehydration of low-starch vegetables. In the case of the vegetables studied (parsnips, rutabagas, and sweet potatoes), the dipping method is not appreciably effective if the raw slices are dipped. Blanching denatures the cytoplasm and a greater amount of pectin solution is soaked up by blanched slices than by raw slices. Pectin dipping is very successful with dehydrated sliced carrots in which the coating also enhances the retention of carotene during subsequent storage.[1721]

It is well known that undesirable changes affecting the physical structure of dehydrated vegetables occur during their storage. For example, the amount of water which is taken up by such materials upon soaking or cooking materially decreases at times, resulting in an undesirable texture and a lower ratio of rehydration. Baker and Murray[1722] found that these changes are intimately associated with the colloidal properties of the pectin contained in the dehydrated tissue. These authors expressed the colloidal usefulness of the pectins in dehydrated products by their jelly grade as defined in Chapter XXIII and calculated from viscosity measurements and reached the conclusion that the grade of the pectin is definitely related to the quality of dehydrated fruits and vegetables Straight-line relationships were found in the case of apples and peaches and the authors suggest that this method may also be used for the grading of dehydrated carrots. The viscosities of the solutions from sweet potatoes, beets, raisins, currants, prunes, and pears were too low to give sufficiently exact results to demonstrate any relationship to eating quality.

VII. "CALCIUM TREATMENT"

Although it has been known for many years that, under certain conditions, treatment with calcium has a firming action on many plant tissues, it was not until 1937 that the systematic development of such methods

[1719] C. W. Wilson, U. S. Pat. 1,975,998 (1934).
[1720] R. M. Reeve, Food Research, 8, 146 (1943).
[1721] R. M. Reeve, Food Inds., 14, 51 (1942).
[1722] G. L. Baker and W. G. Murray, Food Research, 12, 129 (1947).

commenced.[1723] Calcium treatment is now widely used for firming many food products of plant origin[1724] and, since its effectiveness is believed to be associated with the presence of pectic constituents in the tissue, this subject will be discussed briefly here.

The use of calcium chloride for firming canned whole tomatoes was suggested by the author,[1725] and Kertesz, Tolman, Loconti, and Ruyle[1726] made a detailed investigation of the practical ways of using this method, which is now of considerable importance for the tomato canning industry. In order to satisfy the exacting color requirements for canned tomatoes, ripe fruits must be used. However, ripe fruit of sufficient firmness to prevent excessive disintegration is available only for comparatively short periods and much of the pack is either deficient in color, or in firmness, or "wholeness." Since the price differential between tomatoes which are whole and those which fall to pieces is considerable, it is beneficial to have a method which prevents the excessive softening which occurs during processing. The calcium treatment accomplishes this to a great extent, enabling the canner to pack a better product for a longer period of time.

The calcium treatment of tomatoes may be accomplished either by dipping the peeled tomatoes in a solution[1726] of calcium chloride or by adding some calcium salt to the can. The dipping method is now used only to an insignificant extent, if at all. Addition of the calcium salt to the can is simple. This may be done by dissolving some calcium chloride in the juice which is added to the can or, much more commonly, by the use of combination table salt–calcium salt tablets.[1727] Government regulations in this country[1728] and in others permit the use of calcium. Because of the hygroscopicity of such tablets made from table salt and calcium chloride, difficulties have been encountered in tablet-dispensing machines. The loss of tablets from opened packages in the humid air of canneries is also considerable. This led to the introduction of calcium sulfate,[1729–1730] which, when properly mixed with table salt, dissolves in the tomato juice in the can during processing and affords the same benefits. In addition to the sulfate, calcium citrate and phosphates are now

[1723] Z. I. Kertesz, *Canner*, **88** (7), 26 (1939).

[1724] Z. I. Kertesz, Proc. Natl. Canners Assoc. Tech. Session, N. C. A. Information Letter 1170, Jan. 28 (1948).

[1725] Z. I. Kertesz, *Canner*, **88** (24), 14 (1949).

[1726] Z. I. Kertesz, T. G. Tolman, J. D. Loconti, and E. H. Ruyle, *New York State Agr. Expt. Sta.*, Tech. Bull. 252 (1940).

[1727] Such combination tablets are manufactured by Scientific Tablet Co., St. Louis. Missouri, and by the major salt-producing companies.

[1728] *Federal Register*, **5**, 2282 (1940); **12**, 825, 3021 (1947).

[1729] C. H. Martin, U. S. Pat. 2,333,873 (1943).

[1730] M. Siegel, *Canning Age*, **24**, 92 (1943).

also permitted in canned tomatoes.[1728] The permissible quantity in this country is defined as 0.07% calcium chloride or an equivalent proportion of the other noted calcium salts, calculated on the basis of the weight of the finished canned tomatoes. Both the calcium chloride and the calcium sulfate combination tablets are now extensively used. Apparently, calcium which is applied in the field does not find its way into the fruit and does not cause a firming effect.[1731] In calcium-treated canned tomatoes a steady equalization of the **calcium in the tomato** fruit in the cans takes place until a fairly constant gradient is reached in about 30 days.[1732]

In economic importance, the calcium treatment of sliced apples is perhaps equal to that of canned whole tomatoes.[1733] The calcium may be applied in the soaking tank,[1734–1736] in the blanching water, or as a separate bath. As the result of studies of the benefits which may be derived from various calcium salts,[1737] calcium lactate is now considered to be superior to the cheaper chloride because of the absence of any effect on the flavor. Calcium treatment has been successfully used for both frozen and canned sliced apples, for fresh sliced apples prepared for the bakery trade,[1738] and for baked apples.[1736] There are apparently no governmental objections to the reasonable use of this method of counteracting the detrimental effects of heat and freezing on the firmness of apple tissue.[1739]

Calcium firming has been used for many other products. If raspberries are treated before canning, they hold their shape much better.[1724] Calcium treatment also prevents excessive sloughing off of canned potatoes and softening of sulfured fruit,[1740,1741] canned peaches, olives, etc., but the results are not always favorable with pears, strawberries,[1742] etc. For further details of calcium treatment only reference is made to a review of this subject[1724] and to the specific articles quoted above.

The role of pectic substances in the effectiveness of calcium treatment of tomatoes and apples—the two best known and most important examples of the application of this principle—will now be considered. In the early days of calcium treatment of canned tomatoes,[1725] it was assumed

---

[1731] C. B. Sayre, Z. I. Kertesz, and J. D. Loconti, *J. Am. Soc. Agr.*, **32**, 389 (1940).

[1732] Z. I. Kertesz and J. D. Loconti, *Canner*, **92** (10), 11 (1941).

[1733] Z. I. Kertesz, *Farm Research*, **13** (1), 6 (1947).

[1734] W. B. Esselen, Jr., W. J. Hart, and C. R. Fellers, *Quick Frozen Foods*, **9**, (5), 66 (1946).

[1735] C. H. Hills, C. S. Nevin, and M. E. Heller, *Fruit Products J.*, **26**, 356 (1947).

[1736] J. J. Powers and W. B. Esselen, Jr., *Fruit Products J.*, **25**, 200 (1946).

[1737] K. Holgate and Z. I. Kertesz, *Fruit Products J.*, **28**, 37 (1948).

[1738] Z. I. Kertesz, *Farm Research*, **16** (1), 3 (1950).

[1739] Natl. Canners Assoc., Information Letter 1194, July 24, 1948.

[1740] F. E. Atkinson and C. C. Strachan, *Fruit Products J.*, **21** (1), 5 (1941).

[1741] J. G. Woodroof and S. R. Cecil, *Georgia Agr. Expt., Sta.*, Bull. 238 (1945).

[1742] E. G. Grab, J. B. Wegener, and B. H. Baer, *Food Packer*, **24**, 39 (1948).

that enzymic action during peeling of the fruit was a necessary prerequisite to the effectiveness of the firming treatment. It was believed that tomatoes contain only high-ester pectinic acids which are not capable of forming gel-like structures (causing increased firmness) with calcium. The situation now seems to be vastly more complicated. First of all, it is known that comparatively low-ester fractions occur in the pectinic acids of ripe tomatoes (Chapter XIII), which may be assumed to be capable of forming insoluble compounds with calcium. Second, it is clear that the calcium reacts with and firms other tissue components than those which are on the outer portion of the peeled fruit. Third, it is now also known that nonpectic constituents of plant tissues also react at times to treatment with calcium, although the nature of these compounds can only be guessed at the present time. Fourth, the possibility cannot be excluded that enzyme action resulting in a certain extent of deesterification occurs during the transient period of heating when tissue organization has already been disturbed by "thermal maceration" but the enzymes present have not yet been inactivated.[1694,1695] That some reaction of this sort may be involved is indicated by the fact that canned tomatoes seem to react better to calcium firming than do raw tomatoes; unfortunately, no evidence on this point is available.

Loconti and Kertesz[1743] have presented three items of evidence that calcium firming of canned tomatoes is the result of the formation of calcium pectates or pectinates. Unfortunately, little was known at that time concerning the behavior of low-ester pectins with polyvalent ions, which led to the use of a somewhat confusing nomenclature. Using the current terminology, these results may be summarized as follows.

(1) Model experiments have proved that calcium pectate is digested by commercial pectinases only to a limited extent. Treatment of calcium-firmed tomato tissue yields a fraction of calcium pectate (or acid calcium pectinate) which must be formed because of the calcium treatment since no corresponding fraction is found in the untreated tomatoes.

(2) Dilute alkali does not dissolve calcium pectate unless a sufficient number of treatments is used to reduce the calcium content. When tomato tissue is treated to a limited extent with alkali, a fraction is left in the insoluble portion which, upon further treatment with acid and alkali, proves to be calcium pectate. The calcium in this alkali-insoluble fraction accounts for the bulk of the calcium taken up by the tomato tissue.

(3) Calcium-firmed tomatoes quickly lose their firmness upon immersion in a dilute solution of ammonium citrate. When these tomatoes are again treated with calcium chloride solution, they do not regain their firmness because the pectic constituents which were originally capable of combining with the calcium are removed by the ammonium citrate.

[1743] J. D. Loconti and Z. I. Kertesz, Food Research, 6, 499 (1941).

Reexamination of this entire question in the light of present knowledge of low-ester pectins would be most desirable. Nevertheless, it can be stated with reasonable certainty that the major reaction in the calcium firming of canned tomatoes occurs between the calcium and the pectic constituents.

The calcium treatment of apples is more complicated and even less is known concerning the nature of the reaction which takes place. The effectiveness of the treatment varies, depending on the variety and maturity of the apples. Calcium shows little effect on definitely overripe fruit. The amount of calcium which is taken up from a solution by apple slices and the amount of calcium which causes significant firming also varies almost from lot to lot. The relationship between the type of pectic constituents in the apple tissue and the effectiveness of the calcium treatment has not as yet been explored, nor have the compounds which are formed been isolated as in the case of canned tomatoes. Hills, Nevin, and Heller[1735] attempted to use a solution of pectin-methylesterase, prepared by the method given in Chapter XIV, to reduce the ester content of pectinic acids *in situ* in order to increase the reactivity to calcium. However, the slices treated in this manner did not respond sufficiently to calcium to warrant such a treatment on a commercial scale nor was it entirely clear whether the slight effectiveness was due to deesterification or to other reactions which may have taken place during the treatment of the tissue.

It would seem, therefore, that the situation concerning any exact knowledge of the reactions which take place upon the treatment of plant tissues with calcium is rather unsatisfactory. This is unfortunate because improvements in the methods of treatment could almost certainly be expected with better understanding of the reactions involved. However, there seems to be unusual agreement among the various investigators dealing with this topic that the pectic constituents in fruits and vegetables are responsible for the firming observed upon treatment with calcium.

It may be noted (although this point is of little practical importance) that other polyvalent ions, such as magnesium, strontium, and barium, have been shown to exert similar firming action to that observed with calcium.[1723]

VIII. PECTIC SUBSTANCES IN DAIRY PRODUCTS

The so-called "pectin phenomenon in milk" depends on the emulsion-breaking effect of pectin. Joseph reported[1744] that the addition of 0.2–0.3% pectin to fresh, pasteurized, skimmed, or homogenized milk coagulates it in 10–30 minutes. In addition to the use of rennet, acids, and heating, this provides a fourth method of coagulating the casein of milk.

[1744] G. H. Joseph, *J. Soc. Chem. Ind.,* **49,** 159 (1930).

The reaction does not occur with evaporated, condensed, and reconstituted dried milk. With goat milk coagulation is slow and incomplete. Coagulation occurs at pH values as high as 6.4–6.5 and is not prevented by heating the milk to 176–212°F. (80–100°C.) for 5 minutes. A coagulate prepared by the addition of 0.8% pectin contained 78% of the proteins, 16% of the lactose originally in the milk, and all the added pectin.

Ziegelmayer later made an extensive study[1745] of this reaction and found that it is reversible inasmuch as the precipitated casein can be easily dissolved in milk or water. This author discusses the usefulness of the precipitation method for various dairy products and states that the addition of such precipitated casein to some cheeses improves them in some respects. In addition, the digestibility of cheese made from pectin-precipitated casein is claimed to be better than that of cheese made by customary processes.

A special pectin product named Lattopekt, a mixture of dried skim milk and pectin, was put on the market for use in milk products.[1672] Many other reports have dealt with this reaction. Flora and Hadaway[1746] used apple pectin to reduce curd tension in milk. Wilson and Finley described a beverage powder[1747] containing pectin and "modified" milk. Hertl[1748] used Lattopekt to improve the quality of cheese and prevent it from drying out. Eldridge,[1749] Cultrera and Bellini,[1750] Kieferle and Sonnleitner,[1751] Plaween and Kersten,[1752] and Plaween, Kersten, Feix, and Scheinberger[1753] used pectin in making cheese, usually in combination with customary procedures. Ziegelmayer[1754] stated that, in process cheese, pectin causes increased swelling and greater water-holding capacity. Feix[1755] suggested the use of pectin in producing an artificial rind on cheese.

Griebel and Zeglin developed a specific method[1756] for showing the presence of pectin in the curd. It is believed that pectin is now used in cheese making to a very limited extent, if at all.

[1745] W. Ziegelmayer, *Kolloid-Z.*, **70**, 211 (1935).
[1746] C. C. Flora and C. W. Hadaway, *J. Dairy Sci.*, **24**, 534 (1941).
[1747] C. P. Wilson and J. A. Finley, U. S. Pat. 1,940,036 (1933).
[1748] L. Hertl, *Mlekarske Listy*, **27**, 210 (1935); through *C. A.*, **30**, 7232 (1936).
[1749] E. E. Eldridge, U. S. Pat. 1,693,025 (1928).
[1750] I. R. Cultrera and B. Bellini, *Ann. chim. applicata*, **28**, 389 (1938); through *C. A.*, **33**, 2601 (1939).
[1751] F. Kieferle and F. Sonnleitner, *Deut. Molkerei-Z.*, **55**, 2 (1934).
[1752] A. V. Plaween and G. Kersten, U. S. Pat. 1,953,734 (1934).
[1753] A. V. Plaween, G. Kersten, R. Feix, and E. Scheinberger, U. S. Pat. 1,953,734 (1934).
[1754] W. Ziegelmayer, *Deut. Molkerei-Z.*, **55**, 902 (1934); through C. A., **28**, 5144 (1934).
[1755] R. Feix, German Pat. 626,383 (1936); through *C. A.*, **30**, 3538 (1936).
[1756] C. Griebel and H. Zeglin, *Z. Untersuch. Lebensm.*, **74**, 16 (1937).

Pectin has also been used in ice creams as a stabilizer. It does not seem as if pectin would offer outstanding benefits over the gums which are customarily used and recently developed products like carboxymethyl-cellulose. In the past it has been applied to a considerable extent only when the regular supply of stabilizers was cut off, as during World War II. Of the reports dealing with this subject those by Milford,[1757] Benley and Watts,[1758] Cole,[1759] and Antonov[1760] will be noted here.

IX. PECTIC SUBSTANCES IN CONFECTIONS

Pectin has been used extensively in the manufacture of confections.[1761] The original gumdrop, made from gum arabic and a minimum amount of sugar, was necessarily chewy, gummy, and tough. The need for a confection more closely akin to a jelly than a gum, and which would be more tender, sweeter, and brighter in color, resulted in the starch gums which dominated the market until pectins of consistent quality became available for the manufacture of such products. In addition to having better consistency, such products made with pectin are more suitable for large-scale production by streamlined methods. Special pectin preparations for the confectionery trade are marketed by some manufacturers. As a rule, the proportion of pectin used in confections is considerably higher than in fruit jellies, inasmuch as a much stiffer consistency is required. The soluble solids contents of such products ranges from 75 to 85% and considerable latitude is allowed to the manufacturer in producing a variety of textures, depending on the amount of pectin used and on the final solids contents. There is, of course, a similarity between such products and the "solid jams" noted in Section I-7 (a) of this chapter. Confections using pectin are made both with fruit ingredients and with artificial color and flavor; they are also used coated in various ways and in combination with starch gums. There is an almost endless variety of such products.[1602]

Cruess, Frian, Janz, Lawrence, Miller, and Cytron[1762] described several formulas for the manufacture of fruit jelly candies, one of which is quoted here as an example. The formula used is as follows:

[1757] C. G. S. Milford, U. S. Pat. 2,070,455 (1937).
[1758] L. S. Benley and B. Watts, *Food Research,* 4, 101 (1939).
[1759] W. C. Cole, *Food Inds.,* 13, 57 (1941).
[1760] P. Antonov, *Myasnaya i Molochnaya Prom., 1946* (4), 47; through *C. A.,* 41, 5645 (1947).
[1761] W. V. Cruess, *Fruit Products J.,* 25, 166 (1946).
[1762] W. V. Cruess, R. Frian, R. Janz, D. Lawrence, G. Miller, and B. Cytron, *Fruit Products J.,* 29, 46 (1949).

Ingredient	Parts by weight
Fruit juice (apple, orange, pineapple, prune, or grape)..........	40
Corn or invert sirup.......................................	30
Sucrose..	30
Pectin (powdered, 150 grade).............................	1.25
Citric acid...	0.5

The pectin is mixed with the sugar. The fruit juice is heated to boiling, and the pectin–sugar mixture is added, followed by the sirup. The mixture is cooked down to 11°F. (6.1°C.) above the boiling point of water; then the citric acid (dissolved in water) is added and it is again cooked down to the above temperature. The mixture is then poured on an oiled slab, cut, and rolled in confectioners' sugar, if desired.

With the introduction of low-ester pectins, candies containing much lower proportions of sugar can now be manufactured. Hall and Fahs[1763] described the following general formula for such products:

To 28 oz. of boiling water 0.33 oz. of a low-ester pectin, mixed with 12 oz. of sucrose and 36 oz. of corn sirup, is added. (The low-ester pectin used by Hall and Fahs was not a commercial product but was prepared by the Western Regional Research Laboratory, U. S. D. A., at Albany, California.) Now 0.5 g. of calcium saccharate dissolved in 0.5 oz. of water is added and the mixture is boiled down to the finishing temperature of 228°F. (109°C.). At this time flavoring and coloring materials are added together with 2 g. of sodium citrate dissolved in 0.5 oz. of water. The mixture is poured on an oiled slab or is cast to starch to set. When set, it is "sanded" with sugar or coated with chocolate. This product shows good storage behavior.

X. USES OF PECTIC SUBSTANCES IN BAKERY PRODUCTS

Apples in various forms have been used frequently to improve the quality of bread. At times favorable results are obtained but they are far from consistent.[1764] It was known for some time that the benefits derived from the use of apples are due to the pectic constituents; this led to several investigations of the use of pectic substances in bakery products. The usual purpose of the addition of pectin is to enhance the water-holding ability of the cake or bread and to retard staling.[1765] Epstein[1766]

[1763] H. H. Hall and F. J. Fahs, *Confectioner,* 31 (6), 10 (1946).

[1764] J. G. Malloch, *Sci. Agr.,* 19, 83 (1938).

[1765] Pomosin Werke Ges., German Pat. 347,512 (1929); through *C. A.,* 26, 5157 (1932).

[1766] A. K. Epstein, U. S. Pat. 1,964,940 (1934); reissue 19,933 (1936).

described the use of pectin in cakes and suggests that the pectin be dissolved first in glycerol and then mixed with the milk or water used in
making the batter. Wahl recommends[1767] that the pectin be added with
the sugar solution and states that, by the use of pectin, both the texture
and the yield of sweet rolls and cakes are improved. The proportion of
pectin may be about 5% of the weight of the flour used. Waldschmidt-
Leitz and Bayer[1768] suggested that calcium pectate be incorporated in the
form of an aqueous suspension, jelly, or dry product at the rate of 10–60
milligram per cent of the flour used in the dough to improve baking
quality.

Pectin has also been incorporated in bakery products, cereal breakfast
foods, etc. in such a manner as to increase the bulk of feces (Ch. XXVIII).
When a pectin powder is incorporated for such a purpose,[1769] the particles
should be coated with a material like stearic acid to prevent dissolution
and even the swelling of the pectin while in contact with the liquid of the
dough and prior to ingestion.

Pectic acid has also been used in leavening powder,[1770] in which it
lengthens the useful life of the mixture, controls the release of carbon
dioxide, and leaves no undesirable mineral residue. In using a mixture
composed of 65% pectic acid, 25% sodium bicarbonate, and 10% starch,
about 13% of the available carbon dioxide is evolved.

XI. PECTIN AS EMULSIFYING AGENT IN FOOD PRODUCTS

Pectin has been known for many years as an efficient emulsifying agent.
Rooker[1771] suggested the use of pectin in essential oil emulsions, for the
emulsification of castor oil and mineral oil, for mayonnaise, and for
emulsifying spray ingredients. Of these uses, a few examples of the use of
pectin as an emulsifying agent in food products will be discussed here.

Lotzkar and Maclay[1772] studied the comparative emulsifying efficiencies
of pectin (200 grade, rapid set) and of gum tragacanth, gum karaya, and
gum acacia. At pH values below 3 pectin is as good an emulsifier as gum
tragacanth, and for cottonseed oil it is slightly superior to this gum. As
an emulsifying agent for mineral oil, pectin is clearly superior to gum
tragacanth and gum acacia and as good as gum karaya.

There are numerous patents on the general use of pectins as emulsifying

[1767] A. S. Wahl, U. S. Pat. 1,795,980 (1931).
[1768] E. Waldschmidt-Leitz and A. Bayer, German Pats. 722,398 (1942); 733,272
(1942); and 726,253 (1942).
[1769] C. G. Spalding, U. S. Pat. 2,145,016 (1939).
[1770] W. E. Baier, U. S. Pat. 2,436,086 (1948); Food Inds., 20, 185 (1948).
[1771] W. A. Rooker, Fruit Products J., 7 (1), 11 (1927).
[1772] H. Lotzkar and W. D. Maclay, Ind. Eng. Chem., 35, 1294 (1943).

agents, but only those of Loesch[1773] and of Bender and Loesch[1774] will be noted here.

Pectin has been extensively used as an emulsifying agent in salad dressings and mayonnaise,[1775] especially at times when gums are not available. When present in a proportion of 0.2%, a 100 grade pectin emulsifies the egg yolk. Rooker described a method[1602] of making salad dressing with pectin. Ripa[1672] quotes an English recipe which consists of the following ingredients:

Olive oil	45.40 l.
Egg yolks	9.50 kg.
Table salt	0.68 kg.
Sucrose	0.57 kg.
Mustard, dry	0.23 kg.
Vinegar, spiced	0.57 l.
Vinegar (5%)	3.40 l.
Water	1.41 l.
Pectin powder	28–42 g.

A more recent household recipe[1776] for mayonnaise uses the following ingredients: 1 gallon of salad oil, 16 fresh egg yolks, $1^7/_8$ cups of lemon juice or 5% vinegar, 8 level teaspoonsful each of salt, powdered mustard, and sucrose, 1 spoonful of spices, $^7/_8$ cup of (distilled) water, and $1^3/_4$ level teaspoonsful of 100 grade pectin.

Pectin has also been used as an emulsifying agent in egg substitutes, mostly in conjunction with dried skim milk and some other minor ingredients. Such products were manufactured in Germany during World War II.

The main problem in using pectin for such purposes is not its effectiveness, which is well established, but its cost as compared with those of the common gums. The use of pectin emulsions for nonfood purposes will be discussed in Chapter XXVIII.

XII. PECTINS IN SUGAR MANUFACTURE

When the sucrose is extracted from beet slices during the course of sugar manufacture,[1595] some pectin also usually passes into solution; this may cause several difficulties. First, the pectin increases the viscosity of the extract and thus may reduce the efficiency of filtration. Second, the presence of comparatively little pectin seriously interferes with crystal-

[1773] H. G. Loesch, U. S. Pat. 1,625,641 (1927).
[1774] W. A. Bender and H. G. Loesch, U. S. Pat. 1,759,182 (1930).
[1775] A. Musher, French Pat. 843,617 (1938); through *Chem. Zentr.*, 1940, I, 3049.
[1776] G. H. Joseph, *Food Ind. South Africa*, 1 (2), 25 (1948).

lization. Elion[1777] stated that 20 milligram per cent pectin in a sirup prevents the crystallization of sucrose.

Farnell[1778] found only 0.55–1.22% total pectic substances in sugar cane and stated that the usual extraction procedure dissolves little pectin. In the manufacture of cane sugar, the cane is milled and then the juice is expressed. Little additional water, if any, and no heat are used in this procedure. Browne[1779] found in a sample of cane juice only 0.1% pectin and gums while in molasses the proportion rose to 2.0%. Hachihama[1780] has also studied the pectin from sugar cane.

In contrast, the sucrose from the sliced beets or "cosettes" is extracted in the neighborhood of 185°F. (85°C.) and thus considerable pectin may be dissolved during heating in addition to the water-soluble pectic fraction which is already present. Freezing of the beets,[1781] damage of any kind,[1782] and almost any extent of invasion by microorganisms apparently increase the amount of pectin (and hemicelluloses) extracted during the diffusion process and thus increase later difficulties.

Kharin and Moiseenko[1783] state that the colloids in the diffusion juice consist of pectins and albumins. Aggeev[1784] and Silin and Silina[1785] studied the conditions under which the pectin from beets is dissolved. The latter authors found 0.13% pectin in a sample of factory juice, only 76% of which was removed by carbonation. Aggeev[1786] suggests that "anti-peptizing" agents be used to decrease the solubility of pectic substances during diffusion, and also recommends the removal of pectic substances which are already dissolved with calcium. Baerts and Vanderwijer[1782] made a study of pectins in sugar beet manufacture and found that the furfurogenic substances (which include pectins) in the diffusion juice increase with poorly working knives, too high temperatures in the diffusion battery, and with slowing down or stoppage of the operations. Alkaline water also increases the extraction of these compounds. Hot liming removes pectins and other "furfurogenic" substances (mostly pentosans) more

[1777] L. Elion, *Deut. Destillateur-Z.*, **51,** 233 (1930); through *Chem. Zentr.*, 1930 I, 3368.

[1778] R. G. Farnell, *Intern. Sugar J.*, **25,** 630 (1923).

[1779] C. A. Browne, *J. Am. Chem. Soc.*, **41,** 1432 (1919).

[1780] Y. Hachihama, *J. Soc. Chem. Ind. Japan,* **36,** 258B (1933); through *C. A.,* **33,** 4122 (1939).

[1781] H. Claassen, *Centr. Zuckerind.,* **50,** 221 (1942); through *C. A.,* **37,** 6922 (1943).

[1782] F. Baerts and R. Vanderwijer, *Sucr. belge,* **55,** 167 (1936); through *C. A.,* **30,** 7898 (1936).

[1783] S. E. Kharin and E. A. Moiseenko, *Colloid J. (U. S. S. R.),* **6,** 739 (1940); through *C. A.,* **35,** 7748 (1941).

[1784] L. M. Aggeev, *Trudy Voronezh. Khim. Tekhnol. Inst.,* **5–6,** 51 (1940); through *C. A.,* **37,** 6151 (1943).

[1785] P. M. Silin and Z. A. Silina, *J. Sugar Ind. U. S. S. R.,* **5,** 606 (1931); through *C. A.,* **27,** 5210 (1933).

[1786] L. M. Aggeev, *Trudy Voronezh. Khim. Tekhnol. Inst.,* **2,** 32 (1938); through *C. A.,* **35,** 8337 (1941).

effectively than cold liming. The color of the thin juice from sound beets is improved by such precipitation of calcium pectate in a gelatinous form.

Partly in order to avoid the difficulties experienced because of pectic substances during beet sugar manufacture, Bonelli[1787] developed a new patented process in which the cleaned, pulped beets are extracted with dilute lime. Among the benefits of this method of sugar manufacture is almost complete precipitation of the extracted pectic materials in the initial phases of extraction.

Just as in the case of beet sugar, pectic materials are also extracted in the manufacture of artichoke sirup and inhibit the crystallization of the fructose.[1788] These interfering pectic substances can be eliminated by treatment with pectinase.

XIII. VARIOUS OTHER USES OF PECTIC SUBSTANCES IN FOODS

Reference will be made here to uses of pectic substances in foods which did not logically fall into the previous classifications used in this chapter.

Tressler[1789] used pectin in making fruit purees for use in "variegated" ice creams. The use of pectin in such products is desirable because the puree must possess a smooth texture and a heavy body so that it does not run out of the ice cream when it melts. The use of about 0.5–1.0% 100 grade pectin (in addition to the pectin naturally contained in the fruit) accomplishes this. Preston[1790] described a pectin–sugar preparation, suitable for jellies, sweetmeats, bread, etc., made by chilling a mixed solution of pectin and sugars. A modified pectin jelly made from low-ester pectin and beaten to give smoothness may be used in chocolate creams to reduce sweetness.[1791] Pectin may also be used in bakery glazes and icing[1592] and in puddings.[1792]

Whitfield[1793] suggested that, in order to reduce corrosion in tin cans, the material to be canned be brought to a pectin content of more than 0.25% "in terms of high-grade pectin." This is claimed to result in the formation of a protective film on the inner surface of the can, thus preventing corrosion. A solution of partially digested pectin was suggested for the fining of alcoholic beverages.[1794]

[1787] See W. G. Cass, *Chem. Eng. News,* 25, 1388 (1947).
[1788] H. E. Harrison and D. T. English, *Trans. Illinois State Acad. Sci.,* 27, 73 (1934).
[1789] D. K. Tressler, *Food Inds.,* 14, 49 (1942).
[1790] R. M. Preston, U. S. Pat. 1,949,657 (1933).
[1791] Anonymous, *Food Inds.,* 18, 390 (1946).
[1792] Anonymous, *Food Materials and Equipment,* 5, 3 (1945).
[1793] S. M. L. Whitfield, British Pat. 524,877 (1940); through *C. A.,* 35, 6688 (1941).
[1794] African Sisal and Produce Co. Ltd., and R. J. Browne, British Pat. 558,089 (1943); through *C. A.,* 39, 583 (1945).

Pectins of various sorts have been used extensively for coatings of foods.[1795]   Dickinson and Myers[1796] used a coating with nickel pectinate to protect and preserve beef sides and the like in storage.[1797]   Pectin glacé has been used to a considerable extent for candied fruit.[1798,1799]   It seems that the recently developed low-ester pectins are very useful for such purposes. As an example, a procedure given by Maclay and Owens[1800] will be described:

A low-ester pectin, sufficient to make a 2–2.5% dispersion, is mixed in water with vigorous stirring. If a plasticizer is necessary it can be mixed with the pectin. After complete dispersion the pH is adjusted to a value compatible with the product to be dipped, but it should be between 4 and 6. The solution is then heated to about 160°F. (71°C.) and hot calcium chloride solution, sufficient to give a calcium–pectin ratio of 0.016, is added slowly with rapid agitation. Meat, fruit, or other products should be dipped for a period of time necessary to give a coherent coating. 3 seconds has been found suitable for a number of products. This treatment is followed by dipping in dilute calcium chloride solution to tan the gelled coating and prevent adhesion between drying surfaces. Drying of the gelled coating to a thin film can be carried out in a current of air at a temperature below 140°F. (60°C.). Thickness of the film is controlled by the temperature of the product and of dispersion, by the concentration of pectin or calcium, and by the length of time of dip. In certain applications, such as the coating of frozen food, the pectinate coating is not dried but left in its gel form.

Such coatings[1801] have been found successful for candies in which they prevent undesirable stickiness. It has also been suggested for coating various fruit products, such as figs, dates, and raisins. Freezing burn in frozen fish is prevented by such pectinate coatings. Mold inhibitors, antioxidants, etc., may be incorporated in the coating film. The dry film withstands temperatures up to 180°F. (82°C.). Schultz, Miers, Owens, and Maclay[1802] have studied the permeability of pectinate films to water vapor.

This list by no means exhausts the purposes for which pectic substances have been suggested. Any survey of the literature reveals many other proposed uses, some useful, some questionable, and some absurd. Many such claims appear in patents.

Some further pectin relations in foodstuffs will be discussed in Chapter XXIX in connection with the uses of pectic enzymes.

[1795] W. V. Cruess, U. S. Pat. 1,532,476 (1925).
[1796] A. C. Dickinson and P. B. Myers, U. S. Pat. 2,245,576 (1941).
[1797] C. R. Moulton, Natl. Provisioner, Dec. 13, 1941, p. 12.
[1798] Anonymous, Fruit Products J., 28, 347 (1949).
[1799] Anonymous, Food Inds., 17, 571 (1945).
[1800] W. D. Maclay and H. S. Owens, Chemurgic Digest, 6, 325 (1947).
[1801] H. S. Owens and T. H. Schultz, U. S. Pat. 2,517,595 (1950).
[1802] T. H. Schultz, J. C. Miers, H. S. Owens, and W. D. Maclay, J. Phys. & Colloid Chem., 53, 1320 (1949).

CHAPTER XXVIII

Applications of Pectic Substances in Nonfood Products

I. PECTIC SUBSTANCES IN PHARMACEUTICAL PREPARATIONS

1. Pectin and the "Apple Diet"

The fate of ingested pectin was discussed in Chapter XVII. The use of pectin and pectin-containing fruits in the case of diarrhea, dysentery, and other similar disorders will be dealt with briefly here.

Scraped apples have been used in Europe for centuries as a home remedy for diarrhea and dysentery. The printed recommendation of the use of the fruit treatment (apples preferred) is said to have appeared in an English book in 1775.[1803] However, it seems that thorough clinical investigations of this topic did not commence until the late 1920's and the first major reports are those of Heisler[1804] and Moro.[1805] In the American literature the first report of the use of apples in the treatment of diarrhea appeared in 1933.[1806] Since that time this subject has been discussed in many articles of which only a very few will be quoted here. For the clinical aspects of this problem the reader must be referred to the medical literature and to the various reviews of this topic.[1807-1812]

The "apple diet," pectin, and pectin preparations are now extensively used for the treatment of diarrhea, especially in infants and children.[1803]

[1803] Anonymous, *J. Am. Med. Assoc.,* **109,** 1636 (1937).
[1804] A. Heisler, *Dennoch Landarzt,* Verlag der Aerztliche Rundschau, 1928; quoted from reference 1803.
[1805] E. Moro, *Klin. Wochschr.,* **8,** 2414 (1929).
[1806] T. L. Birnberg, *Am. J. Diseases Children,* **45,** 18 (1933).
[1807] G. H. Joseph, *Bull. Natl. Formulary Comm.,* **9,** (1), 2 (1940).
[1808] H. Baril, *Union Med. Canada,* **66,** 841 (1937).
[1809] J. E. Bittner, *J. Am. Med. Assoc.,* **108,** 509 (1927).
[1810] I. A. Manville, E. M. Bradway, and A. S. McMinis, *Northwest Medicine,* **35,** 441 (1936).
[1811] C. A. Tompkins, *J. Indiana State Med. Assoc.,* **28,** 278 (1935).
[1812] G. W. Kutscher, Jr., *North Carolina Med. J.,* **1,** 107 (1940).

The magnitude of the problem involved is indicated by Felsen,[1813] who stated that this disease in 1939 outranked typhoid as a health problem. Felsen found, in 16 states, about 16,000 cases per year and, in 9 states, the mortality averaged 17.8%.

The recommended doses vary widely and apparently precautions must be taken to prevent dehydration of the patients in spite of the high water content of apples. Water or weak tea is usually offered in addition and at times even parenteral administration of fluid is necessary. Usually the patient is changed to a more substantial diet after the first appearance of a well-formed stool. In addition to apples, bananas,[1814,1815] and yellow turnips[1816] have also been used for such purposes with similar success. There are only very few reports which are outright unfavorable, on the use of such diets, of which the article of Smith and Fried[1817] might be noted here.

Various theories have been advanced which ascribe the success of the diet to different components of apples. The astringent tannic acid,[1805] as well as the malic or other fruit acids present in apples,[1818] have been considered by some to be the active ingredients[1804]; there is some evidence to support these assumptions. However, while it is true that certain fruit juices have been shown to have an action similar to that of scraped apples, applesauce which has been rendered alkaline has proved just as effective as the untreated fruit.[1819] Malyoth[1820] is usually credited with the suggestion that the active ingredient in the apple diet is pectin or, more correctly, the various pectic constituents of apples. Most investigators now support this latter contention which is well substantiated by the extensive successful use of pectin and pectin–agar mixtures instead of scraped apples. However, it would seem to be a mistake to exclude the possibility that other constituents beside the pectin may contribute to the effectiveness.[1821] Indeed, in some experiments in which applesauce was fed to rats suffering from induced diarrhea,[1822] the pectic constituents of applesauce proved to be of the greatest efficiency in curing the rats; the effectiveness of the pectin, however, was increased by the presence of other constituents,

[1813] J. Felsen, *J. Am. Med. Assoc.*, 112, 46 (1939).

[1814] C. J. Joslin, J. E. Bradley, and T. A. Christensen, *J. Pediat.*, 12, 66 (1938).

[1815] H. W. von Loesecke, *Bananas*. 2nd Ed., Interscience, New York, 1950.

[1816] V. Lepps, *Acta Paediat.*, 21, 289 (1937); through *C. A.*, 33, 692 (1939).

[1817] E. E. Smith and R. L. Fried, *J. Pediat.*, 10, 495 (1937).

[1818] R. M. Smock and A. M. Neubert, *Apples and Apple Products*. Interscience, New York, 1950.

[1819] J. S. Hunt, *Arch. Pediat.*, 53, 736 (1936).

[1820] G. Malyoth, *Klin. Wochschr.*, 10, 1255 (1931); 13, 51 (1934).

[1821] M. P. Borowsky, *Am. J. Diseases Children*, 51, 1487 (1936).

[1822] Z. I. Kertesz, M. S. Walker, and C. M. McCay, *Am. J. Digestive Diseases*, 8, 124 (1941).

especially the cellulosic fraction which usually comes under the blanket term of "crude fiber." This latter fraction showed a slight desirable effect even in the absence of pectin.

The mechanism of the effectiveness of pectin in the treatment of these diseases is not clear. It has been suggested that the detoxication effect of galacturonic acid (see below) is responsible for the benefits obtained. Baumann and Forschner-Böcke[1823] ascribe the curative effect to colloidal absorption and removal of toxins, while Bittner,[1824] de Navarre,[1825] and others believe that enlargement of the stool volume and sweeping of the intestines with a plug of well-formed feces is the effective factor. It is interesting to note in this connection that, as noted in Chap. XVII, ingested pectin is usually digested in the normal human, apparently by the bacterial enzymes produced in the colon. However, in the case of dysentery, diarrhea, and other intestinal upsets, the pectin passes through and may be found in the feces. This difference must be due to the changed bacterial flora in the large intestine in such diseases; bacteriological investigations with organisms isolated from normal and diarrhetic feces, however, have thus far failed to give a clear explanation of this observation (see Chapter XVI).

It seems that further research is needed to explain the effectiveness of the apple diet and of pectin. Meanwhile, the apple diet, pectin, and combinations of pectin with other colloids are extensively used in the treatment of these diseases, especially in infants and children. Dried apple powder has been prepared under the sponsorship of the Münich Children's Clinic since 1931 and has been stated to give results equal to, or better than, raw apples. Of course, one great advantage of such preparations is the consistent composition and properties which are not easily attained with raw apples, especially after the normal storage period has passed. Ripa[1826] notes such dry preparations sold in Germany under the names of Santuron and Aplona. Appella is a domestic apple powder produced for such purposes.[1827] Infants receive 30–45 g. of apple powder daily.[1803] In severe cases Leffkowitz[1828] recommends that a 2–5% suspension of the apple powder in weak tea be used.

The use of pectin instead of apples in the treatment of such diseases was one of the reasons for the inclusion of a definition of "Pectin N.F." in the recent editions of the *National Formulary*[1829]; this definition was

[1823] T. Baumann and H. Forschner-Böcke, *Z. Kinderheilk.*, **56**, 515 (1934).
[1824] J. E. Bittner, Jr., *Northwest Medicine*, **35**, 445 (1936).
[1825] G. de Navarre, *Chemist and Druggist*, **122**, 235 (1935).
[1826] R. Ripa, *Die Pektinstoffe*. 2nd ed., Serger und Hempel, Braunschweig, 1937.
[1827] Manufactured by Appella Corp., Seattle, Washington.
[1828] M. Leffkowitz, *Therap. Gegenwart*, **73**, 44 (1932); quoted from reference 1803.
[1829] *National Formulary, VIII*. Committee on National Formulary of the American Pharmaceutical Association, Washington, D. C., 1945.

given in Chap. XXIII. Of the combination preparations, pectin–agar,[1830] alone or in combination with Dextri-Maltose[1831–1833] (containing 6.3% 100 grade pectin) and Kaopectate, a kaolin–pectin preparation,[1834] may be noted here as examples. The acid nickel pectinate[1835] Nipectin[1836] has also been suggested for such purposes.[1837] The effectiveness of this latter preparation is claimed to depend on the alleged bactericidal action of nickel pectinate. Tomectin[1837a] is a mixture of nickel pectinate and dried tomato pulp designed for the treatment of simple diarrhea. Intestisan[1838] is another preparation sold for such purposes.

Pectin has also been used to a limited extent to relieve constipation. Here the feces-forming and lubricating effects of pectin are obviously very important. Fruits rich in pectic constituents have often been used for such purposes. Halliday and Joseph[1839] described a supplemental therapeutic food which consists of citrus albedo which is freed from sugars and then flaked. Spalding[1840] suggested a method of coating pectin particles to inhibit their swelling in baked products so that they may swell upon ingestion and increase peristaltic action.

It would seem that further research leading to clarification of the action mechanism of the apple diet and of pectin preparations used in therapy may easily lead to improvements both in the preparations used and the efficiency of their curative action. Unfortunately, at least to the author's knowledge such research is not being pursued on any significant scale.

2. Use of Pectin in Wound Treatment

Its application in surgical dressings is one of the most striking developments among the many uses of pectin.[1841,1842] Thomson[1843] studied the healing time of infected soft tissue wounds of various kinds and found a

[1830] C. A. Tompkins, U. S. Pat. 2,139,139 (1938).

[1831] G. Washburn, J. Am. Dietetic Assoc., 14, 34 (1938).

[1832] J. A. Bybee, Med. Record Annals, 35, 934 (1941).

[1833] Manufactured by Mead Johnson and Co., Evansville, Indiana.

[1834] Manufactured by Upjohn Co., Kalamazoo, Michigan.

[1835] P. B. Myers, U. S. Pat. 2,259,767 (1941).

[1836] Manufactured by Eli Lilly and Co., Indianapolis, Indiana.

[1837] L. H. Block, A. Tarnowski, and B. H. Green, Am. J. Digestive Diseases, 6, 73 (1939).

[1837a] Manufactured by Ayerst, McKenna, and Harrison, Ltd., Rouses Point, New York.

[1838] G. Ohl, Deut. Gesundheitsw., 1, 480 (1946).

[1839] T. W. Halliday and G. H. Joseph, U. S. Pat. 2,452,750 (1948).

[1840] C. G. Spalding, U. S. Pat. 2,145,016 (1939).

[1841] Anonymous, "Pectin, a Review of Its Therapeutic Uses," Research Department, General Foods Corporation, New York, 1938.

[1842] Anonymous, Research and Invention (Ohio State University Research Foundation), 2 (3), (1938).

[1843] J. E. M. Thomson, Ind. Med., 7, 441 (1938).

definite beneficial action upon proper administration of a 2% pectin solution as a dressing. The pectinized gauze seems to absorb the decomposed tissue materials and debris, and the wound becomes nonpurulent, looks clean, and heals rapidly. The pectin treatment also seems to stimulate the formation of healthy granulations and, at the same time, discourages excessive, anemic granulations. Thomson felt that the effectiveness of the treatment depends on stimulation of the natural defense mechanism against infections.

Haynes, Tompkins, Washburn, and Winters[1844] obtained very satisfactory results when aqueous pectin solutions were used for treating wounds, including osteomyelitis and other deep wounds, as well as superficial wounds which had not responded to other treatments. Fantus and Dyniewicz[1845] reported excellent results in using a pectin paste to treat bed sores. From an investigation for three years on the use of pectin solutions (2–10%), Tompkins, Crook, Haynes, and Winters[1846] concluded that pectin therapy results in a prompt response with cleaner wounds and rapid growth of highly vascular granulation tissue. The method seems to be of particular value with the chronic type of lesion which often resists all other therapeutic efforts. Hamilton[1847] found that nickel pectinate does not affect wound healing but that it does accelerate epithelization.

It has been rumored that pectin was applied during the recent war in German military practice for wound dressings, but the author has no exact information concerning this matter.

This beneficial effect of pectin in wound healing has been attributed to its alleged bactericidal action[1844] but most workers in the field now believe that other effects[1848] are more important. Here again the exact mechanism is still unknown.

3. Use of Pectin as a Hemostatic Agent

In Chapter XVII the effect of pectin on blood clotting was discussed in some detail. Some of the practical uses of pectin as a hemostatic agent will be dealt with here.

For some time pectin solutions, administered intravenously, subcutaneously, or orally, have been used extensively for the prevention of bleedings of all kinds. Preparations made for this purpose[1849] have been on the

[1844] E. Haynes, C. A. Tompkins, G. Washburn, and M. Winters, *Proc. Soc. Exptl. Biol. Med.*, **36**, 839 (1937).

[1845] B. Fantus and H. A. Dyniewicz, *Science*, **90** (Supplement, Aug. 25), 7 (1939).

[1846] C. A. Tompkins, G. W. Crook, E. Haynes, and M. Winters, *Surg. Gynecol. Obstet.*, **72**, 222 (1941).

[1847] J. E. Hamilton, *Surgery*, **15**, 242 (1944); through *C. A.*, **39**, 4678 (1945).

[1848] A. G. Olsen, *Am. J. Digestive Diseases*, **7**, 515 (1940).

[1849] Turon Gesellschaft, German Pat. 666,591 (1938).

market in Europe since the early thirties. The best known of these is Sangostop,[1850] which was sold for injections or oral use and contained about 3 and 5% pectin, respectively. Apparently such preparations usually also contain some calcium and have an acid reaction. Sangostop has also been applied on tampons and its effect in such cases is claimed to be almost instantaneous. A further similar German preparation is Hämophobin.[1851]

Corresponding French preparations were sold under the names Coagucit and Arhemapectine. The latter[1852] contained, according to Ripa,[1826] 1.5% pectin, 0.05% calcium chloride, and 0.7% sodium chloride and was packed in sterile 1-cc. ampoules. Corresponding pectin solutions were also sold in some other European countries. These preparations have been widely used in Europe and have been official in Germany since 1939. There is a very extensive medical literature on their application but, apparently, the interest of the medical profession in this country has not been aroused by the many reports on pectin as a useful hemostatic agent. There are three summaries in the literature on this subject,[1807,1841,1853] of which Deuel's excellent review is the most recent.

In evaluating the results reported by various authors, the previously emphasized difficulty is repeatedly encountered: the hemostatic effect was in most cases judged only subjectively. Indeed, the measurement of such effects *in vivo* is difficult and, for the present, the only available criterion is the opinion expressed by various authors.

The benefits of pectin as a hemostatic agent have been observed in a great variety of bleeding, internal and external. It has been applied as a prophylactic treatment before operations of all kinds, including tooth extraction, in hemorrhages of all sorts, as well as in gynecological treatments.

There are several reports on the successful use of pectin solutions in the case of hemophilia. For the medical literature the reader must be referred to the review by Deuel,[1853] who quotes the major reports up to 1945.

4. Pectin as Blood Plasma Substitute

Properly prepared solutions of colloidal plasma substitutes (or replacement solutions) have certain advantages over plasma. They are usually readily available in large quantities and in sufficiently pure form, and are nonantigenic.[1853a] However, they may cause conglomeration and increased sedimentation of erythrocytes and do not furnish any material for

[1850] Made and sold by Turon Gesellschaft, Frankfurt am Main, Germany.
[1851] H. Barth and H. Rampelt, *Pharmazie*, **2**, 504 (1947); through *Chem. Zentr.*, 1948, I, 1084.
[1852] Made by Laboratorium R. Gallier, Paris.
[1853] H. Deuel, *Schweiz. med. Wochschr.*, **75**, 661 (1945).
[1853a] Anonymous, *J. Am. Med. Assoc.*, **126**, 1154 (1944).

restoration of the lost plasma. They may show further objectionable properties when used repeatedly and in large amounts.[1854]

Some of the plasma substitutes, as the dextran formed from sucrose solutions by *Leuconostoc mesenteroides*[1855] and the polyvinyl pyrrolidone developed in Germany during World War II, are very expensive. The current price of the latter is $12 to $14 per pound.[1856] The current price of high-purity pectin suitable for such purposes is about one-third to one-fourth the cost of polyvinylpyrrolidone (PVP) preparations.

A pectin solution was used during World War II as a plasma substitute[1857-1859] and retained a limited use in postwar years. The pectin is usually applied in a 1%, pyrogen-free, buffered solution, intravenously. However, since the osmotic efficiency rather than high viscosity is important in a serum substitute,[1860] the viscosity of the pectin solution is reduced at times by heating (see Chapter VII). The viscosity in such cases is adjusted to be somewhat greater than that of human plasma but less than that of blood.[1861,1862] Joseph[1863] recently reviewed this field.

It is clear from the discussion in Chapter XVII that the pectin is only of temporary use since most of it is excreted in about 36 hours in the urine.[1864] Jacobson and Smyth[1865] found that injection of a 0.75% solution of pectin caused a much greater and much more prolonged increase in plasma volume than did the injection of the same volume of physiological salt solution. If a pectin solution is used in excess, some pectin may be deposited in the body as a compound of unknown composition.[1866] Kozoll, Volk, Steigmann, and Popper[1861] suggest that some of the nonexcreted pectin may be deposited in the spleen. The view of Bryant, Palmer, and Joseph[1867] that pectin is not deposited in the kidneys or the liver of rabbits which had large amounts of pectin solutions injected into the blood

[1854] Anonymous, *J. Am. Med. Assoc.*, **136**, 557 (1948).
[1855] W. E. Laurence, *The New York Times*, December 24, 1950; Section 4, p. 7.
[1856] Anonymous, *Chem. Eng. News*, **29**, 3 (1951).
[1857] Anonymous, *Science Digest*, **10**, 36 (1941).
[1858] F. W. Hartman, V. Schelling, H. N. Harkins, and B. Brush, *Am. Surgery*, **114**, 212 (1941).
[1859] Anonymous, *The New York Times*, Aug. 14, 1941, p. 10.
[1860] G. A. Bradasch, *Anesthesiology*, **5**, 1 (1944), through *J. Am. Med. Assoc.*, **124**, 1015 (1944).
[1861] D. D. Kozoll, B. W. Volk, F. Steigmann, and H. Popper, *J. Lab. Clin. Med.*, **31**, 30 (1946).
[1862] Made by Frederick Stearns and Co., Detroit, Mich.
[1863] G. H. Joseph, *Pectin Sols for Parenteral Use*. Research Department, California Fruit Growers Exchange, Ontario, California, 1950.
[1864] H. N. Harkins, *Michigan State Med. Soc. J.*, **41**, 287 (1942).
[1865] S. D. Jacobson and C. J. Smyth, *Proc. Soc. Exptl. Biol. Med.*, **50**, 218 (1942).
[1866] H. Popper, B. W. Volk, K. A. Meyer, D. D. Kozoll, and F. Steigman, *Arch. Surgery*, **50**, 34 (1945); through *C. A.*, **39**, 2563 (1945).
[1867] E. F. Bryant, G. H. Palmer, and G. H. Joseph, *Proc. Soc. Exptl. Biol. Med.*, **49**, 279 (1942).

stream was noted in Chapter XVII. However, Hueper[1868] feels that pectin, even if partly degraded, is apparently retained in the liver, kidney, bone marrow, spleen, and arteries, and may give rise to various difficulties.

Further research on this matter is needed to decide whether the objections to such possible retention of pectin in the body are strong enough to counteract the benefits derived from its use. However, the fact that pectin solution is a suitable plasma substitute, or, more correctly,[1863] a replacement solution, is clearly established. High and consistent purity, easy availability in large quantities, and at low prices, and the simplicity of the preparation of the parenteral solution from the dry preparation provide many advantages over other materials suggested for the same purpose.

Pectin and gelatin have also been used in the processing of plasma in blood banks.[1869]

5. Pectin in Detoxication of Poisonous Metals

In 1825 Braconnot[1870] suggested that pectic substances are good antidotes for heavy metal poisoning because of the insolubility of the compounds formed. This fact was also observed by Fellenberg,[1871] who correctly concluded that, with an increased proportion of free acid groups in the pectinic acid, the formation of such insoluble metal derivatives is enhanced. Stuewer and Olsen[1872] state that some heavy metal ions, such as lead, react so readily with pectin that they can be quantitatively removed from solution as a pectic precipitate; for example, if a solution containing lead is passed through a filter bed consisting of calcium pectate, the lead can be entirely removed from the solution.

Thus, the simultaneous presence of pectin and of heavy metals minimizes the toxic effect of the latter. Such is the case with lead spray residues on apples.[1873] Murer and Crandall[1874] found a 24% reduction in lead retention when rats were fed 5% pectin, as compared with a pectin-free diet. Manville, Reithel, Yamada, Spencer, and Richardson[1875] reported results in reducing the toxicity by feeding apples when lead and arsenic

[1868] W. C. Hueper, Science, 102, 233 (1945).

[1869] M. J. Levine and R. E. Hoyt, Am. J. Clin. Path., 16, 40 (1946); through C. A., 40, 2885 (1946).

[1870] H. Braconnot, Ann. chim. phys., 30, 96 (1825).

[1871] T. Fellenberg, Biochem. Z., 85, 118 (1918).

[1872] R. F. Stuewer and A. G. Olsen, J. Am. Pharm. Assoc., 29, 303 (1940).

[1873] J. B. Shields, H. H. Mitchell, and W. A. Ruth, J. Nutrition, 18, 87 (1939).

[1874] H. K. Murer and L. A. Crandall, J. Nutrition, 23, 249 (1942).

[1875] I. A. Manville, F. J. Reithel, P. M. Yamada, T. W. Spencer, and J. R. Richardson, J. Ind. Hyg. Toxicol., 22, 36 (1940).

were given to rats, guinea pigs, and rabbits. The largest doses of apples gave complete protection during the experimental periods.

Rosenfeld, Roboz, and Beath[1876] found that selenium absorption in rats was reduced from 70% on a pectin-free diet to 46% when pectin was fed in addition. However, the pectin even in the highest concentration did not give sufficient protection to keep the animals alive.

Since pectic constituents are a normal part of our diet, one may well wonder to what extent we are all indebted to these compounds for health, or, at least, for being alive.

6. Pectic Substances in Various Other Pharmaceuticals

Brunthaler[1877] claims to have observed benefits upon administering 20 cc. of a 3% solution of purified pectin to infants with symptoms suggestive of poliomyelitis. More extensive clinical tests are needed to verify this observation. Micheel and Dörner[1878] synthesized compounds of pectinic acids with proteins for immunological purposes. Pectin has been used to lower the toxicity[1879] and increase the solubility[1880] of sulfa drugs. The increase in solubility is observed with pectin as well as neutral sodium pectinate; in addition to sulfonamides, other drugs, such as gitaligenin, gitalin, gitoxin, protactin, aesculin, and theophylline, are similarily affected.[1880]

Pectin has been used extensively to reduce the rate of absorption of various drugs. A pectin–insulin mixture, free from pectin decomposition products and zinc, is sold under the name Decurvon.[1881-1883] The insulin enters the blood stream slowly. The solution is suitable for hypodermic injection and contains 2.5–3.5% pectin. Similar effects have been observed in using penicillin together with pectin, intramuscularly,[1884] or with a pectin hydrolyzate,[1885] orally. Such penicillin-pectin preparations are now commercially produced.[1886] The action of many other drugs, such

[1876] I. Rosenfeld, E. Roboz, and O. A. Beath, paper given at the San Francisco meeting of the American Chemical Society, March, 1949.

[1877] E. Brunthaler, *Monatschr. Kinderheilk.*, **88**, 53 (1941).

[1878] F. Micheel and H. Dörner, *Z. physiol. Chem.*, **280**, 92 (1944).

[1879] G. J. Martin and M. R. Thompson, U. S. Pat. 2,366,742 (1945); through *C. A.*, **39**, 3125 (1945).

[1880] R. Becher and S. Leya, *Experientia*, **2**, 459 (1946).

[1881] F. Wuhrman, *Schweiz. med. Wochschr.*, **69**, 1275 (1939).

[1882] B. B. A. Brahn and T. Langner, *Nederland. Tijdschr. Geneesk.*, **83**, III, 4621 (1939); through *C. A.*, **34**, 515 (1940).

[1883] B. B. A. Brahn, U. S. Pat. 2,294,016 (1943); through *C. A.*, **37**, 1015 (1943).

[1884] B. L. Zinnamon and V. P. Seeberg, *Venereal Disease Inform.*, **26**, 31 (1945); through *C. A.*, **39**, 4390 (1945).

[1885] R. Murray and M. Finland, *Proc. Soc. Exptl. Biol. Med.*, **62**, 242 (1946).

[1886] Anonymous, *J. Am. Med. Assoc.*, **143**, 941 (1950).

as adrenaline, ephedrine, sex hormones, and streptomycin, can also be prolonged by injecting them together with pectin.[1887]

II. PECTIC SUBSTANCES IN PASTES, COSMETICS, SOAPS, ETC.

Pectic pastes have been used successfully in certain external conditions, such as external ulcers. This led to the development of specifications for pectin pastes which were discussed at a symposium.[1886-1891]   At the present time *National Formulary VIII*[1829] carries descriptions of two types of pectin pastes. These may be prepared in the following manner:

PECTIN PASTE (PASTA PECTIN, PAST. PECTIN)

Pectin.	75 g.
Glycerol.	180 g.
Benzoic acid.	2 g.
Isotonic "three chlorides" solution to make.	1000 g.

The benzoic acid is dissolved in 825 cc. of the isotonic salt solution heated to 100°C., and then the previously mixed pectin and glycerol are added with stirring. The stirring is continued until a homogeneous paste is formed. The paste is stored in tight containers and avoiding excessive heat. It may deteriorate in a few months to show some liquefaction.

THIN PECTIN PASTE (PASTA PECTINI TENUIS, PAST. PECTIN. TEN.)

This paste is prepared in the same manner but using only 35 g. of pectin and 70 g. of glycerol.

There are descriptions of many similar products in the literature.[1892] Some of these use pectin in combination with other colloids[1893-1895] or crude pectin preparations made by heating citrus albedo.[1896,1897]   Goldner[1898] described various pectin pastes and pectin skin varnishes containing sulfanilamide, sulfathiazole, zinc oxide, sulfur, and other active ingredients. This author stated that pectin, when used alone, produces coarse emulsions but that a satisfactory texture can be obtained by using a 1:1

[1887] H. Welch, H. L. Hirsch, and S. R. Taggart, *Science News Letter*, **52**, 210 (1947).
[1888] J. L. Powers and E. C. Beeler, *Bull. Natl. Formulary Comm.*, **9** (1), 24, 31 (1940).
[1889] A. G. Olsen, *Bull. Natl. Formulary Comm.*, **9** (1), 28 (1940).
[1890] G. H. Joseph, *Bull. Natl. Formulary Comm.*, **9** (1), 34 (1940).
[1891] K. B. Rosen, *Bull. Natl. Formulary Comm.*, **9** (1), 35 (1940).
[1892] E. Bourdet, *Parfumerie*, **1**, 99 (1943); through *C. A.*, **40**, 4480 (1946).
[1893] J. G. Mousson and Co. and H. Korper, German Pat. 601,475 (1934).
[1894] J. G. Mousson and Co., German Pat. 620,843 (1935).
[1895] Pomosin Ges., Belgian Pat. 443,990 (1942); through *C. A.*, **39**, 590 (1945).
[1896] G. Kruse, German Pat. 617,310 (1935).
[1897] B. Rosenfeld, British Pat. 500,281 (1939); through *C. A.*, **33**, 5590 (1939).
[1898] K. J. Goldner, *Am. J. Pharm.*, **114**, 41 (1942).

mixture of pectin and gum acacia. Pectin is stated to be incompatible with tannin, salicylic acid, and alkalis. Manchey and Schneller[1899] described lotions, creams, and pastes made with mixtures of pectin and quaternary ammonium salts. Lesser[1900] and Rae[1901] used pectin in hair pomades. Toni[1902] described the use of pectin gels as ointment excipients.

Pectin has also been used in tooth paste.[1903]

Because of its high absorptive power, Ziegelmayer[1904] recommends that pectin be added to soaps. Pectin has apparently been used extensively in Italian soaps as a filler.[1905] The following composition was given for a liquid soap:

Soap	50–60%
Pectin	22.5%
Sodium silicate solution (at 38 Bé)	27.5%

It is claimed that the texture of soap cakes is much improved by the presence of pectin, the detergent power is increased, and the pectin also has a beneficial effect on the skin. A paste containing 8–15% dry matter, including some citrus pectin, was marketed in Italy under the name Tergina.[1906] This soap was apparently very effective.[1907]

III. PECTIN AND PECTINATE FILMS AND FIBERS

Several references were made on previous pages to films and fibers prepared from pectin, pectinates, etc. Henglein and Schneider[1908] nitrated crude pectins and precipitated the nitropectin with water. The nitropectin was then dissolved in an organic solvent and used to make threads and foils insoluble in water. Of all such products by far the most promising are the pectinate films[1909] recently described by Maclay and Owens.[1910] These authors state that such products may be prepared in at least three different ways:

[1899] L. L. Manchey and G. H. Schneller, U. S. Pat. 2,372,159 (1945).

[1900] M. A. Lesser, *Drug & Cosmetic Ind.*, 45, 549 (1939).

[1901] J. Rae, *Mfg. Chem.*, 15, 363 (1944).

[1902] G. Toni, *Bull. chim. farm.*, 85, 3, 21 (1946); through *C. A.*, 40, 6755 (1946).

[1903] Deuts. Pektinges., German Pat. 551,888 (1932); quoted from R. Ripa, *Die Pektinstoffe*, 2nd ed., Serger und Hempel, Braunschweig, 1937.

[1904] W. Ziegelmayer, *Deut. Nahrungsm. Rundschau*, 1935, 65; quoted from Ripa.

[1905] Anonymous, *Soap*, 17 (1), 63 (1941).

[1906] F. Wittka, *Seifensieder-Ztg.*, 67, 397 (1940); through *C. A.*, 35, 339 (1941).

[1907] H. Tarchi, *Chim. ind. agr. biol.*, 16, 127 (1940); through *Chem. Zentr.*, 1940, II 2241.

[1908] F. A. Henglein and G. Schneider, *Ber.*, 69, 309 (1936); German Pat. 680,396 (1939).

[1909] T. H. Schultz, H. S. Owens, and W. D. Maclay, *J. Colloid Sci.*, 3, 53 (1948).

[1910] W. D. Maclay and H. S. Owens, *Chemurgic Digest*, 6, 32 (1947).

(1) By extrusion of a low-ester pectinic acid solution through a rectangular orifice into a bath containing polyvalent ions and acid.

(2) By evaporation of a sodium acid pectinate solution containing a plasticizer, followed by treatment with a polyvalent cation.

(3) By dipping, for a few seconds, an object into a solution containing a dispersion of calcium sodium pectinate held at a temperature above the gelling point and drying it, or by spraying it first with a solution of sodium acid pectinate followed by a solution of calcium chloride. The application of such a dip for coating was discussed in Chapter XXVII.

These authors summarize the properties of pectinate films as follows: They possess strength between 7 and 14 kg./mm.^{2} and are extensible to about 3–9%; they can be plasticized with glycerin which decreases the strength somewhat; their wet strength is one third to one fifth of the dry strength. The pectinate films show water-vapor permeability similar to that of cellulose films. The main difficulties preventing the commercial use of these films are high plasticizer requirements and low wet strength. Their permeability to water vapor has been studied by Schultz, Miers, Owens, and Maclay,[1911] who concluded that for uses requiring high resistance to the passage of moisture such films should be given a supplementary wax coating.

Fibers of pectin and pectinic acid have been prepared by extrusion of a solution into an ethanol bath. Such fibers from low-ester pectinic acids and pectic acid have been made by extrusion into a solution containing a polyvalent cation. Recently Maclay and Owens[1910] described the following method of preparing calcium pectinate yarns:

A 3% solution of sodium acid pectinate is forced through a candle filter and thence pumped through a spinneret which is immersed in a coagulating solution of the salt of a metal of the desired type of fiber. The fiber is then washed with water to remove excess salt and stretched during drying. Calcium pectinate yarns of 25 filaments and stretched 100% during drying exhibit excellent molecular orientation, have strengths as high as 2.9 g. per denier, and extensibilities of 6–9%. Fibers of other pectinates, such as zinc, with strengths comparable to those of the calcium salts have also been made. The wet strength of such fibers is only about one fifth of the dry strength.

Zinc pectinate films plasticized with glycol bori-borate are flame resistant, offering the possibility of use on decorative objects such as colored transparent ribbons.[1912]

[1911] T. H. Schultz, J. C. Miers, H. S. Owens, and W. D. Maclay, *J. Phys. & Colloid Chem.*, **53**, 1320 (1949).

[1912] W. D. Maclay and H. S. Owens, *Modern Packaging*, Sept. 1948.

IV. USE OF PECTIC SUBSTANCES IN BACTERIOLOGICAL CULTURE MEDIA

Culture media for plates and slants require gel-producing constituents which can meet exacting specifications. Agar has been the standard gel-forming agent for some time, but pectin has also been used in specific media and in days of agar shortages. Some investigations were discussed in Chapter XVI in which pectin was used in liquid media. The use of pectin and pectinate gels in bacteriological work will be discussed here.

Funck[1913] and Zimmerman[1914] have suggested the use of pectin for such purposes; and McCready, Owens, and Maclay[1915] described the use of fibrous sodium pectate[1916] in the form of an acid sodium-calcium salt for bacteriological gels. Baier and Manchester[1917] have dealt in detail with this subject and the discussion below is taken for the most part from their paper.

Any gel to be used in bacteriological work must be heat reversible and nontoxic to the organisms; it should not be easily liquefied, should withstand autoclaving, and should remain sufficiently fluid for pouring at 43°C. (109°F.).

The common high-ester pectins are not particularly suitable for such purposes because they require more than 50% sugar solids for proper jelly formation. Pectic acid and sodium pectate form gels which do not have very suitable textures and are not brilliantly clear as is desirable for plate counts.

Baier and Manchester used a sodium ammonium pectate described by Baier and Wilson[1918] and described several formulas which have been found successful. Of these a "standard method" suggested for water and sewage sample culture is made as follows:

Sodium hydroxide (1 N)	8.0 cc.
Calgon (sodium hexametaphosphate), food grade....	2.5 g.
Beef extract	3.0 g.
Peptone	5.0 g.
Sodium ammonium pectate	30.0 g.
Gum acacia (optional)	(0.5 g.)
Distilled water	1000.0 cc.

[1913] E. Funck, *Klin. Wochschr.*, **16**, 1546 (1937).

[1914] W. Zimmerman, *Zentr. Bakt. Parasitenk.*, **144**, I, 65 (1939); through *C. A.* **33**, 9356 (1939).

[1915] R. M. McCready, H. S. Owens, and W. D. Maclay, *Science*, **97**, 428 (1943).

[1916] C. W. Wilson, U. S. Pat. 2,132,065 (1938); reissue 21,077 (1939).

[1917] W. E. Baier and T. C. Manchester, *Food Inds.*, **15**, 94 (1943).

[1918] W. E. Baier and C. W. Wilson, *Ind. Eng. Chem.*, **33**, 287 (1941).

The alkali and Calgon are added to the water in a 2-liter beaker, after which the beef extract and peptone are also added and the solution is weighed and then heated on a steam bath. Now the pectate and the acacia (if any) are added with constant stirring and the heating is continued at 85°C. (185°F.) or higher for 15 min. with occasional stirring. The pH is now determined and adjusted to 7.7 ± 0.1 and the temperature is raised to boiling over a wire gauze and low flame. The solution is boiled for 5 min., the weight is adjusted to that originally determined, and the mixture is boiled up again and passed through four thicknesses of cheese cloth into flasks or Hasson bottles.[1919] The containers are sterilized at 15 lbs. pressure for 15 minutes. The final pH of the gels is about 6.6.

The gel produced is fairly firm with good tenacity and stands incubation well at 40°C. (104°F.). Some molds and bacteria cause liquefaction. The solidified stock medium may be remelted, although somewhat higher temperatures than for agar gels are needed. Baier and Manchester also describe the preparation of media with Tryptone, milk, and potato extract and discuss in detail the applications and limitations of the pectate media as compared with the standard gels prepared with agar. Jones[1920] described the preparation of bacteriological media with commercial low-ester pectins.

V. VARIOUS OTHER USES

There is practically no end to the list of various further uses for which pectic substances have been recommended. Only a few examples will be cited here.

Crude extracts from sugar beets have been used frequently as adhesives,[1826] but it may very well be that other compounds which are present (hemicelluloses, saponins) have more to do with the adhesive properties than the true pectin content. Rooker[1921] notes that although a 3–6% solution of (purified) pectin makes a good desk mucilage, effective on paper as well as on tin, wood, or glass,[1922] it can scarcely compete with the much cheaper materials now used for this purpose. A disadvantage of pectin is that microorganisms attack and destroy it easily and, therefore, suitable preservatives must be added. On the other hand, as Rooker states, pectin solutions do not develop, upon spoiling, the offensive odors common to present-day mucilages. A 2–3% solution of pectin has been found useful for tipping the ends of cigars.[1922]

One of the quaint uses for pectin and pectates is in the quenching of

[1919] R. Hasson, *J. Milk Technol.*, 5, 243 (1942).
[1920] D. R. Jones, *Nature*, 158, 625 (1946).
[1921] W. A. Rooker, *Fruit Pectin*. Avi, New York, 1928.
[1922] "A Handbook on the Uses of Nutr-Jel Powdered Apple Pectin," Speas Co., Kansas City, Missouri (about 1946).

steel and other alloys. The heat conductivity of a 0.2–4.0% pectin solution is in the same range as that of oils used in quenching and the pectin solutions have the advantage that the extent of effectiveness can be easily controlled by changing the concentration.[1923-1926] In some of the solutions pectin contents as high as 40% were recommended[1924,1925] and it is difficult to see how such solutions can be prepared from a pectin of any quality even if some gum arabic is used with it, as suggested.

Pectin and pectin hydrolyzates have been suggested as creaming and thickening agents for rubber latex.[1927-1930] Ripa[1826] states that if 70 cc. of a 10% pectin solution is added to 1 liter of latex, phase separation occurs and the liquid latex concentrate takes up about one seventh of the original volume. The use of pectin has also been suggested in the making of sponge rubber.[1931] In the synthetic rubber industry pectates have been used as antistick agents.[1932] Fibrous pectate pulp (Chapter XXV) and some sodium phosphate are dispersed with strong agitation in hot water; the solution or rather dispersion is then used to coat paper for packaging raw synthetic rubber. Such coatings work in a very interesting manner because the crating adheres strongly to the synthetic rubber and, when the package is opened, the pectate film cleaves from the paper. Pectate coatings were suggested earlier for paper used for other purposes,[1933] but it is said that the difficulties met in applying the highly viscous solutions and the extreme reactivity of the latter in forming gels with any trace of polyvalent ions has prevented extensive usage. Wurz[1934] states that parchmentizable bleached sulfite pulp contains more polygalacturonic acid than pulps which are not parchmentizable.

In addition to coating paper, pectic substances have also been used to coat aluminum foil. This product[1935] was sold in Germany under the name of Biofan and was used as an impervious cover for the surface of

[1923] R. Ripa, U. S. Pat. 1,876,170 (1932).
[1924] Pomosin Werke, German Pats. 577,711 (1933); 596,825 (1934); quoted from Ripa, *Die Pektinstoffe,* 2nd ed., Serger und Hempel, Braunschweig, 1937.
[1925] Deut. Pektinges., French Pat. 753,251 (1933); quoted from Ripa.
[1926] C. W. Wilson, U. S. Pat. 2,178,925 (1942).
[1927] Deut. Pektinges., German Pat. 560,259 (1932).
[1928] C. W. Wilson, *Rubber Age,* May, 1942, p. 121.
[1929] California Fruit Growers Exchange, French Pat. 804,366 (1936); quoted from Ripa.
[1930] C. W. Wilson, U. S. Pat. 2,421,108 (1947).
[1931] C. W. Wilson, U. S. Pat. 2,381,706 (1945).
[1932] Anonymous, *Chemurgic Digest,* 3, 176 (1944).
[1933] O. Wurz and O. Swoboda, *Papier-Fabr.,* 37, 125 (1939); through *C. A.,* 33, 5153 (1939).
[1934] O. Wurz, *Papier-Fabr.,* 35, 185 (1937); through *C. A.,* 31, 2747 (1937).
[1935] Manufactured by Rheinische Blattmetal A.-G., Grevenbroich, Niederrhein.

jars of jams and similar products. Another form of this product had the foil coated with paper impregnated with pectin.[1936]

Ripa[1826] describes a German patent on the use of pectin to increase the density of wood. Ehrlich[1937] described the use of pectin in growing giant ammonium chloride crystals. This method was the subject of several patents issued to Seidler.[1938]

Baker[1939] suggested the use of pectic substances in plastics. A hard, tough resin made with citrus protopectin as the plastic filler has also been described.[1940] Holzcker[1941] described a synthetic resin made by the condensation of phenol and pectic acid.

Schulz[1942] used solutions containing pectin, casein, and phosphate or citrate buffer (at pH 5.5–6.5) to make foaming products. Dumanski, Granskaya, and Novikov[1943] note its use for increasing foaming power. Stuewer and Olsen[1872] prepared organic derivatives of pectinic acids with the aim of obtaining foam-producing agents.

The presence and role of pectic substances in cotton fibers were mentioned earlier (Chap. XIV). Sookne and Harris[1944] state that about 85% of the acid groups in cotton are furnished by the pectic substances, apparently mostly pectic acid. The presence of acid groups is important from the standpoint of dyeing properties.[1945] The pectic substances from textile fibers can be removed by boiling with dilute solutions of sodium, potassium, and ammonium citrate, oxalate, and other chemicals,[1946] an operation usually called "degumming." Addition of pectin to cotton pulps decreases the beating time required to give maximum breaking strength.[1947] Pectin has been used to a limited extent as a sizing agent.[1948] Comparative tests on the use of pectin and starch for finishing textiles have shown that there is practically no difference in the strength of the warp. Pectin-treated fibers can be worked on both Platt and Northrup

[1936] C. L. Hinton, B.I.O.S. Final Report 388, Item 22, H. M. Stationery Office, London, 1946.

[1937] F. Ehrlich, Z. anorg. Chem., 26, 38, 203 (1931).

[1938] P. Seidler, German Pats. 463,184 (1928); 467,184 (1928); and 467,788 (1928).

[1939] G. L. Baker, Sci. Monthly, 40, 48 (1935).

[1940] Anonymous, Food Inds., 21, 1706 (1949).

[1941] R. Holzcker, U. S. Pat. 2,157,488 (1939).

[1942] M. Schulz, German Pat. 686,879 (1940); through Chem. Zentr., 1940, I, 3198.

[1943] A. V. Dumanski, T. A. Granskaya, and N. V. Novikov, Schriften zentral. biochem. Forsch. Inst. Nahr. u. Genussmittelind. U. S. S. R., 3, 361 (1933); through C. A., 28, 2970 (1934).

[1944] A. M. Sookne and M. Harris, J. Research Natl. Bur. Standards, 25, 47 (1940).

[1945] P. P. Victorov and G. I. Fridlyand, J. Applied Chem. (U. S. S. R.), 12, 113 (1939); through C. A., 33, 6602 (1939).

[1946] C. Prinot, Compt. rend., 213, 503 (1941).

[1947] D. M. Musser and H. C. Engel, Paper Trade J., 115, (8), 35 (1942).

[1948] S. Lyubimov, Rekonstruktz. Textil. Prom., 11 (1), 47 (1932); through C. A., 27, 3827 (1933).

looms. Satisfactory results have been obtained with pectin even without the addition of auxiliary substances such as glycerin, soap, or tallow, which are generally used in conjunction with starch. The pectin is soluble in water and thus can be washed out easily.[1922] Köhler[1949] described a method to show the presence of pectin in textile products.

Pectin has been frequently suggested as an emulsifying agent for a variety of purposes,[1826] some already noted before. As Rooker[1921] states, it is doubtful whether pectin can compete with other much cheaper emulsifying agents of at least equal efficiency. Sauer and Sanzenbacher[1950] prepared colloidal metal sols which were stabilized with pectin. Rossen[1951] prepared an emulsifying agent consisting of a mixture of pectin and skim milk.

Wilson[1952] and Baier[1953] prepared insecticides from various alkaloids and pectic acid. Wilson[1954] suggested the use of metal pectates for the clarification of liquids containing suspended solids.

Sheehy and Burke[1955] suggested the use of pectin in poultry feed to prevent feather picking, while Otto[1956] described a pectin-iodine preparation to prevent dysentery in poultry.

References to other suggested uses for pectic substances could be continued here endlessly. Needless to say, pectin manufacturers and institutions interested in agricultural by-product utilization are constantly searching for such possible outlets. All the known major uses were discussed in Chapters XXVII and XXVIII, however, with important possible uses listed in the last sections.

The role of pectic substances in cacao, coffee, and tea fermentation, and in tobacco curing will be discussed in Chapter XXIX.

[1949] W. Köhler, *Kunstseide u. Zellwolle*, 22, 202 (1940); through *C. A.*, 35, 2334 (1941).

[1950] E. Sauer and Sanzenbacher, *Kolloid Z.*, 79, 55 (1937).

[1951] N. J. Rossen, Danish Pat. 63,636 (1945); through *C. A.*, 40, 4234 (1946).

[1952] C. W. Wilson, U. S. Pat. 2,207,185 (1940).

[1953] W. E. Baier, U. S. Pat. 2,207,694 (1940).

[1954] C. W. Wilson, U. S. Pat. 2,419,930 (1947).

[1955] E. J. Sheehy and E. M. Burke, *J. Eire Dept. Agr.*, 37, 42 (1940); through *C. A.*, 35, 1096 (1941).

[1956] R. Otto, German Pat. 706,630 (1941); through *C. A.*, 36, 2085 (1942).

CHAPTER XXIX

Applications of Pectic Enzymes

I. USE OF COMMERCIAL PECTINASES FOR FRUIT JUICE AND WINE CLARIFICATION

Pectic enzymes were discussed in Chapter XIV and the production of commercial pectinases, in Chapter XV. Some of the uses of such enzymes in fruit juice and wine clarification, a subject previously mentioned in Chapter XXVII, will be dealt with here.

As noted on previous pages, commercial pectinases were developed in this country in order to produce brilliant fruit juices economically, whereas concurrent German work on such enzymes aimed primarily at the reduction of viscosity in such fruit juices. The reason for this latter effort was the extensive use in Europe of clear fruit juices and of such juices rendered sterile by germ-proofing filtration (Chapter XXVII). The enzymic method is considered by some as the most desirable procedure of fruit juice clarification.[1957]

Some of the pectinases now on the market were discussed before. The most important commercial pectinases sold in this country are the "Pectinols". Of these Pectinol A is recommended for apple juice, Pectinol W for grape juice and grape wine, and Pectinol M for the clarification of miscellaneous fruit juices and wines made from blackberries, strawberries, raspberries, peaches, etc.[1958] The use of pectinases for the clarification of apple juice and wines will be illustrated briefly here.

There are several possible ways in which these enzymes may be used. One is to add the enzyme to the ground apples before pressing. Although this is likely to increase the yield of juice obtained, such methods were not used in the past because of the haste with which the juice had to be pressed in order to prevent excessive enzymic darkening. However, a recent development in juice technology makes the future use of pectinases feasible.

[1957] R. E. Marshall, *Michigan State College Agr. Expt. Sta.*, Circ. Bull. 206 (1947).

[1958] Anonymous, "Pectinols," Trade pamphlet published by Rohm and Haas Co., Philadelphia, Pa. (about 1944).

When ascorbic acid is added to the juice immediately after grating or grinding the apples, this almost completely prevents darkening.[1959,1960] Thus, when the enzyme is added simultaneously, it can be afforded an opportunity to act before pressing and then to continue its action in the pressed juice. Naturally, such a method will make apple pomace useless for pectin production.

The pectinase is now applied to the expressed juice. There is little need to enter a discussion here of the mechanism of clarifying action since it has already been noted on several occasions on previous pages. The major reaction is hydrolysis of the pectic polyuronides with resulting destabilization of the colloidal systems responsible for the cloudiness.

There is considerable variation in the ease with which different lots of apple juice clarify.[1961] Juice made from overripe apples requires a larger proportion of the enzyme and experience must be relied upon to determine the exact amounts to use under varying conditions. In addition to the character of the juice, clarification depends on: (1) the amount of enzyme, (2) the temperature, and (3) the length of time allowed. As an example,[1957] juice made from firm, ripe apples and 12–14 oz. of Pectinol A per 100 gallons of juice requires about 12–15 hours at 60–65° (15.6–18.3°C.). If the juice must be clarified in 4 hours, about 3 times as much enzyme must be added. These pectinases are active between 32° and 140°F. (0° and 60°C.), with an approximate optimum at 100°F. (37.8°C.). The enzyme is destroyed by heating for 10 min. to 140°F., and increasingly more quickly as the temperature is elevated.[1958]

As the time of clarification or "breaking" approaches, the apple juice seems to become even more cloudy than it was before.[1962] Once flocculation starts, the colloids which are in part responsible for the turbidity settle rapidly and can be removed by filtration or centrifuging, or the clear apple juice can be simply siphoned off from the sediment. In commercial practice some filtration is usually applied in order to obtain a brilliant juice. Interestingly enough, some precipitate also occurs when a pectin solution is "clarified," even if the pectin is used highly purified.[1963] This precipitate interested several workers[1964–1966] but little attention is now paid to it.

[1959] C. S. Pederson, *Fruit Products J.*, **26**, 294 (1947).
[1960] K. Holgate, J. C. Moyer, and C. S. Pederson, *Fruit Products J.*, **28**, 110 (1948).
[1961] J. J. Williams, *Food Inds.*, **5**, 294 (1933).
[1962] Z. I. Kertesz, *New York State Agr. Expt. Sta.*, Bull. 589 (1930).
[1963] J. J. Willaman and Z. I. Kertesz, *New York State Agr. Expt. Sta.*, Tech. Bull. 178 (1931).
[1964] F. Ehrlich and F. Schubert, *Biochem. Z.*, **168**, 13 (1926).
[1965] Z. I. Kertesz, "Pectic Enzymes," in F. F. Nord and R. Weidenhagen, eds., *Ergebnisse der Enzymforschung*. Vol. V. Akadem. Verlagsgesellschaft, Leipzig, 1936, p. 233.
[1966] S. A. Waksman and M. C. Allen, *J. Am. Chem. Soc.*, **55**, 3408 (1933).

It should also be clear that, because of the presence of many enzymes other than those acting on pectic substances (Chapter XV), commercial pectinases may attack a variety of compounds in the apple juice. Proteins[1967] and hemicelluloses,[1968] for example, have been shown to be hydrolyzed.

The enzymic clarification of apple juice is rarely allowed to proceed until pectic components of the juice are completely hydrolyzed. Actually, clarification takes place rather early in the hydrolysis.[1962,1963,1969] The various changes which occur in pectin solutions upon treatment with a commercial pectinase were illustrated in Tables 59 and 60. In both experiments the amount of pectin present (as determined by the calcium pectate method) dropped less than 50% when the solutions were already completely clarified. Such behavior can be foretold from the rapid loss of colloidal properties (as viscosity) during the early phases of hydrolysis. In apple juice, some 60–80% of the pectin is usually lost for calcium pectate precipitation when clarification is stopped by inactivation of the enzymes.

It was mentioned in Chapter XXVII that sediments form at times in enzyme-clarified apple juice and that such secondary precipitations can be prevented by the addition of some pectin. For the technological details of enzymic clarification of apple juice, only reference will be made here to the many excellent discussions of this topic.[1957,1970–1973]

Widmer[1974] used a combination enzyme–gelatin clarification method with apple juice and states that removal of the pectin is essential for efficient concentration of the clear juice. Cox[1975] destroyed the bothersome quick-setting pectin naturally present in cranberries and then used a slow-setting citrus pectin to make cranberry jelly. Serbinova[1976] states

[1967] D. C. Carpenter and W. F. Walsh, *New York State Agr. Expt. Sta.*, Tech. Bull. 202 (1932).

[1968] R. L. Messier, *Dissertation*, Cornell University, 1945.

[1969] A. Mehlitz and H. Maass, *Biochem. Z.*, **276**, 66 (1935).

[1970] A. Mehlitz, *Süssmost*. 2nd ed., Serger und Hempel, Braunschweig, 1936.

[1971] D. K. Tressler, M. A. Joslyn, and G. L. Marsh, *Fruit and Vegetable Juices*. Avi. New York, 1939.

[1972] F. E. Atkinson and C. C. Strachan, *Canada Dept. Agr.*, Tech. Bull. **68** (1949).

[1973] V. L. S. Charley, editor, *Recent Advances in Fruit Juice Production*. Commonwealth Bureau of Hort. and Plantation Crops, London, 1950.

[1974] A. Widmer, *Schweiz. Z. Obst- u. Weinbau*, **49**, 530 (1940); through *C. A.*, **36**, 7227 (1942).

[1975] R. E. Cox, *Food Inds.*, **5**, 348 (1933).

[1976] N. I. Serbinova, *Konservnaya i Plodoovoshchn. Prom.*, **10** (4), 11 (1939); through *C. A.*, **36**, 2944 (1942).

that enzymic clarification with a mold pectinase had no effect on the ascorbic acid (vitamin C) content of black currant juice. Charley[1977] made a systematic comparison of various methods applicable for the clarification of cider.

Cruess, Rivera, Chong, and Gibson[1978] found that the treatment of fresh prunes with 0.1% Pectinol W permitted the pressing of prune juice with an 86% yield. Without the treatment, only a negligible quantity of juice could be pressed from the fruit.

In addition to their use in fruit juices, pectinases are also extensively used in winemaking. Popova, Burovaya, and Puchkova[1979] used an enzyme produced from *Botrytis cinerea* (*Sclerotinia Fucheliana*) for this purpose, while Besone and Cruess[1980] and Hickinbotham and Williams[1981] applied commercial pectinases made in the United States and Germany, respectively. A special grade of pectinase is now marketed for winemaking.[1958] It may be applied in a variety of ways. When added to sulfited white must allowed to settle for racking before fermentation, it hastens clearing and reduces the volume of lees. When added to crushed grapes which are allowed to stand overnight, both the free run and the total yield of must increase.[1982]

The enzyme is applied in various proportions, such as 1 lb. per 1000 lbs. of crushed grapes or a few pounds per 100 gallons of must. Arguments have been advanced for the use of the pectinase in both red and white wines, and especially in the manufacture of the Spanish type of sherry. In some countries the pectinase is almost universally applied in winemaking.

Treatment with pectinase has been claimed, not only to hasten clarification of the wine, but also to enhance the deposition of argols,[1983] increase the ease of filtration, and improve the bouquet and flavor of the finished product.[1984]

[1977] V. L. S. Charley, *Long Ashton (Bristol) Agr. Expt. Sta. Annual Rept. for 1934,* p. 191 (1935).
[1978] W. V. Cruess, W. Rivera, G. Chong, and A. Gibson, *Fruit Products J.,* 110, (1) 22 (1950).
[1979] E. M. Popova, L. N. Burovaya, and M. G. Puchkova, *Biokhimiya,* 4, 742 (1940); through *C. A.,* 34, 5556 (1940).
[1980] J. Besone and W. V. Cruess, *Fruit Products J.,* 20, 365 (1941).
[1981] A. R. Hickinbotham and J. L. Williams, *J. Dept. Agr. S. Australia,* 43, 491, 596 (1940).
[1982] W. V. Cruess and J. Kilbuck. *Wines and Vines,* 28, 23 (1947).
[1983] A. Baouman, *Génie civil,* 123, 173 (1946); through *C. A.,* 40, 7509 (1946).
[1984] J. Kilbuck, A. B. Nussbaum, and W. V. Cruess, paper given at the San Francisco meeting, American Chemical Society, March, 1949.

II. USE OF COMMERCIAL PECTINASES IN ANALYTICAL WORK AND IN PREPARATION OF GALACTURONIC ACID

There are some indications that pectic enzymes will eventually become recognized tools for the analysis of plant products. There are several older reports dealing with such applications of pectic enzymes in the form of crude fungus extracts.[1985] Turning to commercial pectinases, at least one manufacturer has put on the market a pectinase, Pectinol 100D, for such purposes.[1986] Loconti and Kertesz[1987] used the latter enzyme in the evaluation of the role of pectic constituents in tomato juice. Frush and Isbell[1988] used the same enzyme and suggested that a fraction to be called "pectic enzyme soluble substances" be included in analyses of food products (see Chapter VIII for more details). Meade, Fish, and Dustman[1989] used Pectinol A in the analysis of apple tissues.

The action of pectinase solutions on sections of human tissue was studied by McManus and Saunders.[1990] Although various changes were observed by these authors, it would seem likely that these did not occur as the result of the action of pectic enzymes but more likely were caused by various other admixed enzymes.

The main difficulty with the use of such impure enzymes for analytical purposes is the presence in these preparations of many other enzymes. This subject was discussed in Chapters XIV and XV. It would seem that, until specific enzymes void of other enzymes are obtainable, the complex preparations which are now sold must be used with care and discrimination. However, there is no doubt that the eventual use of such specific enzymes is the most promising approach in the analysis of such complex mixtures as plant tissues.

Pectolytic enzymes have been used extensively in the preparation of galacturonic acid. This subject was discussed previously in considerable detail in Chapter II.

III. USE OF PECTIN-METHYLESTERASE (PECTASE) FOR VARIOUS PURPOSES

It has been mentioned that this enzyme is now commercially available. The preparation of pectin-methylesterase was given in Chapter XIV. Its

[1985] M. H. Branfoot (Carré), "A Critical and Historical Study of the Pectic Substances of Plants," Dept. Sci. Ind. Research Brit. Food Invest., Special Rept. No. 33 (1929).

[1986] Rohm and Haas Co., Philadelphia, Pa.

[1987] J. D. Loconti and Z. I. Kertesz, Food Research, 6, 499 (1941).

[1988] H. L. Frush and H. S. Isbell, J. Research Natl. Bur. Standards, 33, 401 (1944).

[1989] R. C. Meade, V. B. Fish, and R. B. Dustman, Plant Physiol., 23, 98 (1948).

[1990] J. F. A. McManus and J. C. Saunders, Science, 111, 204 (1950).

use for the partial and complete deesterification of pectinic acids was also discussed in detail.

An interesting use of pectin-methylesterase is in the stabilization of the cloud in orange juice. For the extraction of the enzyme, minced orange flavedo is made into a slurry and the pH is adjusted to 6.0. The enzyme solution is then filtered off and, at times, further purified by the use of ion exchange resins. The enzyme can then be used for the partial deesterification of the natural pectin in orange juice: such a treatment is said to enhance the stability of the "cloud."

Willaman[1991] described an ingenious method of thickening or congealing various food products in which eggplant powder is used as a source of pectin-methylesterase. For making a tomato aspic, the following ingredients are added to 100 cc. of canned tomato juice:

Apple pectin	1.00 g
Eggplant powder	0.05 g.
Calcium acetate	0.13 g.
Confectioner's sugar	2.00 g.

The mixture is stirred into the tomato juice until dissolved, and the solution is then allowed to stand at about 122°F. (50°C.) until it has congealed to a solid gel. This occurs in about 55 minutes.

This scheme was also used by Willaman for the preparation of various salads, chocolate milk pudding, etc.

We have noted in Chapter XXII that pectin-methylesterase is used commercially to reduce the ester content of pectin in order to lengthen the setting time.

IV. PECTIC ENZYMES IN RETTING OF TEXTILE FIBERS

The useful fibers of flax, hemp, and other fiber plants, such as jute, etc., must be loosened from the stem that contains them. This is usually accomplished by a process known as "retting" which allows separation of the fiber bundles from the cortex and wood and effects at least partial digestion of the cementing material between the fibers in the bundles. Mitscherlich[1992] first attributed these changes to the pectolytic enzymes produced by microorganisms, a view which is now generally accepted.[1993]

Retting may be accomplished both by anaerobic and by aerobic methods. The former is usually done in slowly flowing waters and pools, whereas, in the aerobic method, the plant material is retted in vats supplied with aeration or by the methods known as "dew" or "land" retting.

[1991] J. J. Willaman, U. S. Pat. 2,373,729 (1945).
[1992] H. Mitscherlich, *Ann. chem. pharm.*, **75**, 305 (1850).
[1993] S. C. Prescott and C. G. Dunn, *Industrial Microbiology*. McGraw-Hill, New York, 1940.

Anaerobic retting is primarily accomplished by bacterial action, aerobic retting by the action of fungi. Thaysen and Bunker[1994] differentiate among the preliminary, physical, biological, and mechanical stages in retting. Both the production of microorganisms capable of forming pectolytic enzymes and pectolysis occur mostly in the biological phase.

This subject was touched upon in Chapter XIX and the excellent reviews of this subject by Branfoot[1985] and Thaysen and Bunker[1994] were noted. Prescott and Dunn[1993] more recently summarized the bacteriological knowledge concerning retting.

In anaerobic retting *B. amylobacter, Plectridium pectinovorum,* and *Cl. felsineum (B. felsineus) (Clostridium butyricum)* seem to be the organisms most commonly found and thought to be responsible for the retting action. Carbone,[1995] in a retting process named after him, used mass cultures of the latter organisms with success. In aerobic retting *B. comesii,* as well as molds and other bacteria, seems to be involved.

The loosening of the fiber bundles is due to the removal of various cementing tissue components, presumably mostly of pectic nature. Some investigators of these changes, as Zamyslov,[1996] Couchman,[1997] and Hessler[1998] found a considerable decrease in pectic substance content in the retted hemp and flax fibers as compared with the starting material. This occurred despite the removal of some tissue constituents, thus changing the sample in a manner which would have resulted in an increase in the pectic content, if the latter had been untouched (see Chapter XIV).

Comparatively little is known, however, concerning the enzymes involved in retting. While there are many organisms which, in pure cultures, are capable of attacking pectin and performing retting,[1999] only a few have been used for the production of enzymes which are then—in the absence of the living organism—capable of retting. At times true fermentation rather than pectolysis may be involved. Katagiri and Nakahama[2000] compared the pectin-decomposing enzymes produced by retting bacteria and found that crude preparations showed remarkable specificity in their actions toward various fiber plants, such as flax, kenaf, hemp, and ramie. It would seem that mixtures of enzymes may be involved rather than pectolytic enzymes alone; this matter, however, is not clear at the present

[1994] A. C. Thaysen and H. J. Bunker, *The Microbiology of Cellulose, Hemicellulose, Pectin and Gums.* Oxford Univ. Press, London, 1927.

[1995] D. Carbone, *Faserforsch.,* **2,** 170 (1922).

[1996] A. D. Zamyslov, *Biokhimiya,* **5,** 479 (1940); through *C. A.,* **35,** 4961 (1941).

[1997] J. F. Couchman, *J. Council Sci. Ind. Research (Australia),* **12,** 183 (1939).

[1998] L. E. Hessler, *J. Am. Soc. Agron.,* **37,** 146 (1945).

[1999] I. A. Makrinov, *Arch. sci. biol. Petrograd,* **18,** 440 (1915), quoted from Branfoot, reference 1985.

[2000] H. Katagiri and T. Nakahama, *J. Agr. Chem. Soc. Japan,* **16,** 1151 (1940), through *C. A.,* **35,** 6799 (1941).

time. Hajo[2001] reviewed the role of enzymes in the enzymic retting of flax. An enzyme mixture named Hiparol, secreted by *Thielaviopsis paradoxa* (DeSeynes) V. Hohn appears to be more active than bacterial enzymes in the retting of jute and coconut husk fibers.[2002] Watson and Baruah[2003] compared the effectiveness of Hiparol with that of bacterial enzymes on six fiber plants important in India. Prevot and Raynaud[2004] compared the pectolytic properties of *Cl. corallinum* with those of other similar species. Bonnet[2005] used bacterial enzymes to remove pectic constituents and proteins from linen and cotton.

In summary, it may be said that thorough reconsideration of the role, as well as the use, of pectolytic enzymes in the retting of plant fibers would be most desirable. With improved understanding of the structure of pectic substances, increased knowledge of at least some pectolytic enzymes, and especially with the much more exact methodology of pectic enzymes which has been developed recently, such further research may easily result in better understanding and improvement of retting processes. After all, there are other outstanding examples, such as the tanning industry, to illustrate what properly developed enzymes and controlled enzyme action can do for an industry.

V. ROLE OF PECTIC ENZYMES IN "FERMENTATION" OF TOBACCO, TEA, AND COCOA AND COFFEE BEANS

These subjects are noted here because of the probability that pectic enzymes participate in these processes. However, as will be shown below, this is still more of an assumption than an established fact.

After drying, tobacco leaves are placed in heaps and are dampened to attain a moisture content of 20–25%. Thereupon, fermentation takes place which may raise the temperature of the leaves as high as 158°F. (70°C), although it is usually kept at about 122°F. (50°C.) by repacking the heaps. Bacteria of the *Escherichia coli* type are said to play a major role in this fermentation,[2006] but this has not been convincingly demonstrated and it is not clear just what does happen. From our standpoint, the important fact is that the pectic constituents of the tobacco leaves undergo

[2001] Hajo, *Melliand Textilber.*, **21**, 536 (1940); through *C. A.*, **36**, 7326 (1942).

[2002] P. Baruah and H. K. Baruah, *Science and Culture*, **11**, 369 (1946); through *C. A.*, **40**, 7645 (1946).

[2003] C. M. Watson and H. K. Baruah, *Textile Mfr.*, **72**, 434 (1946); through *C. A.*, **40**, 7645 (1946).

[2004] A. R. Prevot and M. Raynaud, *Compt. rend.*, **222**, 1531 (1946).

[2005] L. Bonnet, *Teintex*, **8**, 175 (1943); through *C. A.*, **38**, 6104 (1944).

[2006] A. C. Thaysen, in *A System of Bacteriology in Relation to Medicine*. H.M. Stationery Office, London, 1929.

changes. Tobacco leaves are a rich source of pectin-methylesterase (see Chap. XIV) and apparently during certain phases of fermentation, this enzyme acts on the pectinic acids which are naturally present in the leaves, causing the formation of free methanol.[2007] This mixing of the enzyme and substrate may occur through partial plasmolysis resulting from exposure to the comparatively high temperatures. Neuberg and Scheuer[2008] and Neuberg and Kobel[2009] discovered this reaction by tracing the origin of the methanol found in fermented tobacco leaves. It seems, however, that during fermentation some hydrolysis of the pectic constituents also occurs and, since pectolytic enzymes seem to be absent from the leaves, such hydrolysis probably occurs because of the presence of bacterial enzymes. There now seems to be revived interest in this subject.[2009a]

The changes which occur in the pectic constituents of tea leaves during their curing or fermentation are suspected rather than known. Roberts[2010] states that changes in the pectic constituents are probable but have been investigated very little.

After the cacao pods are picked, the seeds are removed and scooped into heaps or placed in baskets or boxes in which they are then "fermented" or "cured." The raw seeds are encased at this time in a mass of white, mucilaginous pulp which must be removed. It seems that attempts to perform this operation with enzymes or pure cultures of microorganisms have thus far been unsuccessful. The fermentation takes 2–7 days during which most of the liquefied mucilaginous mass oozes away.[2011] The yeast *Saccharomyces theobroma* is supposedly involved in this process,[2012] but it is almost certain that several organisms participate when the fermentation takes a desirable course. The process now depends on chance infection. Acetic, lactic, and butyric acids, ethanol, esters, and no doubt many other compounds are formed during the process.[2007] Most investigators emphasize the several pronounced changes which occur in the odor emanating from the heap, which seems to indicate a succession of dominant microorganisms during different periods of the fermentation.[2011]

The suggestion has also been made that fermentation is the result

---

[2007] G. Gabel and G. Kiprianoff, *Biochem. Z.*, **212**, 337 (1929).

[2008] C. Neuberg and M. Scheuer, *Biochem. Z.*, **243**, 461 (1931).

[2009] C. Neuberg and M. Kobel, *Biochem. Z.*, **189**, 232 (1927); **229**, 455 (1930).

[2009a] W. G. Frankenburg, in F. F. Nord, ed., *Advances in Enzymology*, Vol. X, Interscience, New York, 1950.

[2010] E. A. H. Roberts, in F. F. Nord and C. H. Werkman, eds., *Advances in Enzymology*. Vol. II, Interscience, New York, 1942, p. 113.

[2011] W. T. Clarke, "Chocolate and Cocoa," in R. E. Kirk and D. F. Othmer, eds., *Encyclopedia of Chemical Technology*, Vol. III, Interscience, New York, 1949, p. 889.

[2012] A. Preyer, *The Fermentation of Cacao*. London, 1913.

of enzymes occurring in the cacao tissue.[2013] The few chemical analyses now available[2014] do not give a clear picture of the pectic changes involved; in fact, it is not even known whether pectic substances make up any substantial portion of the material surrounding the raw beans.

The situation is rather similar with coffee beans.[2015] Fermentation in this case is done in water and aims at removal of the bulk of the fleshy tissue surrounding the beans. Perrier[2016] states that the mucilaginous coating adhering to the coffee beans is freed during the fermentation process by the action of pectinases.

VI. PECTIC ENZYMES IN PLANT DISEASES

The destructive effect of many microorganisms on plant material, especially fruits and vegetables, has long been recognized. Early investigators blamed the tissue softening and destruction on the decomposition of cellulose by "cytases" which were allegedly excreted. It was not until 1886 that DeBarry[2017] established, for *Sclerotinia libertiana*, that the detrimental effect occurs to a large extent through the action of microbial enzymes which affect the pectic constituents. The formation of pectolytic enzymes by various microorganisms was discussed earlier (Chapter XIV), as well as their utilization of pectic substances (Chapter XVI). The action of such enzymes on plant tissues of economic importance will be dealt with briefly here.

The rigidity of plant tissue depends to a great extent on the adhesion of cells and cell layers (Chapter XII). This adhesion is, generally speaking, accomplished by the cementing effect of the intercellular pectic substances, especially those in the middle lamella (Chapter X). Most plant diseases related to the destruction of pectic constituents in the tissue result from the digestion of these cementing structures by the pectolytic enzymes which are excreted into the surrounding medium by various microorganisms. The digestion of the middle lamella results in reduction of the original structure into a mass of separate cells surrounded by a large amount of clear, light colored liquid.[2018] This maceration of the tissue is usually designated as "soft rot." Many plant pathologists believe that the ability

[2013] H. C. Brill, *Philippine J. Sci.*, **A10**, 123 (1915).

[2014] A. W. Knapp, *Cacao Fermentation*. Bale, London, 1937.

[2015] L. W. Elder, "Coffee," in R. E. Kirk and D. F. Othmer, eds., *Encyclopedia of Chemical Technology*. Vol. IV, Interscience, New York, 1949, p. 223.

[2016] A. Perrier, *Compt. rend.*, **193**, 547 (1931).

[2017] A. DeBarry, *Comparative Morphology and Biology of the Fungi, Mycetozoa and Bacteria*. Oxford, 1887.

[2018] S. G. Paine, in *A System of Bacteriology in Relation to Medicine*. H.M. Stationery Office, London, 1929.

of fungi to secrete extracellular pectolytic enzymes which soften the tissue in advance of the hyptal tips is one of the key biochemical features accounting for the pathogenicity of these various soft rot organisms. On the other hand, it seems that the secretion of pectolytic enzymes is not a common means of access of the pathogenic organisms to the tissues. In most cases, such organisms enter the plant only after mechanical injury, such as puncturing, cracking, or bruising.

A tremendous amount of valuable research on pectic enzymes has been done by plant pathologists; their accomplishments have been ably reviewed by Branfoot,[1985] Paine,[2018] and others. It is disheartening that very little work of this sort seems to be in progress at present; a survey of the literature indicates that the bulk of information on hand dates from before 1930 and that scarcely any substantial reports were published for many years on this important subject. Furthermore, most handbooks and textbooks which appeared during the past decade pay little attention to the role of pectic constituents and pectolytic enzymes in plant diseases. Foster's recent volume[2019] may be mentioned as a notable exception.

The interest in the role of pectic enzymes in plant pathology was the incentive for many of the interesting investigations of protopectin (see Chapters III, X). Table 61 lists some of the microorganisms which are known to produce pectolytic enzymes and some of the factors which influence the formation of such enzymes have been discussed. Mention has already been made of the role of pectic enzymes and of pectic changes in the softening of pickles[2020] and it may be added that Cruess[2021] found similar participation of pectolytic enzymes in the stem-end softening of olives. However, the relationship between the ability to form pectolytic enzymes and pathogenicity (soft rotting ability) is not always satisfactory[2021a] and thus it seems likely that factors other than pectic enzymes enter the picture.

There is considerable evidence that the presence of pectic substances of some kind is needed for the production of pectolytic enzymes, which may, therefore, be classified as adaptive enzymes. But, as Foster states, there are substantial variations in this respect among different fungi, as the previously quoted work of Gäumann and Böhni[2022] and Phaff[2023] illustrates. The situation seems to be even more complex in the case of

[2019] J. W. Foster, *Chemical Activities of Fungi*. Academic Press, New York, 1949.
[2020] T. A. Bell, J. L. Etchells, and I. D. Jones, *Food Technol.*, **4**, 157 (1950).
[2021] W. V. Cruess, *Fruit Products J.*, **27**, 44 (1947).
[2021a] R. P. Elrod, *J. Bact.*, **44**, 433 (1942).
[2022] E. Gäumann and E. Böhni, *Helv. Chim. Acta*, **30**, 24, 1591 (1947).
[2023] H. Phaff, *Arch. Biochem.*, **13**, 67 (1947).

the production of pectin-methylesterase. Under the conditions used by Phaff, the pectic enzymes produced by *Penicillium chrysogenum* were almost entirely extracellular, but one might wonder whether this would be the case when the organism grows in a plant tissue, since changes of conditions materially affect the retention or excretion of enzymes.[2022-2024] It is to be hoped that the investigations of Phaff and of Gäumann and Böhni may be the beginning of a new era of activity in this interesting and economically important field of microbial formation of pectic enzymes and their action on plant tissues.

[2024] Z. I. Kertesz, *Plant Physiol.*, 6, 249 (1931).

S